SO-AXL-349

PROGRESS
IN
HETEROCYCLIC CHEMISTRY

Volume 8

Books

CARRUTHERS: Cycloaddition Reactions in Organic Synthesis
GAWLEY & AUBÉ: Principles of Asymmetric Synthesis
HASSNER & STUMER: Organic Syntheses based on Name Reactions and
Unnamed Reactions
PAULMIER: Selenium Reagents & Intermediates in Organic Synthesis
PERLMUTTER: Conjugate Addition Reactions in Organic Synthesis
SIMPKINS: Sulphones in Organic Synthesis
WONG & WHITESIDES: Enzymes in Synthetic Organic Chemistry

Journals
BIOORGANIC & MEDICINAL CHEMISTRY
BIOORGANIC & MEDICINAL CHEMISTRY LETTERS
JOURNAL OF PHARMACEUTICAL AND BIOMEDICAL ANALYSIS
TETRAHEDRON
TETRAHEDRON: ASYMMETRY
TETRAHEDRON LETTERS

Full details of all Elsevier Science publications, and a free specimen copy of any Elsevier Science journal, are available on request from your nearest Elsevier Science office.

PROGRESS

IN

HETEROCYCLIC CHEMISTRY

Volume 8

A critical review of the 1995 literature preceded by two chapters on current heterocyclic topics

Editors

H. SUSCHITZKY
Department of Chemistry and Applied Chemistry, University of Salford, UK

and

G. W. GRIBBLE
Department of Chemistry, Dartmouth College, Hanover, New Hampshire, USA

PERGAMON

U.K.   Elsevier Science Ltd, The Boulevard, Langford Lane,
        Kidlington, Oxford OX5 1GB, U.K.

U.S.A. Elsevier Science Inc., 660 White Plains Road, Tarrytown,
        New York 10591-5153, U.S.A.

JAPAN   Elsevier Science Japan, Higashi Azabu 1-chome Building 4F,
        1-9-15 Higashi Azabu, Minato-ku, Tokyo 106, Japan

First Edition 1996

Library of Congress Cataloging in Publication Data

A catalog record for this book is available from the Library of Congress

British Library Cataloguing in Publication Data

A catalogue record for this book is available from the British Library

ISBN 0 08 0427960

*Printed and bound in Great Britain
by Biddles Ltd, Guildford and King's Lynn*

Contents

Foreword vii

Advisory Editorial Board Members viii

Chapter 1: **Geminal Diazides of Heterocycles** 1
Th. Kappe and C. O. Kappe, *Institut fur Organische Chemie,*
Karl-Franzens Universitat, Graz, Austria

Chapter 2: **Radical Methods in the Synthesis of** 14
Heterocyclic Compounds
Mukund P. Sibi and Jianguo Ji, *North Dakota State University, Fargo, USA*

Chapter 3: **Three-Membered Ring Systems** 44
A. Padwa, *Emory University, Atlanta, GA, USA* and S. S. Murphree, *Bayer Inc.,*
Charleston, SC, USA

Chapter 4: **Four-Membered Ring Systems** 66
J. Parrick, and L. K. Mehta, *Brunel University, Uxbridge, UK*

Chapter 5: **Five-Membered Ring Systems**

Part 1. **Thiophenes & Se, Te Analogs** 82
R. K. Russell, *The R. W. Johnson Pharmaceutical Research Institute, Raritan,*
NJ, USA and J. B. Press, *Galenica Pharmaceuticals, Inc., Frederick, MD, USA*

Part 2. **Pyrroles and Benzo Derivatives** 103
R. J. Sundberg, *University of Virginia, Charlottesville, VA, USA*

Part 3. **Furans and Benzo Derivatives** 121
St. Reck and W. Friedrichsen, *University of Kiel, Germany*

Part 4. **With More than One N Atom** 146
S. A. Lang, Jr, *Wyeth-Ayerst Research, Pearl River, NY, USA* and
V. J. Lee, *Microcide Pharmaceuticals Inc., Mountain View, CA, USA*

Part 5. **With N and S (Se) Atoms** 163
R. Tanaka, *Suntory Institute for Biomedical Research, Osaka, Japan*

Part 6. **With O & S (Se, Te) Atoms** 178
R. A. Aitken and L. Hill, *University of St. Andrews, UK*

v

Part 7. **With O & N Atoms** 192
G. V. Boyd, *The Hebrew University, Jerusalem, Israel*

Chapter 6: Six-Membered Ring Systems

Part 1. **Pyridine and Benzo Derivatives** 209
J. E. Toomey, Jr and R. Murugan, *Reilly Industries, Inc., Indianopolis, IN, USA*

Part 2. **Diazines and Benzo Derivatives** 231
M. P. Groziak, *Southern Illinois University, Carbondale, IL, USA*

Part 3. **Triazines, Tetrazines and Fused Ring Polyaza Systems** 255
D. T. Hurst, *Kingston University, Kingston upon Thames, UK*

Part 4. **With O and/or S Atoms** 277
J. D. Hepworth and B. M. Heron, *University of Central Lancashire, Preston, UK*

Chapter 7: Seven-Membered Rings 298
D. J. LeCount, Formerly of *Zeneca Pharmaceuticals, UK,*
1, Vernon Avenue, Congleton, Cheshire, UK

Chapter 8: Eight-Membered and Larger Rings 320
G. R. Newkome, *University of South Florida, Tampa, FL, USA*

Subject Index 337

Foreword

Progress in Heterocyclic Chemistry (PHC) Volume 8 reviews critically the heterocyclic literature published mainly in 1995. The first two chapters are review articles. Chapter 1 by T. Kappe deals with "Geminal Diazides of Heterocycles," and Chapter 2 by M. Sibi and J. Ji provides extensive coverage of the important emerging area of "Radical Methods in the Synthesis of Heterocyclic Compounds." The unusual length of the latter contribution attests to the rising power of this methodology in heterocycle construction.

The remaining chapters deal with recent advances in the field of heterocyclic chemistry arranged by increasing ring size. Once again, the reference system follows the system employed in *Comprehensive Heterocyclic Chemistry* (Pergamon, 1984).

We are pleased to have Chapter 5.5 on "Five-Membered Ring Systems with N and S (Se) Atoms" in Volume 8, since this chapter was not covered in Volume 7.

We thank all authors for providing camera-ready scripts and disks, and, especially, for adopting our new uniform format. In this regard, we welcome comments from readers about the style and presentation.

We are much indebted to David Claridge of Elsevier Science for his invaluable help with the presentation of Chapters and with the new format.

Finally, we wish to acknowledge retiring editor Eric Scriven for his outstanding contribution in all previous volumes of this series as co-editor.

Once again, we hope that our readers will find PHC-8 to be a useful and efficient guide to the field of modern heterocyclic chemistry.

H. Suschitzky
G. W. Gribble

vii

Editorial Advisory Board Members
Progress in Heterocyclic Chemistry

1996–1997

PROFESSOR H. W. MOORE (CHAIRMAN)
University of California, Irvine, CA, USA

DR D. BELLUS
Ciba Geigy Ltd
Basel, Switzerland

PROFESSOR J. BERGMAN
Royal Institute of Technology
Stockholm, Sweden

PROFESSOR D. BOGER
Scripps Research Institute
La Jolla, CA, USA

PROFESSOR D. CORNINS
North Carolina State University
Raleigh, NC, USA

PROFESSOR S. DENMARK
University of Illinois
Champaign-Urbana, IL, USA

PROFESSOR T. GILCHRIST
University of Liverpool
Liverpool, UK

PROFESSOR T. HIND
Chiba University, Japan

PROFESSOR K. MORI
Science University of Tokyo
Tokyo, Japan

DR P. ORNSTEIN
Eli Lilly Co
Indianapolis, IN, USA

PROFESSOR S. RYCHNOVSKY
University of California
Irvine, CA, USA

PROFESSOR B. STANOVNIK
University of Ljubljana
Ljubljana, Slovenia

Professor S. Weinreb
Pennsylvania State University
University Park, PA, USA

The International Society of Heterocyclic Chemistry is pleased to announce the establishment of its home page on the World Wide Web. Access can be gained from the following locations:

For USA, Americas, Japan:

http://euch6f.chem.emory.edu/ishc.html

for Europe:

http://www.ch.ic.ac.uk/ishc/

Chapter 1

Geminal Diazides of Heterocycles

Thomas Kappe and C. Oliver Kappe
Institut für Organische Chemie, Karle-Franzens-Universität Graz, A-8010 Graz, Austria

1.1. DIAZIDO-QUINOLINEDIONES

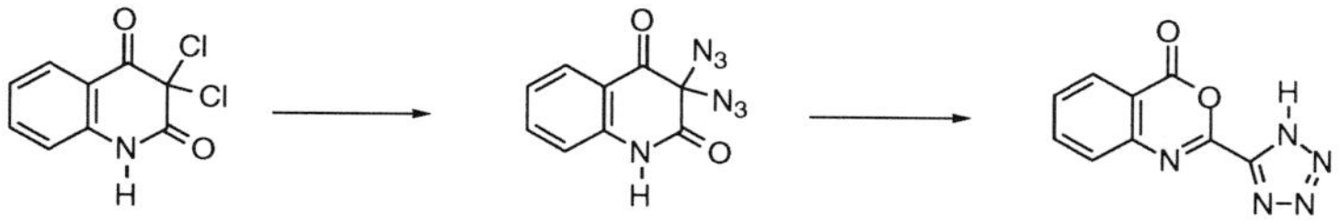

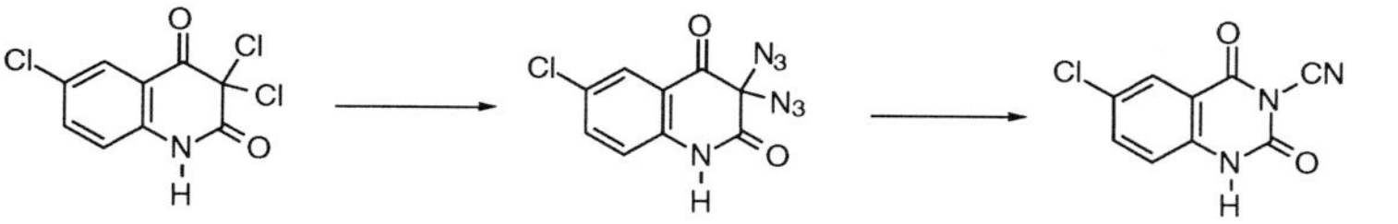

A short historical review on the development of the chemistry of quinolines containing the "diazido malonyl" moiety seems to be appropriate. The synthesis of "dichloro malonyl" heterocycles (e.g. **1**) was reported over 30 years ago [62M1376] [63M447], and in the following years the exchange of the halogen atoms against nucleophiles (alkoxides [64AG(E)754] [65M889], amines [68M990] [68M2157]) were studied. In 1970-72 [72TH000] we studied the reaction of **1a** with sodium azide which resulted in a high yield production of **2a**. This type of geminal diazide proved to be a good starting material for a number of transformations. Firstly, the thermolysis of this compound above 110 °C afforded (with loss of dinitrogen) the tetrazolyl-benzoxazinone **3** in 83 % yield. However, in 1976 the synthesis of **2b** was described by H. W. Moore [76TL2513] and much to our surprise the product of its thermolysis (with loss of two molecules of dinitrogen) was assigned structure **4b** (48 % yield).

In the following years we repeated the thermolysis of type **2** compounds with a variety of substituents in the benzene nucleus, and found that by refluxing the diazides **2** in aromatic hydrocarbons (such as toluene or xylene) two substances were formed - their ratio depended on the nature of the substituents in the benzene nucleus [79TH000] [79MI000]. At the time we had no doubts about the structure of **4** proposed by Moore. This situation changed when in 1983 a paper by D. J. LeCount [83JCS(P1)813] appeared in which the synthesis of **4a** from 2-amino-3,1-benzoxazin-4-one and sodium cyanamide was described. Though LeCount did not prepare **4b**, he concluded from his data for **4a** that the structure of **4b** must be wrong. A spectroscopic investigation by us showed the other products of the thermolysis to be the isomeric diazo quinoline-2,4-diones **6** [84CC338]. Compound **6** had been prepared previously by M. Regitz [65LA(687)214]; and the substance was known to us, as we had used it earlier for the preparation of azo dyes [72TH000] and their copper complexes [75ZN(B)773].

The formation of **3** and **6** proceeds obviously through the same intermediate **5**, formed from **2** with loss of dinitrogen *via* an α-azido-nitrene. Further loss of dinitrogen leads directly to the diazo ß-diketones **6** (if the quinolones **2** are substituted at the nitrogen atom only this type of compound is obtained [96UP000].

The ration of **3/6** is strongly dependend on the nature of R

The reaction to give **3** involves a cleavage of the bond between C-3 and C-4. The intermediate **7** undergoes acylation at the amid carbonyl oxygen to afford **3**. If the reaction of **2** is performed in a high boiling alcohol (e.g. in butanol) the ring opened anthranilic esters **8** are formed (amines yield anthranilic amides corresponding to **8** [68M990] [68M2157]).

The formation of tetrazole derivatives from geminal diazides has been observed and correctly interpreted already in 1931 [31CB1555]. The thermal decomposition of dimethyl diazidomalonate was reinvestigated by R. M. Moriaty [85JOC3710] after our short report in 1984 [84CC338].

The reaction of **2** in refluxing acetic acid (containing some water) leads directly to the free acid **8** (R = H), which is of course also readily obtained from **3** by hydrolysis.

An attempt to ringclose the free acid **8** to the benzoxazinone **3** with the help of acetic anhydride led to an unexpected result: If **8** (or preferable **3**) is heated in acetic anhydride the oxadiazolyl benzoxazine **12** is obtained. However, the outcome of this reaction is not surprising since R. Huisgen [68AG359] and others, have shown, that the acylation of tetrazoles give 1,3,4-oxadiazoles *via* N-acylnitrilimines (such as **11**) by 1,5-dipolar electrocyclic ringclosure.

Hydrolysis of **12** gives the open chain derivative of anthranilic acid, oxalic acid and acetylhydrazine **13** [72TH000].

The action of concentrated sulfuric acid at 0 °C on the geminal diazide **2** gives in high yield (> 90 %) the N-oxamoyl anthranilic acid **14** [72TH000]. This compound can be further hydrolyzed to anthranilic acid **15** or converted into the ester **16**. N-Alkyl derivatives of **2** behave in a similar manner; cf. the conversion of **18** to **19**. The latter compound may be easily degradated to 1,2,3,4-tetrahydroquinoline-1-carboxylic acid in the same way. Only the N-phenyl derivative of **2** reacts differently and affords acridone **17** in 65 % yield. The cleavage of the C-3 - C-4 bond in these reactions is again noteworthy.

Consideration of the mechanism has to account for the fact, that hydrazoic acid and dinitrogen is liberated during the course of the reaction. The similarity to the Schmidt reaction is obvious, and it should be mentioned that quinisatine (2,3,4-trioxo-tetrahydroquinoline) reacts with sodium azide and sulfuric acid at 0 °C in moderate yield to give **14**. [96TH000].

The reduction of **2**, either catalytically or with zinc in acetic acid, leads to 3-amino-4-hydroxy-2-quinolone **20** [72TH000]. These amino compounds are rather unstable; they dimerize with loss of ammonia to "bis-amines", which in turn are readily oxidized to dyes similar to those obtained from ninhydrin and primary amines [68M1205] [68M1543]. The amino derivatives **20** are therefore conveniently converted into O,N-diacetyl derivatives, the N-acetyl derivative **21**, or its dehydrated form, the oxazolo derivative **22** [95MI000]. The variety of biological activity of oxazolo-quinolines of type **22** has been detected only in recent years [94JHC1647].

The pharmacological activity of two of the geminal diazides should be mentioned: N-alkylderivatives of **2** are blood platelet aggregation inhibitors (TXA_2 antagonists) [90MI000], while the 6,8-dinitro derivative of **2** [79TH000] shows good activity as antiulcer agent [96UP000].

1.2. DIAZIDO-PYRIDAZINES AND DIAZIDO-PYRIMIDINES

Searching for other 6-membered "diazido malonyl N-heterocycles" we have selected the pyridazine derivative **25** and diazido barbituric acids **32** as model systems, since they are available easily and in large quantities. Compound **25** is obtained in the usual way by chlorination of **23** with sulfuryl chloride and exchange of the halogen atoms with sodium azide.

Substance **23** in turn is available from 3,5-dichloro-6-phenylpyridazine, an intermediate in the production of a well known herbicide (Pyridate^R) by a two-step or three-step synthesis [87TH000]. The thermolysis of **25** (with N-Me) e.g. in boiling 1-butanol leads to the butyl ester **27** [85TH000] [87TH001]. Hydrolysis of this ester yields (under subsequent decarboxylation) compound **28** . The same compound is directly obtained from **25** when heated in water containing solvents such as dioxane or acetic acid. The intermediate of an unstable spiro-tetrazole **26** - as in the quinoline series - must be postulated; and it is interesting to note again, that the bond cleavage in the parent heterocyclic ring system occurs between the keto-carbonyl group and the sp^3 C-atom of the tetrazole (C-4 - C-5 bond) and not in the amid-carbonyl group, which would lead to the isomeric structure **29** [87TH001]. However, there are some differences from the quinoline diazides: if the N-unsubstituted compound **25** was heated, no tetrazolyl-1,3-oxazine was found, only the 4-diazo-3,5-dioxo-pyridazine could be isolated [85TH000]. This diazo ketone was obtained when the amine **30** was diazotized. Interestingly, the amine **30** (obtained in the usual way by reduction of **25**) proved to be more stable than 3-amino-4-hydroxy-2-quinolones (**20**) [85TH000].

Investigations of the reactivity of 5,5-diazidobarbituric acid are leading to somewhat different results [96M000]. The synthesis of **32** is easily accomplished *via* the dichloro-barbiturates **31**. Heating of the dimethyl derivative **32b** in boiling toluene leads to the 5-diazo barbituric acid **33** in 44 % yield, a compound which was independently synthesized from dimethylbarbituric acid using Regitz's procedure with *p*-toluenesulfonic acid azide [64LA(676)101]. Treatment of **31a** with water leads under ring-opening and decarboxylation to dichloroacetyl urea [59JOC1383] [63M935]. Under the same conditions, we expected the formation of diazidoacetyl urea from **32a,b** (cf. next chapter). However, the products obtained were the parabanic acids **34a,b**. The ring-contraction of 5,5-dihydroxybarbituric acid (alloxan hydrate) *via* benzylic acid rearrangement, decarboxylation, and oxidation to parabanic acid is a well studied process [61JA2579]. A similar mechanism can be assumed for the transformation of **32** to **34**. The most surprising result was obtained when **32a** was heated in boiling 1-butanol: colorless prisms sublimed into the condenser which were identified as ammonium azide **35** (33 % yield!). No other product could be isolated from the reaction mixture. The mechanism of the reaction is rather obscure, although it is known that hydrazoic acid can be liberated from diazido malonyl heterocycles (cf. chapter 1.1.) with acids. It might be speculated that **32a** itself is acidic enough to liberate hydrazoic acid, and that further fragmentation of the urea moiety liberates the necessary ammonia for the salt formation. Heating of **32a** in benzyl alcohol leads to benzyl allophanate **36** in 41 % yield, while **32b** gives under the same conditions the tetrazole carboxamide **37** in 42 % yield. The reaction of **32b** in refluxing butanol provides **37** in 16 % yield apart from some parabanic acid **34b** (18 %).

1.3. DIAZIDOACETYL DERIVATIVES OF HETEROCYCLES

In many cases N-substitued anilines or azomethines (resp. enamines) react with two equivalents of diethyl malonate to give pyrono derivatives of 2-quinolones or 2-pyridones in good yield [84JHC1881] [89JHC1555] [88TH000] [90TH000]. Chlorination of these compounds with sulfuryl chloride and aqueous work up yields dichloroacetyl derivatives of quinolones and pyridones which in turn react with sodium azide to afford a variety of diazidoacetyl derivatives of type **38**.

Since these products are, therefore, readily available as starting materials we have studied their further use. The diazido compounds **38** are not very stable. They loose readily dinitrogen (usually on crystallization from alcohol) and give the tetrazolyl derivatives **39**. Treatment of **39** with acetic anhydride leads in the usual way (cf. the conversion of **3** *via* **9-11** to **12**) to the oxadiazolyl derivative **40**. The carbonyl group in this structure can be reduced with sodium borohydride to the methylene group. Careful hydrolysis of this compound (**41**) with acid, yields the hydrazide **42**, while alkaline hydrolysis of both affords the acid **43** [84JHC1881].

Heterocyclic acetic acids of this type are potential antiinflammatory agents, and we found this method to be very convenient for their synthesis.

Another way to potential antiinflammatory activity is to mimic a carboxylic acid by a tetrazole moiety (compare the pK_a 4.8 for tetrazole itself). A good example is Intrazol^R which is closely related to Indomethacin (an indolyl-3-acetic acid derivative). Therefore we have also reduced the carbonyl group in **39** yielding compounds of type **44** [84JHC1881]. Unfortunately no compound of this series showed antiinflammatory activity.

Dichloroacetyl compounds which are acidic enough to form salts with sodium azide can not react with the azide anion. The phenolic dichloroacetyl compounds from which **38** is obtained must form a strong hydrogen bridge to the carbonyl group by which the acidity is drastically reduced. The formation of tetrazolo-derivatives is not the only way, by which dichloroacetyl compounds can react. We have also studied the reaction of some other aromatic dichloroacetyl derivatives, namely those of structures **45** (R^1, R^2 = H, NO_2), and **49** [79TH000] with sodium azide. Much to our surprise [79TH000] the products of the reaction were the aroyl azides **46** and **50**. Later, G. Mann et al. [83S191] extended the reaction to a number of ω,ω-dibromoacetophenones and gave a mechanistic explanation for the reaction pathway. The acid azides of type **46** and **50** are of course valuable intermediates since they give on heating isocyanates, which can react with other nucleophiles to urethanes or ureas. If no nucleophile is present they may undergo cyclization as shown for **47** yielding' the benzimidazole **48**. We intend to use the potential of these transformations for further reactions.

1.4. DIAZIDOMETHYL PYRIMIDINES

The reaction of ethyl acetoacetate, benzaldehyde, and urea leads to ethyl 1,2,3,4-tetrahydro-6-methyl-2-oxo-4-phenyl-5-pyrimidinecarboxylate. This reaction (the so called Biginelli reaction) was discovered over 100 years ago [93T6937]. Interest in these dihydropyrimidines has increased rapidly mainly due to their close structural relationship to the pharmacologically important dihydropyridine calcium channel blockers of the nifedipine-type [93T6937]. The dibromo (**51**) and monobromo derivatives (**55**) of the most simple Biginelli compounds mentioned above are readily obtained by bromination [93T6937], and the reactions of these derivatives with sodium azide have been studied recently [90LA505] [91JCS(P1)1342].

The action of sodium azide on the dibromo compound **51** did not afford the expected diazido derivative but furnished the nitrile **52** with loss of dinitrogen and hydrogen bromide. The reaction was conveniently carried out in hexamethylphosphoric triamide (HMPT) at 35 °C. If DMF was used as a solvent no reaction took place at temperatures below 60 °C. At higher temperatures the initially formed nitrile **52** reacted with a second equivalent of sodium azide to yield the tetrazole **53**, which was also obtained by direct action of sodium azide on **52**, using 1-methyl-2-pyrrolidone (NMP) as solvent and triethylamine hydrochloride as catalyst. Although the structure of **52** was supported by analytical and spectroscopical data it was decided to prove its structure by an independent synthesis: it is known that azides having an adjacent methylene group can be decomposed to give nitriles under certain conditions. Thus, palladium(0)-catalyzed decomposition of 6-(azidomethyl)pyrimidine **54** in the presence of diphenylacetylene as hydrogen acceptor led to the formation of nitrile **52** in 39 % yield. The reaction was carried out in refluxing xylene under nitrogen atmosphere, using palladium black as catalyst. The required monoazide **54** was obtained from **55** by halide displacement [90LA505].

To explore further the structural requirements for this unexpected nitrile formation (**51** → **52**) the reaction of the 1-methyl derivative **56** with sodium azide was examined. In this case the diazido derivative **57** was obtained instead of the nitrile **58**. In a control experiment the nitrile **58** was also prepared by methylation of **52** with trimethyl phosphate in the presence of potassium carbonate. **58** reacted in analogy to **52** with sodium azide to furnish the tetrazole **59**. Attempted decomposition of the geminal diazide **57** in refluxing DMF failed to give the tetrazole **59** (which is very surprising in view of the easy conversion of **38** to **39**) [90LA505].

In addition, the reaction was extended to the 4-unsubstituted tetrahydro-pyrimidines **60**. Here the same reaction pattern as before was observed: The 1-unsubstituted derivative led to the 6-cyanopyrimidine **61**, whereas the 1-methyl derivative afforded the geminal diazide **62** [90LA505].

An interesting conversion of the geminal diazidomethyl pyrimidines **57** and **62** was observed when heated at reflux in DMF [91JCS(P1)1342]. The resulting products (**63a** R = H, 86 %; **63b** R = Ph, 46 %) have the structure of a pyrazolo[4,3-d]pyrimidine bearing the ester group at N-2, as shown by an X-ray crystal analysis. This reaction summarizes nicely what has been shown before: dinitrogen elimination from **57/62** leads to an α-azido nitrene which eliminates again dinitrogen to give the diazo compound **64**. This α,β-unsaturated diazo system would be expected to undergo spontaneous 1,5-electrocyclization to the pyrazolopyrimidine **65**. However, the ^{13}C NMR spectrum showed no signal which could be assigned to a sp^3 carbon, but rather two signals in the aromatic region. A thermal van Alphen Hüttel rearrangement (well known for 3,3-disubstituted 3*H*-pyrazoles) seemed therefore likely to have occurred. In principle the ethoxycarbonyl group could have migrated to N-1 or N-2; the X-ray analysis solved this problem. Saponification of the ester group by sodium hydroxide and acidification resulted in the formation of the N-unsubstituted pyrazolopyrimidine [91JCS(P1)1342].

In addition to the thermal decomposition the photochemical reaction of geminal diazide **62** was also studied. Irradiation of an acetone solution of **62** under an inert gas atmosphere afforded a complex mixture of products which could not be separated or identified. However, if the reaction was carried out in the presence of oxygen the uracil derivative **66** was obtained in 48 % yield. Surprisingly, in addition to the oxidation of the CH_2 group, the 6-diazidomethyl function was completely lost during the reation [91JCS(P1)1342]. At the present time no mechanistic explanation for this unusual behavior can be presented. On the other hand, photooxidation of compound **63** leads straightforward to compound **67** [91JCS(P1)1342].

ACKNOWLEDGMENTS

T.K. thanks his numerous students and post-graduate coworkers, whose names are found in the references, for their dedicated work in the field of heterocyclic azido chemistry.

1.5. REFERENCES

31CB1555	R. Götzky, *Ber. Dtsch. Chem. Ges.* **1931**. *64*, 1555.
59JOC1383	F. Bier-Slezak, H. A. McElray, *J. Org. Chem.* **1959**, *24*, 1383.
61JA2579	H. Kwart, R. W. Spayd, C. J. Collins, *J. Am. Chem. Chem.* **1961**, *83*, 2579, and references cited therein.
62M1376	E. Ziegler, R. Salvador, T. Kappe, *Monatsh. Chem.* **1962**, *93*, 1376.
63M447	E. Ziegler, T. Kappe, *Monatsh. Chem.* **1963**, *94*, 447.
63M935	T. Kappe, E. Ziegler, *Monatsh. Chem.* **1963**, *94*, 935.
64AG(E)754	E. Ziegler, T. Kappe, *Angew. Chem., Int. Ed. Engl.* **1964**, *3*, 754.
64LA(676)101	M. Regitz, *Liebigs Ann. Chem.* **1964**, *676*, 101.
65LA(687)214	M. Regitz, S. Stadler, *Liebigs Ann. Chem.* **1965**, *687*, 214.
65M889	E. Ziegler, T. Kappe, *Monatsh. Chem.* **1965**, *96*, 889.
68AG359	R. Huisgen, *Angew. Chem.* **1968**, *72*, 359.
68M990	T. Kappe, E. Lender, E. Ziegler, *Monatsh. Chem.* **1968**, *99*, 990.
68M1205	H. Wittmann, W. Dreveny, E. Ziegler, *Monatsh. Chem.* **1968**, *99*, 1205.

68M1543   H. Wittmann, W. Dreveny, E. Ziegler, *Monatsh. Chem.* **1968**, *99*, 1543.

68M2157   T. Kappe, E. Lender, E. Ziegler, *Monatsh. Chem.* **1968**, *99*, 2157.

72TH000   G. Lang, Ph.D. Thesis, University of Graz, 1972.

75ZN(B)773   T. Kappe, R. Korchid-Zadeh, H. Steiniger, *Z. Naturforsch., Teil B* **1975**,*30*, 773.

76TL2513   G. Landen, H. W. Moore, *Tetrahedron Lett.* **1976**, 2513.

79MI000   T. Kappe, E. Pongratz, G. Lang, *7th International Congress of Heterocyclic Chemistry*, Tampa, Florida, USA, **1979**, Abstr. p. 200.

79TH000   E. Pongratz, Ph.D. Thesis, University of Graz, 1979.

83JCS(P1)813   D. J. LeCount, *J. Chem. Soc., Perkin Trans. 1* **1983**, 813.

83S191   G. Weber, S. Hauptmann, H. Wilde, G. Mann, *Synthesis* **1983**, 191.

84CC338   T. Kappe, G. Lang, E. Pongratz, *J. Chem. Soc., Chem. Commun.* **1984**, 338.

84JHC1881   K. Faber, T. Kappe, *J. Heterocyl. Chem.* **1984**, *21*, 1881.

85JOC3710   R. M. Moriaty, B. R. Bailey, I. Prakash, R. S. Miller, *J. Org. Chem.* **1985**,*50*, 3710.

85TH000   S. Zengerer, Ph.D. Thesis, University of Graz, 1985.

87TH000   P. Kaiser, Ph.D. Thesis, University of Graz, 1987.

87TH001   A. Pfaffenschlager, Ph.D. Thesis, University of Graz, 1987.

88TH000   P. Roschger, Diploma Thesis, University of Graz, 1988.

89JHC1555   C. O. Kappe, T. Kappe, *J. Heterocycl. Chem.* **1989**, *26*, 1555.

90LA505   C. O. Kappe, *Liebigs Ann. Chem.* **1990**, 505.

90MI000   E. Malle, W. Stadlbauer, G. Ostermann, B. Hofmann, H. J. Leis, G. M. Kostner, *Europ. J. Med. Chem.* **1990**, *25*, 137.

90TH000   P. Roschger, Ph.D. Thesis, University of Graz, 1990.

91JCS(P1)1342   C. O. Kappe, G. Färber, *J. Chem. Soc., Perkin Trans 1* **1991**, 1342.

93T6937   C. O. Kappe, *Tetrahedron* **1993**, *49*, 6937.

94JHC1647   W. Steinschifter, W. Fiala, W. Stadlbauer, *J. Heterocycl. Chem.* **1994**, *31*, 1647, and references cited therein.

95MI000   T. Kappe, R. Aigner, M. Jöbstl, P. Hohengassner, *Heterocyclic Commun.*, **1995**, *1*, in press

96M000   T. Kappe, N. J. Krake, A. Khattab, *Monatsh. Chem.* **1996**, *127*, in press

96UP000   T. Kappe, C. O. Kappe, unpublished results.

96TH000   K. Langhans, Ph. D. Thesis, University of Graz, 1996.

Chapter 2

Radical Methods in the Synthesis of Heterocyclic Compounds

Mukund P. Sibi and Jianguo Ji
North Dakota State University, Fargo, ND, USA

INTRODUCTION

Radical reactions have found increased application in the preparation of simple as well as complex heterocyclic compounds. Heterocycle syntheses in which radical reactions are used for the key bond construction are discussed in this review. Functional group interconversion such as reductions using radical methods are not included. Several reviews and key articles that discuss radical methodologies for heterocycle synthesis were published in 1995 [95BCSF1003] [95JA6603] [95MI217] [95 MI313] [95MI355] [95 MI515] [95SL217] [95T7095] [95T7579] [95T13103].

THREE MEMBERED RING

An interesting method for the preparation of epoxides using radical methodology has been reported [95AJC233]. Addition of cyclohexyl iodide **1** under reductive or non reductive conditions to ethyl t-butylperoxymethylpropenoate **2** at refluxing temperatures furnished the epoxide **4** in moderate yield. The reaction proceeds through an intramolecular homolytic displacement.

FOUR MEMBERED RING

Radical methods have found limited use in the preparation of four-membered heterocycles. Intramolecular cyclization of α-bromoeneamide (**5**) has been examined for the synthesis of β-lactams. The reaction proceeds cleanly through a 4-*exo-trig* pathway to furnish **6**. As had been previously established, this regioselectivity is dependent on the nature of the substituent on the olefin. This methodology has been applied in the synthesis of β-lactam antibiotics ($\pm$)-PS-5 (**7**) and (+)-thienamycin [95JOC1276] [95SL912].

A similar cyclization strategy has been used for the synthesis of a key methylcarbapenem intermediate **10** [95SL915]. The note worthy aspect of this work is the establishment of three contiguous chiral centers during the radical reaction.

Sakamoto and co-workers have explored a very interesting photochemical method for the preparation of β-lactams [95JOC7088]. The reaction proceeds through a hydrogen abstraction from achiral acyclic monothioimide **11**. When the photolysis is conducted in the solid state, absolute asymmetric induction takes place and the lactam **13** is produced with low enantiomeric excess.

	12	**13**	**14**
benzene, 20 °C	24%	47% (0%,ee)	12%
solid (0 °C)	48%	17% (8%,ee)	20%
solid (-45 °C)	64%	16% (20%,ee)	19%

FIVE MEMBERED RING

Formation of five-membered heterocycles through radical methodologies has been investigated extensively. Inter-, intramolecular, and cascade reactions have been reported for the synthesis of heterocycles. In the case of intramolecular cyclizations, 5-*exo* pathway is the preferred mode of reactivity. Rate constant for the formation of pyrrolidine by radical ring closure has been reported [95AJC2047].

An efficient modification of the manganese(III) mediated malonate radical addition to styrene has been examined. Use of cerium(IV) nitrate in methanol at room temperature results in the direct formation of the butyrolactone **17** in low yield along with other byproducts [95JCS(P1)1881]. Other intermolecular single electron processes for the formation of lactones have been reported [95JOC458] [95BCSF843].

Hwu *et al.* have examined the dependence of the metal oxidant on the mode of reactivity in silicon-controlled allylation of 1,3-dioxo compounds [95JOC856]. The use of manganese(III) acetate furnished the dihydrofuran product **22** only. On the other hand, use of cerium(IV) nitrate resulted in the formation of both acyclic (**23**) as well as the cyclized compound, with the product distribution dependent on the nature of the allylsilane. Facile synthesis of dihydrofurans by the cerium(IV) mediated oxidative addition of 1,3-dicarbonyl compounds to cyclic and acyclic alkenes has also been reported [95JCS(P1)187].

Sato and co-workers have investigated interesting chiral Lewis acid mediated radical addition to α–methylene-γ-butyrolactone **24** [95JOC3576] [95CC1043]. In this transformation the Lewis acid activates the carbonyl group for radical addition as well as functions as a chiral reagent. Stereocontrol of hydrogen-transfer reactions involving acyclic radicals bearing heterocyclic groups has also been investigated [95JOC288].

BuI, Bu$_3$SnH
Et$_3$B, toluene
-78 °C-20 °C
47%

24   **25** 28% ee

Intramolecular radical cyclization reactions are extensively used for the formation of heterocycles. These reactions are generally carried out under reductive conditions using tin or silicon hydride reagents. The tin hydride reagent can be used catalytically. An example of this type of protocol is shown in the formation of tetrahydrofuran nucleus [95SL95]. An added feature of this reaction is that tributyltin halide is used as a source of tin radicals as well as a Lewis acid in the regioselective reductive cleavage of product ketal (**27** → **28**). A new tetrahydrofuran annulation protocol by tandem radical cyclization followed by reductive deoxygenation has been reported [95TL1127].

Bu$_3$SnCl (0.2 eq)
NaBH$_3$CN (2 eq)
AIBN (cat), t-BuOH
reflux, 2 h 80%

26   **27**   **28**

The effect of selenium additives in the trapping of radical intermediates has been investigated [95JOC84]. The reaction of the iodoether **29** with tin hydride alone furnished the benzopyran **31** as the major product, a result arising from initial 5-*exo-trig* cyclization followed by rearrangement and indicating that the hydrogen atom transfer is slower than rearrangement. This was accompanied by minor amounts of the benzofuran **30**, a product from the normal 5-*exo-trig* cyclization followed by reduction. Addition of 10% of diphenyldiselenide gave the benzofuran as the major product, a result of more efficient hydrogen atom transfer from hydrogenphenylselenide (the product from reaction between diphenyldiselenide and tributyltin hydride). This is an example of polarity reversal catalysis.

Bu$_3$SnH, AIBN
Benzene, reflux

29   **30**   **31**

Additive	30/31 ratio
-	1/4
Ph$_2$Se$_2$	9/1

An intramolecular reductive addition of α,α–difluoro acetal radicals to olefins in a 5-*exo-trig* mode has been reported [95TL3531]. The reaction with the corresponding α–bromo-α,α–difluoroacetates gave no cyclized products. This method provides ready access to α,α–difluoro-γ-lactones **34** in good yields.

Intramolecular addition of acyl radicals to enoates proceeds in high yields. The acyl radicals are generated conveniently from acyl selenides. The application of this methodology in the stereoselective synthesis of *cis*-2,5-disubstituted tetrahydrofuran-3-ones is illustrated [95TL31].

Intramolecular addition of carbon-centered radicals to alkynes under reductive conditions has been examined by Dulcére and Rodriguez. Alkyl radical generation from **39** resulted in the formation of a substituted tetrahydrofuran **40**, a nucleoside analog [95SL923]. An improved 5-*exo-dig* process for the formation of iodomethylene lactone has been reported [95T4665].

A similar cyclization as described above has been used for the carbocyclization of bromopropargyl ethers **41** in the pyrimidinedione series using tributyltin hydride [95SL705]. If the reaction is carried out using triethylamine, carbocyclization with bromine transfer takes place (**41 → 42**). The authors suggest that this reaction proceeds through a radical pathway.

Intramolecular addition of heteroatom radicals to olefins constitutes a convenient method for the synthesis of heterocycles. The photochemical ring closure reaction of oxyl radical derived from **44** provides access to tetrahydrofuran **45** [95JOC6706]. The regioselectivity in this cyclization is excellent, however, the stereoselectivity is only modest. The stereoselectivity was dependent on the temperature of the reaction.

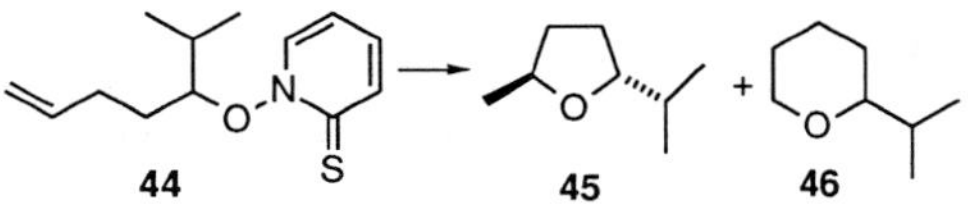

45 (t/c) : **46**

hv, 15 °C, NpSH (1.2 eq)   98 (75:25) 2
hv, 30 °C, Bu$_3$SnH, TBB   98 (69:31) 2

44   **45**   **46**

An alternative to reductive radical cyclization procedures is the use of group transfer methods. A novel group transfer cyclization reaction involving an organotellurium compound **47** has been described [95CC2515]. The bicyclic product **48** is formed as a 2:1 mixture of isomers at the terminus.

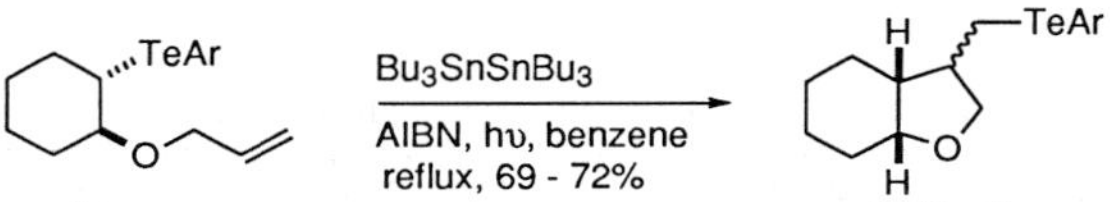

Bu$_3$SnSnBu$_3$

AIBN, hυ, benzene
reflux, 69 - 72%

47   **48** (2 : 1)

A new radical chain group transfer reaction which does not involve tin reagents has been reported. The reaction proceeds by a photosensitized electron transfer reductive activation of PhSeSiR$_3$ using 1,5-dimethoxynaphthalene as the sensitizer [95ACIE2669]. In contrast to the tellurium transfer described above, the selenium transfer reaction gave higher diastereoselectivity (4:1 vs 2:1).

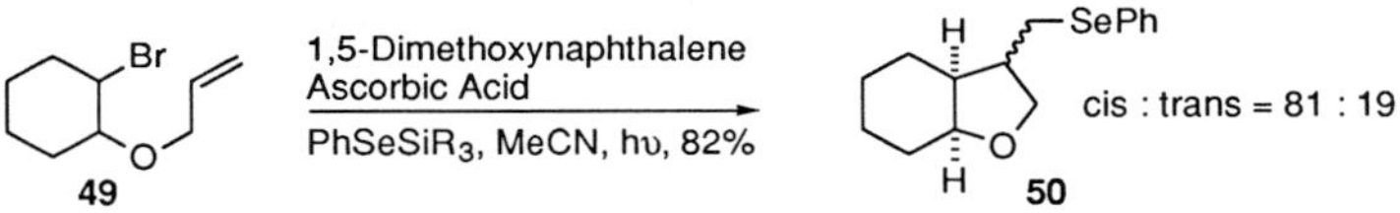

1,5-Dimethoxynaphthalene
Ascorbic Acid

PhSeSiR$_3$, MeCN, hυ, 82%

cis : trans = 81 : 19

49   **50**

A novel radical-induced C-N bond formation has been reported [95TL323]. The reaction involves the treatment of an alkyl iodide **51** with iso-amylnitrite and a trialkyltin radical precursor. The reaction is postulated to proceed through the formation of trialkyltin nitrite.

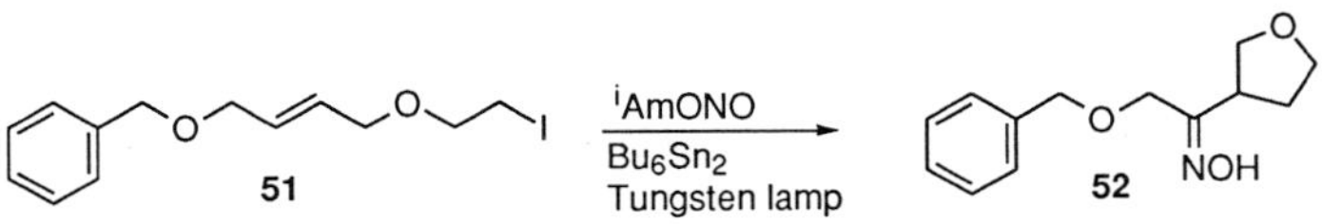

^{i}AmONO
Bu$_6$Sn$_2$
Tungsten lamp

51   **52**   NOH

The development of new radical initiators is an area of active investigation. Tada *et al.* have described a (triphenyltin)cobaloxime complex as a reagent for radical generation from bromides [95JOC6635]. This is an alternative to reductive processes involving tin hydride and allows for the introduction of an additional functional group in the product.

Intramolecular addition of vinyl radicals to olefins as a method for heterocycle synthesis has been examined. The vinyl radicals can be conveniently generated from vinyl bromides and samarium(II) diiodide [95JOC7424]. The intermediate radical after cyclization undergoes a further electron transfer from samarium to furnish a carbanion which is quenched at the end of the reaction. A samarium(II) diiodide mediated aryl radical cyclization onto a dihydrofuran has been reported [95T8555].

Molander and co-workers have studied the stereoselective intramolecular addition of ketyl radicals to olefins [95JOC872]. The ketyl radicals are generated from ketone by treatment with samarium(II) diiodide. A similar reaction sequence using **61** gave only elimination products.

Samarium(II) diiodide mediated ketyl radical addition to alkyne results in the formation of an alkene after radical cyclization [95SL277]. Compound **65**, a product from one such reaction, has been converted to the carbohydrate portion of miharamycin A, a nucleoside antibiotic.

Tandem radical addition strategies are powerful tools for the construction of complex heterocycles. Several variations in the tandem sequence are possible: intermolecular radical addition followed by intramolecular reaction; intramolecular radical reaction followed by intermolecular trapping; intramolecular addition followed by intramolecular trapping. Several factors need to be controlled in order for this methodology to be successful. Some of these are (1) preferential intermolecular attack of the radical precursor to one end of the substrate (2) regioselectivity (*exo* or *endo*) in the intramolecular addition of the intermediate radical, (3) stereochemistry in the intermolecular addition, and (4) the method of termination. The tandem addition of tosyl radical to oxa substituted diolefin **66** has been reported [95JOC6040]. The tosyl radical adds preferentially at the less substituted olefin producing the intermediate **67**. This radical undergoes intramolecular cyclization with high 5-*exo* selectivity to produce the cyclized radical which is terminated by chlorine abstraction from tosylchloride. Several aspects of the cyclization are noteworthy. The reaction proceeds with very high 1,2-diastereoselection and moderate 1,5-diastereoselection. The observed diastereoselectivity has been corroborated by theoretical calculations.

Multicomponent tandem addition reactions have been investigated by Russell and co-workers. Addition of t-butyl radical to the allyl acrylate **70** with termination from dimethyldisulfide furnishes butyrolactone **71** as a diastereomeric mixture (remote center). However, the ring junction stereochemistry is exclusively *trans* [95JA3645].

A very interesting tandem intermolecular radical addition followed by an intramolecular reaction has been reported [95BCSJ1999]. The reaction involves the addition of malonic acid amide radical to a 1,5-dialkene **72** at the internal carbon forming a stable diaryl radical. Oxidation to a diaryl cation followed by cyclization generates a pyrrolidinone or a lactone. A second radical intermediate is then generated by the manganese(III) reagent and it undergoes a radical cyclization oxidation sequence to furnish the spiro lactone **73**.

Enynes are also excellent substrates for tandem addition reactions. Pandey and co-workers have reported a photoinduced electron transfer (PET) promoted reaction of a selenium radical addition to an enyne [95T1483]. The high stereoselectivity observed in this cyclization is noteworthy.

The use of perfluoroalkyliodide in group transfer tandem additions has been examined by Wang and Lu for the preparation of butyrolactones [95T2639]. The mild reaction conditions, high chemical yield, and excellent control of alkene stereochemistry are the highlights of this methodology.

Intramolecular radical cyclization followed by trapping of the intermediate with an enone has been investigated by Fraser-Reid and co-workers [95JOC3871] as a method for the synthesis of highly functionalized C-glycosyl derivatives. The control of the anomeric stereochemistry as well as the facial selectivity in the addition to the chiral enone is impressive.

Arene diazonium tetrafluoroborates are good precursors for aryl radicals [95JOC4991]. Tetrathiafulvalene (TTF) serves as a useful catalyst for the generation of aryl radicals from diazonium salts [95JCS(P1)1349]. A tandem addition sequence involving the preparation of a benzofuran starting from an enyne and using TTF as catalyst has been reported [95JCS(P1)623].

82 → TTF, Me_2CO / H_2O, 4 days / 64% → **83** + **84** 83:84 = 84:16

Radical methods have been used as the key bond forming reactions in the synthesis of heterocycle fragments which are components of biologically active natural products. In a simple and efficient alternative to acyl selenides, the intramolecular cyclization of acyl cobalt species has been investigated [95HCA447]. The acyl radical is generated cleanly by photolysis of **85** and the intermediate organocobalt species undergoes a β-elimination to regenerate an alkene. The lactone **86** served as a key intermediate in the synthesis of (+)-multifidene **87**.

85 → hυ / CH_2Cl_2, reflux → **86** → **87** (+)-Multifidene

Radical methods are useful for the synthesis of highly functionalized enantiomerically pure cyclopentane derivatives [95SL918]. Reductive cyclization of the arabinolactone **88** furnished the *cis*-lactone **89** in quantitative yield. Exhaustive reduction with borane-dimethylsulfide gave the functionalized cyclopentane **90**.

88 → Bu_3SnH, AIBN / EtOAc, reflux 1.5 h / quant. → **89** → $BH_3 \cdot Me_2S$ → **90**

Carbocyclization of a radical derived from butyrolactone **91** onto an alkyne under reductive conditions gave the bicyclic lactone **92** in moderate yield [95JOC8179]. This intermediate was used in the total synthesis of (+)-eremantholide A **93**.

91 → Bu_3SnH, AIBN / toluene, reflux / 66% → **92** → **93** (+)-Eremantholide A

Srikrishna and co-workers have described cyclopentannulation of allyl alcohols by radical cyclizations as protocols for the synthesis of sesquiterpenes. The total synthesis of 4-epibakkenolide-A **98** wherein two radical annulations were used for key carbon-carbon bond formations is illustrated [95CC469]. Radical cyclizations based on the 5-*exo-dig* pathway have been used as the key step in the total synthesis of sporothriolide and 4-epi-ethisolide [95TL2661] and in an approach to eriolanin skeleton [95TL2067].

Intramolecular cyclization of the acetal derived from propargyl alcohol **100** under reductive conditions gave the acetal **101** in high yield [95SL893]. Compound **102** has been converted to (3S, 4R)-luffariolide E.

Radical cyclization with iodine atom transfer of a highly functionalized propiolic ester **103** using dibenzoyl peroxide as an initiator gave the α-methylene-γ-butyrolactone **104** in good yield [95T11257]. The relative stereochemistry at carbon atoms 4 and 5 are established during the reaction. The intermediate **104** has been converted to the anti-tumor agent (-)-methylenolactocin **105**.

The manganese(III) acetate mediated oxidative cyclization of β-ketoesters has been utilized to construct a pentacyclic compound in low yield [95CC403]. The intermediate radical **107** formed from an initial 6-*endo-trig* reaction undergoes further lactonization in the presence of copper(II) acetate. The compound **108** has the basic skeleton found in fungal metabolite sesquiterpene phenols.

106	Mn(OAc)$_3$ Cu(OAc)$_2$ HOAc 58 °C, 5 h 25%	**107** **108**

A short and highly stereoselective route to lignan natural products (±)-dihydrosesamin and (±)-lariciresinol using radical methods has been reported [95JCS(P1)927]. These cyclizations proceed in good yields and the stereochemistry at two contiguous chiral centers are established.

109 → NBS (0.4 eq) CH$_2$Cl$_2$, -15 °C-rt → **110** → Bu$_3$SnH AIBN, benzene 10 h → **111**

Ar=3,4-methylenedioxyphenyl
Ar=4-benzyloxy-3-methoxyphenyl

dihydrosesamin 80% (7:1)
lariciresinol 90% (7:1)

Pancrazi and co-workers have reported a 6-*endo-trig* cyclization of enyne **112** in a synthetic approach to the A-B ring of forskolin [95TL7247]. The tandem addition process using tributyltin hydride provides the tricyclic compound **113** in 60% yield.

112 → Bu$_3$SnH AIBN, Toluene heat, 60% → **113** **114** Forskolin

Enantioselectivity in the oxidative homocoupling of radicals generated from 3-acyl-2-oxazolidone **115** has been investigated [95JOC1100]. The α-acyl radical of **115** was generated by treatment with LDA, titanium tetrachloride, and in the presence of an amine reagent. The dimerization of the acyl radical gave 2,3-disubstituted succinates **116** and **117** in good yield and high diastereoselectivity. The RR isomer **116** was converted to the lignan natural product (-)-hinokinin **118**.

115   **116:117** RR : RS = 85 : 15   **118** (-)-Hinokinin

The synthesis of nitrogen containing heterocycles through radical methods has received considerable attention. Several interesting transformations have been examined for the preparation of nitrogen heterocycles. Intramolecular free radical additions to carbon-nitrogen double bonds have been investigated as a method for the synthesis of nitrogen heterocycles [95T2039]. Reductive cyclization of **119** provides 9-alkylcarbazole **120** through a 5-*exo-trig* pathway. Minor amount of the phenanthridine **121**, a product from the alternative 6-*endo* cyclization or through rearrangement is also obtained. Intramolecular tandem radical cyclization of imines has been reported [95TL5623].

119   **120** 45%   **121** 19%

Beckwith and Storey have developed a tandem translocation and homolytic aromatic substitution sequence en route to spiro-oxindoles [95CC977]. Treatment of the bromoaniline derivative **122** with tin hydride at 160 °C generated the aryl radical **123** which underwent a 1,5-hydrogen atom transfer to give intermediate **124**. Intramolecular homolytic aromatic substitution and aromatization gave the spiro-oxindole **125**. Intramolecular aryl radical cyclization on to a pyrrole nucleus has been used to prepare spirocyclic heterocycles [95TL6743].

122   **123**   **124**   **125**

Synthesis of bridged azabicyclic compounds using radical translocation reaction followed by cyclization has been reported [95JCS(P1)1801]. Treatment of bromoamide **126** with tributyltin hydride at reflux produced a mixture of **127**, the 5-*exo-trig* product, **128**, product of a 6-*endo* process, along with the reduction product **129**.

126   **127** 42% (66:34)   **128** 30%   **129** 12%

Aryl radicals are easily generated form the corresponding halides using samarium(II) diiodide and amine ligands. They can be trapped intramolecularly by an alkene in either a 5-*exo* or a 6-*endo* pathway [95TL949] [95TL1365]. The product ratio has some dependency on the nitrogen ligand used with the samarium species.

130   **131**   **132**   131:132 = 81:19

Synthesis of pyrrolidin-2-ones by cyclization through the generally disfavored 5-*endo-trig* mode has been reported [95JCS(P1)1115]. Treatment of the disulfanyl acetal **133** under reductive conditions furnished continine **134**, a nicotine metabolite in high yield. Reaction of the corresponding dichloro or monochloro compound gave none or very small amounts of the cyclized compounds.

133   **134** (±)-Continine

The addition of sulfur radicals to isocyanides produces imidoyl radicals as intermediates. The stereocontrolled 5-*exo-trig* cyclization of imidoyl radicals in the synthesis of substituted (alkylthio)pyrrolines, pyroglutamates, and thiopyroglutamates has been reported [95JOC6242]. The intermediate **137** is not isolated but undergoes further thermal reaction to furnish a pyroglutamate derivative.

Intramolecular cyclization of N-alkenyl-2-bromoindoles has been described. The formation of five as well as six-membered ring in the radical cyclization proceeds in good yield [95TL4857]. A novel intramolecular free radical aromatic *ipso* substitution reaction has been reported [95CC1353]. Treatment of **138** with tributyltin hydride generates an alkyl radical which attacks the alkene at the carbon bearing the sulfur substituent. This is followed by elimination of the sulfur substituent to provide the cyclized products **139** in moderate yields. The efficiency of the reaction is dependent on the size of the ring formed and on the sulfur substituent.

Preparation of fluorinated organic compounds is important. Uneyama and co-workers have investigated the generation and reactions of trifluoroacetimidoyl radicals [95BCSJ1497]. The imidoyl radicals can be generated under three different conditions and it undergoes clean 5-*exo* cyclizations to provide 3-substituted indoles in moderate yields.

Das and co-workers have described the generation of α–aminoalkyl radicals from cyclic secondary amines using anthraquinone-photocatalysis [95JCS(P1)1797]. The conjugate addition of the α–aminoalkyl radical to enoates has been examined. The cyclized compound is obtained directly from the reaction. The chemical yield of **149** is low and it is accompanied by **148**, a product arising from nucleophilic addition of the amine to the crotonate.

Preparation of chiral nitroxide radicals is important because of their potential as molecules with unique optoelectronic properties. The radical enolate **151** was generated from **150** on treatment with samarium(II) diiodide at low temperatures [95JOC6820]. The intermediate enolate was acylated to provide the stable free radical **152** in good yield.

Tandem radical additions have also been utilized for the synthesis of nitrogen containing heterocycles. These reactions have the same requirements as those discussed for the oxygen heterocycles. The reductive addition of phenylsulfanyl radicals to the unsaturated amide **153** has been investigated [95JCS(P1)19]. The nucleophilic radical adds selectively to the enamide followed by 5-*exo*-cyclization to give **154** in excellent yield with high *trans* selectivity.

Tandem addition of sulfonyl radical followed by capture of the intermediate alkyl radical with aryldiselenide (disulfide) has been investigated for heterocycle formation. The sulfonyl radical can be conveniently generated from the corresponding sodium salt in aqueous acetic acid [95SC3549]. The chemical yields for the preparation of both nitrogen and oxygen heterocycles are moderate to good, however the stereoselectivity is poor.

A group transfer tandem addition of bromotrichloromethane to diallyl amine **157** has been reported [95SC3529]. The radical reaction can be initiated using either azobisisobutyronitrile (AIBN) or manganese(III) acetate electrochemically. It should be noted that the *cis* diastereomer is formed as the major product.

Strategies involving tandem radical additions play an important role in the construction of nitrogen containing natural products. Intramolecular reductive tandem addition has been used for the construction of *Pseudocopsinine* and *Aspidosperma* alkaloid models [95SL507]. The reaction establishes two contiguous chiral centers in **160** but proceeds in low yield. A reductive 5-*exo* aryl radical cyclization onto an enamine furnished a key intermediate in the synthesis of isoindolobenazepine alkaloid chilenine [95TL6733].

Boger and co-workers have examined intramolecular radical addition followed by intermolecular trapping en route to simplified analogs of CC-1065 and duocarmycin alkylation subunits [95JOC1271]. The trapping of the alkyl radical with TEMPO provides a convenient method for the introduction of oxygen containing functional groups.

The use of an azide as an efficient radical acceptor with concomitant nitrogen elimination has been applied for the preparation of an intermediate in aspidospermidine synthesis [95CC1409]. Reductive cyclization of **165** at reflux temperature furnished **166**, the ABCE tetracyclic portion of aspidospermidine **167**, in 95% yield. The cyclization establishes three contiguous chiral centers.

Curran and co-workers have explored cascade radical reactions, a formal [4+1] annulation strategy, for the synthesis of camptothecin and analogs [95ACIE2683]. Treatment of the pyridone **168** with phenyl isocyanide and hexamethylditin furnished the intermediate **169**. Formation of the five-membered ring followed by radical attack onto the aromatic ring gave the natural product **170** in 45% yield. Similar routes were employed for the synthesis of topotecan, irinotecan, and GI-147211C.

An asymmetric synthesis of novel tin functionalized carbopenem system through radical cyclization of an enyne has been reported [95TA1055]. Treatment of the β-lactam **171** with tributyltin hydride resulted in the addition of tin radical to the alkyne followed by 5-*exo* cyclization to provide **172** in 80% yield. The product was obtained as a 88:12 mixture of diastereomers.

Radical methods have found limited application in the synthesis of sulfur heterocycles. A tandem tosyl radical addition and intramolecular trapping by a thiophene ring has been investigated [95SL763]. Cyclization under sonication or thermal conditions gave the thiophene in 77-81% chemical yield.

Axon and Beckwith have examined diastereoselective radical addition to methyleneoxazolidinones as a method for the synthesis of α-amino acids [95CC549]. Treatment of the oxazolidinone 176 with the iodo sugar 177 under reductive conditions gave 178 in high yield as a single diastereomer. The stereochemistry of the hydrogen atom transfer step is controlled by the bulky t-butyl group. Compound 177 on reduction gave the C-glycosyl alanine 179.

The use of solid-state photochemical reaction for heterocycle synthesis has been investigated [95JOC4682]. Photolysis of S-phenyl N-(benzoylformyl)thiocarbamates 180 gave oxazolidindiones 183 in low yields along with other byproducts. The photolysis product 183 is produced in 46% ee and the experiment constitutes an example of *absolute* asymmetric synthesis.

The temporary silicon connection method introduced by Stork is a useful protocol for the preparation of silaoxacycles. The C-Si bond in the silaoxacycles is readily converted to C-OH with retention of stereochemistry by oxidative procedures. Utimoto and co-workers have developed a novel method for the synthesis of triols using the temporary silicon connection method [95BCSJ625]. Treatment of the silacycle 184 with tin hydride furnished a mixture of silacycles, which were converted to the triacetate 187 without isolation. The *endo* isomer 185 was formed as the major compound.

Fraser-Reid and co-workers have examined serial radical cyclization of pyranose-derivatives [95AJC333] in the stereocontrolled synthesis of Woodward's reserpine precursor [95JOC3859]. Treatment of the bromosilane **188** under reductive conditions resulted in a 5-*exo* followed by a 6-*exo* cyclization. The intermediate radical eliminates phenylsulfinyl radical to provide the alkene **189** as the product. The intermediate has been converted to the reserpine precursor **190**. The temporary silicon method has been utilized for the synthesis of brassinolide side chain [95SL850].

Formation of bonds to heteroatoms using radical methods have received sparse attention. Fong and Schiesser have reported the first example of an amidyl radical attack on selenium [95TL7329]. The reaction of **191** with benzoyl peroxide at high temperature gave the clinically important ebselene **192** in moderate yield. Use of di-t-butylperoxide gave a low yield of the target molecule. N-alkyl analogs of ebselen were prepared in high yields using similar radical cyclization protocol.

A simple method for the preparation of 1,3-dithiol-2-ones **196** using radical methodology has been reported [95CC1429]. The reaction involves heating of diisopropyl xanthogen disulfide **193** with a terminal alkyne at 80 °C in the presence of a radical initiator. The reaction conditions are compatible with a variety of functional groups on the alkyne.

SIX MEMBERED RING

Formation of six-membered rings by radical cyclization is less common as compared to the construction of five-membered rings. Of the two available pathways for ring formation, the 6-*exo-trig* (*dig*) mode is more accessible. Examples on the use of the alternate 6-*endo-trig* pathway for ring formation are also known.

In an elegant demonstration of the utility of radical methodologies in natural product synthesis, Lee *et al.* have applied two independent cyclizations to construct the *cis*-2,6-disubstituted pyran fragment of dactomelyne [95JA8017]. Reductive cyclization of the trichloro alkene **197** gave a dichloropyran which was dehalogenated to furnish **198** in good yield. A second radical cyclization of dibromoalkene **199** allows for the formation of the other pyran ring with the desired *trans* relationship of the C-Br and the acetic acid side chain. The bicyclic compound **200** has been converted to dactomelyne **201**.

A 6-*exo-trig* cyclization of a pyran derived radical onto an oxime has been employed as the key step in the synthesis of *Amaryllidace* alkaloid (+)-7-deoxypancratistatin [95JA7289]. Treatment of **202** under reductive cyclization conditions gave **203** as a single stereoisomer in good yield. The compatibility of the radical reaction conditions with the dense functionality present in **202** is noteworthy.

The fragmentation of nitrate esters to carbon radicals under thermal or photochemical conditions has been exploited by Batsanov and co-workers in the stereoselective construction of δ-lactones [95JCS(P1)1281]. Treatment of **205** with tin hydride in refluxing benzene gave the 6-*exo-trig* cyclization product **206** in good yield and high stereoselectivity.

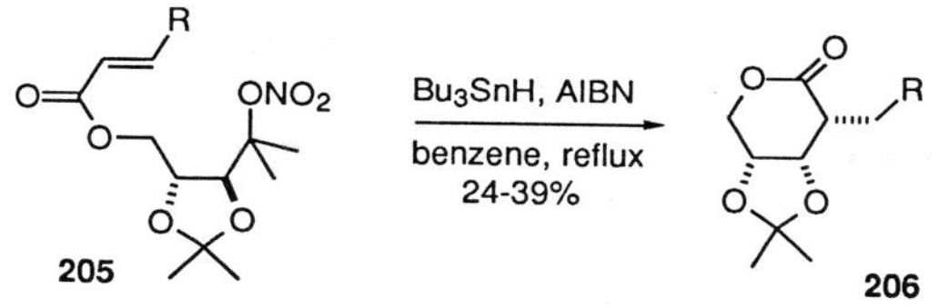

205 → **206**

Bu$_3$SnH, AIBN

benzene, reflux
24-39%

An enantioselective reduction of an α–iodolactone under radical conditions has been reported [95CC481]. Treatment of **207** with tin hydride, magnesium(II) iodide and in the presence of a chiral amine gave the δ-lactone **208** in good yield and moderate enantioselectivity. This is one of the first examples of chiral Lewis acid mediated enantioselective radical reactions.

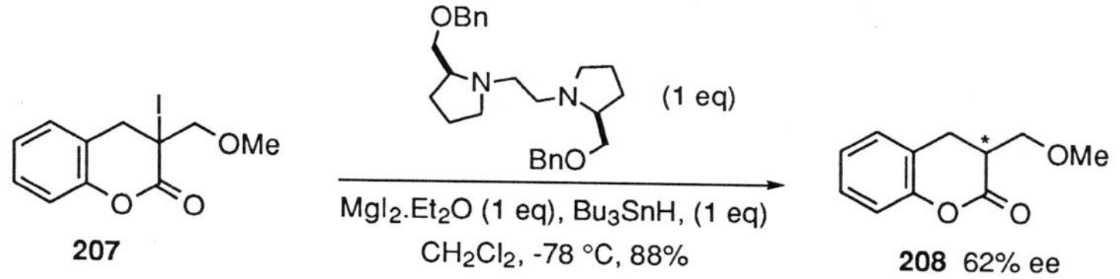

207 → **208** 62% ee

(1 eq)

MgI$_2$.Et$_2$O (1 eq), Bu$_3$SnH, (1 eq)
CH$_2$Cl$_2$, -78 °C, 88%

Several different radical methods are available for the synthesis of six-membered nitrogen heterocycles. A manganese(III) acetate promoted addition of amino malonate radical to an alkene has been utilized for the preparation of an intermediate in the synthesis of loracarbef [95JOC6176]. The intermediate tertiary radical obtained by the 6-*exo-trig* process is trapped intramolecularly by one of the ester groups of the malonate.

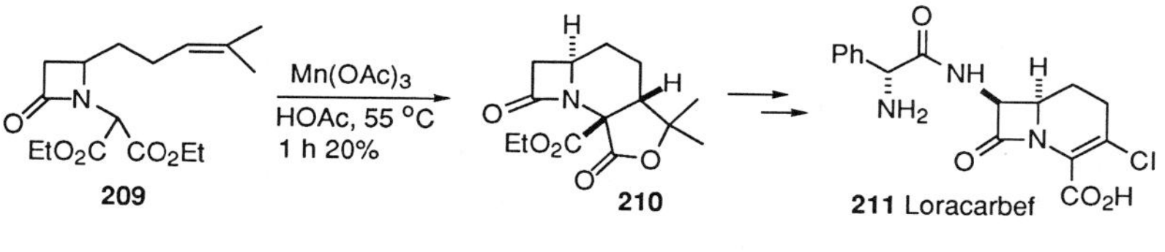

209 → **210** → **211** Loracarbef

Mn(OAc)$_3$
HOAc, 55 °C
1 h 20%

The intermolecular addition of an alkyl radical to an enaminoketone in a 6-*exo-trig* mode has been investigated [95TL417]. Reductive cyclization of **212** provides a diastereomeric mixture of **213** in excellent yield. Compound **213** has been transformed to the piperidine alkaloid dihydropinidine **214**.

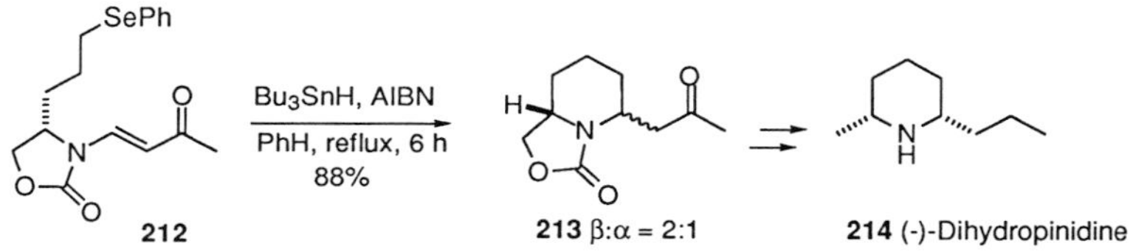

212

Bu$_3$SnH, AIBN
PhH, reflux, 6 h
88%

213 β:α = 2:1

214 (-)-Dihydropinidine

α–Halo amides are useful substrates for the preparation of nitrogen containing heterocycles by radical methods [95JOC7161]. Bonjoch *et. al* have reported the first synthesis of melinonine-E **217**, a quaternary indole alkaloid, by using a 6-*exo-trig* radical cyclization of an α–halo amide as the key step [95CC2141].

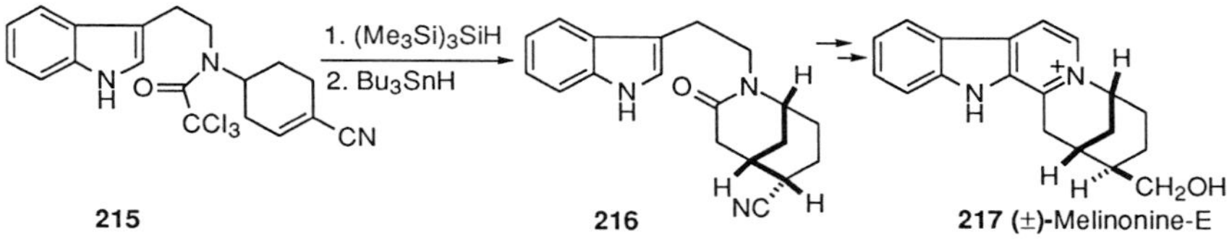

215

1. (Me$_3$Si)$_3$SiH
2. Bu$_3$SnH

216

217 ($\pm$)-Melinonine-E

Imines have been employed as radical acceptors in the preparation of nitrogen heterocycles [95AJC291]. A highly selective 6-*endo-trig* radical cyclization onto a chiral aldehyde imine has been developed by Werstiuk *et al*. Reductive cyclization of **218** provides a 3.8:1 diastereomeric mixture of the tetrahydroisoquinoline **219**. A minor amount of **220**, a product arising from a 5-*exo* cyclization is also produced.

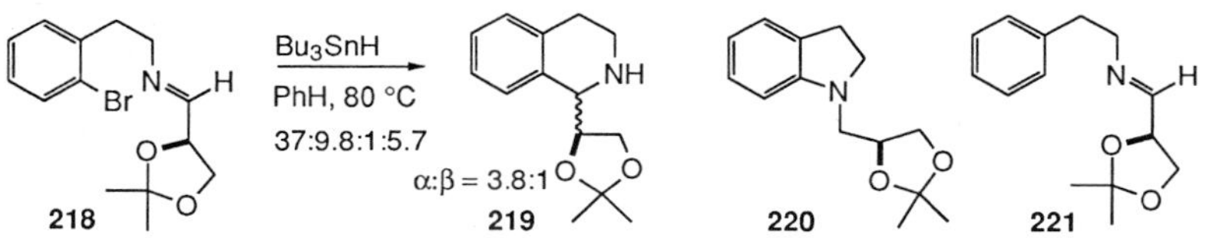

218

Bu$_3$SnH
PhH, 80 °C
37:9.8:1:5.7
α:β = 3.8:1

219

220

221

An unusual 1,2-aryl radical rearrangement from carbon to nitrogen has been investigated by Kim and Do [95CC1607]. Treatment of the azide **222** with tin hydride in refluxing benzene gave the phenanthridine **223**. The yield of **223** was high when R was a phenyl group while the aminofluorene **224** was the major product when R was a methyl group.

222

Bu$_3$SnH (0.2 eq)
AIBN (0.05 eq)
12-83%

223 R = Ph 83%
R = Me 12%

224 R = Ph 14%
R = Me 78%

Tandem radical additions have been used in the preparation of piperidines. Substituted nitrogen containing heterocycles with ring sizes ranging from 5-8 have been synthesized by radical methods [95JCS(P1)19]. Addition of sulfur radicals to **225** occurs selectively at the enamide portion followed by an intramolecular 6-*exo* cyclization to produce a diastereomeric mixture of **226** in good yield.

225

(PhS)$_2$, PhSH, hυ
82%

226 (cis:trans = 65:22)

Other reported procedures for the preparation of nitrogen heterocycles involve the use of [bis(1-adamantylcarbonyloxy)iodo]arenes in substitution and addition reactions [95JCS(P1)2135], radical cation [4+2] cycloaddition with 2-vinylindoles [95ACIE1900], reactions of trifluoroacetimidol radicals [95BCSJ1497], synthesis of thienoquinoline and thienoisoquinolines via photocyclization [95S1131], and intramolecular homolytic aromatic substitutions [95TL4307].

Hwu *et al* have investigated the intermolecular carbon radical addition to diallyl silanes and allylvinyl silanes [95JOC2448]. Addition of α–keto radical generated at high temperature using manganese((IV) dioxide to dimethyldiallyl silane **228** furnished the silacycle **231** in good yield with the intramolecular step proceeding through an 6-*endo-trig* mode. It is interesting that the product arising from the kinetically favored 5-*exo-trig* cyclization is not formed in this cyclization.

227 **228**

MnO$_2$ (2.5eq)
HOAc, 140 °C
81%

229 **230** **231**

1,2-dioxanes are common structural features present in compounds exhibiting high biological activity against malaria. The O-O bond in 1,2-dioxanes can be installed through an intramolecular peroxy radical addition to an alkene [95JHC1783]. A process involving the addition of peroxy radical to an olefin followed by trapping of the intermediate radical with molecular oxygen has been utilized in the synthesis of yingzhaosu C **234**, an antimalarial isolated from the roots of a rare perennial vine yingzhao [95TL4167].

232   O$_2$, PhH / t-BuOOH di t-butyl peroxyoxalatte   **233**   **234** Yingzhaosu C

LARGE RINGS

Very few reports describe the use of radical methods in the construction of large ring heterocycles (>7). A peroxydicarbonate-mediated hydrogen atom abstraction from an aldimine followed by cyclization onto an aromatic ring has been applied to the synthesis of dibenzoxazepines **237** [95T12143]. The yield of the heterocyclic product is low.

235   DPDC (2 eq) PhH, 60 °C / 24-54 h / 11-19%   **236**   **237**

An unusual 8-*endo-trig* radical cyclization has been reported. Selective addition of sulfanyl radical to the enamide portion of **239** followed by cyclization gave the 8-membered heterocycle **239** in low yield along with the adduct **240** [95JCS(P1)19]. Formation of larger rings using the same methodology was unsuccessful.

238   (PhS)$_2$, PhSH, hυ   **239** 19%   +   **240** 26%

A radical fragmentation sequence has been used for the preparation of 8-membered cyclic imides [95H49]. Treatment of the carbinolamide **241** with diacetoxyiodobenzene gave the imide **244** in low yield. The major product in this reaction is a 5-membered cyclic imide, a product arising from an alternative C-C bond cleavage.

Synthesis of 12- and 13-membered sulfur-containing lactones by homolytic macrocyclization of mercaptoacetic esters and alkynes has been investigated [95S307]. Reaction of the mercaptoester **245** with alkynes using triethyl borane radical initiation gave the macrolactones **247** and **248** in low yield [95TL2293]. Remote asymmetric induction is observed during the cyclization.

Other radical methods for heterocycle synthesis involve $S_{RN}1$ reactions. The synthesis of indoles [95BCSF306], imidazoles [95JOC8015], imidazopyrimdines [95T9643], and substituted 1,3-dioxanes [95JCS(P1)609] have been reported.

REFERENCES

95ACIE1900 Gürtler, C. F.; Blechert, S.; Steckhan, E. *Angew. Chem., Int. Ed. Engl.* **1995**, *34*, 1900.

95ACIE2669 Pandey, G.; Poleshwar Rao, K. S. S. *Angew. Chem., Int. Ed. Engl.* **1995**, *34*, 2669.

95ACIE2683 Curran, D. P.; Ko, S.-B.; Josien, H. *Angew. Chem., Int. Ed. Engl.* **1995**, *34*, 2683.

95AJC233 Degueil-Castaing, M.; Navarro, C.; Ramon, F.; Mailard, B. *Aust. J. Chem.* **1995**, *48*, 233.

95AJC291 Tomaszewski, M. J.; Warkentin, J.; Werstiuk, N. H. *Aust. J. Chem.* **1995**, *48*, 291.

95AJC333 Lopéz, J. C.; Gómez, A. M.; Fraser-Reid, B *Aust. J. Chem.* **1995**, *48*, 333.

95AJC2047 Della, E. W.; Knill, A. M. *Aust. J. Chem.* **1995**, *48*, 2047.

95BCSF306 Beugelmans, R.; Chbani, M. *Bull. Soc. Chim Fr* **1995**, *132*, 306.

95BCSF843 Nédélec, J-Y.; Lachaise, I.; Nohair, K.; Paugam, J. P.; Hakiki, M. *Bull. Chem. Soc. Fr.* **1995**, *132*, 843.

95BCSF1003 Carboni, B.; Vaultier, M. *Bull. Soc. Chim Fr* **1995**, *132*, 1003.

95BCSJ625 Matsumoto, K.; Miura, K.; Oshima, K.; Utimoto, K. *Bull. Chem. Soc. Jpn.* **1995**, *68*, 625.

95BCSJ1497   Dan-oh, Y.; Matta, H.; Uemura, J.; Watanabe, H.; Uneyama, K. *Bull. Chem. Soc. Jpn.* **1995**, *68*, 1497.

95BCSJ1999   Nishino, H.; Hashimoto, H.; Korp, J. D.; Kurosawa, K. *Bull. Chem. Soc. Jpn.* **1995**, *68*, 1999.

95CC403   Crombie, B. S.; Redhouse, A. D.; Smith, C.; Wallace, T. W. *J. Chem. Soc., Chem. Commun.* **1995**, 403.

95CC469   Srikrishna, A.; Viswajanani, R.; Sattigeri, J. A. *J. Chem. Soc., Chem. Commun.* **1995**, 469.

95CC481   Murakata, M.; Tsutsui, H.; Hoshino, O. *J. Chem. Soc., Chem. Commun.* **1995**, 481.

95CC549   Axon, J. R.; Beckwith, A. L. J. *J. Chem. Soc., Chem. Commun.* **1995**, 549.

95CC957   Kar, S., Lahiri, S. *J. Chem. Soc., Chem. Commun.* **1995**, 957.

95CC977   Beckwith, A. L. J.; Storey, J. M. D. *J. Chem. Soc., Chem. Commun.* **1995**, 977.

95CC1043   Urabe, H.; Kobayashi, K.; Sato, F. *J. Chem. Soc., Chem. Commun.* **1995**, 1043.

95CC1353   Caddick, S.; Aboutayab, K.; West, R. I. *J. Chem. Soc., Chem. Commun.* **1995**, 1353.

95CC1409   Kizil, M.; Murphy, J. A. *J. Chem. Soc., Chem. Commun.* **1995**, 1409.

95CC1429   Gareau, Y. *J. Chem. Soc., Chem. Commun.* **1995**, 1429.

95CC1607   Kim, S.; Do, J. Y. *J. Chem. Soc., Chem. Commun.* **1995**, 1607.

95CC2141   Quirante, J.; Escolano, C.; Bosch, J.; Bonjoch, J. *J. Chem. Soc., Chem. Commun.* **1995**, 2141.

95CC2515   Engman, L.; Gupta, V. *J. Chem. Soc., Chem. Commun.* **1995**, 2515.

95H49   Hernández, R.; Melian, D.; Prange, T.; Suarez, E. *Heterocycles* **1995**, *41*, 439.

95HCA447   Hemamalini, S.; Scheffold, R. *Helv. Chim. Acta.* **1995**, *78*, 447.

95JA3645   Russell, G. A.; Li, C.; Chen, P. *J. Am. Chem. Soc.* **1995**, *117*, 3645.

95JA6603   Curran, D. P.; Xu, J.; Lazzarini, E. *J. Am. Chem. Soc.* **1995**, *117*, 6603.

95JA7289   Keck, G. E.; McHardy, S. F.; Murry, J. A. *J. Am. Chem. Soc.* **1995**, *117*, 7289.

95JA8017   Lee, E.; Park, C. M.; Yun, J. S. *J. Am. Chem. Soc.* **1995**, *117*, 8017.

95JCS(P1)19   Naito, T.; Honda, Y.; Miyata, O.; Ninomiya, I. *J. Chem. Soc., Perkin. Trans. 1* **1995**, 19.

95JCS(P1)187   Nair, V.; Mathew, J. *J. Chem. Soc., Perkin. Trans. 1* **1995**, 187.

95JCS(P1)271   Morikawa, T.; Washio, Y.; Harada, S.; Hanai, R.; Kayashita, T.; Nemoto, H.; Shiro, M.; Taguchi, T. *J. Chem. Soc., Perkin. Trans. 1* **1995**, 271.

95JCS(P1)609   Beugelmans, R.;Madjdabadi, A. A.; Gharbaoui, T.; Lechevallier, A. *J. Chem. Soc., Perkin. Trans. 1* **1995**, 609.

95JCS(P1)623   Fletcher, R. J.; Lampard, C.; Murphy, J. A.; Lewis, N. *J. Chem. Soc., Perkin. Trans. 1* **1995**, 623.

95JCS(P1)927   Maiti, G.; Adhikari, S.; Roy, S. C. *J. Chem. Soc., Perkin. Trans. 1* **1995**, 927.

95JCS(P1)1115   Sato, T.; Chono, N.; Ishibashi, H.; Ikeda, M. *J. Chem. Soc., Perkin. Trans. 1* **1995**, 1115.

95JCS(P1)1281   Batsanov, A. S.; Begley, M. J.; Fletcher, R. J.; Murphy, J. A.; Sherburn, M. S. *J. Chem. Soc., Perkin. Trans. 1* **1995**, 1281.

95JCS(P1)1349   Murphy, J. A.; Roome, S. J. *J. Chem. Soc., Perkin. Trans. 1* **1995**, 1349.

95JCS(P1)1797   Das, S.; Kumar, J. S. D.; Shivaramayya, K.; George, M. V. *J. Chem. Soc., Perkin. Trans. 1* **1995**, 1797.

95JCS(P1)1801   Sato, T.; Kugo, Y.; Nakaumi, E.; Ishibashi, H.; Ikeda, M. *J. Chem. Soc., Perkin. Trans. 1* **1995**, 1801.

95JCS(P1)1881 Nair, V.; Mathew, J. *J. Chem. Soc., Perkin. Trans. 1* **1995**, 1881.

95JCS(P1)2135 Togo, H.; Taguchi, R.; Yamaguchi, K.; Yokoyama, M. *J. Chem. Soc., Perkin. Trans. 1* **1995**, 2135.

95JHC1783 Ouyang, J.; Nishino, H.; Kurosawa, K. *J. Het. Chem.* **1995**, *32*, 1783.

95JOC84 Crich, D.; Yao, Q. *J. Org. Chem.* **1995**, *60*, 84.

95JOC288 Guindon, Y.; Slassi, A.; Rancourt, J.; Bantle, G.; Bencheqroun, M.; Murtagh, L.; Ghiro, E.; Jung, G. *J. Org. Chem.* **1995**, *60*, 288.

95JOC458 Ohno, T.; Ishino, Y.; Tsumagari, Y.; Nishiguchi, I. *J. Org. Chem.* **1995**, *60*, 458.

95JOC856 Hwu, J. R.; Chen, C. N.; Shiao, S.-S. *J. Org. Chem.* **1995**, *60*, 856.

95JOC872 Molander, G. A.; McKie, J. A. *J. Org. Chem.* **1995**, *60*, 872.

95JOC1100 Kise, N.; Tokioka, K.; Aoyama, Y.; Matsumara, Y. *J. Org. Chem.* **1995**, *60*, 1100.

95JOC1271 Boger, D. L.; McKie, J. A. *J. Org. Chem.* **1995**, *60*, 1271.

95JOC1276 Ishibashi, H.; Kameoka, C.; Iriyama, H.; Kodama, K.; Sato, T.; Ikeda, M. *J. Org. Chem.* **1995**, *60*, 1276.

95JOC2448 Hwu, J. R.; Chen, B.-L.; Shiao, S.-S. *J. Org. Chem.* **1995**, *60*, 2448.

95JOC3576 Urabe, H.; Yamashita, K.; Suzuki, K.; Kobayashi, K.; Sato, F. *J. Org. Chem.* **1995**, *60*, 3576.

95JOC3859 Gómez, A. M.; López, J. C.; Fraser-Reid, B. *J. Org. Chem.* **1995**, *60*, 3859.

95JOC3871 López, J. C.; Gómez, A. M.; Fraser-Reid, B. *J. Org. Chem.* **1995**, *60*, 3871.

95JOC4682 Sakamoto, M.; Takahashi, M.; Fujita, T.; Nishio, T.; Iida, I.; Watanabe, S. *J. Org. Chem.* **1995**, *60*, 4682.

95JOC4991 Wassmundt, F. W.; Pedemonte, R. P. *J. Org. Chem.* **1995**, *60*, 4991.

95JOC6040 Bertrand, M. P.; De Riggi, I.; Lesueur, C.; Gastaldi, S.; Nouguier, R.; Jaime, C.; Virgili, A. *J. Org. Chem.* **1995**, *60*, 6040.

95JOC6176 Crocker, P. J.; Miller, M. J. *J. Org. Chem.* **1995**, *60*, 6176.

95JOC6242 Bachi, M. D.; Melman, A. *J. Org. Chem.* **1995**, *60*, 6242.

95JOC6635 Tada, M.; Kaneko, K. *J. Org. Chem.* **1995**, *60*, 6635.

95JOC6706 Hartung, J.; Gallou, F. *J. Org. Chem.* **1995**, *60*, 6706.

95JOC6820 Tamura, R.; Susuki, S.; Azuma, N.; Matsumoto, A.; Toda, F.; Ishii, Y. *J. Org. Chem.* **1995**, *60*, 6820.

95JOC7088 Sakamoto, M.; Takahashi, M.; Shimizu, M.; Fujita, T.; Nishio, T.; Iida, I.; Yamaguchi, K.; Watanabe, S. *J. Org. Chem.* **1995**, *60*, 7088.

95JOC7161 Kitagawa, O.; Kikuchi, N.; Hanano, T.; Aoki, K.; Yamazaki, T.; Okada, M.; Taguchi, T. *J. Org. Chem.* **1995**, *60*, 7161.

95JOC7424 Capella, L.; Montevecchi, P. C.; Navacchia, M. L. *J. Org. Chem.* **1995**, *60*, 7424.

95JOC8015 Chahma, M.; Combellas, C.; Thiébault, A. *J. Org. Chem.* **1995**, *60*, 8015.

95JOC8179 Takao, K-i.; Ochiai, H.; Yoshida, K-i.; Hashizuka, T.; Koshimura, H.; Tadano, K.; Ogawa, S. *J. Org. Chem.* **1995**, *60*, 8179.

95MI217 Davies, A. G. In *Comprehensive Organometallic Chemistry II* ; Abel, E. W., Stone, F. G. A., Wilkinson, G., Eds.; Pergamon: Oxford, 1995; vol. 2, pp. 217.

95MI313 Colvin, E. W. In *Comprehensive Organometallic Chemistry II* ; Abel, E. W., Stone, F. G. A., Wilkinson, G., Eds.; Pergamon: Oxford, 1995; vol. 11, pp. 313.

95MI355 Sato, T. In *Comprehensive Organometallic Chemistry II* ; Abel, E. W., Stone, F. G. A., Wilkinson, G., Eds.; Pergamon: Oxford, 1995; vol. 11, pp. 355.

95MI515   Krief, A. In *Comprehensive Organometallic Chemistry II* ; Abel, E. W., Stone, F. G. A., Wilkinson, G., Eds.; Pergamon: Oxford, 1995; vol. 11, pp. 515.

95S307   Demchuk, D. V.; Lazareva, M. L.; Lindeman, S. V.; Khrustalyov, V. N.; Struchkov, Y. T.; Ismagilov, R. F.; Troyansky, E. I.; Nikishin, G. I. *Synthesis* **1995**, 307.

95S1131   Marzinzik, A. L.; Rademacher, P. *Synthesis* **1995**, 1131.

95SC3529   Lachaise, I.; Nohair, K.; Hakiki, M.; Nédélec, J. Y. *Synth. Commun.* **1995**, *25*, 3529.

95SC3549   Chuang, C.-P.; Wang, S.-F. *Synth. Commun.* **1995**, *25*, 3549.

95SL53   Aitken, R. A.; Bradbury, C. K.; Burns, G.; Morrison, J. J. *Synlett* **1995**, 53.

95SL95   Srikrishna, A.; Viswajanani, R. *Synlett* **1995**, 95.

95SL217   Feldman, K. S. *Synlett* **1995**, 217.

95SL277   Fairbanks, A. J.; Sinaÿ, P. *Synlett* **1995**, 277.

95SL507   Parsons, P. J.; Penkett, C. S.; Cramp, M. C.; West, R. I.; Warrington, J.; Saraiva, M. C. *Synlett* **1995**, 507.

95SL705   Dulcère, J.-P., Baret, N.; Rodriguez, J.; Faure, R. *Synlett* **1995**, 705.

95SL763   Chuang, C.-P.; Wang, S.-F. *Synlett* **1995**, 763.

95SL850   Koreeda, M.; Wu, J. *Synlett* **1995**, 850.

95SL893   Hareau-Vittini, G.; Kocienski, P. J. *Synlett* **1995**, 893.

95SL912   Ishibashi, H.; Kodama, K.; Kameoka, C.; Kawanami, H.; Ikeda, M. *Synlett* **1995**, 912.

95SL915   Ishibashi, H.; Kameoka, C.; Kodama, K.; Ikeda, M. *Synlett* **1995**, 915.

95SL918   Horneman, A. M.; Lundt, I.; Søtofte, I. *Synlett* **1995**, 918.

95SL923   Dulcère, J. P.; Rodriguez, B. J. *Synlett* **1995**, 923.

95T1483   Pandey, G.; Sekhar, B. B. V. S. *Tetrahedron* **1995**, *51*, 1483.

95T2039   Gioanola, M.; Leardini, R.; Nanni, D.; Pareschi, P.; Zanardi, G. *Tetrahedron* **1995**, *51*, 2039.

95T2639   Wang, Z.; Lu, X. *Tetrahedron* **1995**, *51*, 2639.

95T4665   Mawson, S. D.; Routledge, A.; Weavers, R. T. *Tetrahedron* **1995**, *51*, 4665.

95T7095   Majetich, G.; Wheless, K. Tetrahedron **1995**, *51*, 7095.

95T7579   Dalko, P. I. *Tetrahedron* **1995**, *51*, 7579.

95T8555   Holzapfel, C. W.; Williams, D. B. G. *Tetrahedron* **1995**, *51*, 8555.

95T9643   Roubaud, C.; Vanelle, P.; Maldonado, J.; Crozet, M. P. *Tetrahedron* **1995**, *51*, 9643.

95T11257   Mawson, S. D. Weaver, R. T. *Tetrahedron* **1995**, *51*, 11257.

95T12143   Leardini, R.; McNab, H.; Nanni, D. *Tetrahedron*, **1995**, *51*, 12143.

95T13103   Bunce, R. A. *Tetrahedron,* **1995**, *51*, 13103

95TA1055   Alcaide, B.; Benito, J. L.; Rodríguez-Campos, I. M.; Rodríguez-López, J.; Rodríguez-Vicente, A.; Sierra, M. A.; García-Granda, S.; Gutíerrez-Rodríguez, G. *Tetrahedron: Asymm.* **1995**, *6*, 1055.

95TL31   Evans, P. A.; Roseman, J. D. *Tetrahedron Lett.* **1995**, *36*, 31.

95TL323   Fletcher, R. J.; Kizil, M.; Murphy, J. A. *Tetrahedron Lett.* **1995**, *36*, 323.

95TL417   Lee, E.; Kang, T. S.; Joo, B. J.; Tae, J. S.; Li, K. S.; Chung, C. K. *Tetrahedron Lett.* **1995**, *36*, 417.

95TL949   Cabri, W.; Candiani, I.; Colombo, M.; Franzoi, L.; Bedeschi, A. *Tetrahedron Lett.* **1995**, *36*, 949.

95TL1127   Srikrishna, A.; Viswajanani, R.; Yelamaggad, C. V. *Tetrahedron Lett.* **1995**, *36*, 1127.

95TL1365   Santagostino, M.; Kilburn, J. D. *Tetrahedron Lett.* **1995**, *36*, 1365.

95TL2067   Cossy, J.; Ranaivosata, J.-L.; Bellosta, V. *Tetrahedron Lett.* **1995**, *36*, 2067.

95TL2293   Troyansky, E. I.; Ismagilov, R. F.; Strelenko, Y. A.; Samosphin, V. V.; Demchuk, D. V.; Nikishin, G. I.; Lindeman, S. V.; Khrustalyov, V. V.; Struchkov, Y. T. *Tetrahedron Lett.* **1995**, *36*, 2293.

95TL2661   Sharma, G. V. M.; Krishnudu, K. *Tetrahedron Lett.* **1995**, *36*, 2661.

95TL3531   Itoh, T.; Ohara, H.; Emoto, S. *Tetrahedron Lett.* **1995**, *36*, 3531.

95TL4167   Boukouvalas, J.; Pouliot, R.; Fréchette, Y. *Tetrahedron Lett.* **1995**, *36*, 4167.

95TL4307   Araneo, S.; Fontana, F.; Minisci, F.; Recupero, F.; Serri, A. *Tetrahedron Lett.* **1995**, 36, 4307.

95TL4857   Dobbs, A. P.; Jones, K.; Veal, K. T. *Tetrahedron Lett.* **1995**, *36*, 4857.

95TL5623   Bowman, W. R.; Stephenson, P. T.; Young, A. R. *Tetrahedron Lett.* **1995**, *36*, 5623.

95TL6733   Ishibashi, H.; Kawanami, H.; Iriyama, H.; Ikeda, M. *Tetrahedron Lett.* **1995**, *36*, 6733.

95TL6743   Jones, K.; Ho, T. C. T.; Wilkinson, J. *Tetrahedron Lett.* **1995**, *36*, 6743.

95TL7247   Anies, C.; Billot, L.; Lallemand, J.-Y.; Pancrazi, A. *Tetrahedron Lett.* **1995**, *36*, 7247.

95TL7329   Fong, M. C.; Schiesser, C. H. *Tetrahedron Lett.* **1995**, *36*, 7329.

Chapter 3

Three-Membered Ring Systems

Albert Padwa
Emory University, Atlanta, GA, USA

S. Shaun Murphree
Bayer Inc., Charleston, SC, USA

3.1 INTRODUCTION

The chemistry of three-membered heterocycles continues to be bullish. From biologically important target molecules to synthetically useful and versatile reagents to mechanistically challenging theoretical aspects, these systems represent a varied and almost limitless terrain of substrates, in spite of the *de facto* simplicity of the functional groups themselves. As always, this review is not designed to be an exhaustive compilation of events regarding three-membered systems, but rather an update of selected highlights and recent contributions to ongoing threads of research reported in the year's literature, which are of particular interest to the synthetic chemist. The organization is much the same as that of previous years.

3.2 EPOXIDES

3.2.1 Preparation of Epoxides

Epoxides have been prepared by a variety of methods, but by far the most significant method is the epoxidation of olefins. The attractiveness of this approach lies in the ready availability of the necessary substrates, as well as an arsenal of well-characterized protocols for their epoxidation; the Sharpless epoxidation of allylic alcohols provides a classic example. Of course, of particular advantage in this methodology is the possibility to construct chiral epoxides. While the Sharpless conditions, as well as other related systems, represent an inestimable workhorse for the synthetic chemist, research is quite active in other areas, particularly those applying to the asymmetric epoxidation of achiral, non-functionalized substrates. Dominating this playing field are the Jacobsen-type catalysts, chiral (salen)Mn complexes of varying constitution (*e.g.,* 1). No longer newcomers, these catalysts promote the predictable, if not always well-understood, asymmetric epoxidation of double bonds. Of course, the variety of catalysts of this type have arisen from the need to *"fine-tune"* reaction conditions for certain substrates, an effort which is ongoing.

1a: R_1 = Ph; R_2 = OSi(i-Pr)$_3$; R_3 = t-Bu
1b: R_1 = Ph; R_2 = R_3 = H
1c: R_1 = -(CH$_2$)$_4$- ; R_2 = R_3 = t-Bu

1

For example, Jacobsen has reported the use of low-temperature conditions to improve the enantioselectivity of certain (salen)Mn epoxidations. A series of recalcitrant olefins were subjected to catalyst **1a** in the presence of N-methyl morpholine N-oxide (NMO) as an additive and MCPBA as a terminal oxidant in methylene chloride at -78°C; the results were then compared to the analogous reaction in an optimized room temperature set of conditions (*i.e.*, aqueous NaOCl as terminal oxidant and 4-phenylpyridine N-oxide (4-PPNO) as additive). Of course, the epoxidations at lower temperatures were correspondingly slower; some substrates were unreactive under these conditions (*e.g., cis*-ethyl cinnamate). However, all olefins which underwent epoxidation at -78°C did so with slight to marked improvement in ee's. The example of **2b** represents the first such epoxidation of a free carboxylic acid-bearing substrate with (salen)Mn catalysts [95TL5457]. Katsuki has also observed slightly increased ee's by adding NaCl to the aqueous hypochlorite system, thus allowing for sub-zero (-18°C) reaction temperatures [95SL827].

1a, m-CPBA
NMO, CH$_2$Cl$_2$, -78°C

2a; R=F
2b; R=CO$_2$H

3a; R=F
3b; R=CO$_2$H

Tetrasubstituted olefins are particularly difficult to epoxidize enantioselectively with (salen)Mn catalysts. Nevertheless, Jacobsen has reported moderate to high enantioselectivities with certain tetrasubstituted olefins by careful selection of reaction parameters. Curiously enough, the more bulky catalysts appear to be the most effective for these substrates, as

catalyst (3 - 5 mol%)
4-phenyl pyridine-N-oxide (20 mol%)
CH$_2$Cl$_2$, 0°C

4a; R=Et
4b; R=Ph

4a; R=Et
4b; R=Ph

exemplified by the epoxidation of chromene derivative **4a** with the catalyst **1a** with 97% ee. On the other hand, the somewhat bulkier substrate **4b** was only reactive with the simple, salicyl-aldehyde-derived salen complexes (*e.g.,* **1b**), which represents an unusually high ee for the aryl-unsubstituted catalysts [95TL5123].

These results contradict Jacobsen's earlier mechanistic theories, which would have predicted a *"top-on"* approach for the sterically demanding tetrasubstituted olefins (Figure 1) and thus inferior results compared to the less-substituted olefins, which were assumed to approach from a skewed *"side-on"* disposition.   Furthermore, his observation that trisubstituted olefins were epoxidized in an opposite stereochemical sense compared to other olefins required invoking a stepwise mechanism, wherein the radical intermediate is steered by the pendant chiral catalyst [94JOC4378]. At the current time, these results fail to coalesce into a clear unified predictive model.

Figure 1

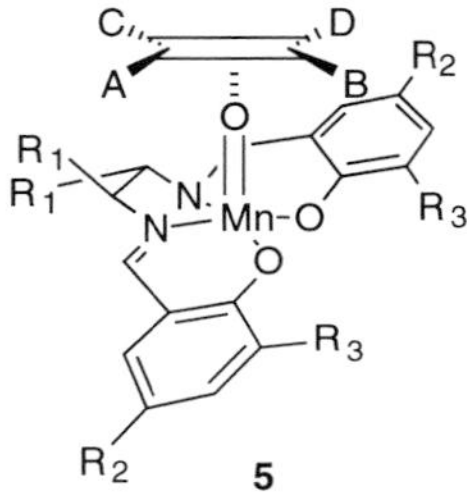

Indeed, the mechanism of these (salen)Mn catalysts' activity is still of considerable controversy.   Katsuki, for instance, who has focused recently on the reactivity of binap-derived catalysts (*e.g.,* **6**) with various *cis*-olefins [95SL827] as well as cyclic trisubstituted olefins [95SL197], maintains that all observations can be rationalized solely on the basis of steric and electronic steering of the substrate during the approach to the catalyst. According to

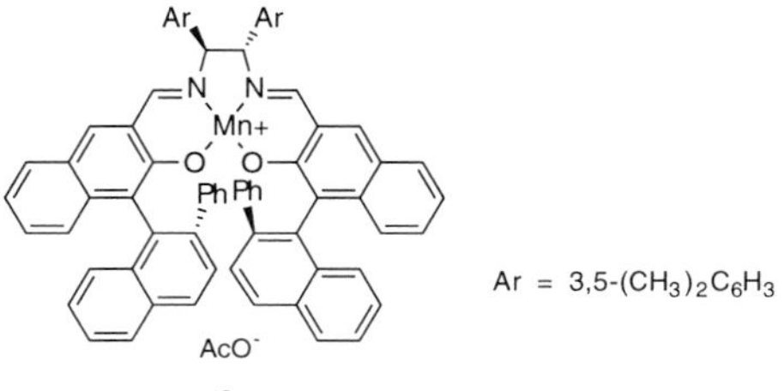

$Ar = 3,5\text{-}(CH_3)_2C_6H_3$

6

this scenario, olefins approach the metal-oxo bond along the nitrogen-manganese bond axis (Figure 2). In the case of olefins with unsaturated substituents, π,π-interaction between the salen benzene ring and the unsaturated substituent either augments or overrides steric interactions.

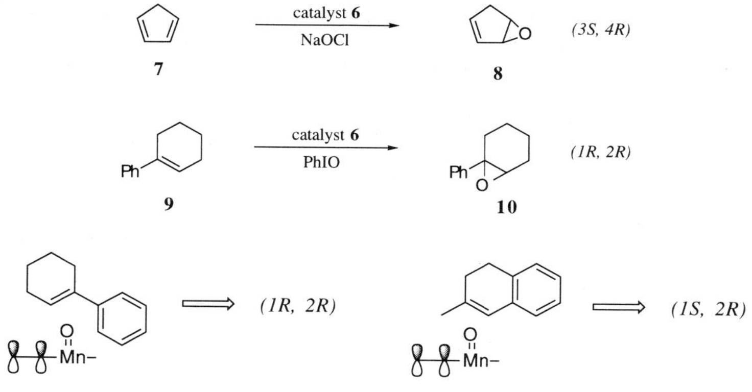

Figure 2

Perhaps the most intriguing contribution to this dialog is that of Norrby and Akermark [95JA11035], who propose the intermediacy of a metallaoxetane in the epoxidation reaction. Molecular modeling indicates that the formation of such an intermediate would bring about a significant change in the catalyst landscape and create a chiral pocket. The literature results are rationalized by a mechanism wherein a reversible formation of a metallaoxetane is followed by the irreversible rearrangement to a bound epoxide (Scheme 1). The formation of the epoxide can proceed either directly (path A) or *via* homolytic cleavage, rotation, and coupling (path B), when a stabilized radical can be formed.

Scheme 1

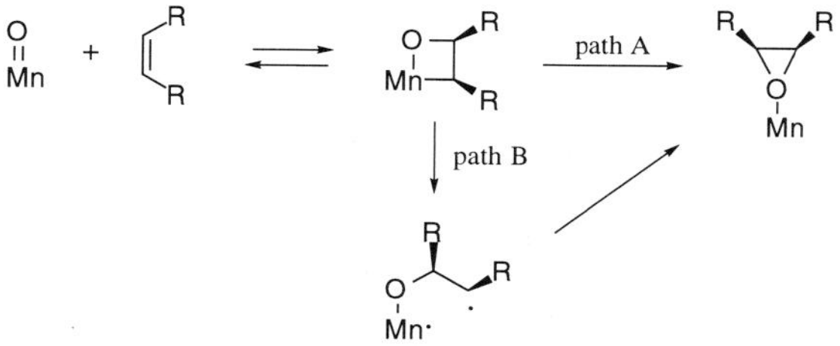

In a related study, Jorgensen has examined the regio- and enantioselective catalytic epoxidation of conjugated aliphatic dienes using achiral and chiral manganese salen complexes and sodium hypochlorite or iodosylbenzene as the terminal oxidant. For most substrates, the less substituted diene is epoxidized; however, in the case of isoprene, the more highly substituted double bond is the more reactive. Jorgensen proposes an intermediate of type **11**, the formation of which is dependent upon steric factors as well as HOMO/LUMO interactions [95TL319].

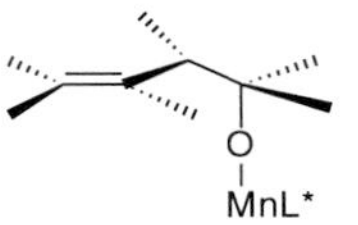

11

Regardless of the mechanism, the chiral (salen)Mn-mediated epoxidation of unfunctionalized alkenes represents a methodology with constantly expanding generality. Very mild and neutral conditions can be achieved, as illustrated by Adam's epoxidation of chromene derivatives **12** using Jacobsen-type catalysts and dimethyldioxirane as a terminal oxidant [95TL3669]. Similarly, periodates can be employed as the stoichiometric oxidant in the epoxidation of *cis*- and *trans*-olefins [95TL319].

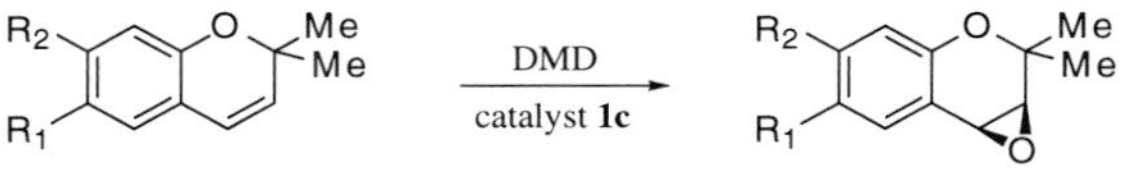

$$\xrightarrow[\text{catalyst 1c}]{\text{DMD}}$$

12   **13**

An aggravating phenomenon associated with the (salen)Mn complexes is that the epoxidation of *trans*-olefins proceeds typically with low ee's. Remarkably, however, the analogous chromium complexes (*e.g.,* **14**) catalyze such epoxidations with greater selectivity than for the corresponding *cis*-olefins under the same conditions. Here the mechanism is presumed to involve an electrophilic process, which is supported by the fact that only electron-rich alkenes are effectively epoxidized. In the case of *trans*-ß-methyl-styrene (**15**), enantioselectivities of *ca.* 80% are observed [95TL7739].

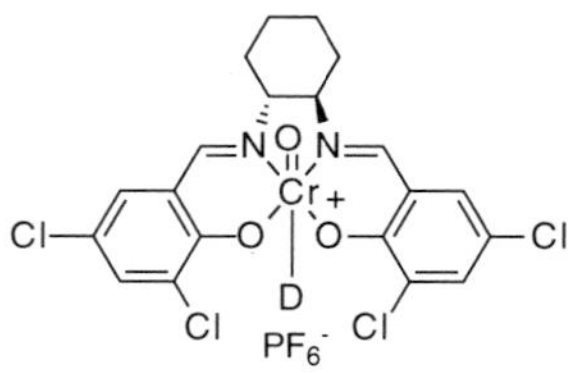

1 4

D = pyridine-N-oxide

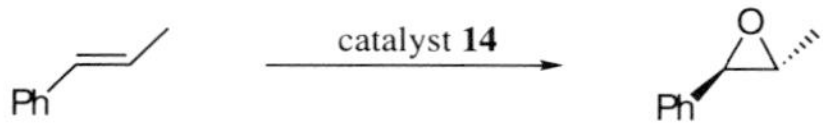

$$\xrightarrow{\text{catalyst 14}}$$

15   **16**

Another notoriously ill-behaved group of substrates are the terminal alkenes, which lack the steric definition necessary for most catalytic systems. As an alternative methodology, the enzyme chloroperoxidase has been examined for the epoxidation of 2-methyl-1-alkenes (*e.g.*, **17**). Yields tend to be low; ee's, although variable, can be quite high [95JA6412]

$$EtCO_2 \xrightarrow[\text{34\% yield; 94\% ee}]{\text{chloroperoxidase}} EtCO_2$$

17   **18**

Of course, as in the case of the classic Sharpless epoxidation, the oxidant can be directed to a given face by a preexisting directing group on the substrate itself. The role of the traditional allylic hydroxy group can also be filled by other remote functionalities. For example, whereas amino–alkenes cannot be epoxidized by usual methods (competing N-oxidation), protonation by an arenesulfonic acid and subsequent treatment with m-CPBA allows for chemoselective epoxidation. Furthermore, when properly disposed, the pendant ammonium functionality can serve as a potent directing group for the oxidant. Thus, under these conditions cyclohexenylamine **19** affords exclusively the *syn* epoxide **20** [95JOC3692].

$$\xrightarrow[]{\text{ArSO}_3\text{H} \quad \text{MCPBA}}$$

19   **20**

In the case of dual functionality, the two sites may interact in either a constructive or destructive fashion. This was illustrated by a set of stereoselective epoxidations on a series of allylic carbamates which were appended with a carbomethoxy group a hydroxymethyl group or an acetoxymethyl group. In all cases, *threo* epoxides were favored (*syn* to the carbamate) upon treatment with MCPBA, which indicates the strong directing power of the carbamate group. However, the magnitude of the *syn:anti* ratio was dependent upon the type and configuration of the other functionality. A relatively low ratio was observed when the two groups compete for face selectivity, whereas *"cooperative coordination"* leads to higher ratios. From the magnitude of the perturbation, the following order of directing ability was proposed: carbamate>methyl ester>homoallylic alcohol=acetate [95JOC1026].

Coordination with heteroatoms is not an absolute prerequisite for efficacy in directional control. Thus, the stereochemistry observed in the epoxidation of alkoxy-substituted cyclohexenyl ketones **21** has been explained on the basis of a Felkin-Ahn transition

$$\xrightarrow[\text{Triton B}]{\text{TBHP}}$$

21   **22**

state, where the approach of the nucleophilic peroxide is controlled by the protected alcohol *via* the sterics imposed by conformational effects [95TL6611].

Similarly, a non-coordinative model can be used to rationalize the observed stereocontrol in the nucleophilic epoxidation (*t*-BuOOLi) of hydroxy substituted vinyl sulfones 23 and 26, where the stereochemical course of the reaction can be controlled by the appropriate choice of protecting group. Thus, in the case of terminal alkenes 23, the unprotected hydroxy functionality leads to predominantly *syn* products, while protection with the bulky triisopropylsiloxy group effectively reverses the selectivity. The opposite of this phenomenon is seen in the case of the styrene derivatives 26. Although hydrogen-bonding effects could not be ruled out, a sufficient model can be constructed from consideration of 1,2-allylic strain between the phenylsulfonyl group and the R'-substituent, as well as 1,3-allylic strain, which favors conformers with the alkyl group outside. Attack of the nucleophile thus proceeds at the sterically less hindered face [95JCS(P1)141].

Denmark has developed a practical dioxirane-mediated protocol for the catalytic epoxidation of alkenes, which uses Oxone as a terminal oxidant. The olefins studied were epoxidized in 83-96% yield. Of the many reaction parameters examined in this biphasic system, the most influential were found to be the reaction pH, the lipophilicity of the phase-transfer catalyst, and the counterion present. In general, optimal conditions feature 10 mol% of the catalyst 1-dodecyl-1-methyl-4-oxopiperidinium triflate (30) and a pH 7.5-8.0 aqueous-methylene chloride biphasic solvent system [95JOC1391].

It is known that sub-stoichiometric amounts of amine N-oxides are effective additives in metallo-catalyzed epoxidation reactions, increasing yield and/or selectivity. Meyers has reported a remarkable instance where chiral unsaturated lactams (*i.e.*, 32) can be epoxidized in high yields by the action of either trimethylamine-N-oxide (TMNO) or N-methyl morpholine N-oxide (NMO) in the absence of a metal catalyst. These conformationally restricted substrates are stereospecifically epoxidized by the nucleophilic addition of the oxide on the least hindered face of the double bond [95TL1613].

          32   33   34

Another relatively simple system for the epoxidation of tri- and *cis*-disubstituted olefins is formamide-hydrogen peroxide in an aqueous medium. This reagent has the advantage of being pH-independent, which makes it attractive for biochemically mediated transformations. No reaction was observed in the case of *trans*-disubstituted and terminal olefins. With bifunctional alkenes, the more reactive double bond is selectively epoxidized [95TL4015].

          35   36

Also in the realm of novel reaction conditions, Marson and co-workers observed an interesting phenomenon during the initially problematic attempts to epoxidize the vinyl-hydroxylactam derivative **37**. Normal Sharpless conditions (VO(acac)$_2$/TBHP) resulted not in the expected epoxidation, but rather in an eliminative oxidation to give the imide **38**. Other Lewis acids were examined in hopes of activating the substrate toward the desired reactivity. Surprisingly, the combination of TBHP and SnCl$_4$ effected not only the epoxidation of the terminal alkene, but also resulted in the displacement of the hydroxy group by the peroxide nucleophile, to give the peroxyepoxide **39**. The diastereoselectivity of the epoxidation in this case is opposite to that observed in analogous carbocyclic systems [95TL5979].

          38   37   39

The notorious propensity for terminal olefins to undergo non-selective epoxidation has been overcome in one case by the stepwise formation of the epoxide. Thus, a Merck group capitalized on the chiral environment of oxazolidine **40** by first carrying out a diastereoselective iodohydration using N-iodo succinimide (NIS) under a carefully chosen set of conditions, then effecting ring-closure to give the epoxide **42** in 97:3 diastereoselectivity [95TL2195].

40   **41**   **42**

Certain chiral epoxides can be prepared from ß-hydroxyselenides (*e.g.*, **43**), typically intermediates for allylic alcohol synthesis. The novel reactivity of these substrates seems to be restricted to those cyclic compounds in which the hydroxy and the selenoxide groups can achieve an antiperiplanar disposition [95TL5079].

43   **44**

Finally, Sato and co-workers have added a twist to the known preparation of epoxides from the action of sulfur ylides on carbonyl compounds. In this version, the requisite sulfur ylides are formed by desilylation of [(trimethylsilyl)methyl]sulfonium salts (*e.g.*, **45**) in DMSO. This avoids the strongly basic conditions typically encountered in the preparation of sulfur ylides [95SYN649].

45   **46**   **47**

3.2.2 Reactions of Epoxides

Epoxides undergo a repertoire of fairly well-characterized reactions, perhaps the most typical being the nucleophilic ring opening process. Since the epoxide in question is usually found in a compound with multiple functionality, many new methodologies seek to optimize chemo- and regioselectivity. Fortunately, the oxirane lone pair provides a convenient handle to effect activation of the heterocycle toward C-O bond cleavage; thus, efficient catalysts are of particular interest.

For example, organoimido complexes of Group VI transition metals have been shown to catalyze the ring cleavage of styrene oxide (**48**) by trimethylsilyl azide. The observed regioselectivity corresponds to the formation of the more stable carbocation. The catalytic activity of the imido complex is a function of the electrophilicity at the metal center. Amines can also be used as the nucleophile, but the reaction is not as smooth, presumably due to interaction with the catalyst [95TL107].

$$\text{48} \xrightarrow[\text{TMSN}_3]{\substack{\text{W(t-BuN)}_2\text{(t-BuNH)}_2 \\ \text{95\%}}} \text{49}$$

During the past year, Collin has shown that $SmI_2(THF)_2$ catalyzes the ring-opening of epoxides by trimethylsilylazide and trimethylsilylcyanide, as well as by primary and secondary amines. With the TMS nucleophiles, the same regioselectivity is observed as with the previous example, TMS-azide giving better selectivity than TMS-cyanide. Amines tend to attack the less hindered carbon center of the epoxide ring, although the selectivity is amine-dependent. Yields in all cases are fair to very good [95TL1649].

$$\text{50} \xleftarrow[\text{TMSN}_3]{\substack{\text{SmI}_2\text{(THF)}_2 \\ \text{50\%}}} \text{48} \xrightarrow[\text{Et}_2\text{NH}]{\substack{\text{SmI}_2\text{(THF)}_2 \\ \text{87\%}}} \text{51}$$

Yamamoto has reported that ytterbium triisopropoxide, prepared *in situ* from $Yb(OTf)_3$ and $LiOPr^i$ in THF, can be used in a very mild, highly efficient, and widely applicable procedure for the azidolysis of epoxides. In every case except styrene oxide, products are derived from the attack of azide at the less hindered carbon atom. The method appears to be quite tolerant of functionality, leaving preexisting tosyl, acyl, and siloxy groups intact (*e.g.*, **52 → 53**) [95CC1021].

$$\text{52} \xrightarrow[\text{Yb(i-PrO)}_3]{\text{TMSN}_3} \text{53}$$

Jacobsen has succeeded in carrying out the analogous transformation in an asymmetric fashion using (salen)Mn(III) complexes, thus demonstrating a new role for these catalysts. Epoxides fused to five-membered rings provided for the highest levels of enantioselectivity, while six-membered rings and acyclic systems led to slightly lower ee's. Ether, olefin, and

$$\text{54} \xrightarrow[\substack{\text{TMSN}_3 \\ \text{80\% yield} \\ \text{98\% ee}}]{\text{catalyst 1c} \quad \text{CSA}} \text{55}$$

carbonyl-containing functional groups on the substrate were all tolerated by the catalyst (*e.g.,* **54 → 55**) [95JA5897].

The ring opening reaction is by no means limited to conventional nucleophiles. For example, catalytic amounts of ceric ammonium nitrate in the presence of excess nitrate ion promotes the smooth conversion of epoxides to ß-nitrato alcohols in good to excellent yields. Regioselectivity is best with monosubstituted epoxides containing a halomethyl or alkoxymethyl group (*i.e.,* **56**), where the product arises from a formal nucleophilic attack onto the unsubstituted epoxide carbon. The reaction is actually presumed to go through a one-electron transfer to form an oxiranium radical cation (**57**), which is then captured by the nitrate ion [95TET909].

The hydride ion can also serve as a nucleophile in these nucleophilic oxirane cleavage reactions. In fact, Iyer [95SC2267] and Dragovich [95JOC4922] have independently reported on the regio-specific ring opening of epoxides by way of a palladium-catalyzed transfer hydrogenolysis using ammonium formate as the hydrogen source. Under these conditions, hydride attacks at the less hindered carbon atom (*e.g.,* **59 → 60**), except in the case of aryl-substituted epoxides, where ring opening occurs exclusively at the benzylic position (*e.g.,* **48 → 61**).

Still other epoxide cleavage processes can be nucleophile induced, but without direct attack at a heterocyclic carbon. A good illustration of this phenomenon is seen in the alkylative elimination of epoxy tosylhydrazones (**62**). Optically pure allyl alcohols have been prepared from these precursors, themselves derived from the corresponding chiral epoxy aldehydes, by reaction with Grignard reagents. The eliminative ring opening proceeds with retention of configuration about the resultant carbinol carbon, producing exclusively *trans*-olefins (**65**) in consistently good yields [95TL307].

Epoxides can be converted to chlorocarbonyl compounds (*e.g.*, **69**) by concomitant chloride induced ring opening and oxidation using mild Swern-type reaction conditions. The regio-chemistry is dependent upon epoxide composition. Disubstituted epoxides give chloroketones in high yields; terminal epoxides give the products of attack at the unsubstituted carbon. The one exception to this rule is styrene oxide which, like trisubstituted epoxides, yields the product of the most stable carbocation intermediate. Epoxy homoallylic alcohol arrays give enedione systems [95TET2467].

66   **67**   **68**   **69**

The propensity for epoxides to undergo various rearrangements under Lewis acidic conditions is also well-known. Typically, Lewis acid *"catalysts"*, such as $BF_3 \cdot OEt_2$, must be used in quantities approaching stoichiometric amounts due to their instability under the reaction conditions. However, Yamanoto has recently demonstrated that tris(pentafluoro phenyl)boron, an air-stable and powerful Lewis acid, was not only active in catalytic quantities, but also effective in mediating the alkyl-shift rearrangement of epoxide **70** with

70   **71**   **72**

much higher selectivity than conventional Lewis acid catalysts. Solvent effects were significant: changing the solvent from toluene to methylene chloride resulted in a drastic reduction in selectivity, with hydride-shift rearrangement becoming a competitive process [95SL721].

Similarly, Jung and D'Amico have shown that chiral tertiary allylic epoxides undergo a stereospecific rearrangement in the presence of $BF_3 \cdot OEt_2$ to give optically active quaternary aldehydes **74**. The stereospecificity of the process is rationalized on the basis of hindered rotation of the intermediate carbocation. Furthermore, eclipsing interactions hinder the

73   **74**   **75**

alignment necessary for hydride shift. Only in cases of low migratory aptitude (*i.e.,* cyclohexylmethyl, phenethyl) does hydride migration become significant [95JA7379].

The high energy differential associated with ring opening can be used advantageously to drive otherwise entropically challenged reactions. For example, Marson has demonstrated a curious reactivity of certain alkynyl epoxy alcohols (*e.g.,* **76**), which undergo a high-yielding $TiCl_4$-catalyzed 7-*endo-tet* cyclization to give bicyclo[5.3.0]decenone systems (*e.g.,* **77**). The predominance of the observed mode of cyclization over the more favored 6-*exo-tet* process is rationalized on the basis of chelation control, in which the *vic*-diol array plays a pivotal role [95TL7145].

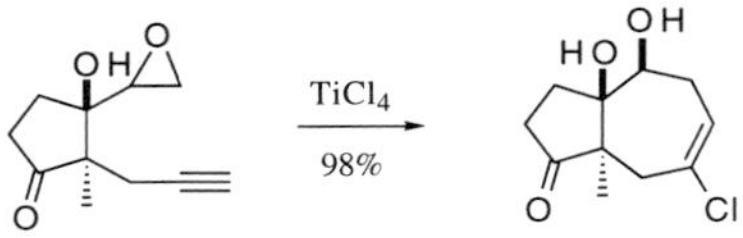

76   **77**

Indeed, these epoxide-facilitated ring closure reactions show advantages over other methods. For example, Clive and Magnuson were able to access a desired tricyclopentanoid intermediate **79** for the synthesis of (±)-ceratopicanol by the Cp_2TiCl-mediated cyclization of the bicyclic epoxide **78**. Attempts to construct this system through conventional enyne radical cyclizations yielded only the bridged product (*i.e.,* **81**) [95TL15].

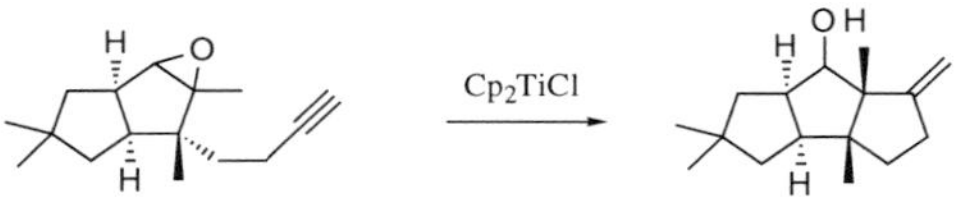

78   **79**

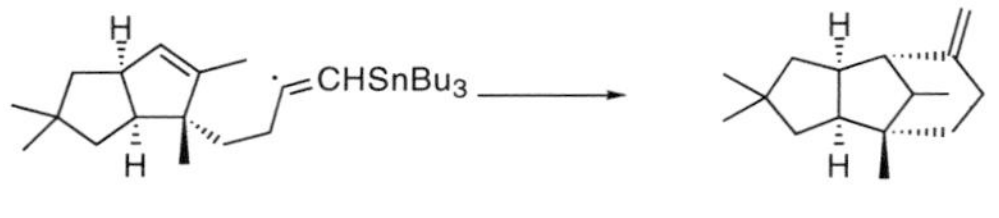

80   **81**

Alternatively, novel allenylidene-tetrahydrofurans such as **84** can be prepared by the tributyltin hydride-mediated radical cyclization of bromoalkynyl-oxiranes **82**, where the epoxide

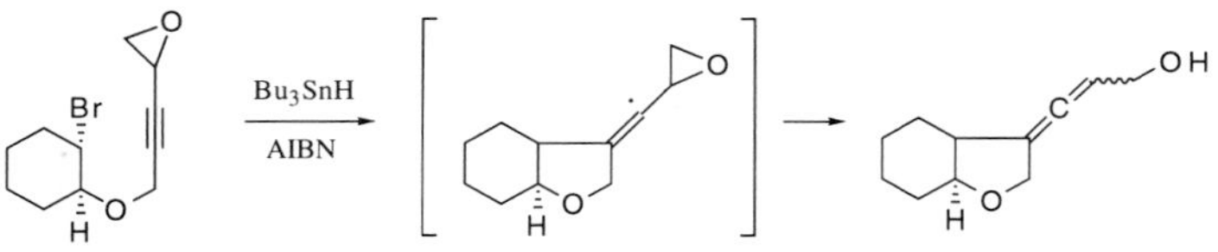

82   **83**   **84**

ring serves as an efficient radical terminator. The reaction proceeds through the normal 5-*exo* mode [95CC897].

3.3   AZIRIDINES
3.3.1 Preparation of Aziridines

In regard to aziridine synthesis, there are two basic strategies of comparable importance, namely (1) the addition of an amine component onto some C_2 fragment such as an olefin, or (2) the addition of a C_1 component onto a C-N substrate such as an imine (Scheme 2, Paths A and B, respectively). The former approach bears at least conceptual similarity to the classical olefin epoxidation protocols, yet exhibits significant mechanistic differences.

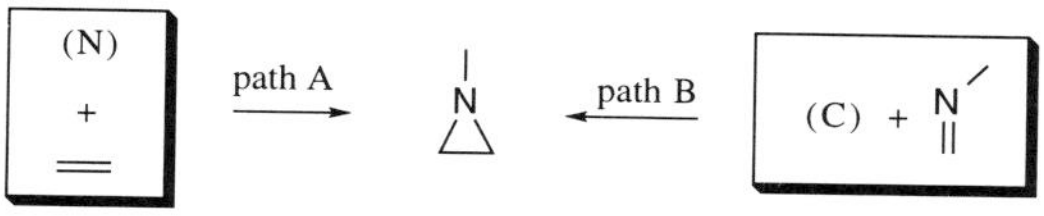

Scheme 2

For example, Jacobsen has studied the asymmetric aziridination of alkenes using (diimine)-copper(I)-catalysts **85**. The results support the intermediacy of a discrete Cu(III)-nitrene intermediate and thus suggests mechanistic similarity (particularly regarding transition state geometry) to asymmetric cyclopropanation [95JA5889].

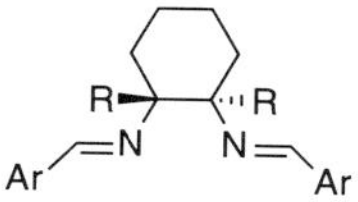

85

This nitrene-addition approach was used by Knight to synthesize vinyl aziridines from 1,3-dienes using PhI=NTs and a copper catalyst. The more electron-rich double bond is selectively transformed in most cases. When the electronic difference is negligible, the regioselectivity is then determined by steric hindrance. A mixture of *cis* and *trans* isomers is usually obtained [95SL949].

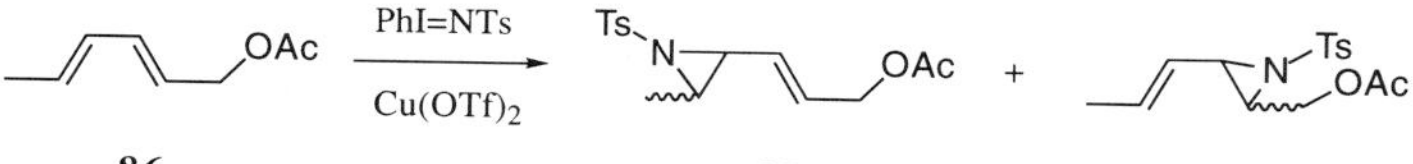

86   **87**   **88**

A strictly nucleophilic approach can also be used for an [(N) + (C=C)] protocol. Thus, the chiral iodo-unsaturated bicyclic lactam **89** undergoes stereoselective conjugate addition with primary amines to give the tricyclic aziridine **90**, which can be subsequently transformed into the chiral 3,4-aziridinopyrrolidine **91** by reductive cleavage. Yields of up to 90% can be achieved and facial selectivity is greater than 98:2 [95TL3491].

89   90   91

In contrast with the corresponding preparation of epoxides, this approach to aziridine formation is not overwhelmingly predominant. Nevertheless, the [(C) + (C=N)] protocol can play an important preparative role. Jacobsen has been active in this area as well, focusing on the asymmetric synthesis of aziridines by a carbenoid transfer to imines (*i.e.,* **92**) using copper(I) salts in association with bis(dihydro–oxazole) ligands **93**, a process which yields modest ee's [95ACIE676]. Jorgensen has also reported a similar racemic version of this protocol which features the copper(II)triflate-catalyzed group-transfer from ethyl diazoacetate to various imines (**95**) to give the corresponding aziridines **96** as a mixture of *cis* and *trans* isomers; however, he reports low ee's for the corresponding chiral approach using chiral ligand **93a** [95CC1401].

92   94   93

93a: R = Ph; R' = Me
93b: R = t-Bu; R' = H

95   96

A recently reported novel asymmetric aziridination route involves the action of methylene transfer reagents on chiral sulfinimines **97**, whereby the selectivity is conferred by the asymmetric sulfinyl center. The stereochemical outcome of this reaction is dependent upon the methylene transfer reagent. Thus, dimethyloxosulfonium methylide provided predominantly isomer **98**, whereas the use of dimethylsulfonium methylide led to the formation of **99** as the major product [95TL295].

97   98   99

3.3.2 Reactions of Aziridines

Similar to the epoxides, the most frequently encountered synthetic transformation for aziridines is nucleophilic ring-opening, whereby carbon- and heteroatom-based nucleophiles are comparably important. As an example of the former type, aziridine-2-carboxylates **100** can be ring-opened with higher order cuprates to give the protected amino acid derivatives **101**, corresponding to attack at the less-substituted aziridine carbon [95TL151].

100 $\xrightarrow{R_2CuCNLi_2}$ **101**

There is, of course, no paucity of examples using heteroatom-based nucleophiles. For example, aziridine-2-t-butyl carboxylate **102** reacts with primary amines to give the dialkylated diamino-propionic acid derivatives **103**, which are interesting precursors for the synthesis of cyclosporin analogs. Again, attack occurs overwhelmingly at the ß-carbon [95TL4955].

102 $\xrightarrow{NH_2R}$ **103**

Hydroxymethylaziridine **104** undergoes ring opening in the presence of either carbon- or heteroatom-based nucleophiles upon treatment with two equivalents of potassium hydride to provide the vic-aminoalcohol derivative **106**. The key step of the reaction is considered to be an aza-Payne rearrangement of the deprotonated aziridine-methanol to the epoxide **105**, which then undergoes nucleophilic attack at the less substituted oxirane carbon to give the observed product. The process is carried out in one pot, is amenable to various nucleophiles (*e.g.*, thiols, TMS-cyanide, higher order cuprates), and proceeds with very good diastereoisomeric excess [95TL6247].

104 $\xrightarrow{KH}$ **105** $\xrightarrow{Nu^-}$ **106**

Ketoaziridines **107** can be reductively cleaved by samarium iodide in the presence of a proton source to form aminoketones **112** in good to excellent yields. The mechanism is assumed to include the intermediate hydroxymethine radical **108**, which is formed by a single electron transfer. This species either undergoes immediate further reduction to the corresponding anion **109**, followed by ring opening, or engages in a homolytic ring cleavage (*i.e*,

108→ 111) before accepting another electron. The reaction is rapid and is tolerant of many nitrogen protecting groups [95JOC6660].

The aziridine ring may also be opened in an electrophilic fashion. For example, the aziridine nucleus of the functionalized allyl silane **113** undergoes intramolecular ring opening in the presence of boron trifluoride etherate to give the aminomethyl vinyl cyclohexane **114** in 90% yield as a 2.7:1 mixture of *cis* and *trans* isomers [95TL3793].

Alper and co-workers have reported the first enantiospecific palladium-catalyzed cycloaddition of aziridines with heterocumulenes. Thus, N-butyl phenylaziridine **115** reacts with p-chlorophenyl isothiocyanate in the presence of $(PhCN)_2PdCl_2$ to form thiazolidinimine **117** in good yield. This reaction proceeds with retention of configuration at the aziridine carbon center [95JA4700]. Nadir and Basu have reported a very similar reaction involving the aziridine sulfonamide **118** and using sodium iodide as a catalyst. Based on spectroscopic evidence, these conditions provide the isomeric 2-imidazolidine-thione **120** rather than the thiazolidinimine. The reaction is believed to proceed *via* initial attack of iodide at the benzylic position to give an intermediate iodoamide **119**, which then condenses with the heterocumulene [95JOC1458].

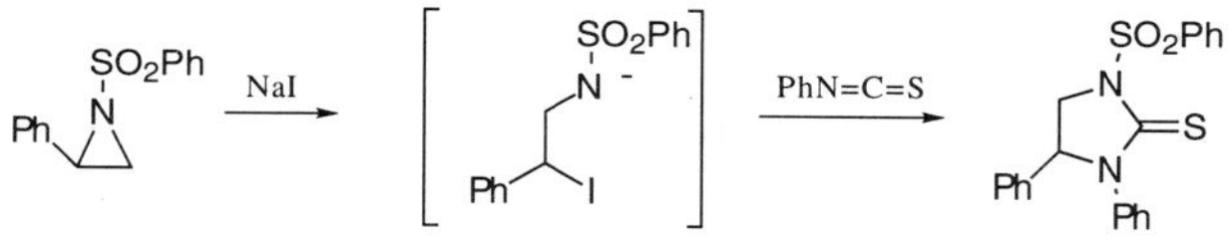

118 **119** **120**

Coldham [95TL3557] and Somfai [95TL1953] have independently investigated the ring expansion of vinyl aziridines to piperidines *via* the aza-Wittig rearrangement. Thus, Coldham has prepared the unsaturated *cis*-piperidines **123** as single diastereoisomers in fair to good yield from the keto–aziridines **121** using a one-pot, two-step procedure. The stereochemical outcome is rationalized on the basis of the chelated intermediate **122**. In a related manner, Somfai has used this protocol for the enantioselective total synthesis of indolizidine 209D (**126**).

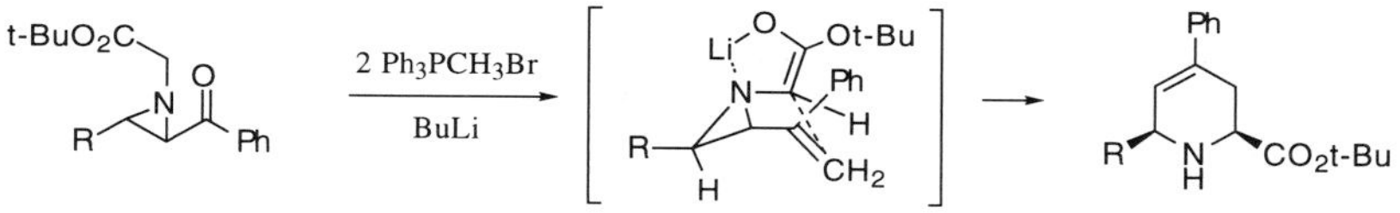

126 **127** **128**

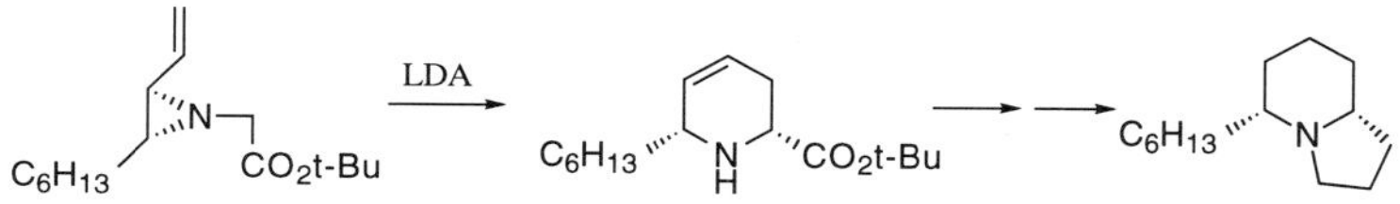

124 **125** **126**

Finally, chiral *2H*-azirine-2-carboxylic esters **128** can be prepared from the corresponding aziridines **127** under mild Swern oxidation conditions. This method, which is effective for both *cis* and *trans* substrates, introduces the double bond regioselectively at the "*non-conjugated*" site [95TL4665].

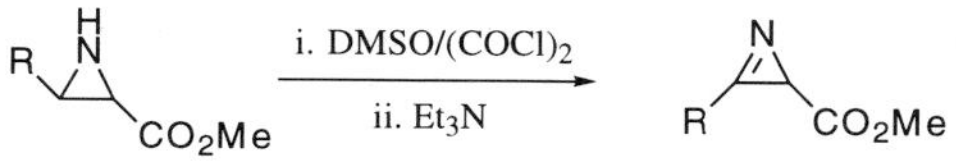

127 **128**

3.4 DIOXIRANES

3.4.1 Preparation of Dioxiranes

The most significant advance in the preparation of dioxiranes is the elucidation of conditions which allow for *in situ* formation of the dioxirane reagent, thus allowing for catalytic quantities of the ketone precursor and use of more economical and readily available terminal oxidants. Thus, Curci has reported on the *in situ* generation of the chiral dioxiranes **129** and **130** in conjunction with sodium perchlorate, NMNO, or peracids for the enantioselective epoxidation of unfunctionalized alkenes [95TL5831]. Similarly, Yang has used the *in situ* generation of methyl(trifluoromethyl)dioxirane (**131**) in homogeneous medium using Oxone as a stoichiometric oxidant for the efficient epoxidation of olefins [95JOC3887].

| 129 | 130 | 131 |

3.4.2 Reactions of Dioxiranes

The chemical reactivity most associated with dioxiranes is the electrophilic transfer of oxygen to electron-rich substrates (*e.g.,* epoxidation, N-oxidation) as well as oxygen insertion reactions into unactivated C-H bonds. The reactivity-selectivity relationships among these types of reactions has been examined in depth by Curci. The reaction kinetics are dependent upon a variety of factors, including electron-donor power of the substrate, electrophilicity of the dioxirane, and steric influences [95PAC811].

Indeed, Adam observed that, whereas acyclic vinyl silanes **132** undergo smooth epoxidation in excellent yield, the cyclic substrates exhibit varying amounts of allylic oxidation as well. The C-H insertion pathway becomes more prominent when the double bond is deactivated by either steric or electronic influences. Thus, the *t*-butyl derivative **134** gives as much as 20% of the allylic oxidation product (**136**) [95TL4991].

| 132 | 133 |

| 134 | 135 (80%) | 136 (20%) |

3.5   OXAZIRIDINES

3.5.1 Preparation of Oxaziridines

Jorgensen has studied the oxidation of imines **137** to oxaziridines **138** catalyzed by transition metal complexes using molecular oxygen as the stoichiometric oxidant. Optimized conditions employ 4 mol% of $CoCl_2$ as catalyst and 3-methylbutanal as co-reductant; substrates containing a C-aryl group are best suited for the protocol. The mechanism is thought to involve an intermediate acyl-peroxo-cobalt species [95JCS(P1)699].

$$R^1 \underset{R^2}{\overset{}{=}}N^{\cdot}R^3 \xrightarrow[CoCl_2]{O_2 - RCHO} R^1 \overset{O}{\underset{R^2}{\overset{}{-}}}\overset{}{N}^{\cdot}R^3$$

$$\mathbf{137} \qquad\qquad \mathbf{138}$$

The 3-aryl-N-BOC-oxaziridines **140** are prepared by the oxidation of the corresponding benzaldimines **139** using the lithium salt of m-CPBA under aprotic conditions. These oxaziridines can then be used as protected-nitrogen transfer agents [95TL1439].

$$X \overset{}{\bigcirc}\overset{}{\underset{H}{=}}N\text{-}BOC \xrightarrow[m\text{-}CPBA]{BuLi} X \overset{}{\bigcirc}\overset{O}{\triangle}N\text{-}BOC$$

$$\mathbf{139} \qquad\qquad \mathbf{140}$$

3.5.2 Reactions of Oxaziridines

Oxaziridines show a diversity of reactivities; perhaps the most synthetically useful behavior is their selective oxidizing ability. For example, fluoro-*cis*-2,3-dialkyloxaziridines **141** function as effective reagents for the selective oxidation of ethers to carbonyl compounds (*e.g.*, **142** → **143**). This protocol was used for the oxidation of methoxy residues on various classes of steroids [95JOC2314].

$$R^1 \overset{O}{\underset{N}{\triangle}}\overset{R^2}{\underset{F}{}} + \quad \overset{OR}{\square\square} \quad \longrightarrow \quad \overset{O}{\square\square}$$

$$\mathbf{141} \qquad\qquad \mathbf{142} \qquad\qquad\qquad \mathbf{143}$$

3.6 REFERENCES

94JOC4378   B. D. Brandes, E. N. Jacobsen, *J. Org. Chem.* **1994**, *59*, 4378.

95ACIE676   K. B. Hansen, N. S. Finney, E. N. Jacobsen, *Angew. Chem., Int. Ed. Engl.* **1995**, *34*, 676.

95CC897   J. -P. Dulcère, E. Dumez, R. Faure, *J. Chem. Soc., Chem. Commun.* **1995**, 897.

95CC1021   M. Meguro, N. Asao, Y. Yamamoto, *J. Chem. Soc., Chem. Commun.* **1995**, 1021.

95CC1401   K. G. Rasmussen, K. A. Jørgensen, *J. Chem. Soc., Chem. Commun.* **1995**, 1401.

95JA4700   J. -O. Baeg, C. Bensimon, H. Alper, *J. Am. Chem. Soc.* **1995**, *117*, 4700.

95JA5889   Z. Li, R. W. Quan, E. N. Jacobsen, *J. Am. Chem. Soc.* **1995**, *117*, 5889.
95JA5897   L. E. Martínez, J. L. Leighton, D. H. Carsten, E. N. Jacobsen, *J. Am. Chem. Soc.* **1995**, *117*, 5897.
95JA6412   A. F. Dexter, F. J. Lakner, R. A. Campbell, L. P. Hager, *J. Am. Chem. Soc.* **1995**, *117*, 6412.
95JA7379   M. E. Jung, D. C. D'Amico, *J. Am. Chem. Soc.* **1995**, *117*, 7379.
95JA11035   P. -O. Norrby, C. Linde, B. Åkermark, *J. Am. Chem. Soc.* **1995**, *117*, 11035.
95JCS(P1)141 R. F. W. Jackson, S. P. Standen, W. Clegg, A. McCamley, *J. Chem. Soc., Perkin Trans. 1* **1995**, 141.
95JCS(P1)699 L. Martiny, K. A. Jørgensen, *J. Chem. Soc., Perkin Trans. 1,* **1995**, 699.
95JOC1026   A. Jenmalm, W. Berts, K. Luthman, I. Csöregh, U. Hacksell, *J. Org. Chem.* **1995**, *60*, 1026.
95JOC1391   S. E. Denmark, D. C. Forbes, D. S. Hays, J. S. DePue, R. G. Wilde, *J. Org. Chem.* **1995**, *60*, 1391.
95JOC1458   U. K. Nadir, N. Basu, *J. Org. Chem.* **1995**, *60*, 1458.
95JOC2314   A. Arnon, R. Bernardi, M. Cavicchioli, G. Resnati, *J. Org. Chem.* **1995**, *60*, 2314.
95JOC3692   G. Asensio, R. Mello, C. Boix-Bernardini, M. E. González-Nuñez, G. Castellano, *J. Org. Chem.* **1995**, *60*, 3692.
95JOC3887   D. Yang, M. -K. Wong, Y. -C. Yip, *J. Org. Chem.* **1995**, *60*, 3887.
95JOC4922   P. S. Dragovich, T. J. Prins, R. Zhou, *J. Org. Chem.* **1995**, *60*, 4922.
95JOC6660   G. A. Molander, P. J. Stengel, *J. Org. Chem.* **1995**, *60*, 6660.
95PAC811   R. Curci, A. Dinoi, M. F. Rubino, *Pure Appl. Chem.* **1995**, *67*, 811.
95SC2267   J. P. Varghese, A. Sudalai, S. Iyer, *Synth. Commun.* **1995**, *25*, 2267.
95SL197   T. Fukuda, R. Irie, T. Katsuki, *Synlett* **1995**, 197.
95SL721   K. Ishihara, N. Hanaki, H. Yamamoto, *Synlett* **1995**, 721.
95SL827   D. Mikame, T. Hamada, R. Irie, T. Katsuki, *Synlett* **1995**, 827.
95SL949   J. G. Knight, M. P. Muldowney, *Synlett* **1995**, 949.
95SYN649   K. Hioki, S. Tani, Y. Sato, *Synthesis* **1995**, 649.
95TET909   N. Iranpoor, P. Salehi, *Tetrahedron* **1995**, *51*, 909.
95TET2467   S. Raina, V. K. Singh, *Tetrahedron* **1995**, *51*, 2467.
95TL15   D. L. J. Clive, S. R. Magnuson, *Tetrahedron Lett.* **1995**, *36*, 15.
95TL107   W. -H. Leung, E. K. F. Chow, M. -C. Wu, P. W. Y. Kum, L. -L. Yeung, *Tetrahedron Lett.* **1995**, *36*, 107.
95TL151   N. J. Church, D. W. Young, *Tetrahedron Lett.* **1995**, *36*, 151.
95TL295   J. L. García Ruano, I. Fernández, C. Hamdouchi, *Tetrahedron Lett.* **1995**, *36*, 295.
95TL307   S. Chandrasekhar, M. Takhi, J. S. Yadav, *Tetrahedron Lett.* **1995**, *36*, 307.
95TL319   P. Pietikäinen, *Tetrahedron Lett.* **1995**, *36*, 319.
95TL1439   J. Vidal, S. Damestoy, A. Collet, *Tetrahedron Lett.* **1995**, *36*, 1439.
95TL1613   C. J. Andres, N. Spetseris, J. R. Norton, A. I. Meyers, *Tetrahedron Lett.* **1995**, *36*, 1613.
95TL1649   P. Van de Weghe, J. Collin, *Tetrahedron Lett.* **1995**, *36*, 1649.
95TL1953   P. Somfai, J. Åhman, *Tetrahedron Lett.* **1995**, *36*, 1953.

95TL2195　　P. E. Maligres, V. Upadhyay, K. Rossen, S. J. Cianciosi, R. M. Purick, K. K. Eng, R. A. Reamer, D. Askin, R. P. Volante, P. J. Reider, *Tetrahedron Lett.* **1995**, *36*, 2195.

95TL3491　　C. J. Andres, A. I. Meyers, *Tetrahedron Lett.* **1995**, *36*, 3491.

95TL3557　　I. Coldham, A. J. Collis, R. J. Mould, R. E. Rathmell, *Tetrahedron Lett.* **1995**, *36*, 3557.

95TL3669　　W. Adam, J. Jekö, A. Lévai, C. Nemes, T. Patonay, P. Sebök, *Tetrahedron Lett.* **1995**, *36*, 3669.

95TL3793　　S. C. Bergmeier, P. P. Seth, *Tetrahedron Lett.* **1995**, *36*, 3793.

95TL4015　　Y. Chen, J. -L. Reymond, *Tetrahedron Lett.* **1995**, *36*, 4015.

95TL4665　　L. Gentilucci, Y. Grijzen, L. Thijs, B. Zwanenburg, *Tetrahedron Lett.* **1995**, *36*, 4665.

95TL4955　　M. E. Solomon, C. L. Lynch, D. H. Rich, *Tetrahedron Lett.* **1995**, *36*, 4955.

95TL4991　　W. Adam, F. Prechtl, M. J. Richter, A. K. Smerz, *Tetrahedron Lett.* **1995**, *36*, 4991.

95TL5079　　P. Ceccherelli, M. Curini, F. Epifano, M. C. Marcotullio, O. Rosati, *Tetrahedron Lett.* **1995**, *36*, 5079.

95TL5123　　B. D. Brandes, E. N. Jacobsen, *Tetrahedron Lett.* **1995**, *36*, 5123.

95TL5457　　M. Palucki, G. J. McCormick, E. N. Jacobsen, *Tetrahedron Lett.* **1995**, *36*, 5457.

95TL5831　　R. Curci, L. D'Accolti, M. Fiorentino, A. Rosa, *Tetrahedron Lett.* **1995**, *36*, 5831.

95TL5979　　M. B. Hursthouse, A. Khan, C. M. Marson, R. A. Porter, *Tetrahedron Lett.* **1995**, *36*, 5979.

95TL6247　　K. Nakai, T. Ibuka, A. Otaka, H. Tamamura, N. Fujii, Y. Yamamoto, *Tetrahedron Lett.* **1995**, *36*, 6247.

95TL6611　　R. J. Linderman, R. J. Claassen II, F. Viviani, *Tetrahedron Lett.* **1995**, *36*, 6611.

95TL7145　　C. M. Marson, A. Khan, J. McGregor, T. J. Grinter, *Tetrahedron Lett.* **1995**, *36*, 7145.

95TL7739　　C. Bousquet, D. G. Gilheany, *Tetrahedron Lett.* **1995**, *36*, 7739.

Chapter 4

Four-Membered Ring Systems

J. Parrick and L.K. Mehta
Brunel University, Uxbridge, UK

4.1 INTRODUCTION

The present account follows the general pattern of earlier surveys in this series. Recently published reviews are mentioned in the appropriate sections with the exception of one that is most conveniently described here. This is a description of transition metal mediated carbonylative ring expansion reactions of heterocyclic compounds (95ACR414) which mentions most of the heterocycles included in this chapter either as starting materials or products.

In the present review the ring systems containing one heteroatom are considered first, except for β-lactams which are given a special section at the end. Interest in azetidines continues to be stimulated by the discovery of the potentially useful trinitro derivative. The requirements for the stereoselective synthesis of substituted oxetane are being explored and derivatives of aluminium are useful in the stereoselective routes to oxetanones. The preparation and subsequent pyrolysis of oxetanones is suggested as an alternative to the Wittig route to olefins. Stereoselective routes to thietanes and thietane 1-oxides are mentioned.

The chemistry of some ring systems having two hetero-atoms, i.e. dioxetanes, dithietanes, oxathietanes and thiazetidines are described. Next, the review considers compounds having either silicon or boron in a four-membered ring. Some thermolysis processes are interesting in the silicon series and the first thermally stable 1,2-dihydro-1,2-diborete is described.

Finally, a section is devoted to developments in β-lactam chemistry. Fused-ring systems are not included though often the purpose of the work on monocyclic systems is to develop synthons for fused-ring compounds. Recent reviews on the use of β-lactams as synthons include (94MI417) (139 references) and (95ACR383) (49 references).

4.2 AZETIDINES

N-Substituted azetidines (3, R^1 = alkyl or aryl, R^2 = H) are obtained in good yield by intramolecular cyclization of N-alkyl-3-bromopropylamines (2, R^1 = alkyl or aryl, R^2 = H), which are themselves readily obtained by borohydride reduction of the corresponding N-alkylidine or N-arylidene compounds (1) (94TL8023). The same general route gives 3-alkoxyazetidines (3, R^2 = O-alkyl or O-aryl) if the appropriate Schiff's base (1, R^2 = O-alkyl or O-aryl) is used (95T5465). Another approach (95SC603) leads to benzyloxymethyl (BOM) protected 3-hydroxyazetidines (5). Here an intermolecular reaction between a primary aliphatic amine and 1,3-bis(4-methylbenzenesulfonyloxy)propane (4), available in four steps from glycerol, gives good yields of (5).

The conversion of pyrrolidines (6) into 1,2-disubstituted azetidines (7) has been achieved using an extrusion reaction (93BSB719).

More chemistry directed towards the development of efficient routes to 1,3,3-trinitroazetidine has been published, including a full paper (95JOC1959) on the work given in a preliminary form (reported in Volume 7 in this series). Two new routes have also been developed (95JOC4943) but, although yields in the later steps of the syntheses are satisfactory, the early step for the formation of the N-nitrosoazetidines (9, R^1 = H, R^2 = NO_2) or (9, R^1 = OH, R^2 = CH_2Br) from (8, R^1 = H) or (8, R^1 = CH_2Br) respectively, proceeds in very poor yield (1-3%).

The CD spectra of optically active 1-nitroso-2-substituted azetidines are analysed by non-empirical quantum chemical calculations. The sign of the Cotton effect for the n-π* transition at 380 nm is determined by the chirality of the chromophore (95JA928).

Nitration of 1-substituted azetidines with N_2O_5 often gives ring-opened products similar to those found for aziridines (95T5073). However, N-acyl azetidines undergo nitrolysis of the substituent to yield N-nitroazetidines in good yields.

3-Amino-3-phenylazetidine is obtained in high yield in three steps from N-benzhydryl-3-azetidinone by using dibenzylamine as an amine equivalent in a modified Strecker reaction (95SC803).

Regiospecific, Pd(II) catalysed, cycloaddition reactions of azetidines to yield ring-enlarged products include the formation of tetrahydro-2-iminopyrimidines (e.g. 10) by reaction with carbodiimides (95JOC253) and tetrahydro-1,3-thiazin-2-imines (e.g. 11) from isothiocyanates (95JOC3092).

4.3 OXETANES AND THIETANES

The synthesis of oxetanes by intramolecular cyclization of alcohols includes the stereoselective synthesis of (13) from the *syn*-form of (12) (94TL6611), the formation of 3-methylene-oxetanes (15) by bromination and subsequent cyclization of (14) (94MI926), and the preparation of enantiomerically pure (17) from optically pure (16) under phase transfer conditions (95S533).

Cycloaddition routes to oxetanes include the preparation of fluorinated oxetanes by electrophilic [2+2]cycloaddition of hexa-fluoroacetone and fluorinated ethenes in the presence of the recently introduced anhydrous aluminium chlorofluoride as a Lewis acid catalyst. The reaction is regiospecific with $CHX=CF_2$ (X = H, F, Cl, Br) to yield (18) (95JOC3419). Photoexcited cyclization routes to oxetanes have been investigated further in order to determine the requirements for stereoselectivity. Silyl enol ethers (19) react with aromatic aldehydes (Paterno-Buechi reaction) to give the isomer (20) as the major product and the diastereoselectivity (65-95%) was optimised when R^1 is a sterically demanding group (94TL5845, 95LA855). Furil undergoes a photo [2+2]cyclization with β-methyl-styrene (94G459).

Oxetanes having ether groups in a side chain (21) undergo rearrangement in the presence of boron trifluoride etherate to give larger rings (22) with accompanying transfer of the terminal ether substituent (94H2165). Lanthanide-induced rearrangements of 2-iminooxetanes yield β-lactams (95JOC1020).

The aldol (23) on treatment with benzenesulphonyl chloride yields the oxetanone (β-lactone) (24) which is an intermediate in the synthesis of the butenolides (25) (95SC479). Aliphatic terminal alkynes or arylalkynes react with nitrones in the presence of a copper based catalyst system to give 1,3,4-trisubstituted β-lactones (95JOC4999).

Spiro-β-lactones (27) are formed in a highly regioselective way by treatment of the cyclohexenylacetic acid (26) with 1,3-dibromo-5,5-dimethylhydantoin and then potassium *tert*-butoxide in anhydrous DMF (94MI327).

Lithium enolates of phenyl esters (28) react with aldehydes or ketones to give *O*-lithiated phenyl β-hydroxyalkanoates (29) which undergo spontaneous intramolecular cyclization to β-lactones (30) (95JOC758). Also, lithium enolates are used in the synthesis of 3-[1-(dialkylamino)alkyl]β-lactones (94JOC7994), which are precursors for α-oxo-β-lactones.

Exceptionally bulky methylaluminium bis(4-bromo-2,6-di-*tert*-butyl)phenoxide is a useful catalyst in producing high stereo-selectivity in the cycloaddition of trialkylsilylketene with aldehydes to give *cis*-3,4-disubstituted-2-oxetanones (95T4011). The complex formed from a trialkylaluminium and the chiral bissulfonamide (31) catalyses the [2+2]cycloaddition of ketene and aldehydes (R^2CHO) to give the 3-substituted-2-oxetanones (32) with 0 to 74% e.e. (94CC2281).

A Michael-type addition of secondary amines or thiols to 3-methylene-2-oxetanones (33) and subsequent pyrolysis of the adduct (34, $X = NR^2_2$ or SR^2) to yield allylic amines (35, $X = NR^2_2$) or sulphides (35, $X = SR^2$) has been proposed as a useful alternative to the Wittig olefination procedure (95JOC578).

The structure, synthesis and biological activity of natural 2-oxetanones and their derivatives has been reviewed (95S729). The synthesis of some novel 3-(hydroxymethyl)-4-(2-substituted ethyl)-2-oxetanones and their biological activity as 3-hydroxy-3-methyl-glutaryl coenzyme-A inhibitors has been reported (94CPB1272, 94CPB2097).

Homochiral (2S,3S)-3-amino-2-phenylthietane (38) has been synthesized as a consequence of a series of reactions in which the thietane ring (37) is formed by the reaction of potassium O-ethyldi-thiocarbonate on the 1,3-ditosylate (36, R = OTs) or diiodide (36, R = I) (94TA1327).

Photocycloaddition of phenyl triphenylsilyl thioketones with electron poor olefins (e.g. acrylonitrile) yield thietanes (e.g. 39) in a regioselective manner and, in some cases, in a highly stereo-selective process (95JCS(P1)2039). Spirothietanes (e.g. 41) are obtained by photocycloaddition of a cyclic thione (e.g. 40) and an alkene (95JCS(P1)561).

Chiral thietanes with mesogenic groups have been used as novel liquid crystals (95SC2665). The oxazole derivatives (42) readily undergo thermal rearrangement to the thietan-3-imines (43) (95CC67).

The oxidation of 3-substituted tetramethylthietanes with MCPBA gives the *cis*-sulfoxide with modest stereoselectivity (8:3 is the best of 4 examples) (94TL5809), and Ti(III) in a mixture of hydrogen peroxide, water and methanol is more selective (94MI281).

4.4 DIOXETANES AND DITHIETANES

The bromide ion catalysed rearrangement of benzofuran dioxetane (44) yields the spiro oxirane (45) by attack of bromide ion at the 3-position of the dioxetane (94JA6713).

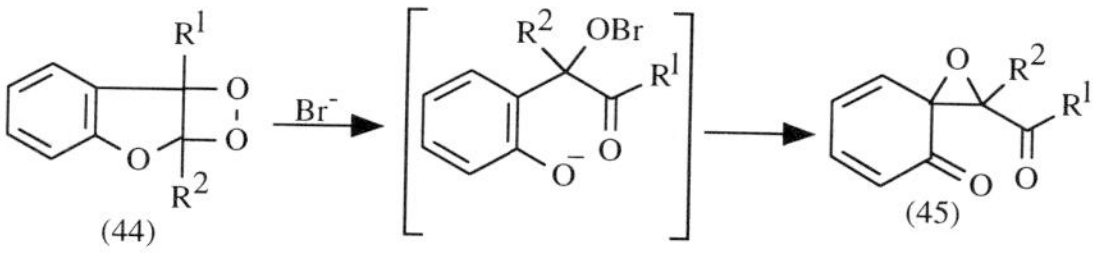

(44) (45)

A review of biologically interesting small-ring disulfides includes some dithietanes (94MI97).

The reaction of carbon disulfide with α-functional phosphonates $[(R^1O)_2P(O)CH_2X]$ in the presence of bases gives dithiolates which, on treatment with *gem*-dihalides (R^2CHBr_2), yield (46) (94MI409). 1,3-Dithietanes (47) on reaction with hydrazides $(RCONHNH_2)$ yield the 1,3,4-oxadiazoles (48) (94H185, 95H1235).

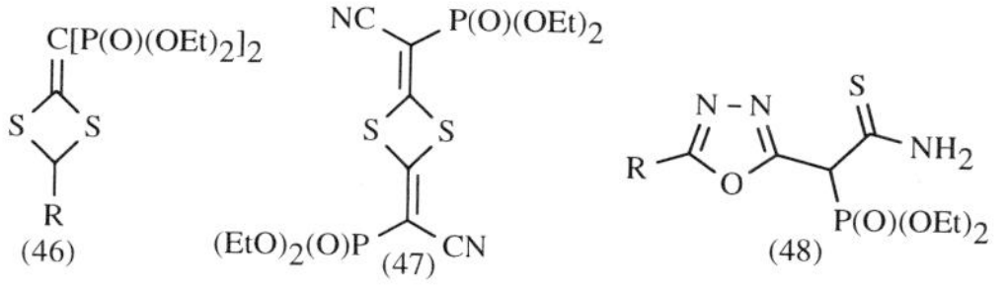

(46) (47) (48)

4.5 OXATHIETANES AND THIAZETIDINES

Two novel reagents for the selective sulfonation of styrene to the β-sultone (49) are reported (94ZOR948). The action of sulfur trioxide on the olefin $CF_2:CFSO_3SiMe_3$, yields the β-sultone (50) (94JFC89).

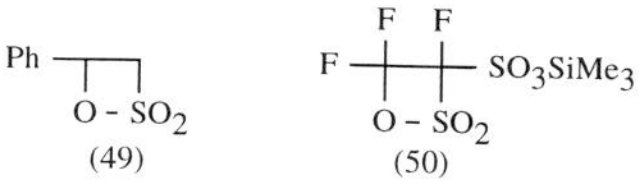

(49) (50)

Some tricyclic 1,3-thiazetidines of type (51) are reported (95CPB63). Selective C-S bond cleavage of 3-aryl-β-sultams (52) with ethylaluminium dichloride gives aryl ketones or aldehydes by a process involving 1,2-aryl shift, imine formation and hydrolysis of the imine (95TL245).

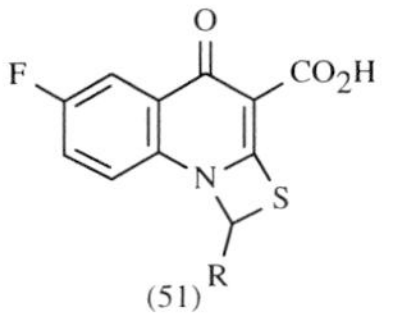

(51) 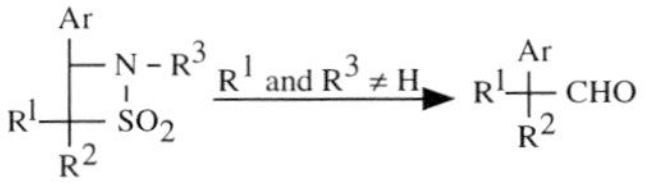 (52)

4.6 SILICON AND BORON HETEROCYCLES

Very low pressure thermolysis of (2-silapropen-2-yl)benzene $(CH_2:Si(Me)C_6H_5)$ causes a 1,3-hydrogen shift from the aryl carbon to the sp^2 silicon with the formation of (53) (94OM4661). In a related reaction, thermolysis of the silacyclobutane (54) yields (55) by a 1,4-hydrogen shift after the four-membered ring has decomposed by loss of ethene (95JOMC4).

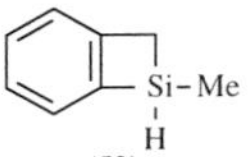

(53) 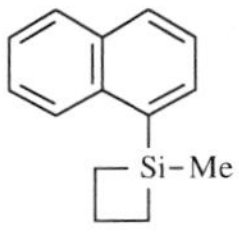 (54) 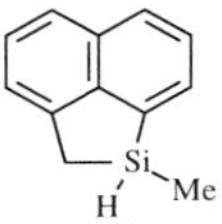 (55)

Silacyclobutene (57) is obtained in high yield on acidification of (56), which is readily prepared from dimethyl-bis-(phenylethynyl)silane (95JA2665).

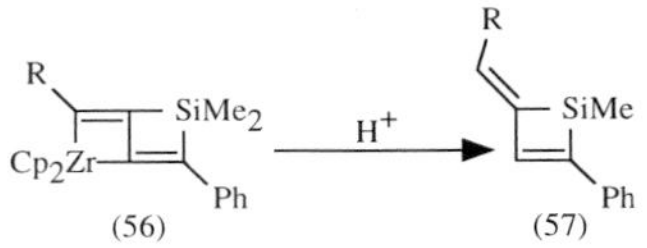

(56) (57)

The boracyclobutenes (58, R^1 = Bu^t, R^2 = H, R^3 = TMS and R^1 = 2,3,5,6-Me$_4$C$_6$H, R^2 = SnMe$_3$, R^3 = 3,5-Bu$^t_2$C$_6$H$_3$) have been prepared and their reactions studied (94AG2394, 94AG2172). The first thermally stable 1,2-dihydro-1,2-diborete (59) has been obtained in two steps in 28% yield (94CB2349). Thermolysis of 1,2-oxaboretamide (60, R = mesityl), the intermediate of a boron-Wittig reaction, gives the expected olefin (95JA6142).

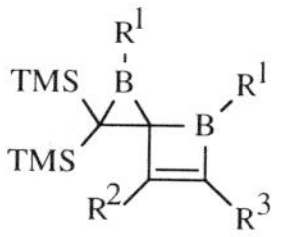

(58) 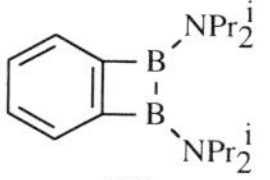　(59) 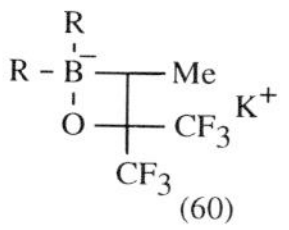　(60)

4.7 AZETIDINONES (β-LACTAMS)

Lithium (α-methylbenzyl)allylamide is used as a differentially protected nucleophile in a high yielding four-step synthesis of homochiral β-lactam (61) (95CC1109). Chiral, non-racemic, β-amido sulfoxides (62) undergo a highly asymmetric Pummerer-type of cyclization giving enantiomerically enriched (e.e. 60-85%) β-lactams (63). The stereoinduction is dominated by the absolute configuration of the sulfoxide (95TL115).

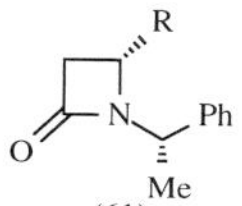

(61) 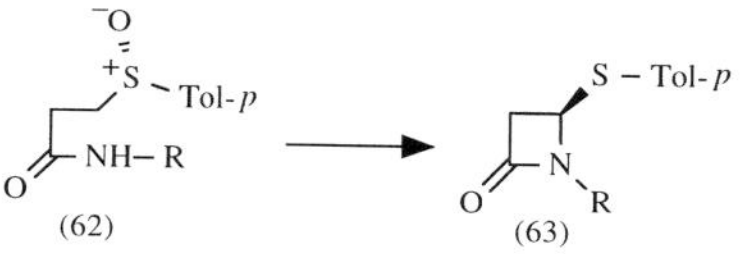　(62)　(63)

Cyclization of 3-halo-*N*-phenylpropionamides using calixarenes gives higher yields than use of crown ethers in a PTC procedure (94JCR(S)342). In a different cyclization procedure, 3-sulfonoxyamides give higher yields than the corresponding 3-chloroamides (95H691) and 3-hydroxy-2-hydroxymethyl-2-methyl-propanamides are cyclized in 55-65% yield in the presence of HMPA and CCl_4 (95CC1279). Certain *N,N*-dimethyl acylthio-amides (e.g. 64) undergo a novel cyclization in the presence of LDA at -78°C to give β-thiolactams (e.g. 65) (readily converted to a β-lactam) by incorporation of a carbon of an *N*-methyl group into the ring (95JA5859). Sulfur is also used to cause regioselective radical cyclization of *N*-[2-(phenylthio)ethenyl]-α-bromoacetamide to (66), though in only 22% yield (95JOC1276).

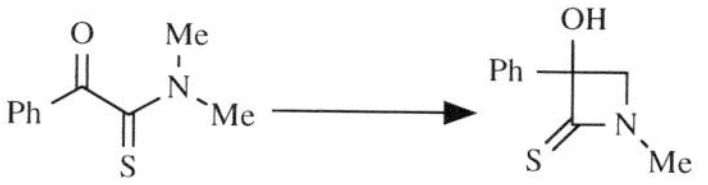

(64)　(65) 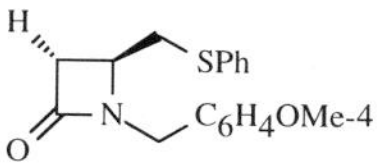　(66)

The addition of imines to either ketenes or enolates continues to be developed. Conditions are reported for the diastereoselective synthesis of 3-alkyl-4-substituted β-lactams from acid chlorides (95TL2555) and preferential formation of *trans* isomers has been found when acid chlorides (PhCH$_2$COCl and AcOCH$_2$COCl) are used in conjunction with microwave heating (95TL213). The use of chiral imines and silylketene acetals in boron reagent mediated reactions to provide asymmetric syntheses of 3-(1-hydroxyethyl)-β-lactams is reviewed (94MI306). N-Imino-β-lactams are formed when 2,3-diaza-1,3-dienes are used as the azine component (94JOC8003).

The effects on stereocontrol at the 4-position of 3,4-disubstituted β-lactams formed from chiral ester enolate-imine condensations caused by changes in the cation are discussed, as are the effects of the structure of the chiral auxiliary and the co-ordinating ability of heteroatoms in the ester (95TL729). Lithium enolates are used in the first asymmetric total synthesis of (67) (94TL7339). Zinc enolates are used in high yielding reactions giving (68, R^1 = Ph or 2-thienyl) (94RTC567) and also in the additions of glycine ester enolates with imines in the presence of α-amino esters as chiral auxilliaries (95JOC4331). Choice of the correct method is important if optimum stereo-control is required (94CL1403). A review (108 references) of the use of organotin and organosilicon compounds in the synthesis and transformation of β-lactams is available (94H2309). Titanium enolates of 2-pyridyl-thioesters with imines bearing a chiral auxiliary, and the α-methylbenzyl group is particularly useful (94T9471). Aromatic imines react enantioselectively (e.e. up to 78%) with a mixture of an enolate derived from 2-pyridylthioesters, an enantiomerically pure aminoalcohol (N-methylephedrine is particularly useful) and boron trichloride-dimethyl sulfide complex in a one-pot procedure (95T8941).

Trans-3,4-disubstituted β-lactams are obtained from 4-substituted precursors upon hydroxylation (moderate yield) (95G65) or by electrophilic attack on the less hindered face of the enolate (95JCS(P1)351, 95JCS(P1)359). A 3-trimethylsilyl substituent is replaceable to give a 3-methoxycarbonylmethyl substituent

(94HCA2147) or a 3-propenylidene substituent (95HCA629).

The ester group of 3-substituted 4-acetoxy-β-lactams is replaceable in reactions with *B*-(1-cyclohexenyl)dialkylboranes to give (69) but variable mixtures of *cis* and *trans* isomers are formed (95JA9604). Also, the 4-acetoxy group is shown to be replaceable to yield a 4-dithioester substituent (95TL771). *Cis*-3-substituted 4-formyl-β-lactams undergo an unusual Baeyer-Villiger rearrangement to form (70) (95TL3401).

(69) (70)

A comparison of the reactivity of C-N or C-P fission in β-lactams and four-membered cyclic phosphonamidates, respectively, shows the latter to be much more reactive (95PAC711). The absolute configuration of some 1,3,4-trisubstituted β-lactams is determined by CD spectra (95TL4217). A ring expansion of 3-amido-1-hydroxy-β-lactams to 4-imidazolin-2-ones by the action of tosyl chloride and organic base is reported (95TL1617).

ACKNOWLEDGEMENTS

We thank Dr. C. J. G. Shaw for his helpful comments.

REFERENCES

93BSB719   M. Rahmouni, M. Abbari, R. Carrie and M. Soufiaoui; *Bull. Soc. Chim. Belg.*, 1993, **102**, 719.

94AG2172   D. Steiner, H.-J. Winkler, S. Wocaldo, S. Fau, W. Massa, G. Frenking and A. Berndt; *Angew. Chem.*, 1994, **106**, 2172.

94AG2394   C. Balzereit, H.-J. Winkler, W. Massa and A. Berndt; *Angew. Chem.*, 1994, **106**, 2394.

94CB2349   D. E. Kaufmann, R. Boese and A.Scheer; *Chem. Ber.*, 1994, **127**, 2349.

94CC2281   Y. Tamai, H. Yoshiwara, M. Someya, J. Fukumoto and S. Miyano; *J. Chem. Soc., Chem. Commun.*, 1994, 2281.

94CL1403   M. Shimizu, T. Ishida and T. Fujisawa; *Chem. Lett.*, 1994, 1403.

94CPB1272   H. Hashizume, H. Ito, N. Kanaya, H. Nagashima, H. Usui, R. Oshima, M. Kanao, H. Tomoda, T. Sunazuka, H. Kumagai and S. Omura.; *Chem. Pharm. Bull.*, 1994, **42**, 1272.

94CPB2097   H. Hashizume, H. Ito, T. Morikawa, N. Kanaya, H. Nagashima, H. Usui, H. Tomoda, T. Sunazuka, H. Kumagai and S. Omura; *Chem. Pharm. Bull.,* 1994, **42**, 2097.

94G459   N. A. Al-Jalal, M. J. Ijam, F. Al-Omran and G. Gopalakrishnan; *Gazz. Chim. Ital.,* 1994, **124**, 459.

94H185   R. Neidlein, M. Jochheim, C. Krieger and W. Kramer; *Heterocycles,* 1994, **39**, 185.

94H2165   A. Itoh, Y. Hirose, H. Kashiwagi and Y. Masaki; *Heterocycles,* 1994, **38**, 2165.

94H2309   G. A. Veinberg and E. Lukevics; *Heterocycles,* 1994, **38**, 2309.

94HCA2147   M. Johner, G. Riha, S. Guetler and H.-H. Otto; *Helv. Chim. Acta,* 1994, **77**, 2147.

94JA6713   W. Adam, M. Ahrweiler and D. Reinhardt; *J. Am. Chem. Soc.,* 1994, **116**, 6713.

94JCR(S)342   S. J. Harris, A. M. Kinahan, M. J. Meegan and R. C. Prendergast; *J. Chem. Res., (S),* 1994, 342.

94JFC89   D. Hass, H. Holfter and U. Schroeder; *J. Fluorine Chem.,* 1994, **69**, 89.

94JOC7994   B. Alcaide, G. Esteban, Y. Martin-Cantalejo, J. Plumet, J. Rodriguez-Lopez, A. Monge and V. Perez-Garcia; *J. Org. Chem.,* 1994, **59**, 7994.

94JOC8003   B. Alcaide, M. Miranda, J. Perez-Castells, C. Polanco and M. A. Sierra; *J. Org. Chem.,* 1994, **59**, 8003.

94MI97   K. Steliou, P. L. Folkins and D. N. Harpp; *Adv. Sulfur Chem.,* 1994, **1**, 97.

94MI281   R. S. Glass, W. P. Singh and B. A. Hay; *Sulfur Lett.,* 1994, **17**, 281.

94MI306   A. Datta and G. I. Georg; *Chemtracts: Org. Chem.,* 1994, **7**, 306.

94MI327   S.-S. Jew, H. Lee and B.-A. Koo; *Arch. Pharmacal Res.,* 1994, **17**, 327.

94MI409   Y.-X. Ding, J.-Q. Yue, J.-N. Dai and R.-X. Lin; *Youji Huaxue,* 1994, **14**, 409.

94MI417   R. Southgate; *Contemp. Org. Synth.,* 1994, **1**, 417.

94MI926   K.-T. Kang, D. C. Ryu, T. M. Sung and J. G. Kim; *Bull. Korean Chem. Soc.,* 1994, **15**, 926.

94OM4661   V. V. Volkova, L. E. Gusel'nikov, E. A. Volnina and E. N. Buravtseva; *Organometallics,* 1994, **13**, 4661.

94RTC567   H. L. van Maanen, H. K. Johann, J. T. B. H. Jastrzebski and G. van Koten; *Recl. Trav. Chim. Pays-Bas.,* 1994, **113**, 567.

94T9471   R. Annunziata, M. Bengalia, M. Cinquini, F. Cozzi and L. Raimondi; *Tetrahedron,* 1994, **50**, 9471.

94TA1327   M. D. Rozwadowska; *Tetrahedron: Asymmetry,* 1994, **5**, 1327.

94TL5809   R. S. Glass, W. P. Singh and B. A. Hay; *Tetrahedron Lett.*, 1994, **35**, 5809.

94TL5845   T. Bach; *Tetrahedron Lett.*, 1994, **35**, 5845.

94TL6611   P. Galtsis and D. J. Parks; *Tetrahedron Lett.*, 1994, **35**, 6611.

94TL7339   D. A. Burnett; *Tetrahedron Lett.*, 1994, **35**, 7339.

94TL8023   N. De Kimpe and D. De Smaele; *Tetrahedron Lett.*, 1994, **35**, 8023.

94ZOR948   Zh. V. Matsulevich, A. V. Borisov and I. V. Bodrikov; *Zh. Org. Khim.*, 1994, **30**, 948.

95ACR383   I. Ojima; *Acc. Chem. Res.*, 1995, **28**, 383.

95ACR414   K. Khumtaveeporn and H. Alper; *Acc. Chem. Res.*, 1995, **28**, 414.

95CC67   G. L'abbe, A. Francis, W. Dehaen and S. Toppet; *J. Chem. Soc., Chem. Commun.*, 1995, 67.

95CC1109   S. G. Davies and D. R. Fenwick; *J. Chem. Soc., Chem. Commun.*, 1995, 1109.

95CC1279   L. Molina, A. Perani, M.-R. Infante, M.-A. Manresa, M. Maugras, S. Achilefu, M.-J. Stebe and C. Selve; *J. Chem. Soc., Chem. Commun.*, 1995, 1279.

95CPB63   J. Segawa, K. Kazuno, M. Matsuoka, I. Shirahase, M. Ozaki, M. Matsuda, Y. Tomii, M. Kitano and M. Kise; *Chem. Pharm. Bull.*, 1995, **43**, 63.

95G65   R. Annunziata, M. Benaglia, M. Cinquini, F. Cozzi and A. Scolaro; *Gazz. Chim. Ital.*, 1995, **125**, 65.

95H691   P. J. Crocker, U. Karlsson-Andreasson, B. T. Lotz and M. J. Miller; *Heterocycles*, 1995, **40**, 691.

95H1235   M. Jochheim, H. G. Krug, R. Neidlein and C. Krieger; *Heterocycles*, 1995, **41**, 1235.

95HCA629   S. Ruf and H.-H. Otto; *Helv. Chim. Acta*, 1995, **78**, 629.

95JA928   G. V. Shustov and A. Rauk, *J. Am. Chem. Soc.*, 1995, **117**, 928.

95JA2665   T. Takahashi, Z. Xi, Y. Obora and N. Suzuki; *J. Am. Chem. Soc.*, 1995, **117**, 2665.

95JA5859   X. Creary and C. Zhu; *J. Am. Chem. Soc.*, 1995, **117**, 5859.

95JA6142   T. Kawashima, N. Yamashita and R. Okazaki; *J. Am. Chem. Soc.*, 1995, **117**, 6142.

95JA9604   T. Rossi, S. Biondi, S. Contini, R. J. Thomas and C. Marchioro; *J. Am. Chem. Soc.*, 1995, **117**, 9604.

95JCS(P1)351   E. J. Thomas and A. C. Williams; *J. Chem. Soc., Perkin Trans. 1*, 1995, 351.

95JCS(P1)359   J. M. Roe and E. J. Thomas; *J. Chem. Soc., Perkin Trans. 1*, 1995, 359.

95JCS(P1)561   T. Nishio; *J. Chem. Soc., Perkin Trans. 1*, 1995, 561.

95JCS(P1)2039   B. F. Bonini, M. C. Franchini, M. Fochi, G. Mazzanti, A. Ricci, P. Zani and B. Zwanenburg; *J. Chem. Soc., Perkin Trans. 1*, 1995, 2039.

95JOC253   J.-O. Baeg, C. Bensimon and H. Alper; *J. Org. Chem.*, 1995, **60**, 253.

95JOC578   W. Adam and V. O. Nava-Salgado; *J. Org. Chem.*, 1995, **60**, 578.

95JOC758   C. Wedler, A. Kunath and H. Schick; *J. Org. Chem.*, 1995, **60**, 758.

95JOC1020   G. Barbaro, A. Battaglia and P. Giorgianni; *J. Org. Chem.*, 1995, **60**, 1020.

95JOC1276   H. Ishibashi, C. Kameoka, H. Iriyama, K. Kodama, T. Sato and M. Ikeda; *J. Org. Chem.*, 1995, **60**, 1276.

95JOC1959   T. Axenrod, C. Watnick, H. Yazdekhasti and P. R. Dave; *J. Org. Chem.*, 1995, **60**, 1959.

95JOC3092   J.-O. Baeg and H. Alper; *J. Org. Chem.*, 1995, **60**, 3092.

95JOC3419   V. A. Petrov, F. Davidson and B. E. Smart; *J. Org. Chem.*, 1995, **60**, 3419.

95JOC4331   H. L. van Maanen, H. Kleijn, J. T. B. H. Jastrzebski, J. Verweij, A. P. G. Kieboom and G. van Koten; *J. Org. Chem.*, 1995, **60**, 4331.

95JOC4943   A. P. Marchand, D. Rajagopal, S. G. Bott and T. G. Archibald; *J. Org. Chem.*, 1995, **60**, 4943.

95JOC4999   M. Miura, M. Enna, K. Okuro and M. Nomura; *J. Org. Chem.*, 1995, **60**, 4999.

95JOMC4   L. E. Gusel'nikov, V. V. Volkova and B. D. Lavrukhin; *J. Organomet. Chem.*, 1995, **492**, C4.

95LA855   T. Bach; *Justus Liebigs Ann. Chem.*, 1995, 855.

95PAC711   M. I. Page, A. P. Laws, M. J. Slater and J. R. Stone; *Pure Appl. Chem.*, 1995, **67**, 711.

95S533   H. Xianming and R. M. Kellogg; *Synthesis*, 1995, 533.

95S729   A. Pommier and J.-M. Pons; *Synthesis*, 1995, 729.

95SC479   H. T. Black, G. A. Brown, D. C. Smith and S. M. Martinie; *Synth. Commun.*, 1995, **25**, 479.

95SC603   J. M. Chong and K. K. Sokoll; *Synth. Commun.*, 1995, **25**, 603.

95SC803   E. Bacque, J.-M. Paris and S. Le Bitoux; *Synth. Commun.*, 1995, **25**, 803.

95SC2665   J. Gay and G. Scherowsky; *Synth. Commun.*, 1995, **25**, 2665.

95T4011   A. B. Concepcion, K. Maruoka and H. Yamamoto; *Tetrahedron*, 1995, **51**, 4011.

95T5073   P. Golding, R. W. Millar, N. C. Paul and D. H. Richards; *Tetrahedron*, 1995, **51**, 5073.

95T5465   N. De Kimpe and D. De Smaele; *Tetrahedron*, 1995, **51**, 5465.

95T8941 R. Annunziata, M. Benaglia, M. Cinquini, F. Cozzi, V. Molteni and L. Raimondi; *Tetrahedron*, 1995, **51**, 8941.

95TL115 Y. Kita, N. Shibata, N. Kawano, T. Tohjo, C. Fujimori and K. Matsumoto; *Tetrahedron Lett.*, 1995, **36**, 115.

95TL213 A. K. Bose, B. K. Banik and M. S. Manhas; *Tetrahedron Lett.*, 1995, **36**, 213.

95TL245 T. Kataoka and T. Iwama; *Tetrahedron Lett.*, 1995, **36**, 245.

95TL729 M. Shimizu, Y. Teramoto and T. Fujisawa; *Tetrahedron Lett.*, 1995, **36**, 729.

95TL771 D. S. Ennis and M. A. Armitage; *Tetrahedron Lett.*, 1995, **36**, 771.

95TL1617 X. Li, C. Niu and M. J. Miller; *Tetrahedron Lett.*, 1995, **36**, 1617.

95TL2555 M. Browne, D. A. Burnett, M. A. Caplen, L.-Y. Chen, J. W. Clader, M. Domalski, S. Dugar, P. Pushpavanam, R. Sher, W. Vaccaro, M. Viziano and H. Zhao; *Tetrahedron Lett.*, 1995, **36**, 2555.

95TL3401 B. Alcaide, M. F. Aly and M. A. Sierra; *Tetrahedron Lett.*, 1995, **36**, 3401.

95TL4217 D. Galle, M. Tolksdorf and M. Braun; *Tetrahedron Lett.*, 1995, **36**, 4217.

Chapter 5.1

Five-Membered Ring Systems: Thiophenes & Se, Te Analogs

Ronald K. Russell
The R. W. Johnson Pharmaceutical Research Institute, Raritan, NJ, USA

Jeffery B. Press
Galenica Pharmaceuticals, Inc., Frederick, MD, USA

5.1.1 INTRODUCTION

As has been the case in previous years, the study of thiophenes has continued unabated in the past year. Of tremendous commercial import, the need to elucidate and improve the removal of sulfur-containing materials from petroleum necessitates further studies of the reactivities of thiophene and its derivatives with homogenous and heterogeneous catalysts. These on-going studies in transition-metal chemistry also require theoretical studies of the electronics, aromaticity and dipolarizability of thiophene-containing compounds which have implications into many areas of synthetic organic and medicinal chemistry. Although extended thiophene derivatives also have tremendous commercial potential as a result of their optochemical and super-conducting electronic properties, this subject was reviewed in detail in our last review and is not covered in this.

One of the interesting aspects of thiophene chemistry is the relative ease and control of introducing substitution at either the 2- and/or the 3- position using routine organic synthetic methods. These derivatives allow study of the resultant electronic effects on the physical properties of thiophenes as well as provide access to novel molecules if the sulfur is removed. In this regard, the thiophene ring might be viewed as a four carbon delivery moiety with the sulfur atom as a protecting group. Since thiophene ring formation is readily accessible from linear materials using a variety of synthetic approaches, incorporation of thiophene into synthetic pathways provides a feasible method to produce useful regioselective results. Synthesis of fused thiophene derivatives continues to be an area of intense study by pharmaceutical and agricultural chemists. The unique electronic properties of thiophene (which is less aromatic than benzene) also provide the platform for some novel electrocyclic chemistry. In addition to thiophene citations, there was a significant increase in reports of selenophene and tellurophene chemistry in contrast to previous years.

An overview of several aspects of thiophene chemistry focused on synthesis of the drugs cetiedil® and ticarcillin® appeared last year <95MI10>. As in the past, there are well over 1,500 literature references during the period of this review (late 1994 through 1995). We have tried to reduce these references to a manageable number to cover the most timely and interesting advances in this area of chemistry. We apologize in advance for our oversights and omissions.

5.1.2 ELECTRONICS, AROMATICITY AND DESULFURIZATION (HDS)

Studies to further understand the electronics and aromaticity of thiophene, benzo[b]- and benzo[c]thiophene, and 2,2'-bithiophene have continued. By studying a combination of geometric, energetic and magnetic criteria of a series of five-membered ring systems, aromaticity and antiaromaticity is well defined with cyclopentadiene as a marginal arene, while phosphole and silacyclopentadienyl anion have increasing aromatic character. In order of aromaticity, pyrrole > thiophene > furan while cyclopentadienyl anion is the most aromatic <95AC(E)337>. *Ab initio* calculations of the geometries, static dipole polarizability and first hyperpolarizability for borole, aluminocyclopentadiene, cyclopentadiene, silacyclopentadiene, pyrrole, phosphole, furan and thiophene show that dipole polarizability is related to the bond distance between C-2 and the heteroatom. The calculated hyperpolarizabilities may be used as a scale of aromaticities and predict the order as benzene > thiophene > pyrrole > furan <95JMT109>. Use of *ab initio* Hartree–Fock–Roothaan studies to calculate linear polarizability (α), first hyperpolarizability (β) and second polarizability (γ) show the α and γ coefficients to order thiophene > pyrrole > furan while β has no trend <95JPC9045>. Analysis of the vibrational frequencies of heteroatom isosteres of indene provides useful refinement of the AM1 Hamiltonian <95MI255, 95MI273>. *Ab initio* determination of the geometric structure and internal rotation of 2,2'-bithiophene predicts an *s-trans-gauche* structure with a torsional angle of 142.2-147°. The flatness of the torsional potential results from destabilization of planar conformers due to the non-bonding interactions of the large sulfur atoms <95JPC4955>.

Diels-Alder reactivity of thiophene and benzothiophene remains poorly understood. AM1 semiempirical studies examining the activation of thiophene for this thermally allowed [4+2] cycloaddition process have shown that the usual synthesis approaches (use of highly reactive dienophiles, substitution on thiophene, increased reaction pressures) have only small effects on rate enhancement. However, use of the corresponding *S*-methylthiophenium salts, which have little aromaticity, should provide excellent activation for Diels-Alder reactions of thiophenes even with poor dienophiles such as ethylene <95JHC483>. This AM1 approach has been applied to examine Diels-Alder reactions of benzo[b]- and benzo[c]thiophenes; the theoretical data agree with experimental results <95JCS(P1)1217>.

There also have been theoretical approaches to some hetero ring-fused thiophene derivatives. *Ab initio* Hartree–Fock geometry optimization calculations were applied to thienopyridine isomers and isosteres and the structural, charge distribution and dipole moment results were interpreted in terms of classical canonical structures. There are two different classes – benzo[c]thiophene has only one canonical structure and preserves C – S single bonds while benzo[b]thiophene has two neutral canonical structures and a shortened $C_2 - C_3$ bond length <95JMT181>. Heat of formation calculations for thienopyridine isomers and their 4-oxygenated derivatives correctly predict preference of the [2,3-b] isomer for the enol form **1** while the [3,2-b] and [3,4-b] isomers prefer the keto form **2** <95JMT171>. Semi-empirical quantum-mechanical calculations for the structural and electronic properties of thieno[3,4-b][1,4]diazepine and 1,5-benzodiazepine systems conclude that both systems achieve pseudo-boat conformation of the 7-membered ring and that the superior anticonvulsant properties of the benzodiazepines **3** must be attributed to electronic differences between the fused thiophene and benzene rings <95MI267>. A computational study of the equilibrium between thieno[2,3-c][1,2,5]oxadiazole 1-oxide and 3-oxide predicts a slight preference for the 1-isomer with the dioxadiazine significantly less stable (Eq. 1) <95JCR(S)120>.

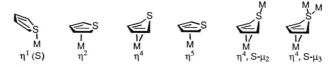

Substituent effects on ^{13}C NMR chemical shifts of some 5-substituted 2-acetylthiophene derivatives and their protonated forms underscore the importance of conjugation effects between the thiophene ring and the protonated acetyl group regardless of 5-substituent <95JCR(S)222>. He I and He II photoelectron spectra of 2-acetyl- and 2-cyanothiophene show the effects of these electron-withdrawing substituents on the π-orbitals of thiophene <95MI399>. Platinum (II) complexes of deprotonated 2-(2-thienyl)pyridine 4 display time-resolved vibrational satellites which are unresolved using conventional spectroscopy <95JPC226, 95JPC13385>.

The need to remove thiophene from crude petroleum has led to a number of studies. The issue of transition metal catalyst poisoning by thiophene has been studied by the spin-coupled valence bond (SC-VB) method to predict that, for a thiophene-Li$^+$ complex, the Li$^+$ ion lies off the C$_2$ axis without sufficient bond strength to poison catalysts <95JCS(F1)749>. A review of organometallic complexes used as models for hydrodesulfurization (HDS) describe known modes of coordination to thiophene (η^1(S), η^2, η^4, η^5) and relate structures to bonding and stabilities to adsorption of thiophene on heterogeneous HDS catalysts <95BSB265>. An extensive review of the mechanism of HDS catalysis is published <95MI353>.

The effects of the transition metals rhodium and iridium on thiophene and its derivatives have received the greatest study. The thermally-generated fragment [(triphos)RhH] reacts with thiophene in THF to produce a C–S insertion intermediate which forms butadienethiolate derivatives upon treatment with electrophiles (Eq. 2) <95JA4333>. Thiophene derivatives reactivity toward [(triphos)RhH] decreases in the order: 2-CO$_2$Et > 2-COMe > 3-COMe >> 3-OMe > thiophene $\approx$ 2-Me > 3-Me; reaction always produces insertion away from the substituent <95O3196>. Among other things, this chemistry provides a useful synthesis of substituted-butadienyl methyl sulfides for which there is no other good methodology <95O4858>. Benzo[b]thiophene reacts with [(triphos)RhH] to produce 2-ethylthiophenol by a ring-opening and subsequent hydrogenation <95JA8567>. The related iridium complex [(triphos)Ir(η^2-C,S-SC$_4$H$_4$)]BPh$_4$ reacts with thiophene in THF and DMSO to produce dramatically different outcomes (Eq. 3) <95CC921>. [(Triphos)MH] fragments (M = Rh, Ir) react with benzo[b]thiophene via C–S insertion to produce

2-vinylthiophenolate derivatives which show a wide array of redox-induced reactivity <95O4390>. The complex Cp*Ir(2,5-Me$_2$T) (5), regardless of η^4 or C,S-coordination to iridium, reacts with electrophiles to produce the same product. It acts as a reducing agent with S$_8$ or O$_2$, as a Lewis acid with SO$_2$, and as a base with CS$_2$ <95ICA61>. In the case of dibenzothiophene, the [(triphos)IrH] fragment reacts with high kinetic selectivity for C–H bond cleavage to give three isomeric complexes at 20° while both C–H and C–S cleavage occurs at 120 - 160°. This is the first report of homogeneous catalytic HDS of dibenzothiophene <95O2342>.

(Eq. 2)

(Eq. 3)

(Eq. 4)

5, M = Ir, Rh

The study of other transition metals as models for HDS has led to the study of Re, Ru, OS, Pt, Mo, and Ni complexes. The focus has been on soluble model complexes that mimic the catalyst systems used in industrial processing of petroleum feed stocks. In many of these model studies, the spectator ligands such as cyclopentadiene are not representative of industrial catalysts. Low d-electron count metals such as Re may provide a better model of HDS. Reaction of ReOCl$_3$(PPh$_3$)$_2$ with thienyllithium reagents produce Li(THF)$_n$ReO(thienyl)$_4$ which are reactive to protic and oxidizing conditions <95IC5220>. Thiophene complexes of ruthenium in ammonia undergo C–S cleavage to give iminium-thiolato derivatives <95O2923>. Novel, isolable 2H-thiophenium complexes form upon treatment of [(4,5-η^2-thiophene)Os(NH$_3$)$_5$](OTf)$_2$ complexes with HOTf (Eq. 4) <95O1559>. Benzothiophene and 1-bromobenzothiophene each react with Os$_3$(CO)$_{10}$(NCMe)$_2$ to form two discrete complexes reacting across the C2–C3 bond of the heterocyclic ring <95O2238>. Thiaplatinacycles form reversibly by insertion across a C–S bond of dibenzothiophene, benzothiophene or thiophene. In the presence of the reducing agent Et$_3$SiH, the benzothiophene complex undergoes 73% desulfurization, while desulfurization of the thiophene complex occurs only to the extent of 4% <95JA2179>.

Among the studies of HDS on surfaces, MoS_2/alumina <95BSB325>, hybrid CoMo/alumina <95MI989, 95MI1037, 95MI401, 95MI52>, molybdenum disulfide particles <95MI281>, $PbMo_6S_8$ <95MI283>, Ni(CO)HZSM5 and other zeolite catalysts <95MI582, 95MI169, 95MI128>, nickel nanoparticles <95MI669>, carbides and nitrides <95JPC16365>, and sulfide bimetallic catalysts <95MI471> are studies worthy of note.

5.1.3 RING SUBSTITUTION

As mentioned in the introduction, the thiophene ring may be substituted regioselectively using routine electrophilic, nucleophilic and organometallic chemistry. This property makes the thiophene ring an extremely useful reactive handle for studying structure-function relationships. In addition, since thiophene may be desulfurized using several alternative strategies, sequential substitution on thiophene may provide the foundation for the controlled construction of unique linear molecules.

Thiophene is an electron rich heteroaromatic compound and an ideal substrate for electrophilic reactions. Selective 5-iodination by bis(trifluoroacetoxy)iodobenzene – iodine provides **6** in excellent yield regardless of the nature of the R substituent <95TL4883>. An inexpensive, rapid laboratory method for iodination of heteroaromatics utilizes lead tetraacetate and molecular iodine <95S926>. The previously reported selective iodinating agent benzyltrimethylammonium dichloroiodide was reinvestigated and found to chlorinate thienyl ketones to **7** and iodinate thienyl esters to **8**. The reagent did produce 5-substituted products exclusively regardless of the nature of the 2-substituent. An unique process that takes advantage of the propensity of thiophene derivatives to chlorinate non-selectively and of the solubility differentials of bisulfite addition products allowed the isolation of **9** in 62% yield in 96% purity (Eq. 5) <95OPP233>. The best method to prepare 2,3,5-trichlorothiophene is the direct chlorination of thiophene using ferric chloride catalysis. Alternatively, 2,5-dichlorothiophene may be chlorinated with thionyl chloride/sulfuryl chloride using aluminum trichloride catalyst <95JHC791>. Vilsmeier formylation of 3-alkylthiophenes is a function of increasing bulk of the 3-alkyl substituent and of the Vilsmeier reagent (Eq. 6) <95H925>. Carbenoids are electron deficient and react with thiophene derivatives to form 3-substituted products exclusively (rather than the more typical 2-substitution result, Eq. 7). In the case of reaction with benzo[*b*]thiophene, cycloadduct **10** forms <95JOC2112>.

Selected substituted thiophene derivatives may also react with nucleophiles. Primary and secondary amines react with 2-bromo-3-substituted-5-nitrothiophenes to produce **11** <95T5403>. Vicarious nucleophilic substitution of hydrogen (VNS) works generally for both 2-nitro- and 3-

nitrothiophene derivatives (Eq. 8) <95T8339>. Potential H_1-antihistaminic benzothieno[2,3-*d*]imidazoles are prepared from 2,3-diamines **12** which, in turn, arise from amine displacement reactions of 3-bromo-2-nitrobenzo[*b*]thiophene <95JHC591>. During the course of these studies, a novel rearrangement occurred with some amines to form **13** rather than the precursor to **12** <95JCS(P1)1243>.

Organometallic chemistry is perhaps the most powerful route to prepare substituted thiophene derivatives. 2-Lithiothiophene, formed either by 2-deprotonation or by lithium–halogen exchange of 2-bromothiophene, undergoes typical reactions such as the addition to the erythropentofuranose to form, after ring closure and deprotection, *C*-deoxyribonucleoside **14** <95S638>. In another application of lithiothiophenes, 2,3-dibromothiophene reacts with *n*-BuLi at -78° and 3-cyanopyridine, then *n*-BuLi and CO_2 at -5° to form **15**; the other regioisomer **16** forms by reaction of 3-bromothiophene to first introduce the 3-ketopyridine moiety and then deprotonation of the 2-position and trapping by CO_2 <95CPB236>. The key step in the formation of the selective dopamine D_1 agonist A-86929 is the conjugate addition of 4-lithio-2-allyl-5-thiophenecarboxamide to a nitroolefin prior to nitro group reduction and ring closure (Eq. 9) <95JMC3445>. Polyfunctionalized thiophenes are formed using lithiation of thiophenecarbonylchromium(0) complexes **17** as the key first step <95JCS(P1)97>. Frequently, lithiothiophenes are too reactive and require transmetallation prior to subsequent reaction. For example, the dioxolane of 3-thiophenecarboxaldehyde may be deprotonated with *n*-BuLi, exchanged with $MgBr_2$, and reacted with (-)-(Ss)-menthyl-*p*-toluenesulfinate to produce **18**; isomer **19** forms using a related modified strategy <95TA2045>. Exchange with $ZnBr_2$ allows reaction of 2-lithiothiophene derivatives with 1-(triphenylphosphorylideneaminomethyl)benzotriazole in a one-pot primary aminomethylation (Eq. 10) <95SC2631>. An alternative strategy to form thienozinc reagents utilizes reaction of 3-iodothiophene with Rieke metal Zn°; these compounds couple with aryl iodides using Pd^0 or Ni^{II} to produce novel biaryls <95JOC6658>. Direct mercuration of 3-substituted thiophenes using $HgCl_2$ produces **20** which forms soluble homopolymers by reaction with copper powder and palladium chloride in pyridine (Eq. 11) <95JA3887>.

(Eq. 9)

(Eq. 10)

M = Li→ZnBr

17

18   **19**   **20**

(Eq. 11)

Stille coupling of stannylthiophenes with 8-silylpurine derivatives provides 8-thienyl-9-(β-D-ribofuranosyl)-2,6-diaminopurines such as **21** <95JHC863>. Similar cross-coupling of 2-tri-*n*-butylstannylthiophene with 2,6-dichloropurines produces selective coupling in the purine 6-position (**22**) <95TL1945>. Palladium-catalyzed reaction of 3-tri-*n*-butylstannylthiophenes with 3-chlorocarbonylpropanoate produces **23** which then reacts with hydrazine to form novel thienylpyridazinone derivatives <95JCR(S)306>. Utilizing selective substitution/exchange strategies, palladium-catalyzed coupling with the three isomers of bromopyridine produce precursors to 3- and 4-(2-, 3-, and 4-pyridyl)-2-hydroxythiophenes exemplified by **24** (Eq. 12) <95JHC435>. Starting with a 2-stannylthiophene, the 5-(2-, 3-, and 4-pyridyl)-2-hydroxythiophene tauomers such as **25** may be prepared <95JHC771>. Pd-catalyzed cross coupling of electron donor-substituted thiophenes with electron-acceptor-substituted halothiophenes using either organozinc or organotin intermediates produces donor-acceptor oligothiophenes such as **26** <95JOC2082>. Suzuki coupling, using either thienyl boronates or thienyl halides, also gives substituted thiophene products. For example, palladium-catalyzed reaction of 5-methyl-2-bromothiophene with 2,4-di-*t*-butoxy-5-pyrimidineboronic acid produces uracil **27** (Eq. 13) <95JHC1159>. Using a similar approach, some 2,4- and 2,5-disubstituted thiophene systems were prepared to study structure-function effects on refractive indices, polarizabilities, as well as other parameters <95MI653>. The alternative strategy using 2-thienylboronic anhydride allows for the preparation of precursors to analogues of the angiotensin II antagonist DuP 753 (Eq. 14) <95BML15>.

21   **22**

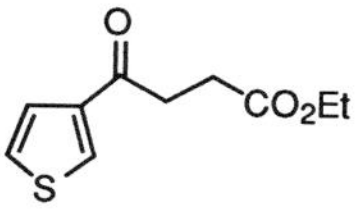

(Eq. 12)

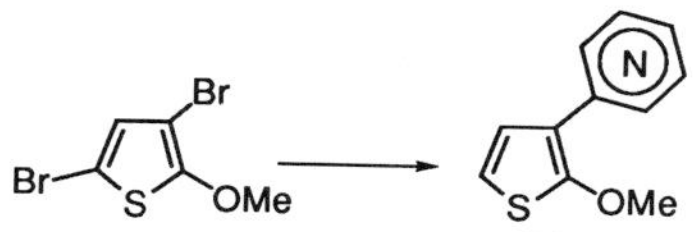

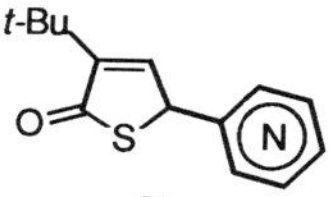

23

25

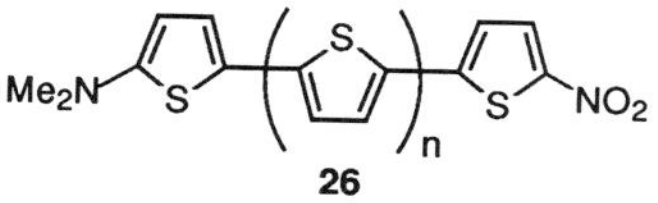

26

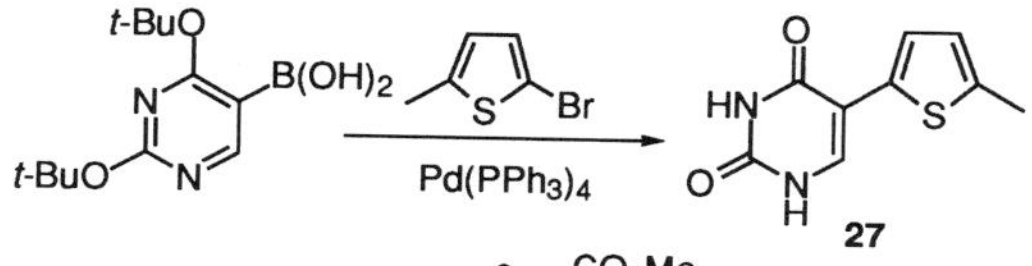

(Eq. 13)

27

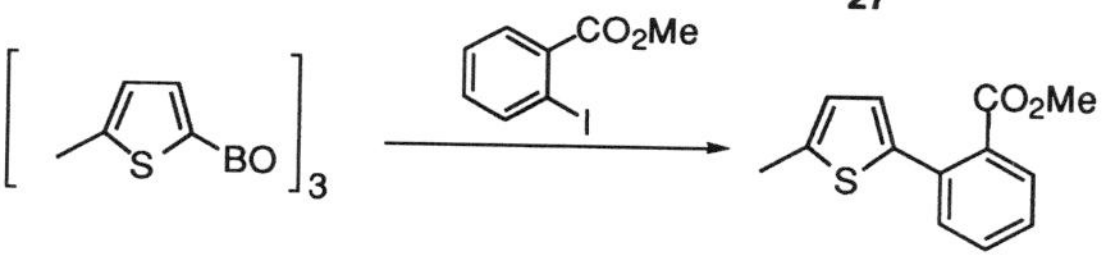

(Eq. 14)

5.1.4 THIOPHENE RING FORMATION

The thiophene ring may be constructed by a variety of means including delivery of sulfur (from numerous sources) to 4-carbon units, radical ring closures, electrocyclic reactions, and use of 2-mercaptoacetate equivalents in a classical Gewald approach. The latter has been used to prepare a large number of thiophene-fused heterocyclic systems. In this past year, ketenethioacetals are reported to convert to condensed thiophenes using a cascade radical reaction (Eq. 15) <95TL2861>. Flash vacuum pyrolysis of phosphorus ylides produces thiophene rings by closure of an acetylene moiety on a methyl sulfide and subsequent radical quenching (Eq. 16) <95SL53>. α-Oxoketene dithioacetals undergo conjugate addition with benzylcopper reagents and subsequent Simmons-Smith reaction to form 2,4-disubstituted thiophenes (Eq. 17) <95TL1925>. Tandem intramolecular Diels-Alder reactions also form thiophene derivatives (Eq. 18) <95AJC593>.

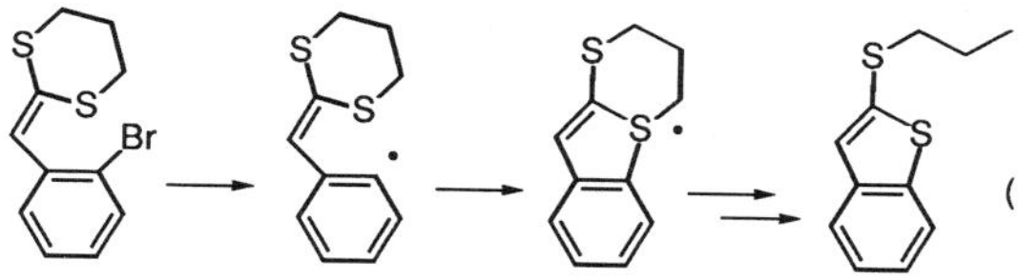

(Eq. 15)

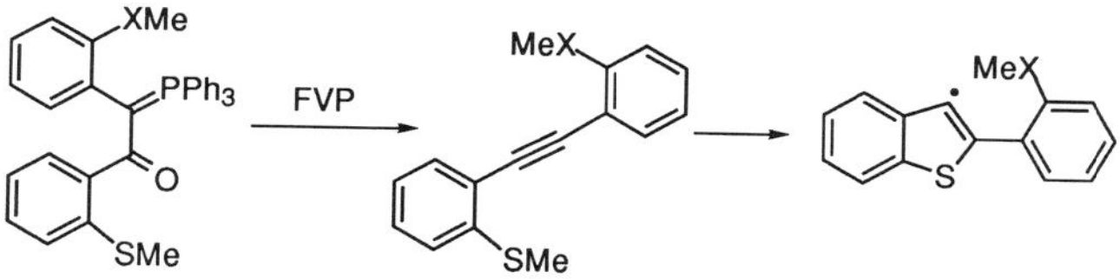

(Eq. 16)

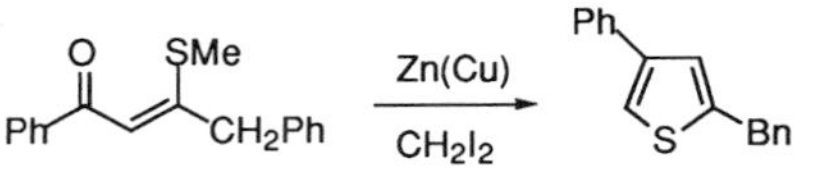

(Eq. 17)

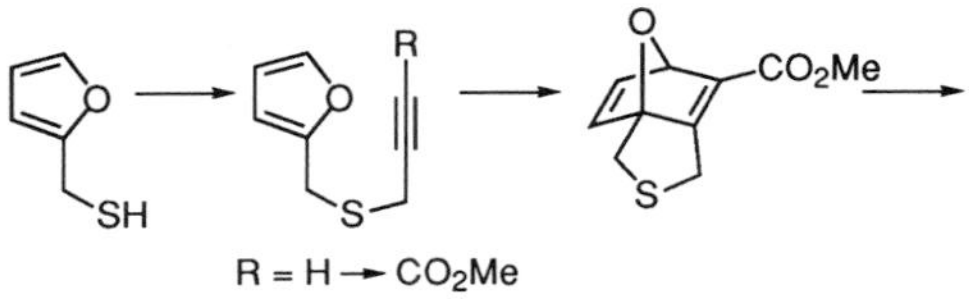

products (Eq. 18)

R = H → CO$_2$Me

Use of sodium sulfide as a sulfur source has provided access to some extremely interesting thiophene derivatives. Reaction with dicyclopropyldiacetylene gives 2,5-dicyclopropylthiophene (Eq. 19); extension of this reaction on "exploding" [*n*]rotanes produces a "crown of thiophenes" (**28**) <95AC(E)781>. Saccharide analogue **29** was prepared using this methodology and has the interglycosidic *O*-linkage replaced with a spacer that has a different orientation than the diyne-linked precursor <95HCA177>. Phosphorus pentasulfide and its Lawesson's reagent (LR) variants also supply sulfur for thiophene ring formation. β,γ-Epoxycarbonyl derivatives formed from allylsilanes and acyl chlorides react with LR to form thiophenes (Eq. 20) <95SC2647>. α-Oligothiophene **30** is formed by LR closure of 1,4-bis(4-methyl-2-thienyl)-1,4-butanedione, which was prepared by a Stetter reaction from 4-methyl-2-thiophenecarboxaldehyde and divinylsulfone <95MI589>. Phosphorus pentasulfide reaction of 2-bromoindanones gives **31** <95PS69>. Disodium 2-aryl succinates react with red phosphorus to form 3-arylthiophenes <95SC235>. Other sulfur sources include thionyl chloride which forms **32** from benzo[*b*]thiophene-2-acrylic acid <95JHC659>. Sulfur dichloride reaction with substituted biphenyls produce dibenzothiophenes <95NJC65>. Condensation of carbon disulfide with 1,3-diketones forms new derivatives of 4,5,6,7-tetrahydrobenzo[*c*]thiophen-4-ones (Eq. 21) <95SC2449>. This reaction has also formed thieno[4,5-*c*; 2,3-*c*']dipyrazoles <95M601>. Ethyl mercaptan serves as an interesting sulfur source when reacted with a cyclic sulfite *en route* to the first example of Dewar benzo[*c*]thiophene (Eq. 22) <95TL3177>.

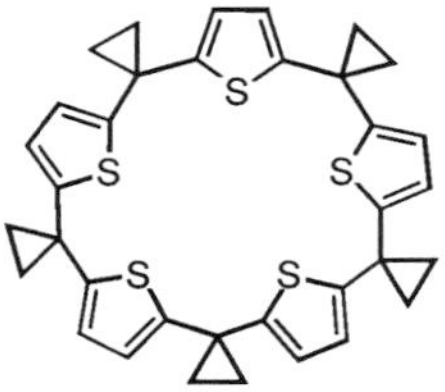

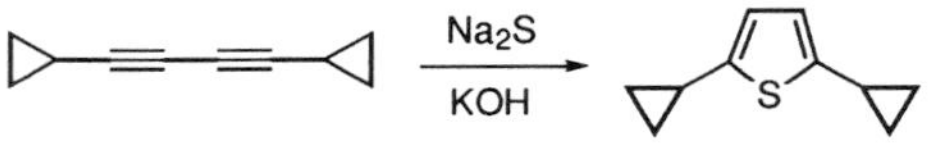

(Eq. 19)

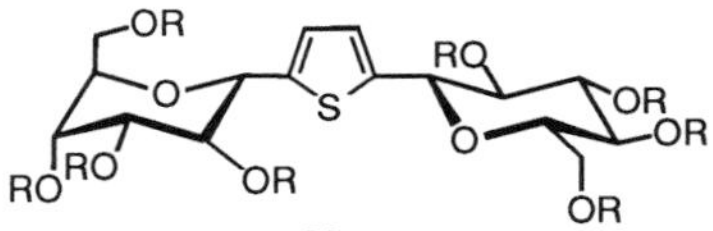

28

29

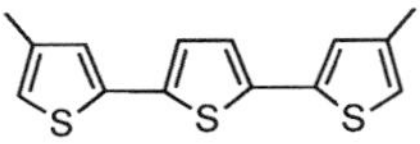

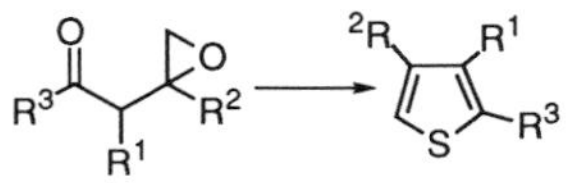

(Eq. 20)

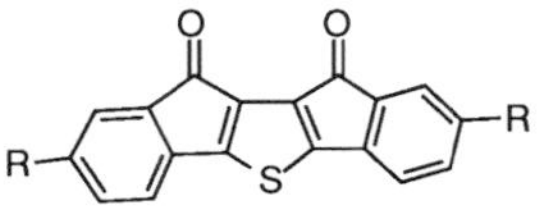

30

31

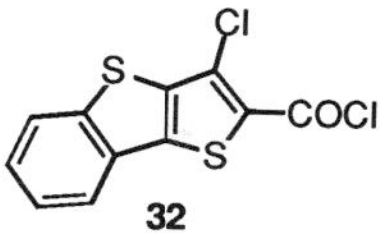

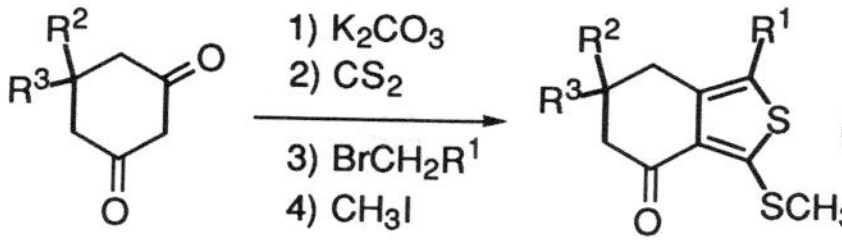

(Eq. 21)

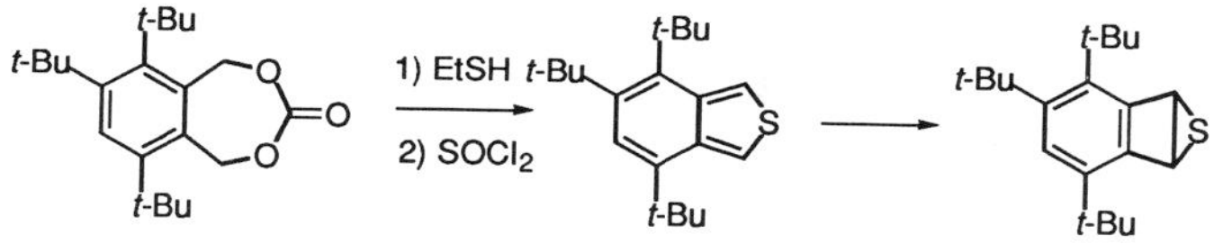

(Eq. 22)

Electrocyclic reactions provide some of the most interesting approaches to thiophene ring construction. Using the intermediacy of α,β-unsaturated sulfines, allenyl sulfones are precursors to a variety of substituted thiophenes (Eq. 23) <95RTC51>. Reaction of diazo compounds with thiones also provide interesting access to the thiophene ring; reaction of $2H$-1-benzothiete produces 2,3-dihydrobenzo[b]thiophenes (Eq. 24) <95TL6047>. A simple synthesis of heterocyclic-fused [c]thiophenes is based upon reaction of bis(arylsulfonyl)diazomethanes with thiones (Eq. 25) <95S87>. Carbenoids alternatively generated from *gem*-dihalides also give rise to electrocyclic thiophene ring formation (Eq. 26) <95JOC5588>. Flash vacuum pyrolysis (FVP) of alkylsulfanylmethylene Meldrum's acid derivatives produces dihydrothiophenes but without preservation of chirality (Eq. 27) <95JCS(P1)1209>. Thermolysis of thiosulfinic S-esters produces thiiranes and 1,3-oxathiolane S-oxides; the former react to form thiophenes (Eq. 28) <95JCR(S)86>. Cycloaddition–extrusion of mesoionic 1,3-tithiolium-4-olate with triphenylphosphirene forms tetraphenylthiophene <95H311>.

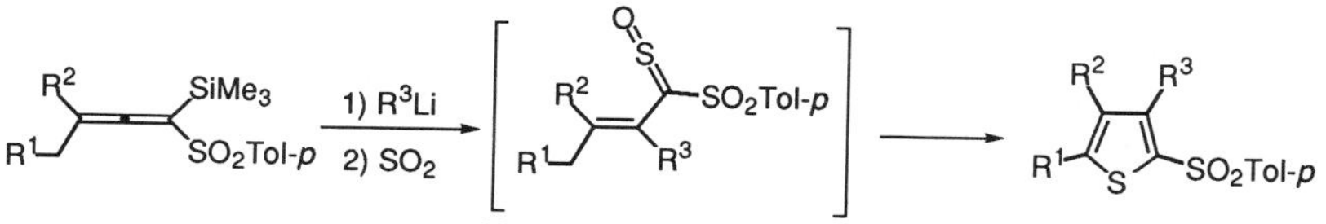

(Eq. 23)

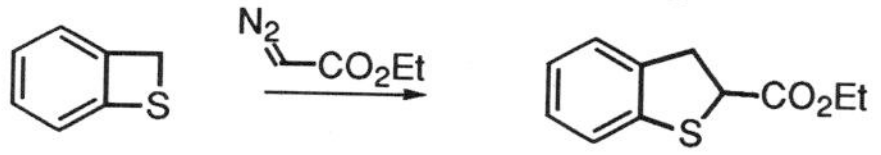

(Eq. 24)

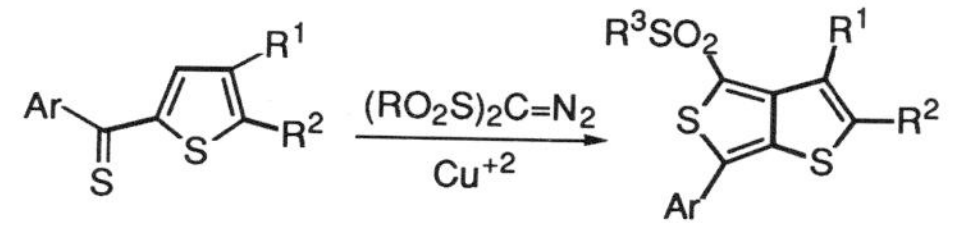

(Eq. 25)

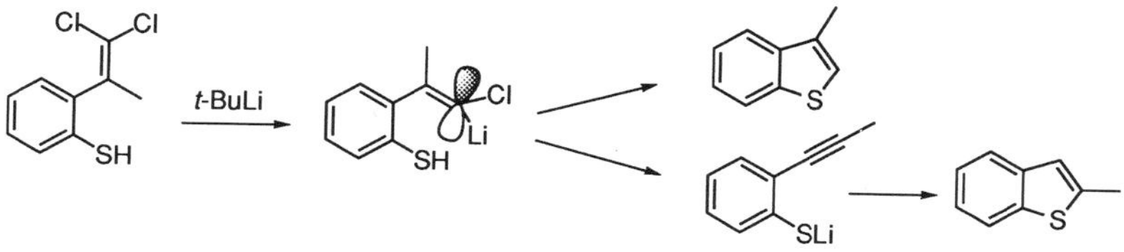

(Eq. 26)

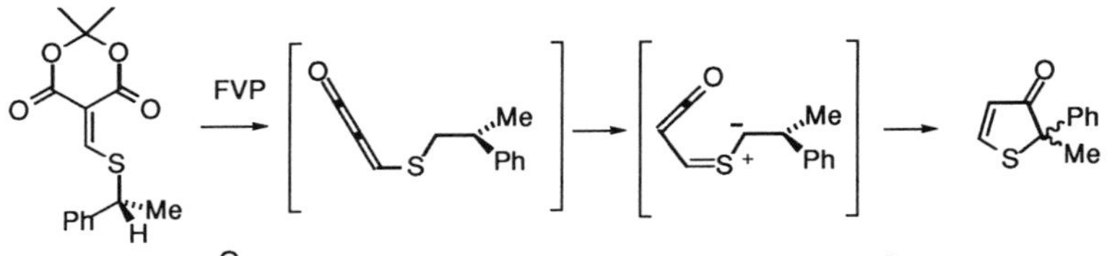

(Eq. 27)

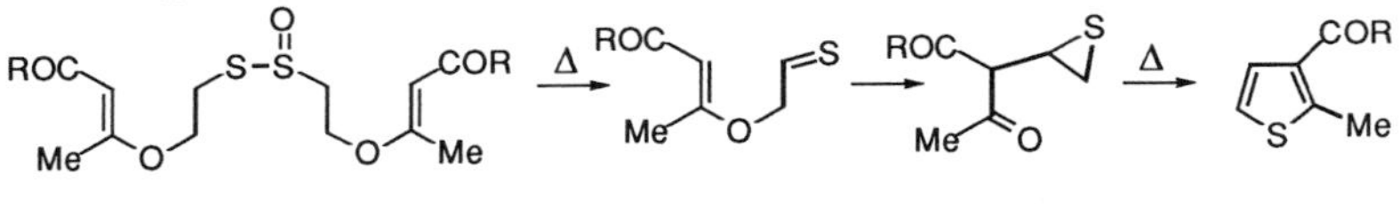

(Eq. 28)

Classical, utilitarian syntheses of thiophene rings continue to be reported. Use of active the methylene moiety of 2-mercaptoacetic acid derivatives in condensation reactions is exemplified by the synthesis of aminothienopyrazoles (Eq. 29) <95MI472>, thienopyridines <94PS85>, fluoro[2,3-b]pyridines (Eq. 30) <95JOC7654>, and monocyclic thiophenes <95H13, 95SC3435>. An extension of this methodology produces thieno[2,3-h][1,6]naphthyridines *via* a Smiles-type rearrangement (Eq. 31) <95H1307>. Poly(cycloalkyl[c]thiophenes) form from cyclododecanone (Eq. 32) <95MI225>. A similar approach using β-trifluoromethyl β-thioacrolein prepares a variety of thiophene derivatives <95JFC121>. Human leukocyte elastase inhibitory thieno[3,4-c]cepham sulfones form using thioacetic acid as a sulfur delivery agent (Eq. 33) <95BML691>.

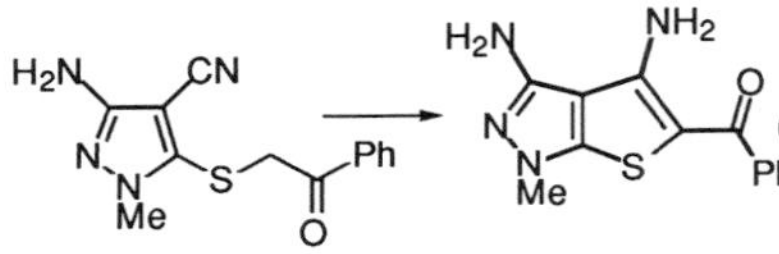

(Eq. 29)

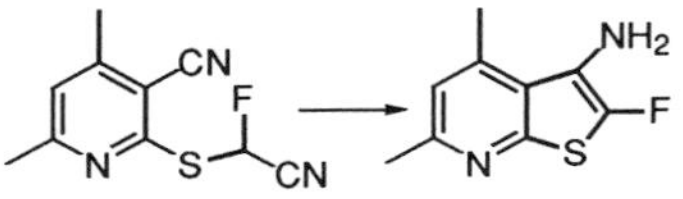

(Eq. 30)

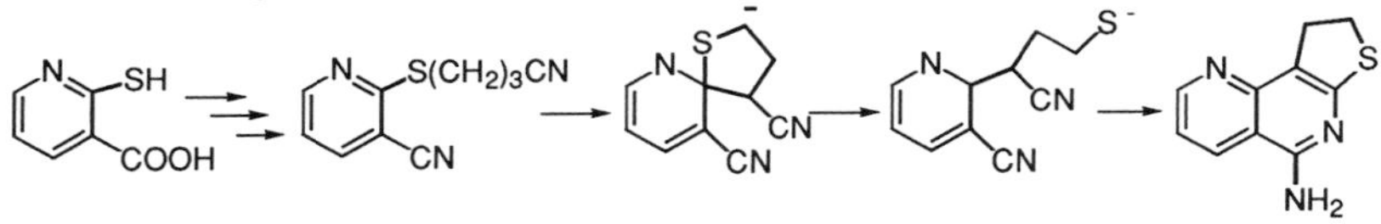

(Eq. 31)

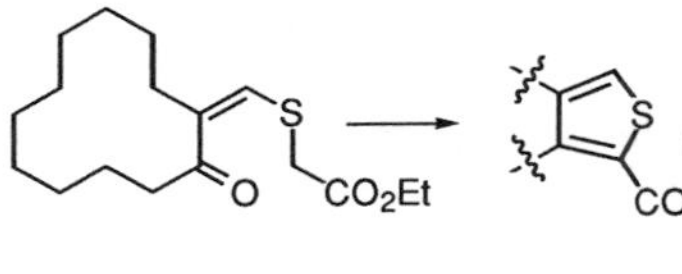

(Eq. 32)

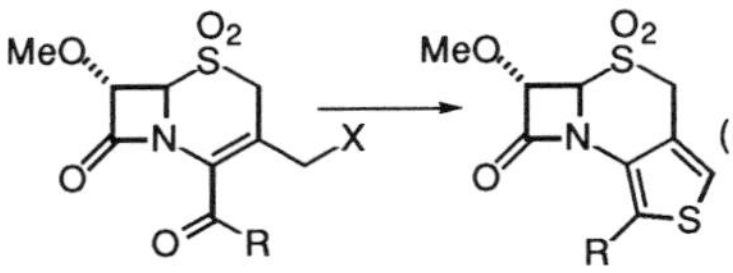

(Eq. 33)

$X = Br \rightarrow SAc \rightarrow SH$

Additional thiophene derivatives prepared using this synthetic approach include thieno[2,3-b]benzo[h]quinolines <95IJC97>, thieno[2,3-d]pyrimidines <95MI887, 95MI1033>, 3-aminothieno[2,3-b]pyridines <95JHC819>, thieno[2,3-c]pyridazines <94PS203>, 5H-1-thia-3,5,6,8-tetraazaacenaphthylenes <95LA1703>, and 3-hydroxythieno[3,2-c]quinolin-4(5H)-ones <95IJC432>.

5.1.5 RING ANNELATION ON THIOPHENE

Formation of fused rings on thiophene usually takes advantage of the ring's activated 2-position to create the final bond of benzothiophene derivatives. As an example of a general synthesis of heterocyclo[*b*]-fused carbazoles, the thermally-generated iminium salt intermediate undergoes intramolecular cyclization to the thiophene derivative (Eq. 34) <95JOC3707>. Radicals generated using sodium *p*-toluenesulfinate allows ring closure to form benzothiophene derivatives (Eq. 35) <95SL763>. Photocyclization also allows ring closure at the 2-position of thiophene to produce thienoquinoline and thienoisoquinoline derivatives exemplified in Eq. 36 <95S1131>. Steric constraint can redirect ring closure on thiophene to the 3-position as shown by the microwave-assisted closure of 2-thenoylbenzoic acids to form **33** <95TL2165>. FVP induces thermal cyclization on 2-substituted-3-methylthiophene derivatives to produce the previously unknown 8*H*-fluoreno[3,4-*b*]thiophene, albeit in poor yield <95TL1303>. A [4+2]cycloaddition reaction of 2,3-dimethylene-2,3-dihydrothiophene to C_{60} produced **34** <95MI125>.

Acid-catalyzed ring closure produces a number of interesting thieno-fused nitrogen heterocycles. Polyphosporic acid-induced ring closure produces thieno[2,3(3,2)-*f*]indolizines which undergo an interesting Diels-Alder reaction (Eq. 37) <95TL83>. Using a similar approach with 3-carboxypiperidine derivatives, methanothienoazoninones **35** are formed <95JHC403>. 2-Piperidine derivatives form thienoazepinones **36** <94BSF986>. Other ring formation takes advantage of the known reactivities of azides, aminoesters and ketoesters. For example, the previously unknown benzothieno[3,2-*c*]isoxazole **37** forms by reaction of a 3-azido moiety <95JCS(P1)2141>. In an investigation of tautomerism of 2-aminoheterocycles, a 2-aminothiophene reacted on nitrogen rather than as an enamine to ultimately produce **38** <95JHC985>. Reaction of ethyl 2-amino-3-thiophenecarboxylate with BMMA produces fused-pyrimidine **39** <95H851>. This starting material may also form thieno[2,3-*d*][1,3]thiazin-4-ones <95LA445>. The 1,2,3-triazine **40** is prepared from 3-amino-2-carboxamidothiophene and is an intermediate for a variety of novel fused-heterocycles <95H37>. Reaction of methyl 4-oxothiolane-3-carboxylate with urea derivatives produces dihydrothieno[3,4-*d*]pyrimidine-2,4-diones <95JHC953>. Nucleophilic displacement of 2-chloro-3-nitrothiophene by methyl 3-mercaptopropionate, reduction and ring closure produces 6,7-dihydrothieno[2,3-*b*][1,4]thiazepin-5(4*H*)-one **41** <95AP313>. Stille coupling of 3-iodopyridine-2-carboxaldehyde with 2-bromo-3-carboxamidothiophene and subsequent ring closure is an improved method for the preparation of thieno[2,3-*b*]naphthyridines <95JHC751>. Paraformaldehyde reaction with 3-hydroxythiophene-2-carboxamide derivatives forms $2H$-thieno[2,3-e]-1,3-oxazin-4($3H$)-one **42** <95JHC103>. Phosphorus pentasulfide reacts with ethyl 3-hydroxythiophene-2-carboxylate to produce $3H$-thieno[3,2-c]-1,2-dithiole-3-thione (**43**) in low yield; an improved synthesis which involves diazotization of the 3-aminothiophene analogue is reported <95JHC847>.

(Eq. 37)

35　　　　36　　　　37　　　　38　　　　39

40　　　　41　　　　42　　　　43

5.1.6 THIOPHENES AS INTERMEDIATES

Extrusion of sulfur dioxide from a ring-fused dihydrothiophene derivative provides an exceptionally easy method for the preparation of heterocyclic o-dimethylene compounds. These compounds are valuable intermediates in intermolecular Diels-Alder reactions. This extrusion method was used to prepare the o-dimethylene compounds **44-46** <95CC1349> as well as quinolinone derivative **47** <95TL5983>. The dihydrothiophene dioxide moiety also played an important role in the formation of the intramolecular Diels-Alder reaction of N-substituted pyrrole **48** <95CC807>.

The treatment of 2,5-dialkyl-3-substituted thiophene-1,1-dioxides with secondary ω-unsubstituted amines provides a convenient entry to azatrienes <95T7035>. 2-Azido-5-methylthiophene was found to decompose to form the single product **49**. This dihydrothiophene product is believed to form via cyclodimerization to a 1,5-dithiocine followed by sulfur extrusion (Eq. 38) <95JCS(P1)613>. The treatment of 2,5-bis(trimethylsilyloxy)thiophene with *pure* bromine in the presence of t-butylammonium bromide (1 mol%) produces maleic thioanhydride <95JOC6676>. 2- (*tert*-Butyldimethylsiloxy)thiophene (TBSOT) was found to undergo diastereoselective coupling with D-glyceraldehyde acetonide to afford the 4,5-threo-5,6-erythro product **50** in 79% yield <95S607, 95TL1941>. The ring opening of benzothiophene with sodamide in liquid ammonia was the first step in the preparation of 1,2-benzodithin **51** <95TL1421>.

Sulfur removal still remains a useful synthetic tool for the preparation of important molecules. A benzothiophene derivative was the starting point for the preparation of 1,11-epithio steriod **52** that was converted to estradiol by the stereoselective removal of sulfur (W-7 Raney Ni) to provide the necessary 9α-H configuration <95TL4467>. Desulfurization of the thienothiophene derivative **53** with a nickel-aluminum alloy in $NaOH/D_2O$ affords perdeuterio heptanoic acid methyl ester <94MI1087>. Thiophene derivatives that contain an electron withdrawing group such as NO_2, CO_2Me or CHO undergo regioselective photochemical Diels-Alder reaction to afford 2-substituted biphenyls <95TL6567>.

5.1.7 INTERESTING THIOPHENE DERIVATIVES

There are numerous examples of biologically interesting molecules containing a thiophene moiety in the 1995 literature. To include all of these reports is well beyond the scope of this review. However, of interest are the reports on compounds like thiophenfurin, **54**, a nucleoside analogue to thiazofurim that exhibits good selectivity towards tumor cells <95JMC3829>. 2'-Deoxyuridine compounds that have a thiophene derivative at the 5-position show moderate to good antiviral activity against HSV-1 <95MI262, 95MI525>. Some carbocyclic 5-(thiophene)-uridines and -cytidines were also investigated for their antiviral activity <95MI1233>. The use of 3-(3-thienyl)alanine **55** as a replacement for phenylalanine was studied in various biologically important peptides <95JMC1242, 95CCC681> as well as in biological polymers <95MI573>. These biological polymers could provide an entry to genetically engineered conducting polymers <95JA536>. Other interesting compounds in this category are, thienodiltiazem analogues **56** <95H709, 95M569, 95LA453>, thienodiazepines **57** <95MI27, 95TL3127> and thiophene derivatives of the hydroxyethylpiperazine class of HIV-1 protease inhibitors as examplified by **58** <95BML185>. The novel thienocyclopentapyran **59** was isolated from the fruits of *Xanthium pungens* (Compositae) <95TL8985>.

54   55   56   57

58   59

Macromolecules containing thiophene units are of interest either as novel molecules that affect metal ion complexation or as molecules that provide unique tests of aromatic vs. nonaromatic character of a ring system. The silicon-bridged thiophene containing macromolecule **60** was prepared to investigate its ability to extract metal ions from an aqueous environment <95JOC7406, 95AG(E)661>. The tetrathia[22]annulene[2.1.2.1] **61** was prepared as the first neutral thiophene containing aromatic annulene <95MI189>. 5,6,17,18-Bisdehydrotetrathia[24]annulene[2.2.2.2] (**63**) was prepared from **62** by formylation (LDA, DMF), McMurry coupling and finally Fritsch-Butternberg-Wiechell rearrangement. Inspite of the planar geometry of **63**, the ^{1}H NMR chemical shifts indicate almost no conjugation around the 24π-electron periphery <95CL499>.

60   61   62   63

5.1.8 SELENOPHENES AND TELLUROPHENES

As in years past, the published thiophene literature dwarfs the selenophene and tellurophene literature. However, there was a significant increase in the number of interesting selenophene and tellurophene references last year. The preparation of η^5-selenophene complexes of chromium, magnesium, ruthenium and iridium were studied <95OM332>. These studies took advantage of the NMR-active selenium isotope ^{77}Se (7.58% natural abundance) as a tool to directly study binding of selenophene derivatives to a catalyst surface.

A number of methods are reported for the preparation of substituted selenophenes. The treatment of lithium 1-alkoxyeneselenolates with propargyl bromide generates the allenic selenoic acid ester that forms **64** in moderate yield after heating (Eq. 39) <95TL2807>. The treatment of β-aryl-β-chloroacroleins with benzyl bromides in the presence of Na_2Se affords the β-selenoacrolein compound that ring closes to selenophene **65** when treated with NaOMe <94PS137>.

Eq. 39

64

65

N-Selenoacylamidines were prepared and reacted with various dienophiles. When the Diels-Alder reactions occur at 0°, the intermediate $4H$-1,3-selenazine **66** forms; this material affords **67** upon thermolysis at 40° (Eq. 40). Compound **67** rearranges to selenophene **68** upon continued heating in ethanol <95TL237>. The oxidation of selenopyran **69** with SeO_2 affords the selenophene **70** <95MI24>. Along with the synthesis of substituted selenophene are reports of the preparation of 5-(selenophene)uridines and -cytidines <95MI1233>, selenolo[3,2-a]pyrrole **71** (as well as telluropyrrole) <95JOM271>, selenolo[2,3-b]pyrrole **72** <95T10323>, pyrimido[4',5'-4,5]selenolo[2,3-b]quinolin-4($3H$)-one **73** <95SC451> and selenasapphyrin <95IC3567>. The selectivity in the bromination of selenophene-2-carbonyl derivatives was investigated in the presence of $AlCl_3$ <95JHC53> and the conductive nature of 2,5-bis(1,3-dithiol-2-ylidene)-2,5-dihydroselenophene complexes was also reported <95CL619>.

Eq. 40

66   **67**   **68**

69   **70**   **71**   **72**   **73**

Treatment of 2,2'-diiodobiphenyl derivatives **74** with Te-Cu in NMP affords the dibenzotellurophenes derivatives **75** <95JOC5274>. The 2,2'-biphenylylenediphenyltellurane **76** was prepared and warmed to 140° until it decomposed to dibenzotellurophene in 69% yield. NMR studies confirmed the formation of **76** which was isolated as a pale yellow solid <95TL2803>. The synthesis and X-ray analysis of air sensitive 21-telluraporphyrin derivatives **77** was reported <95AG(E)2252>.

74 **75** **76** **77**

5.1.9 REFERENCES

94BSF986	D. Berkes, B. Decroix, *Bull. Soc. Chim. France* **1994**, *131*, 986.
94MI1087	H. Tsuzuki, M. Mukumoto, T. Tsukinoki, S. Mataka, M. Tashiro, T. Yonemitsu, Y. Nagano, *J. Label Compound Radiopharm.* **1994**, *34*, 1087.
94PS137	D. Prim, D. Joseph, G. Kirsh, *Phosphorous Surfur* **1994**, *91*, 137.
94PS203	M. S. Abbady, S. M. Radwan, *Phosphorous Sulfur Silicon* **1995**, *86*, 203.
94PS85	A. M. K. Eldean, *Phosphorous Sulfur Silicon* **1994**, *90*, 85.
95AC(E)337	P. v. R. Schleyer, P. K. Freeman, H. Jiao, B. Goldfuss, *Angew. Chem., Int. Ed. Engl.* **1995**, *34*, 337.
95AC(E)781	S. Kozhushkov, T. Haumann, R. Boese, B. Knieriem, S. Scheib, P. Bäuerle, A. de Meijere, *Angew. Chem., Int. Ed. Engl.* **1995**, *34*, 781.
95AG(E)661	B. König, M. Rödel, P. Bubenitschek, P. G. Jones, *Angew. Chem., Int. Ed. Engl.* **1995**, *34*, 661.
95AG(E)2252	L. Latos-Grazynski, E. Pacholska, P. J. Chmielewski, M. M. Olmstead, A. L. Balch, *Angew. Chem., Int. Ed. Engl.* **1995**, *34*, 2252.
95AJC593	J. H. Buttery, J. Moursounidis, D. Wege, *Aust. J. Chem.* **1995**, *48*, 593.
95AP313	T. Erker, *Arch. Pharm. (Weinheim)* **1995**, *328*, 313.
95BML15	G. Estenne, P. Dodey, P. Renaut, G. Leclerc, *Bioorg. Med. Chem. Lett.* **1995**, *5*, 15.
95BML185	B. M. Kim, J. P. Guare, J. P. Vacca, S. R. Michelson, P. L. Darke, J. A. Zugay, E. A. Emini, W. Schleif, J. H. Lin, I. W. Chen, K. Vastag, P. S. Anderson, J. R. Huff, *Bioorg. Med. Chem. Lett.* **1995**, *5*, 185.
95BML691	M. Alpegiani, P. Bissolino, R. Corigli, V. Rizzo, E. Perrone, *Bioorg. Med. Chem. Lett.* **1995**, *5*, 691.
95BSB265	R. J. Angelici, *Bull. Soc. Chim. Belg.* **1995**, *104*, 265.
95BSB325	P. C. H. Mitchell, D. A. Green, *Bull. Soc. Chim. Belg.* **1995**, *104*, 325.
95CC807	T. Suzuki, H. Takayama, *J. Chem. Soc., Chem. Commun.* **1995**, 807.
95CC921	A. Bacchi, C. Bianchini, V. Herrera, M. V. Jiménez, C. Mealli, A. Meli, S. Moneti, M. Peruzzini, R. A. Sánchez-Delgado, F. Vizza, *J. Chem. Soc., Chem. Commun.* **1995**, 921.
95CC1349	H.-H. Tso, N.-C. Yang, Y.-M. Chang, *J. Chem. Soc., Chem. Commun.* **1995**, 1349.
95CCC681	J. Slaninová, M. Czaja, B. Lammek, *Collect. Czech. Chem. Commun.* **1995**, *60*, 681.
95CL499	T. Kawase, H. R. Darabi, R. Uchimiya, M. Oda, *Chem. Lett.* **1995**, 499.
95CL619	K. Takahashi, K. Tomitani, T. Ise, T. Shirahata, *Chem. Lett.* **1995**, 619.
95CPB236	M. Yamguchi, N. Maruyama, T. Koga, K. Kamei, M. Akima, T. Kuroki, M. Hamana, N. Ohi, *Chem. Pharm. Bull.* **1995**, *43*, 236.
95H13	H.-H. Tso, Y.-J. Chen, *Heterocycles* **1995**, *41*, 13.
95H37	C. Peinador, M. C. Veiga, V. Ojea, J. M. Quintela, *Heterocycles* **1995**, *41*, 37.
95H311	T. Kobayashi, H. Minemura, H. Kato, *Heterocycles* **1995**, *40*, 311.
95H709	I. Puschmann, T. Erker, *Heterocycles* **1995**, *41*, 709.
95H851	F. Sauter, J. Frölich, K. Blasl, K. Gewald, *Heterocycles* **1995**, *40*, 851.

95H925	M. R. Detty, D. S. Hays, *Heterocycles* **1995**, *40*, 925.
95H1307	K. Sasaki, A. S. S. Rouf, S. Kashino, T. Hirota, *Heterocycles* **1995**, *41*, 1307.
95HCA177	J. Alzeer, A. Vasella, *Helv. Chim. Acta* **1995**, *78*, 177.
95IC3567	J. Lisowski, J. L. Sessler, V. Lynch, *Inorg. Chem.* **1995**, *34*, 3567.
95IC5220	P. R. Stafford, T. B. Rauchfuss, S. R. Wilson, *Inorg. Chem.* **1995**, *34*, 5220.
95ICA61	J. Chen, R. J. Angelici, *Inorg. Chim. Acta* **1995**, *235*, 61.
95IJC(B)97	E. A. Bakhite, S. M. Radwan, M. M. El-Saghier, *Indian J. Chem.* **1995**, *34B*, 97.
95IJC(B)432	M. C. L. N. Gupta, M. Darbarwar, *Indian J. Chem* **1995**, *34B*, 432.
95JA536	S. Kothakota, T. L. Mason, D. A. Tirrell, M. J. Fournier, *J. Am. Chem. Soc.* **1995**, *117*, 536.
95JA2179	J. J. Garcia, B. E. Mann, H. Adams, N. A. Bailey, P. M. Maitlis, *J. Am. Chem. Soc.* **1995**, *117*, 2179.
95JA3887	M. D. McClain, D. A. Whittington, D. J. Mitchell, M. D. Curits, *J. Am. Chem. Soc.* **1995**, *117*, 3887.
95JA4333	C. Bianchini, P. Frediani, V. Herrera, M. V. Jiménez, A. Meli, L. Rincón, R. Sánchez-Delgado, F. Vizza, *J. Am. Chem. Soc.* **1995**, *117*, 4333.
95JA8567	C. Bianchini, V. Herrera, M. V. Jiménez, A. Meli, R. Sánchez-Delgado, F. Vizza, *J. Am. Chem. Soc.* **1995**, *117*, 8567.
95JCR(S)86	H.-G. Hahn, W. S. Lee, *J. Chem. Res., Synop.* **1995**, 86.
95JCR(S)120	W. Friedrichsen, *J. Chem. Res., Synop.* **1995**, 120.
95JCR(S)222	R. Noto, M. Gruttadauria, S. Rosselli, G. Consiglio, D. Spinelli, *J. Chem. Res., Synop.* **1995**, 222.
95JCR(S)306	P. Powell, M. H. Sosabowski, *J. Chem. Res., Synop.* **1995**, 306.
95JCS(F1)749	P. C. H. Mitchell, G. M. Raos, P. B. Karadakov, J. Gerratt, D. L. Cooper, *J. Chem. Soc., Faraday Trans. 1* **1995**, *91*, 749.
95JCS(P1)97	M. S. Loft, T. J. Mowlem, D. A. Widdowson, *J. Chem. Soc., Perkin Trans. 1* **1995**, 97.
95JCS(P1)613	D. Davies, P. Spagnolo, P. Zanirato, *J. Chem. Soc., Perkin Trans. 1* **1995**, 613.
95JCS(P1)1209	G. A. Hunter, H. McNab, *J. Chem. Soc., Perkin Trans. 1* **1995**, 1209.
95JCS(P1)1243	F. Guerrera, L. Salerno, L. Lamartina, D. Spinelli, *J. Chem. Soc., Perkin Trans. 1* **1995**, 1243.
95JCS(P1)2141	A. DeglInnocenti, M. Funicello, P. Scafato, P. Spagnolo, P. Zanirato, *J. Chem. Soc., Perkin Trans. 1* **1995**, 2141.
95JCS(P2)1217	B. S. Jursic, *J. Chem. Soc. Perkin Trans. 2*, **1995**, 1217.
95JFC121	G. M. Alvernhe, D. Grief, A. J. Laurent, M. Pulst, M. Weissenfels, *J. Fluorine Chem.* **1995**, *70*, 121.
95JHC53	D. N. Antonov, L. I. Belen'kii, S. Gronowitz, *J. Heterocycl. Chem.* **1995**, *32*, 53.
95JHC103	F. Benedini, G. Bertolini, F. Ferrario, A. Motti, A. Sala, F. Somenzi, *J. Heterocycl. Chem.* **1995**, *32*, 103.
95JHC403	D. Berkes, N. Bar, B. Decroix, *J. Heterocycl. Chem.* **1995**, *32*, 403.
95JHC435	Y. Zhang, A.-B. Hörnfeldt, S. Gronowitz, *J. Heterocycl. Chem.* **1995**, *32*, 435.
95JHC483	B. S. Jursic, D. Coupe, *J. Heterocycl. Chem.* **1995**, *32*, 483.
95JHC591	F. Guerrera, L. Salerno, M. C. Sarvá, M. A. Siracusa, *J. Heterocycl. Chem.* **1995**, *32*, 591.
95JHC659	J.-K. Luo, R. F. Federspiel, R. N. Castle, *J. Heterocycl. Chem.* **1995**, *32*, 659.
95JHC771	Y. Zhang, A.-B. Hörnfeldt, S. Gronowitz, *J. Heterocycl. Chem.* **1995**, *32*, 771.
95JHC791	M. Temciuc, A.-B. Hörnfeldt, S. Gronowitz, *J. Hetercycl. Chem.* **1995**, *32*, 791.
95JHC819	Y. W. Ho, I. J. Wang, *J. Heterocycl. Chem.* **1995**, *32*, 819.
95JHC847	M. Pregnolato, P. Borgna, M. Terreni, *J. Heterocycl. Chem.* **1995**, *32*, 847.

95JHC863   V. Ozola, T. Persson, S. Gronowitz, A.-B. Hörnfeldt, *J. Heterocycl. Chem.* **1995**, *32*, 863.
95JHC953   F. Jourdan, J. Renault, A. Karamat, D. Ladurie, M. Robba, *J. Heterocycl. Chem.* **1995**, *32*, 953.
95JHC985   A. M. Almerico, G. Cirrincione, P. Diana, S. Grimaudo, G. Dattolo, E. Aiello, F. Mingoia, *J. Heterocycl. Chem.* **1995**, *32*, 985.
95JHC1159   U. Wellmar, A.-B. Hörnfeldt, S. Gronowitz, *J. Heterocycl. Chem.* **1995**, *32*, 1159.
95JMC1242   D. L. Heyl, M. Dandabathula, K. R. Kurtz, C. Mousigian, *J. Med. Chem.* **1995**, *38*, 1242.
95JMC3445   M. R. Michaelides, Y. Hong, S. DiDomenico, Jr., K. E. Asin, D. R. Britton, C. W. Lin, M. Williams, K. Shiosaki, *J. Med. Chem.* **1995**, *38*, 3445.
95JMC3829   P. Franchetti, L. Cappellacci, M. Grifantini, A. Barzi, G. Nocentini, H. Yang, A. O'Connor, H. N. Jayaram, C. Carrell, B. M. Goldstein, *J. Med. Chem.* **1995**, *38*, 3829.
95JMT109   A. Hinchliffe, H. J. Soscún M., *J. Mol. Struct.* **1995**, *331*, 109.
95JMT171   J. S. Webber, R. G. Woolley, *J. Mol. Struct.* **1995**, *341*, 171.
95JMT181   J. S. Webber, R. G. Woolley, *J. Mol. Struct.* **1995**, *341*, 181.
95JOC2082   F. Effenberger, F. Würthner, F. Steybe, *J. Org. Chem.* **1995**, *60*, 2082.
95JOC2112   M. C. Pirrung, J. Zhang, K. Lackey, D. D. Sternbach, F. Brown, *J. Org. Chem.* **1995**, *60*, 2112.
95JOC3707   A. R. Katritzky, L. Xie, *J. Org. Chem.* **1995**, *60*, 3707.
95JOC5274   H. Suzuki, T. Nakamura, T. Sakaguchi, K. Ohta, *J. Org. Chem.* **1995**, *60*, 5274.
95JOC5588   M. Topolski, *J. Org. Chem.* **1995**, *60*, 5588.
95JOC6658   X. Wu, R. D. Rieke, *J. Org. Chem.* **1995**, *60*, 6658.
95JOC6676   M. J. Kates, J. H. Schauble, *J. Org. Chem.* **1995**, *60*, 6676.
95JOC7406   B. König, M. Rödel, P. Bubenitschek, *J. Org. Chem.* **1995**, *60*, 7406.
95JOC7654   A. W. Erian, A. Konno, T. Fuchigami, *J. Org. Chem.* **1995**, *60*, 7654.
95JOM271   A. G. Mal'kina, R. den Besten, A. C. H. T. M. van der Kerk, L. Brandsma, B. A. Trofimov, *J. Organomet. Chem.* **1995**, *493*, 271.
95JPC226   J. Schmidt, H. Wiedenhofer, A. v. Zelewsky, H. Yersin, *J. Phys. Chem.* **1995**, *99*, 226.
95JPC4955   E. Orti, P. M. Viruela, J. Sánchez-Marín, F. Tomás, *J. Phys. Chem.* **1995**, *99*, 4955.
95JPC9045   V. Keshari, W. M. K. P. Wijekoon, P. N. Prasad, S. P. Karna, *J. Phys. Chem.* **1995**, *99*, 9045.
95JPC13385 H. Wiedenhofer, S. Schützenmeier, A. v. Zelewsky, H. Yersin, *J. Phys. Chem.* **1995**, *99*, 13385.
95JPC16365 S. Ramanathan, S. T. Oyama, *J. Phys. Chem.* **1995**, *99*, 16365.
95LA445   M. Gutschow, S. Leistner, *Liebigs Ann.* **1995**, 445.
95LA453   I. Laimer, T. Erker, *Liebigs Ann.* **1995**, 453.
95LA1703   S. Tumkevicius, *Liebigs Ann.* **1995**, 1703.
95M569   I. Puschmann, T. Erker, *Monatsh. Chem.* **1995**, *126*, 569.
95M601   S. M. Sherif, N. I. Abdel-Sayed, S. M. El-Kousy, R. M. Mohareb, *Monatsh. Chem.* **1995**, *126*, 601.
95MI10   E. Schulz, K. Fahmi, M. Lemaire, *Acros Org. Acta* **1995**, *1*, 10.
95MI24   B. I. Drevko, M. I. Smushkin, L. A. Fomenko, V. G. Kharchenko, *Kim. Geterotsikl Soedin* **1995**, 24.
95MI27   S. Vega, M. S. Gil, V. Darias, C. C. Sanchez Mateo, M. A. Exposito, *Pharmazie* **1995**, *50*, 27.
95MI52   M. Nagai, *Sekiyu Gakkaishi* **1995**, *38*, 52.
95MI125   M. Ohno, N. Koide, S. Eguchi, *Heterocycl. Commun.* **1995**, *1*, 125.
95MI128   M. Sugioka, *Erdöl Kohle, Erdgas, Petrochem.* **1995**, *48*, 128.

| 95MI169 | R. Cid, J. Neira, J. Godoy, J. M. Palacios, A. L. Agudo, *Appl. Catal., A* **1995**, *125*, 169. |

95MI189   M. P. Cava, Z. Hu, *NATO ASI Ser., Ser. C* **1995**, *456*, 189.

95MI225   J. Rühe, A. Berlin, G. Wegner, *Macromol. Chem. Physics* **1995**, *196*, 225.

95MI262   I. Luyten, L. Jie, A. Van Aershot, C. Pannecouque, P. Wigerinck, J. Rozenski, C. Hendrix, C. Wang, L. Wiebe, J. Balzarini, E. De Clercq, P. Herdewijn, *Antiviral Chem. Chemother.* **1995**, *6*, 262.

95MI267   R. Girlanda, G. Martino, M. R. Pelaggi, R. Gitto, *Il Nuovo Cimento*, **1995**, *17*, 267.

95MI281   L. V. Manuilova, V. P. Fedin, Y. V. Mironov, E. M. Moroz, T. V. Pasynkova, V. I. Zaikovskii, T. S. Sukhareva, *React. Kinet. Catal. Lett.* **1995**, *54*, 281.

95MI283   J. W. Benson, G. L. Schrader, R. J. Angelici, *J. Mol. Catalysis A* **1995**, *96*, 283.

95MI353   A. N. Startsev, *Catal. Rev. Sci. Eng.* **1995**, *37*, 353.

95MI399   I. Novak, *Croat. Chem. Acta* **1995**, *68*, 399.

95MI401   K. Inamura, R. Prins, *Stud. Surf. Sci. Catal.* **1995**, *92*, 401.

95MI471   A. N. Startsev, *Kinet. Catal.* **1995**, *36*, 471.

95MI472   K. Gewald, S. Rennert, R. Schindler, H. Schafer, *J. Prakt. Chem./Chem. -Ztg.* **1995**, *337*, 472.

95MI525   J. Liu, A. Van Aerschot, I. Luyten, P. Wigernick, C. Pannecouque, J. Balzarini, E. De Clercq, P. Herdewijn, *Nucleosides Nucleotides* **1995**, *14*, 525.

95MI573   S. Kothakota, M. J. Dougherty, M. J. Fournier, T. L. Mason, E. Yoshikawa, D. A. Tirrell, *Macromol. Symp.* **1995**, *98*, 573.

95MI582   T. I. Karányi, A. Jentys, H. Vinek, *Stud. Surf. Sci. Catal.* **1995**, *94*, 582.

95MI589   T.-M. H. Luo, L.-H. Chen, *J. Chin. Chem. Soc.* **1995**, *42*, 589.

95MI653   A. J. Seed, K. J. Toyne, J. W. Goodby, *J. Mater. Chem.* **1995**, *5*, 653.

95MI669   M. José-Yacamán, H. Terrones, L. Rendón, J. M. Domínguez, *Carbon* **1995**, *33*, 669.

95MI887   M. G. Assy, A. El-Kafrawy, M. M. Hassanien, *Pol. J. Chem.* **1995**, *69*, 887.

95MI989   T. Isoda, S. Nagao, X. Ma, Y. Korai, I. Mochida, *Prepr. Pap. - Am. Chem. Soc., Div. Fuel Chem.* **1995**, *40*, 989.

95MI1033   M. G. Assy, *Pol. J. Chem.* **1995**, *69*, 1033.

95MI1037   P. Blanchard, C. Mauchausse, E. Payen, J. Grimblot, O. Poulet, N. Boisdron, R. Loutaty, *Stud. Surf. Sci. Catal.* **1995**, *91*, 1037.

95MI1233   A. Popescu, A.-B. Hörnfeldt, S. Gronowitz, *Nucleosides Nucleotides* **1995**, *14*, 1233.

95MI1255   W. B. Collier, T. D. Klots, *Spectrochim. Acta (A)* **1995**, *51*, 1255.

95MI1273   T. D. Klots, W. B. Collier, *Spectrochim. Acta (A)* **1995**, *51*, 1273.

95NJC65   M. Cariou, T. Douadi, J. Simonet, *New J. Chem.* **1995**, *19*, 65.

95O1559   M. L. Spera, W. D. Harman, *Organometallics* **1995**, *14*, 1559.

95O2238   R. D. Adams, X. Qu, *Organometallics* **1995**, *14*, 2238.

95O2342   C. Bianchini, M. V. Jiménez, A. Meli, S. Moneti, F. Vizza, V. Herrera, R. A. Sánchez-Delgado, *Organometallics* **1995**, *14*, 2342.

95O2923   Q. Feng, T. B. Rauchfuss, S. R. Wilson, *Organometallics* **1995**, *14*, 2923.

95O3196   C. Bianchini, M. V. Jiménez, A. Meli, F. Vizza, *Organometallics* **1995**, *14*, 3196.

95O4390   C. Bianchini, V. Herrera, M. V. Jiménez, A. Laschi, A. Meli, R. Sánchez-Delgado, F. Vizza, P. Zanello, *Organometallics* **1995**, *14*, 4390.

95O4858   C. Bianchini, M. V. Jiménez, A. Meli, F. Vizza, *Organometallics* **1995**, *14*, 4858.

95OM332   C. J. White, R. J. Angelici, M.-G. Choi, *Organometallics* **1995**, *14*, 332.

95OPP233   J. W. Raggon, J. M. Welborn, J. E. Godlewski, S. E. Kelly, T. G. LaCour, *Org. Prep. Proceed. Int.* **1995**, *27*, 233.

95PS69	F. Bomberg, K. Deters, J. Schulz, K. F. Torges, *Phophorous Sulfur Silicon* **1995**, *91*, 69.
95RTC51	J. B. van der Linden, P. F. T. M. van Asten, S. Braverman, B. Zwanenburg, *Recl. Trav. Chim. Pays-Bas* **1995**, *114*, 51.
95S87	T. Saito, H. Kikuchi, A. Kondo, *Synthesis* **1995**, 87.
95S248	M. D'Auria, G. Mauriello, *Synthesis* **1995**, 248.
95S607	G. Casiraghi, G. Rassu, *Synthesis* **1995**, 607.
95S638	M. Yokoyama, T. Akiba, H. Togo, *Synthesis* **1995**, 638.
95S926	B. Krassowska-Sweibocka, P. Lulinki, L. Skulski, *Synthesis* **1995**, 926.
95S1131	A. L. Marzinzik, P. Rademacher, *Synthesis* **1995**, 1131.
95SC235	A. K. Marwah, P. Marwah, G. S. Rao, B. S. Trivedi, *Synth. Commun.* **1995**, *25*, 235.
95SC451	S. K. Nandeeshaiah, S. Y. Ambekar, *Synth. Commun.* **1995**, *25*, 451.
95SC2449	D. Prim, G. Kirsch, *Synth. Commun.* **1995**, *25*, 2449.
95SC2631	A. R. Katritzky, J. Wang, B. Yang, *Synth. Commun.* **1995**, *25*, 2631.
95SC2647	K.-T. Kang, J. Sun U, *Synth. Commun.* **1995**, *25*, 2647.
95SC3435	H.-H. Tso, H. Tsay, J.-H. Li, *Synthet. Commun.* **1995**, *25*, 3435.
95SL53	R. A. Aitken, C. K. Bradbury, G. Burns, J. J. Morrison, *Synlett* **1995**, 53.
95SL763	C.-P. Chuang, S.-F. Wang, *Synlett* **1995**, 763.
95T5403	V. Frenna, G. Consiglio, C. Arnone, D. Spinelli, *Tetrahedron* **1995**, *51*, 5403.
95T7035	A. Tsirk, S. Gronowitz, A.-B. Hörnfeldt, *Tetrahedron* **1995**, *51*, 7035.
95T8339	M. Makosza, E. Kwast, *Tetrahedron* **1995**, *51*, 8339.
95T10323	D. Wensbo, U. Annby, S. Gronowitz, *Tetrahedron* **1995**, *51*, 10323.
95TA2045	L. D. Girodier, C. S. Maignan, F. P. Rouessac, *Tetrahedron:Asymmetry.* **1995**, *6*, 2045.
95TL83	A. Daich, P. Ohier, B. Decroix, *Tetrahedron Lett.* **1995**, *36*, 83.
95TL237	D. Dubreuil, J. P. Pradère, N. Giraudeau, M. Goli, F. Tonnard, *Tetrahedron Lett.* **1995**, *36*, 237.
95TL1421	W. Schroth, H. Jordan, R. Spitzner, *Tetrahedron Lett.* **1995**, *36*, 1421.
95TL1925	B. K. Mehta, H. Ila, H. Junjappa, *Tetrahedron Lett.* **1995**, *36*, 1925.
95TL1941	G. Rassu, P. Spanu, L. Pinna, F. Zanardi, G. Casiraghi, *Tetrahedron Lett.* **1995**, *36*, 1941.
95TL1945	L.-L. Gundersen, G. Langli, F. Rise, *Tetrahedron Lett.* **1995**, *36*, 1945,
95TL2165	A. Acosta, P. de la Cruz, P. De Miguel, E. Diez-Barra, A. de la Hoz, F. Langa, A. Loupy, M. Majdoub, N. Martín, C. Sanchez, C. Seoane, *Tetrahedron Lett.* **1995**, *36*, 2165.
95TL2803	S. Sato, N. Furukawa, *Tetrahedron Lett.* **1995**, *36*, 2803.
95TL2807	T. Kanda, T. Ezaka, T. Murai, S. Kato, *Tetrahedron Lett.* **1995**, *36*, 2807.
95TL2861	D. C. Harrowven, R. Browne, *Tetrahedron Lett.* **1995**, *36*, 2861.
95TL3127	M. P. Foloppe, P. Sonnet, S. Rault, M. Robba, *Tetrahedron Lett.* **1995**, *36*, 3127.
95TL3177	R. M. El-Shishtawy, K. Fukunishi, S. Miki, *Tetrahedron Lett.* **1995**, *36*, 3177.
95TL4467	M. A. Collins, D. N. Jones, *Tetrahedron Lett.* **1995**, *36*, 4467.
95TL4883	M. D'Auria, G. Mauriello, *Tetrahedron Lett.* **1995**, *36*, 4883.
95TL5983	L. A. White, P. M. O'Neill, B. K. Park, R. C. Storr, *Tetrahedron Lett.* **1995**, *36*, 5983.
95TL6047	H. Meier, D. Gröschl, *Tetrahedron Lett.* **1995**, *36*, 6047.
95TL6567	M. D'Auria, *Tetrahedron Lett.* **1995**, *36*, 6567.
95TL8985	A. A. Mahmoud, A. A. Ahmed, M. Iinuma, T. Tanaka, Y. Takahashi, H. Naganawa, *Tetrahedron Lett.* **1995**, *36*, 8985.

Chapter 5.2

Five-Membered Ring Systems: Pyrroles and Benzo Derivatives

Richard J. Sundberg

University of Virginia, Charlottesville, VA, USA

Progress in pyrrole and indole chemistry will be discussed in the areas of new ring-forming reactions, new methods for synthetic modification, annelation reactions, and new structures and chemistry of transition metal complexes. Several pertinent reviews appeared during 1995. A summary of the history of isolation, synthesis and manufacture of pyrrole appeared. <95JCE875> A review of the use of palladium-catalyzed coupling reactions was published. <95ANH71> Reviews of annelation of indoles by cycloaddition <95ANH121> and electrocyclization <95ANH205> appeared.

5.2.1 METHODS FOR RING FORMATION

A new route to bromopyrroles was developed. It depends on addition of HBr to N-protected γ-aminoynones. When applied to alkynyl ketones, 2-aryl or 2-alkyl 4-bromopyrroles are formed. 2-Alkyl or 2-aryl 3-bromopyrroles can be obtained from acetals of γ-aminoynals. The ketones are made from N-protected propargylamines by C-acylation. The acetals are made from 3,3-diethoxypropyne by addition to an aldehyde followed by introduction of the amino group by reaction with phthalimide under Mitsunobu conditions. <95S276>

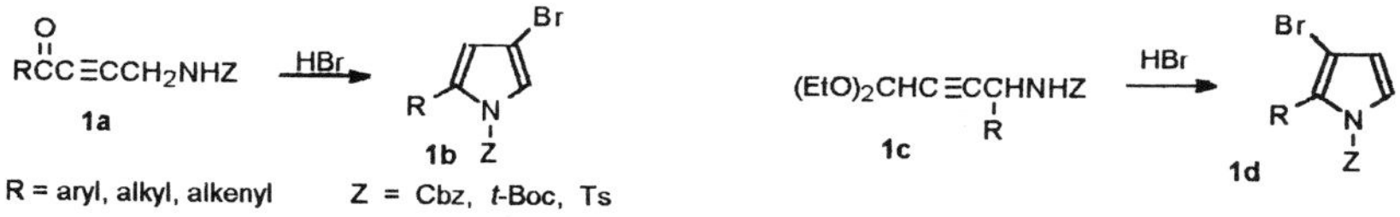

Katritzky and coworkers have developed two new methods of pyrrole synthesis involving condensation of C3-C4-C5 synthons with Schiff bases to obtain 1,2-diaryl pyrroles. The synthon **2a** is obtained by condensation of acrolein, morpholine and benzotriazole, followed by a base-catalyzed elimination. Lithiation gives an anion which adds to the imine. Cyclization occurs on acid treatment. <95TL343> An alternative synthon is obtained by lithiation of **2b**. <95S1315>

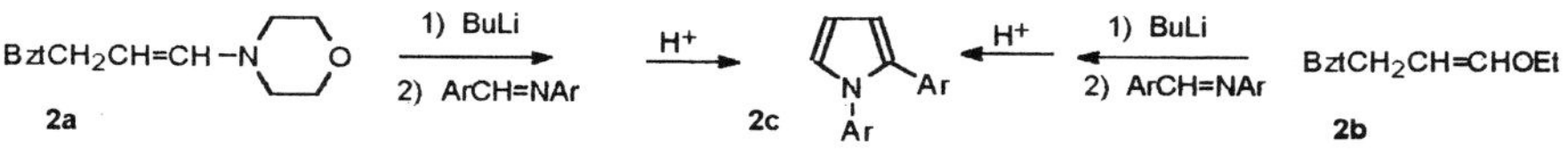

103

Several new examples of the Barton-Zard pyrrole synthesis from nitroalkenes and isocyanoacetate esters demonstrate the broad utility of this procedure. An excellent yield of ethyl 3-(9-anthryl)-4-ethylpyrrole-2-carboxylate was obtained starting with the nitroalkene from anthracene-9-carboxaldehyde and 1-nitropropane. <95TL8457> Burns *et.al.* reported an improved synthesis of benzyl isocyanoacetate which facilitates the synthesis of benzyl pyrrole-2-carboxylate esters by this method. <95SC379> 3-(1-Arylpyrrol-2-yl)pyrrole-2-carboxylates were prepared from 1-aryl-2-(nitrovinyl)pyrroles. <95JHC1703>

1,4-Diaryl-2,3-dinitrobutadienes were found to give primarily 3-aryl-4-(arylethynyl)-pyrrole-2-carboxylates resulting from cycloaddition at one nitroalkene unit and elimination of HNO_2 at the other. <95T5181>

Pyrrol-3-yl glycosides were prepared by condensing fully acetylated aldoses with nitromethane, followed by cycloaddition with TOSMIC. <95JHC899>

The TOSMIC analog *N*-(tosyl)benzyl isocyanide readily reacts with simple acceptors (ethyl acrylate, acrylonitrile, etc.) to give 4-substituted 2-arylpyrroles. Extension to 2,3-diaryl derivatives by use of styryl acceptors required the use of *n*-butyllithium as a base. <95SC795>

Additional examples of preparation of pyrroles from oxazolium oxides were reported. One example is the synthesis of the calcium channel activator FPL64176. The key feature of this synthesis was the prior rather than *in situ* generation of the mesoionic intermediate and the use of a *p*-nitrophenyl group for *N*-protection. <95JOC4947>

Oxazolium oxide cycloaddition was used to prepare 4-perfluoroalkylpyrrole-3-carboxylate esters. <95JFC5> Several 2,3,5-triarylpyrroles were obtained in two steps by cycloaddition between 2,5-diaryloxazolium oxides and an isothiazole dioxide. The initial adducts are thermally decomposed to pyrroles. <95T2455>

A new azomethine ylide containing a dithiolanyl ring was shown to react with typical dipolarophiles to give sulfur-substituted pyrroles. <95TL9409>

Various 4,5-diarylpyrrole-2-carboxylates were prepared by cyclocondensation of α-nitrostyrenes and aryl thioimidates. Dimethyl acetylenedicarboxylate and ethyl propiolate also gave pyrroles. <95BSJ2735>

A new method for the reductive conversion of β-keto-α-nitroesters to pyrroles involves the use of formamidinesulfinic acid (thiourea S,S-dioxide) as the reducing agent. <95TL9469> The ester substituent seems to be required since no reaction occurred with simple α-nitroketones.

Several 3-fluoropyrroles were prepared from α,α-difluoro-γ-iodo-γ-(trimethylsilyl)ketones. Reaction with ammonia gives 3,3-difluoropyrrolines which undergo desilylation and elimination of fluoride on treatment with KF. The required starting materials were made by addition of iododifluoromethyl ketones to vinyl silanes. <95TL5119> This route somewhat extends the range of 3-fluoropyrroles that can be prepared, since a prior procedure required the use of a vinyl acceptor with an electron-withdrawing substituent. <94TL4319>

Modest yields of 1-alkyl-2-phenylpyrroles were obtained by treating N-alkyl-N-allylbenzthioamides with either an alkylating agent or a Lewis acid, followed by a strong base. While this synthesis was designed on the basis of cyclization of a zwitterion intermediate **13c**, there is evidence that an amidine **13d** formed by exchange with the base may actually be involved. <95TL4619>

2-Aryl-5-bromomethyl-4,5-dihydro-$3H$-pyrroles can be formed in 40-70% yield in a two-step process involving addition of 3-butenylmagnesium bromide to an arylnitrile, followed by cyclization with NBS. <95S242>

$ArC{\equiv}N$ + $BrMgCH_2CH_2CH{=}CH_2$ $\longrightarrow$ **14a** **14b** **14c** $\xrightarrow{NBS}$ **14d**

β-Allyl enaminoesters and ketones were cyclized using I_2/Na_2CO_3. <95JOC7357> Dehydrohalogenation leads to pyrrole formation. When the allyl group is incorporated into a cyclohex-2-enyl substituent 7-iodo-3a,4,5,6,7,7a-hexahydroindoles are formed.

15a $\xrightarrow[NaHCO_3]{I_2}$ **15b** $\xrightarrow[105^\circ]{DBU}$ **15c**

An improved method for the well-know preparation of pyrroles from 2,5-dimethoxy-tetrahydrofuran was reported. Alkyl and arylamines, amides and sulfonamides were condensed by using P_2O_5 in dry toluene. <95SC1857>

Blechert and coworkers have extended synthetic methods involving generation and cycloaddition reactions of α-cyanovinylindoles. The cyanovinyl indoles can be generated from arylhydroxylamines by reaction with an aldehyde and cyanoallene. <95S592> The resulting vinylindoles were used as precursors of several kinds of alkaloid structures.

16a + $RCH{=}O$ + $CH_2{=}C{=}CHCN$ $\longrightarrow$ **16d**
16b **16c**

$RCH{=}O$ =

Several new variations of methods for preparation of indoles by Pd-mediated cyclization were reported. Vinylene carbonate was found to be a satisfactory C2-C3 precursor for synthesis of N-acylindolin-2-ols and N-acylindoles from o-iodoacetanilides under Heck conditions. <95H(41)1627>

17a + **17b** $\xrightarrow[(i\text{-}Pr)_2NEt]{Pd(OAc)_2}$ **17c** $\xrightarrow{TsOH}$ **17d**

Larock and Zenner explored the reaction of allenes with N-(o-iodophenyl)-p-toluenesulfonamides. 3-Alkylideneindolines are formed. Enantioselectivity can be achieved in the presence of a chiral ligand. The reactions are believed to occur by addition of an arylPd(II) species to the allene to generate a π-allylPd intermediate which cyclizes. With terminal allenes (R' = H) the reaction is regiospecific and gives 3-methyleneindolines. <95JOC482>

Simultaneous construction of three rings was achieved in Pd-mediated cyclization of the diacetylene **19a** to indolo[2,3-a]carbazole **19c**. <95TL7841> This reaction presumably proceeds by successive oxidative additions to dibromomaleimide and Pd(II)-mediated cyclization.

The diyne **20b**, prepared by oxidative dimerization of the corresponding terminal alkyne, was cyclized to the biindole **20c** using NaOEt. <95SL859>

Furstner and coworkers have continued to explore the titanium-mediated formation of indoles from *o-N*-diacylanilines. The use of a sodium-aluminum oxide mixture prepared from alumina and molten sodium was developed. This material has the advantage over potassium-graphite of being non-pyrophoric. <95S63> Additional specific applications of the reaction were also reported, for example the synthesis of the phytoalexin camalexin, **21b**. <95T773>

A new synthesis of ethyl 7-methoxyindole-3-acetate was accomplished by reductive cyclization of the *o*-nitrobenzyl cyanide **22a**. The indole was then elaboarated to the tetracycle **22d** by an intramolecular Pummerer reaction. <95JHC947>

A procedure for obtaining indole-3-carboxylate ester from the β-pyrrolidino-*o*-nitrostyrene intermediates in the Leimgruber-Batcho indole synthesis was demonstrated. Although ethyl chloroformate is evidently not reactive enough, phosgene followed by methanolysis effects β-carbomethoxylation. Reductive cyclization then gives the indole esters. <95SC95>

Both 3-alkyl and 3-alkylideneoxindoles have been obtained by carbonylative cyclization of *o*-alkynylanilines. Carbonylation in the absence of a reducing agent gives the unsaturated oxindole while inclusion of water and Et_3N leads to the alkyloxindoles. <95TL6243> Since there are now several reliable syntheses of *o*-alkylanilines this may be a practical route to oxindoles.

R = aryl, *t*-butyl

A little-known oxindole cyclization was used to advantage in the course of developing an efficient synthesis of the dopamine receptor agonist Ropinirole. Working from earlier results of Royer <80JHC1531> who obtained oxindoles from β-nitrostyrenes by reaction with $FeCl_3$ and acetyl chloride, the intermediate **25b** was prepared. Of several groups explored for the 4-ethyl functionality, the best results were obtained with a benzoate substituent. <95JHC875>

A palladium-mediated cyclization which provides carbazole-1,4-quinones was improved by development of conditions which require substoichiometirc amounts of $Pd(OAc)_2$. *t*-Butyl hydroperoxide is used for reoxidation of Pd. <95TL1325> The same conditions, however, were only marginally successful (30% yield) for converting diphenylamine to carbazole.

X = H, CH_3, CH_3O R,R' = H,CH_3; CH_3,H; benzo

The industrial scale preparation of indoles from relatively inexpensive starting materials such as aniline and ethylene glycol has been of continuing interest. Some progress in this direction was reported from the laboratories of Tanabe Seiyaku Co. For example, ethylene glycol, propane-1,2-diol and butane-1,2-diol react with *N*-methylaniline over a $Al_2O_3:SiO_2:Na_2O$ catalyst (Neobead P) to give indoles in 40-50% yield. <95JCS(P2)823> A catalyst which promotes *N*-dealkylation by steam and hydrogen at 500-575° was also reported.

5.2.2 Synthetic Modification

One of the more useful means of introducing substituents on the pyrrole ring is Friedel-Crafts acylation because it can be directed to the 2- or 3-position. <85CJC896> In the course of synthesis of 1-alkyl-3-(1-naphthoyl)pyrroles it was found that regioselectivity can be affected by choice of solvent. Use of nitromethane in place of CH_2Cl_2 improved selectivity for C3 <95TL1401> Xiao and Ketcha used 2- and 3-acetyl-1-(phenylsulfonyl)pyrrole as the starting points for synthesis of 2-vinyl and 3-vinyl-1-(phenylsulfonyl)pyrroles. The acetyl pyrroles were reduced to carbinols with $NaBH_4$ and then dehydrated using 0.15 M H_3PO_4 in refluxing dioxane. <95JHC499> A specific variation in Friedel-Crafts acylation conditions also led to a more direct route to Uhle's ketone when it was found that the inclusion of an acid chloride in the reaction medium improved the C4:C2 regioselectivity.<95S506>

ADDITIVE	28b:2cb RATIO	YIELD
none	42:58	69%
CH_3CH_2COCl	92:8	76%
$ClCH_2COCl$	94:6	83%

The first synthesis of simple 2-aminopyrroles was reported. 1-Alkylpyrroles react with *N*-chlorophthalimide to give 2-phthalimidopyrroles. The phthaloyl group can be removed with $NaBH_4$ in 2-propanol. The method can be applied to the parent 2-aminopyrrole by use of a tri-*iso*-propylsilyl substiuent. <95TL9261> The aminopyrroles are not stable neat. In acidic solution, tautomeric equilbrium with a 5-protonated species is indicated by disappearance of the normal coupling of the C5-H as a result of exchange.

Several methods for constructing branched substituents on indole rings have been developed using 1-, 2- or 3-(benzotriazol-1-yl)methylindoles as intermediates. The 2-isomer can be subjected to dilithiation and sequential *C,N*-dialkylation. The Bzt group can then be displaced by reaction with a Grignard reagent, providing a 1,2-disubstituted indole. <95JOC3401>

Bzt = 1-benzotriazolyl   R = *pri*-alkyl ;   R' = $CH_3, C_2H_5, PhCH_2$

Similar methodology was applied to 1-methyl-3-(benzotriazol-1-ylmethyl)indole. This intermediate can be alkylated and the Bzt group can be displaced with nucleophiles, including Grignard reagents or thiolates. <95SC539>

$M^+ {}^- Nu = C_2H_5MgBr$, NaSPh

The 1-(benzotriazol-1-yl)methyl derivatives of indole and carbazole were also used to effect α-silylation/alkylation. <95OM734>

Gramine is a common precursor for indol-3-ylmethylation of enolates and other nucleophiles. Such reactions normally occur by an elimination-addition mechanism. Following development of procedures for 4-substitution via directed lithiation with 1-(tri-*iso*-propylsilyl)-gramine, Iwao and Motoi have developed conditions for tandem nucleophilic substitution of the dimethylamino group. Quaternization followed by reaction with a nucleophile in the presence of TBAF leads to alkylation. <95TL5929> The carbon nucleophiles which were successfully used include nitromethane, methyl acetoacetate, diethyl malonate and diethyl 2-(acetamido)malonate. Phthalimide, thiophenol, TMS-CN and TMS-N₃ were also used as sources of nucleophiles.

N-Protected 3-(bromomethyl)indoles are being used more frequently to introduce indol-3-ylmethyl groups.   Cook and coworkers prepared 3-(bromomethyl)-5-methoxy-1-(phenylsulfonyl)indole by NBS/AIBN bromination of the corresponding 3-methylindole. <95TL3103> This compound proved to be an effective reagent for preparing both D(+) and L(-) 5-methoxytryptophan by stereoselective alkylation of a Schollkopf dihydropyrazine intermediate. <95SC3883>

The Schollkopf intermediate was also used in the preparation of 2-bromo-5-hydroxytryptophan, using 1-(*t*-butoxycarbonyl)-2-bromo-3-(bromomethyl)indole as the alkylating agent. <95TL9133>

The Schollkopf nucleophile was also used in the enantioselective synthesis of β-methyltryptophan. In this case the dihydropyrazine nucleophile undergoes conjugate addition to the sulfone **35a**, which yields a β-methyltryptophan after reductive desulfonylation and hydrolysis. <95JOC4978>

An expeditious enantioselective synthesis of α-methyltryptophan was accomplished using the Seebach oxazolidinone procedure. The oxazolidinone **36b** was prepared from D-tryptophan and pivalaldehyde. Alkylation was carried out without indole-N-protection using 2.2 equiv. of LDA and 1.2 equiv. of methyl iodide. Under these conditions, C-alkylation ocurred preferentially. R-α-methyltryptophan was obtained by hydrolysis of **36c**. <95JOC5719>

A versatile route to β-substituted tryptophan esters was developed beginning with condensation of an indole, an aldehyde and Meldrum's acid. The condensation products can be solvolyzed to half esters and then subjected to Curtius rearrangement. <95TL2057>

An improved procedure for the synthesis of dehydrotryptophans was developed in the course of a synthesis of claviciptic acid. 4-Bromoindole and methyl α-(t-butoxycarbonyl-amino)acrylate reacted in the presence of stoichiometric amounts of Pd(OAc)$_2$ and chloranil to give the dehydrotryptophan **38b** in >80% yield. The chloranil presumably functions to reoxidize Pd^0 formed in the coupling process, but nevertheless lower yields were obtained with substoichiometric amounts of Pd(OAc)$_2$. After enantioselective hydrogenation, a 4-(3-hydroxy-3-methylbut-1-enyl) group was introduced on **38c** using a Heck reaction. <95JOC1486>

Another method for conversion of indoles to tryptophans involves Lewis acid-catalyzed conjugate addition to N-(diphenylmethylene)dehydroalanine. This method was used to prepare 2-alkyl-, 2-bromo-, and 2-methylthiotryptophans. <95S370>

Directed lithiation continues to be a versatile method for synthetic elaboration of pyrroles and indoles. Conditions for lithiation of 1-vinylpyrrole were explored. Lithiation with n-butyllithium with or without TMEDA or KO-t-Bu gave a mixture of C2 and α-vinyl lithiation. Use of a catalytic amount of $(i$-Pr)$_2$NH (12 mol %) with a stoichiometric amount of n-butyllithium/KO-t-Bu at -60 to -80° leads to selective C2 lithiation. <95RTC18> These conditions are believed to reflect a thermodynamic preference for the C2 lithiation. Several typical electrophiles including ketones, aldehydes, DMF, TMS-Cl and alkyl halides gave the expected products, but so far no means for efficient removal of the vinyl group has been found. 1-Carboxy-2-(tributylstannyl)indole, which can be prepared from indole by the Katritzky lithiation-carbonation-lithiation sequence, proved to be a useful intermediate for synthesis of 2-aryl and 2-styrylindoles by Stille coupling. The carboxy group is lost during the coupling process. <95JOC6218> Lithiopyrroles and lithioindoles were also the starting points for introduction of non-carbon substituents. A route to N-protected (t-Boc, phenylsulfonyl) 2-bromopyrroles proceeds via 2-(trimethylstannyl)pyrroles. Bromination is done with NBS at -70°. <95SC1589>

2-Azido and 3-azido-1-methylindole were prepared by azido group transfer from the corresponding lithioindoles using p-toluenesulfonyl azide. <95GCI151>

Snieckus and coworkers found that the 5-(N,N-diethylcarbamoyloxy) group can be used to direct lithiation to C4 of the indole ring. A 1-(t-butyldimethylsilyl) protecting group was used to sterically prevent C2 lithiation. Typical electrophiles such as methyl iodide and DMF were shown to give good yields of 4-substituted products. Other substituents which were successfully introduced include ethoxycarbonyl, acetamido, acetoxy, chloro, iodo, and t-butylthio. The 4-lithiated intermediate was also transmetallated using $ZnBr_2$ and the indol-4-ylzinc reagent underwent Pd-catalyzed coupling with 2-bromopyridine. Successful replacement of the carbamoyloxy group by Grignard reagents using $Ni(acac)_2$ as a catalyst was also reported. <95JOC1484>

Dimethylzincates derived from both 2-lithio and 3-lithio-1-(phenylsulfonyl)indole have been prepared. The zincate reagents react with both allyl bromide and benzaldehyde to give the expected products in 50-60% yield. <95JCS(P1)1207> An indol-2-ylzinc species was found to have enhanced reactivity toward 2-benzylation of indole-3-carboxylates. The dilithio intermediate **42a** could not be directly benzylated, but use of 0.5 mol of $ZnCl_2$ and $Pd(PPh_3)_4$ (1-2 mol %) resulted in good yields. These conditions proved to be applicable to the preparation of the CNS drug candidate **42c** on a 10-25 kg scale. <95JOC6224>

Several other examples of the utility of Pd-mediated reactions in synthesis of aryl and vinyl derivatives of pyrrole and indole were reported. Schmidt and coworkers examined arylation of 1-vinylpyrroles under Heck conditions. Reaction took place at the N-vinyl group. While the parent compound gave a mixture of - and -arylation, 2,3-dialkyl-1-vinylpyrroles preferred -substitution. <95RCB767> Grieb and Ketcha used Suzuki coupling conditions to prepare several 1-

(phenylsulfonyl)-2-arylpyrroles. The pyrrole-2-boronic acid intermediates were prepared from 2-lithio-1-(phenylsulfonyl)pyrrole. <94SC2145> 3-Allylation of methyl 1-(phenylsulfonyl)indole-4-carboxylate was achieved in 70-76% yield by a 3-mercuration and $LiPdCl_4$-catalyzed coupling. <95SL27> Several 4-iodopyrrole-2-carboxaldehydes were converted to the corresponding 4-vinylpyrroles with tri-(n-butyl)vinylstannane under Stille conditions. <95TL7043> Several 4-bromo- and 5-iodopyrrole-2-carboxylate esters were successfully arylated using phenylboronic acid under Suzuki conditions. <95JOC7030> 3-Arylpyrroles were prepared by Pd-mediated coupling of aryl halides with 1-(tri-i-propylsilyl)pyrrole-3-magnesium bromide. <94ZOK1537>

Two new reports have provided examples of the potential utility of indol-2-ylborates for elaboration of indoles. Pd-Catalyzed carbonylation with vinyl triflates was used to prepare 2-(cyclohex-1-enoyl)indoles which were then converted to yuehcukene analogs. <95H(41)1385>

The borate intermediate was also coupled with aryl halides. When a α-ynyl group is present, coupling is followed by a tandem cyclization which leads to 2-[α-(cycloalkylidene)alkyl]indoles. <95CC409>

$R = CH_3, (CH_3)_3Si$ $Y = $ \NCOPh, O=CNCH_3, CH_2C(CO_2Et)_2

Cava and coworkers demonstrated that ceric ammonium nitrate oxidation of 4,6,7-trimethoxytryptamines, followed by cyclization, can efficiently generate the pyrrolo[4,3,2-de]quinoline nucleus which forms the heterocyclic core of a group of marine alkaloids which includes the makaluvamines and discorhabins. <95JOC1800> Previous studies in this area have shown that the methoxy group can subsequently be replaced by amines to provide the natural substances.

The direct oxidative amination of the quinones was also explored. Using the N-tosyl-protected quinone and benzylamine exclusive C6 substitution was achieved. In the absence of the tosyl group C5 substitution is preferred by 3:1. <95JOC3543> Regioselective C6 substitution (8:1) was also observed in the oxidative amination of **46c** using diphenylmethylamine. In both cases the regioselectivity can be attributed to differential substituent interaction with the two quinone carbonyl groups. <95TL7039>

46a   R = H, Ts   **46b**   **46c**   **46d**

Indole was included with alkyl and arylamines in a study which demonstrated the potential of 2-pyridylsulfonyl as an N-protecting group. The group is reductively removed using SmI_2. <95JOC5969> A possible new means for indole debenzylation was uncovered. 1-Benzyl-2-phenylindole and several N-benzylcarbazoles and tetrahydrocarbazoles were found to undergo debenzylation on reaction with methyllithium or LDA. An α-elimination mechanism is proposed. <95TL1671>

Examples of selective side-chain oxidation were reported for two reagents. Ceric ammonium nitrate was found to convert 5-methylpyrrole-2-carboxylates to 5-formylpyrrole-2-carboxylates. <95TL4345> Several examples of oxidation of C2 and C3 methyl groups to formyl in 1-(phenylsulfonyl)indoles with MnO_2 were reported. <95SC2407>

Efficient oxidation of 2-arylindoles to 2-aryl-$3H$-indol-3-ones occurred under photosensitized conditions. The inital oxidation products are trapped by the solvent methanol and the indolones are obtained by vacuum thermolysis. <95SC3831>

47a   **47b**   **47c**

A new fluorinating reagent (F-TEDA-BF) was found to react with pyrrole-2-carboxylates to give 2-fluoropyrroles. <95CC2399> The mechanism has not been established but might involve decarboxylation of an acyl hypofluorite.

48a   **48b**

5.2.3 Annelation Reactions

Radical reactions continue to be explored to define their potential for pyrrole and indole annelation. The cyclization of 2-bromo-1-(but-3-enyl)indole showed the usual preference for 5-*exo* cyclization with yields in the 70-90% range being observed for a variety of substitution patterns. With a 1-(pent-4-enyl) substituent a mixture of 6-*exo* cyclization and reductive dehalogenation was observed. This is similar to what is observed with phenyl radicals and indicates that 2-indolyl radicals are fairly typical aryl radicals. <95TL4857> This is not surprising since the σ-radicals are presumably largely localized at C2 and would not be strongly effected by the π-electron distribution. Cyclization of 1-(ω-iodoalkyl)-3-formylindoles was observed to form 5-7 membered rings by substitution rather than addition. This is attributed to a proton transfer step which generates H_2. The resulting radical anion can then serve as an electron donor in a continuing chain process. <95TL9051> The same skeletons were formed in processes in which a 2-phenylthio or 2-phenylsulfinyl substituent is displaced. The sulfinyl displacement is somewhat more effective, suggesting that an electron-withdrawing group may favor the addition step. <95CC1353>

n	
1	64%
2	75%
3	43%

n		
1	24%	40%
2	50%	50%
3	-	30%

N-(Pent-4-enyl)- pyrroles and indoles were included in a study of cyclizations which are initiated by addition of arenesulfonyl radicals to the terminal alkene. The yield ranged from 55-73% when the radical generation was done by sonication in the presence of Cu(OAc)$_2$. <95SL763>

2-(ethoxycarbonyl)pyrrole
3-cyanoindole

The pyrrole sultine **51b** was prepared to serve as a 3,4-dimethylenepyrrole synthon. The sultine ring is readily generated by reaction of 1-tosyl-3,4-*bis*-(chloromethyl)pyrrole with NaO$_2$SCH$_2$OH (Rongalite). Cycloaddition was observed with several dipolarophiles, but there was competing rearrangement to the less reactive sulfone **51e**. <95CC2537>

X = CO$_2$CH$_3$, Y= bond	5%	42%
X = CO$_2$CH$_3$, Y = H	63%	-
X = CN, Y = H	50%	-

Several cyclopenta[b]indoles were prepared from cyclopenta[b]pyrano[3,4-d]pyrrol-6-one **52a**. <95JCS(P1)1131>

X, Y = CO$_2$CH$_3$, CO$_2$CH$_3$
X, Y = CO$_2$CH$_3$, Si(CH$_3$)$_3$
X, Y = CO$_2$CH$_3$, H (isomer mixture)

5.2.4 Transition Metal Complexes

The potential for transition metal complexes to provide new reactivity patterns continues to be explored by the preparation of complexes and the study of their reactivity patterns. The aminoalkyl substituents of gramine, tryptamine and methyl tryptophanate promoted metalation at C2 of the indole ring by Pt(DMSO)$_2$Cl$_2$. The crystal structure of the gramine product was determined.

<95JOM(496)C1> Indole-3-acetic acid, on the other hand, reacts with Na_2PdCl_4 to give a dimeric product in which the Pt is bound to C3 and N1. <95ICA(235)367>

Well-characterized 2-(chloromercurio) derivatives of 1-acetyl- and 1-(phenylsulfonyl)pyrrole were prepared by reaction of $HgCl_2$. These can be converted to *bis*-(pyrrol-2-yl)mercury compounds or into ruthenium and osmium complexes by transmetallation. In all of these complexes there is coordination between the acetyl or sulfonyl oxygen and the metal, but the chelation is much tighter in the Ru and Os complexes. <95JOM(491)219> To date, the reactivity of these compounds has not been explored.

The chemistry of pyrrol-1-ylbenzylidene pentacarbonyl chromium, molybdenum and tungsten complexes was investigated. Reaction with electrophilic alkenes gives 1-(phenylcyclopropyl)pyrroles. Under photolytic decarbonylation conditions 2 + 2 cycloaddition products were obtained with nucleophilic alkenes, cyclic dienes and imines. <95OM2522>

The work of Harman and coworkers has illustrated how fundamentally changed reactivity patterns can be elicited by use of transition metal coordination complexes. They have studied a series of pentaammineosmium(II) compounds in which the Os is attached at one of the pyrrole "double bonds", rendering the reactivity of the other side of the ring more like that of an enamine. There is also an equilibrium with a species in which the Os is bound at C3-C4. These complexes behave like azomethine ylides and give cycloaddition accross C2-C5. Some of the products obtained are stabilized *2H*- and *3H*-pyrroles. The $Os(II)(NH_3)_5$ moiety provides steric shielding of one face of the pyrrole ring and generally prefers the less substituted of the two alternative π-bonds. These aspects of the complexes can be exploited for the design of stereo- and/or regioselective reactions. The chemistry of these compounds, which encompasses several additional variations, is elaborated in a paper from the Harman group. <95JOC2125>

$E = CH_2=CH\overset{O}{\overset{\|}{C}}R$; RCOCl ; RC$\equiv$N$^+$-X

The cycloaddition reactions generally give *exo* adducts with 1-unsubstituted pyrroles, but 1-methyl and 1-trimethylsilyl substituents favor the *endo* stereoisomers. Cycloaddition has been achieved with *N*-phenylmaleimide, methyl acrylate, methyl crotonate, dimethyl maleate, acrylonitrile and crotonitrile. The rate of cycloaddition is increased by 2,5-dimethyl substitution and this is attributed to the affect on the equilibrium between the 2,3 and 3,4-complexes. The isolation of azanorbornenes from the adducts by oxidative demetallation frequently leads to cycloreversion but azanorbornanes can be isolated by hydrogenation immediately after oxidation. <95JA3405>

η^6-Ruthenium(II) complexes of indole, 2-methylindole and 2,3-dimethylindole were characterized. The strong electron-withdrawing character of the metal substituents is revealed by the pK of the NH groups in these compounds which are in the vicinity of 8. Mixed binuclear complexes of Pd(II) and Cu(II) with these anions were also characterized. <95OM1221>

References

80JHC1531	J. Guillaumel, P. Demerseman, J.-M. Clavel and R. Royer, *J. Heterocycl. Chem.* **1980**, *17*, 1531.
85CJC896	H. J. Anderson, C. E. Loader, R. X. Xu, N. Le, N. J. Gogan, R. McDonald and L. G. Edwards, *Can. J. Chem.* **1985**, *63*, 896.
94TL4319	Z.-M. Qui and D. J. Burton, *Tetrahedron Lett.* **1994**, *35*, 4319.
95ZOK1537	N. A. Bumagin, A. F. Nikitina and I. P. Beletskaya, *Zh. Org. Khim.* **1995**, *30*, 1537; *Chem. Abstr.* **1995**, *123*, 5685v.
95ANH71	A. R. Martin and Z. Qi, *Adv. Nitrogen Heterocycl.* **1995**, *1*, 71.
95ANH121	U. Pindur, *Adv. Nitrogen Heterocycl.* **1995**, *1*, 121.
95ANH205	S. Hibino and E. Sugino, *Adv. Nitrogen Heterocycl.* **1995**, *1*, 205.
95BSJ2735	M. Yokoyama, Y. Menjo, H. Wei and H. Togo, *Bull. Chem. Soc. Jpn.* **1995**, *68*, 2735.
95CC409	M. Ishikura, *J. Chem. Soc., Chem. Commun.* **1995**, 409.
95CC1353	S. Caddick, K. Aboutayab and R. I. West, *J. Chem. Soc., Chem. Commun.* **1995**, 1353.
95CC2399	J. Wang and A. I. Scott, *J. Chem. Soc., Chem. Commun.* **1995**, 2399.
95CC2537	W. S. Chang, W. J. Lin, W.-D. Liu and L.-G. Chen, *J. Chem. Soc., Chem.Commun.* **1995**, 2537.
95GCI151	E. Foresti, M. T. Di Gioia, D. Nanni and P. Zanirato, *Gazz. Chim. Ital.* **1995**, *125*, 151.
95H(41)1385	M. Ishikura, *Heterocycles* **1995**, *41*, 1385.
95H(41)1627	K. Samizu and K. Ogasawara, *Heterocycles* **1995**, *41*, 1627.
95ICA(235)367	M. Takani, H. Masuda and O. Yamauchi, *Inorg. Chem. Acta*, **1995**, *235*, 367.
95JA3405	J. Gonzalez, J. I. Koontz, L. M. Hodges, K. R. Nilsson, L. K. Neely, W. H. Myers, M. Sabat and W. D. Harman, *J. Am. Chem. Soc.* **1995**, *117*, 3405.
95JCE875	H. J. Anderson, *J. Chem. Ed.* **1995**, *72*, 875.
95JCS(P1)1131	C.-A. Harrison, P. M. Jackson, C. J. Moody and J. M. J. Williams, *J.Chem. Soc., Perkin Trans. 1*, **1995**, 1131.
95JCS(P1)1207	Y. Kondo, N. Takazawa, A. Yoshida and T. Sakamoto, *J.Chem. Soc., Perkin Trans. 1*, **1995**, 1207.
95JCS(P2)823	T. Nishida, Y. Tokuda and M. Tsuchiya, *J.Chem. Soc., Perkin Trans. 2*, **1995**, 823.
95JFC5	K. Funabiki, T. Ishihara and H. Yamanaka, *J. Fluorine Chem.* **1995**, *71*, 5.
95JHC499	D. Xiao and D. M. Ketcha, *J. Heterocycl. Chem.* **1995**, *32*, 499.
95JHC875	J. D. Hayler, S. L. B. Howie, R. G. Giles, A. Negus, P. W. Oxley, T. C. Walsgrove, S. E. Walsh, R. E. Dagger, J. M. Fortunak and A. Mastrocola, *J.Heterocycl. Chem.* **1995**, *32*, 875.
95JHC899	J. L. Del Valle, C. Polo, T. Torroba and S. Marcaccini, *J. Heterocycl. Chem.* **1995**, *32*, 899.
95JHC947	I. K. Stamas and H. K. Kotzamani, *J. Heterocycl. Chem.* **1995**, *32*, 947.
95JHC1703	H. Dumoulin, S. Rault and M. Robba, *J. Heterocycl. Chem.* **1995**, *32*, 1703.
95JOC482	R. C. Larock and J. M. Zenner, *J. Org. Chem.* **1995**, *60*, 482.
95JOC1484	E. J. Griffen, D. G. Roe and V. Snieckus, *J. Org. Chem.* **1995**, *60*, 1484.
95JOC1486	Y. Yokoyama, T. Matsumoto and Y. Murakami, *J. Org. Chem.* **1995**, *60*, 1486.
95JOC1800	E. V. Sadanadan, S. K. Pillai, M. V. Latshmikantham, A. D.Billimoria, J. S. Culpepper and M. P. Cava, *J. Org. Chem.* **1995**, *60*, 1800.

95JOC2125   L. M. Hodges, J. Gonzalez, J. I. Koontz, W. H. Myers and W. D. Harman, *J. Org. Chem.* **1995**, *60*, 2125.

95JOC3401   A. R. Katritzky, J.Li and C. V. Stevens, *J. Org. Chem.* **1995**, *60*, 3401.

95JOC3543   Y. A. Jackson, A. D. Billimoria, E. V. Sadanandan and M. P. Cava, *J. Org. Chem.* **1995**, *60*, 3543.

95JOC4947   B. Santiago, C. R. Dalton, E. W. Huber and J. M. Kane, *J. Org. Chem.* **1995**, *60*, 4947.

95JOC4978   G. Shapiro, D. Buechler, M. Marzi, K. Schmidt and G. Gomez-Lor, *J. Org. Chem.* **1995**, *60*, 4978.

95JOC5719   L. Zhang and J. M. Finn, *J. Org. Chem.* **1995**, *60*, 5719.

95JOC5969   C. Goulaouic-Dubois, A. Guggisberg and M. Hess, *J. Org. Chem.* **1995**, *60*, 5969.

95JOC6218   R. L. Hudkins, J. L. Diebold and F. D. Marsh, *J. Org. Chem.* **1995**, *60*, 6218.

95JOC6224   L. E. Fisher, S. S. Labadie, D. C. Reuter and R. D. Clark, *J. Org. Chem.* **1995**, *60*, 6224.

95JOC7030   C. K. Chang and N. Bag, *J. Org. Chem.* **1995**, *60*, 7030.

95JOC7357   H. M. C. Ferraz, E. O. de Oliveira, M. E. Payret-Arrua and C. A. Brandt, *J. Org. Chem.* **1995**, *60*, 7357.

95JOM(491)219G.   R. Clark, M. M. P. Ng, W. R. Roper and L. J. Wright, *J. Organomet. Chem.* **1995**, *491*, 219.

95JOM(496)C1   R. Annunziata, S. Cenini, I. Demartin, G. Palmisano and S. Tollari, *J. Organomet. Chem.* **1995**, *496*, C1.

95OM734   A. R. Katritzky, Q. Hong and Z. Yang, *Organometallics* **1995**, *14*, 734.

95OM1221   S. Chen, V. Carperos, B. Noll, R. J. Swope and M. R. DuBois, *Organometallics* **1995**, *14*, 1221.

95OM2522   I. Merino and L. S. Hegedus, *Organometallics* **1995**, *14*, 2522.

95RCB767   A. F. Shmidt, T. A. Vladimirova, E. Yu. Shmidt and T. V. Dmitrieva, *Russian Chem. Bull.* **1995**, *44*, 767.

95RTC18   A. G. Mal'kina, O. A. Tarasova, H. D. Verkruijsse, A. C. H. T. M. van der Kerk, L. Brandsma and B. A. Trofimov, *Rec. Trav. Chim. Pays-Bas* **1995**, *114*, 18.

95S63   A. Furstner and G. Seidel, *Synthesis* **1995**, 63.

95S242   L. Dechoux, L. Jung and J.-F. Stambach, *Synthesis* **1995**, 242.

95S276   T. Masquelin and D. Obrecht, *Synthesis* **1995**, 276.

95S370   C. Balsamini, G. Diamantini, A. Duranti, G. Spadoni and A. Tontini, *Synthesis* **1995**, 370.

95S506   K. Teranishi, S. Hayashi, S. Nakatsuka and T. Goto, *Synthesis* **1995**, 506.

95S592   S. Blechert, R. Knier, H. Schroers and T. Wirth, *Synthesis* **1995**, 592.

95S1315   A. R. Katritzky, H. Wu, L. Xie, S. Rachwal, B. Rachwal, J. Jiang, G. Zhang and H. Lang, *Synthesis* **1995**, 1315.

95SC95   M. Prashad, L. La Vecchia, K. Prasad and O. Repic, *Synth. Commun.* **1995**, *25*, 95.

95SC379   D. H. Burns, C. S. Jabara and M. W. Burden, *Synth. Commun.* **1995**, *25*, 379.

95SC539   A. R. Katritzky, L. Xie and D. Cundy, *Synth. Commun.* **1995**, *25*, 539.

95SC795   R. Di Santo, R. Costi, S. Massa and M. Artico, *Synth. Commun.* **1995**, *25*, 795.

95SC1589   L. Groenedaal, M. E. Van Loo, J. A. J. M. Vekemans and E. W. Meijer, *Synth. Commun.* **1995**, *25*, 1589.

95SC1857   Y. Fang, D. Leysend and H. C. J. Ottenheijm, *Synth. Commun.* **1995**, *25*, 1857.
95SC2145   J. G. Grieb and D. M. Ketcha, *Synth. Commun.* **1995**, *25*, 2145.
95SC2407   A. K. Mohanakrishnan and P. C. Srinivasan, *Synth. Commun.* **1995**, *25*, 2407.
95SC3831   K.-Q. Ling, *Synth. Commun.* **1995**, *25*, 3831.
95SC3883   P. Zhang and J. M. Cook, *Synth. Commun.* **1995**, *25*, 3883.
95SL27   S. Barbey and J. Mann, *Synlett* **1995**, 27.
95SL763   C.-P. Chuang and S.-F. Wang, *Synlett* **1995**, 763.
95SL859   K. Shin and K. Ogasawara, *Synlett* **1995**, 859.
95T773   A. Furstner and A. Ernst, *Tetrahedron* **1995**, *51*, 773.
95T2455   P. Baggi, F. Clerici, M. L. Gelmi and S. Mottadelli, *Tetrahedron* **1995**, *51*, 2455.
95T5181   C. Dell'Erba, A. Giglio, A. Mugnoli, M. Novi, G. Petrillo and P. Stagnaro, *Tetrahedron* **1995**, *51*, 5181.
95TL343   A. R. Katritzky, H.-X. Chang and S. Verin, *Tetrahedron Lett.* **1995**, *36*, 343.
95TL1325   B. Akermark, J. D. Oslob and U. Heuschert, *Tetrahedron Lett.* **1995**, *36*, 1325.
95TL1401   J. A. H. Lainton, J. W. Huffman, B. R. Martin and D. R. Compton, *Tetrahedron Lett.* **1995**, *36*, 1995.
95TL1671   H. Suzuki, A. Tsukuda, M. Kondo, M. Aizawa, Y. Senoo, M. Nakajima, T. Watanabe, Y. Yokoyama and Y. Murakami and T. Li, *Tetrahedron Lett.* **1995**, *36*, 1671.
95TL2057   L. Jeannin, T. Nagy, E. Vassileva, J. Sapi and J.-Y. Laronze, *Tetrahedron Lett.* **1995**, *36*, 2057.
95TL3103   P. Zhang, R. Liu and J. M. Cook, *Tetrahedron Lett.* **1995**, *36*, 3103.
95TL4345   T. Thyran and D. A. Lightner, *Tetrahedron Lett.* **1995**, *36*, 4345.
95TL4619   I. V. Magadov, A. V. Kornienko, T. O. Zotova and V. N. Drozd, *Tetrahedron Lett.* **1995**, *36*, 4619.
95TL4857   A. P. Dobbs, K. Jones and K. T. Veal, *Tetrahedron Lett.* **1995**, *36*, 4857.
95TL5119   Z.-M. Qui and D. J. Burton, *Tetrahedron Lett.* **1995**, *36*, 5119.
95TL5929   M. Iwao and O. Motoi, *Tetrahedron Lett.* **1995**, *36*, 5929.
95TL6243   K. Hirao, N. Morii, T. Joh and S. Takahashi, *Tetrahedron Lett.* **1995**, *36*, 6243.
95TL7039   E. D. Edstrom and Z. Jones, *Tetrahedron Lett.* **1995**, *36*, 7039.
95TL7043   J. Wang and A. I. Scott, *Tetrahedron Lett.* **1995**, *36*, 7043.
95TL7841   M. G. Saulnier, D. B. Frennesson, M. S. Deshpande and D. M. Vyas, *Tetrahedron Lett.* **1995**, *36*, 7841.
95TL8457   S. Nakajima and A. Osuka, *Tetrahedron Lett.* **1995**, *36*, 8457.
95TL9051   C. J. Moody and C. L. Norton, *Tetrahedron Lett.* **1995**, *36*, 9051.
95TL9133   P. Zhang, R.. Lin and J. M. Cook, *Tetrahedron Lett.* **1995**, *36*, 9133.
95TL9261   M. De Rosa, R. P. Issac and G. Houghton, *Tetrahedron Lett.* **1995**, *36*, 9261.
95TL9409   C. W. G. Fishwick, R. J. Foster and R. E. Carr, *Tetrahedron Lett.* **1995**, *36*, 9409.
95TL9469   B. Quiclet, I. Thevenot and S. Z. Zard, *Tetrahedron Lett.* **1995**, *36*, 9469.

Chapter 5.3

Five-Membered Ring Systems: Furans and Benzo Derivatives

Stephan Reck and Willy Friedrichsen
Institute of Organic Chemistry, University of Kiel, Germany

5.3.1 INTRODUCTION

As in previous years the chemistry of furans and benzofurans was a field of very active research. Again quite a number of natural products with furan moieties (in almost all cases *tetrahydro*furan rings) was isolated. Most of this work was collected - as in the foregoing years - in *"Heterocycles"* and will not be repeated here. Only a few compounds will be mentioned: Quassiols B, C, D (squalene triterpenes from *Quassia multiflora* <95T11959>, meliavolkin 1 (from *Melia volkensii*) <95T2477>, sorocenols A, B (from *Sorocea bonplandii*) <95H1035>, acridone alkaloids <95H187>, tinosinesides A, B <95LA437>, sesquiterpene ethers <95LA1039>, subelliptones C, D <95H279>, spirolides B, C <95CC2159>, halistatin 3 <95CC383>, halogenated furanones (from the marine alga *Delisea pulchra*) <95HCA758>, astribin, asiminensin <95H1731> and others.

5.3.2 REACTIONS

Fluorofurans remain rare compounds. This situation may change, since treatment of 3-bromo-2-furoic acid with Selectfluor^{TM} gave bromofluorofuran, albeit in low yield (27%) <95TL2117>. Starting from 3-bromofuran via alkylation in the 2-position followed by alkylation in the 3-position a number of 2,3-dialkylated furans (e.g., rose furan) was obtained. The olfactory properties of these compounds (as well as their thiophene analogues) were studied <95LA1849>. Benzyltrimethylammonium dichloroiodide appears to be a selective chlorinating agent of furfuryl derivatives containing a carbonyl group <95SYN248>. The reaction of **1** with amines and hydrazines leads to the formation of pyrrolidones **2** <95JOC3975>.

A novel synthetic method for the preparation of two cytotoxic furonaphthoquinones **5a,b** was reported. Regiospecific metallation of 3-furoic acid (**3**) at the 2-position using LDA at -78°C and subsequent treatment with the corresponding aldehydes (R = H, OMe) affords the acids **4** (X = OH) which after reduction (to **4b** with iodotrimethylsilane) and ring closure (Friedel-Crafts) were transformed to **5a,b** <95JCS(P1)1085>.

In the photoreaction of thiobenzamide **6** with substituted furans **7** β-benzoylation was found to be the major reaction.

The aryl ketones **8** arise from an initially formed thietane followed by photochemical fission of the C-S bond and then by hydrolysis of an imine during chromatographic work-up <95JCS(P1)2931>. A 2-alkylation of a furan was effected by a vinylogous Pummerer reaction of the amido-substituted sulfoxide **9** <95JOC7082>.

An intramolecular 2-alkylation was also observed in a sulfonyl free radical induced addition-cyclization <95SL763>. A key intermediate in a new synthesis of pallescensin A (a biologically active labdane diterpene) was prepared by a cationic cyclization reaction with a furan <95SYN1141>. The sonochemical Barbier reaction was extended to carboxylate salts. 2-Furanylketones 10 can be obtained by sonication of a mixture of furan, lithium carboxylate, an alkylchloride, and lithium in THF <95JOC8>.

$$R'Cl + Li + RCOOLi + \underset{O}{\langle\rangle} \xrightarrow[\text{THF, rt}]{))))} \underset{O}{\langle\rangle}\underset{O}{\overset{}{\diagdown}}R$$

10

Nitroderivatives of furan react with carbanions containing leaving groups giving products of replacement of hydrogen with functionalized alkyl substituents <95T8339>. The aldol-type condensations of the silyloxydienes 11 with chiral electrophilic reagents 12 produced versatile templates 13 for a myriad of multifunctional compounds <95SYN607>.

$X^1 = O,N,S$

$X^2, X^3 = O,N$

Sugars, Azasugars, Thiosugars, etc.

The addition of 2-trimethylsilyloxyfuran to 2-acetyl-1,4-naphthoquinone followed by CAN mediated rearrangement gives a pyranonaphthoquinone. Subsequent transformations yield arizonin C1. Compounds of this type were found to exhibit antimicrobacterial activity against pathogenic strains of gram-positive bacterias <95JCS(P1)2855>. Pyranones can be obtained easily by an oxidative ring enlargement of furylcarbinols with iodobenzenediacetate (IBDA)/Mg(ClO$_4$)$_2$. The reaction mechanism can be explained in terms of a SET process <95TL3553>. Polyoxygenated labdane triterpenes were prepared by an oxidative ring opening reaction of a furfuryl alcohol as starting reaction <95T5781>. This type of reaction has been extended to the synthesis of dihydropyridones <95TL4983>. A convenient approach to 2,5-dimethoxy-2,5-dihydrofurans was reported. The reaction of diacetylfurans with monoperoxyphthalate (MMPP) in methanol yields these compounds in high yields <95TL4656>. The photoirradiation of furyl-substituted benzopyrans of type 14 in methanol leads to the formation of pyrano[3,2-b][1]benzopyrans 15. The mechanism of this cleavage/rearrangement was investigated <95JCS(P1)177>.

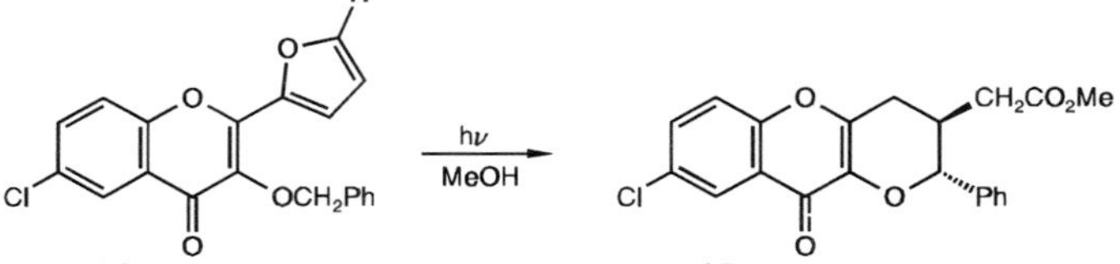

14   **15**

On irradiation, diepoxy[15]annulenone **16** undergoes an intriguing rearrangement, whereby all of the ether and carbonyl oxygens can travel free and change their positions in the rings to give 15 position isomers (e. g., **17**) in all <95CC1213>.

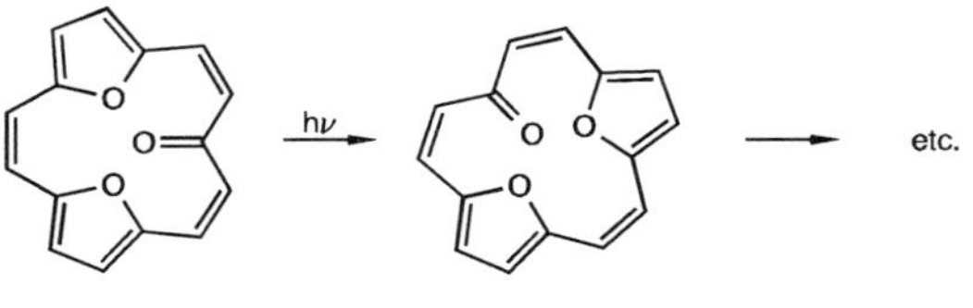

16   **17**

The synthesis of heptaleno[1,2-c]furans and -furanones was also reported <95HCA1437>. In a number of cases furans have been used as starting materials for other heterocycles, e. g., in the synthesis of D-(+)-showdomycin <95CC1017>. Intermolecular cross-carbonylation of aryl iodides with dihydrofurans was achieved with $PdCl_2/PPh_3/CO$ in the presence of a tertiary amine. With 2,3- and 2,5-dihydrofurans, 2-aroyl-4,5-dihydro- and 3-aroyl-2,3-dihydrofurans were obtained as predominant products <95JOC7267>. Pd-catalyzed arylation of 4-alkyl-substituted 2,3-dihydrofurans leads regio- and diastereoselectively to *trans*-2,3-disubstituted 2,3-dihydrofurans, which can be converted to *anti*-aldol derivatives upon ozonolysis <95SL153>. 4-Methyl-N-fluoropyridinium-2-sulfonate was used for the fluorination of dihydrofuran <95JOC6563>. When 2,5-dihydrofuran is treated with ethylmagnesium chloride/(R)-(EBTHI)ZrCl₂ (EBTHI = ethylene-1,2-bis(η^5-4,5,6,7-tetrahydro-1-indenyl)), **18** is formed in 65% yield and excellent enantio-selectivity <95T4383>.

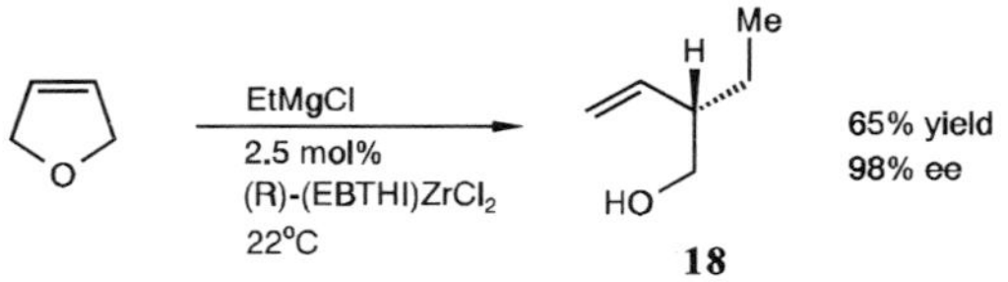

EtMgCl
2.5 mol%
(R)-(EBTHI)ZrCl₂
22°C

65% yield
98% ee

18

Stavudin (2',3'-didehydro-3'-desoxy-thymidine, **21**) shows a strong antiviral activity against AIDS viruses. It was prepared using a dihydrofuran (**20**) as an intermediate. The cyclization step (**19**→**20**) was accomplished with $Mo(CO)_6/Me_3NO$ in 80% yield <95AG356, 95AG(E)350>.

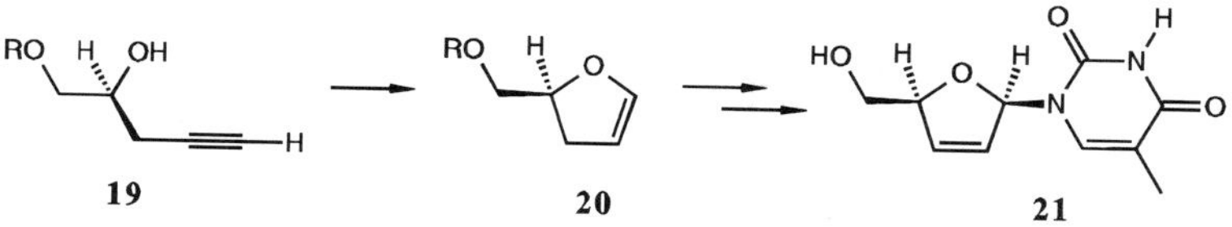

19 → **20** → **21**

R = tBuCO

Diethyl butenylphosphonates were used as starting materials for the synthesis of β-(diethoxyphosphinyl)-β,γ-unsaturated ketones. The authors propose a dihydrofuran as an intermediate <95JOC7027>. The Diels-Alder reaction of the optically active bis(silyl enol ether) **22** with bromoquinone **23** yields (-)-furaquinocin C (**24**). Furaquinacins show wide-ranging biological effects, including in vitro cytotoxicity against HeLaS$_3$ cells, antihypertensive activity, and inhibition of platelet aggregation and coagulation <95JA10755>.

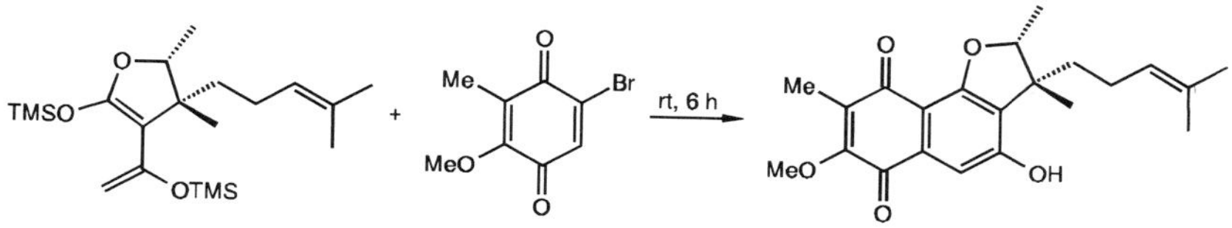

22 + **23** $\xrightarrow{\text{rt, 6 h}}$ **24**

In the preparation of (±)-furaquinacin D (**28**) another strategy was applied. Ring closure of **26** (not isolated, prepared from **25**) to **27** proved to be the key-step in this synthesis <95JA10757>.

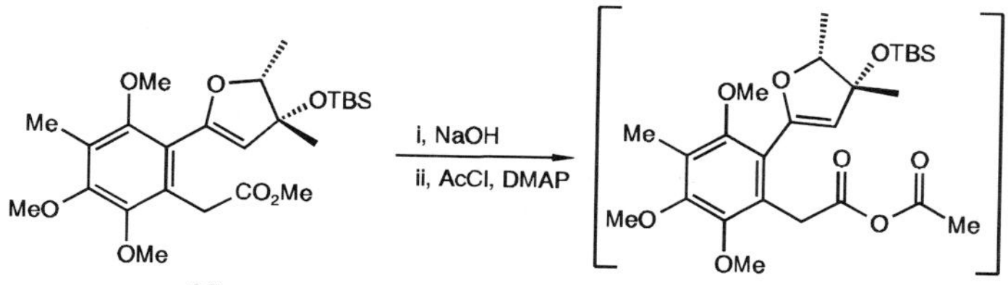

25 $\xrightarrow[\text{ii, AcCl, DMAP}]{\text{i, NaOH}}$ **26**

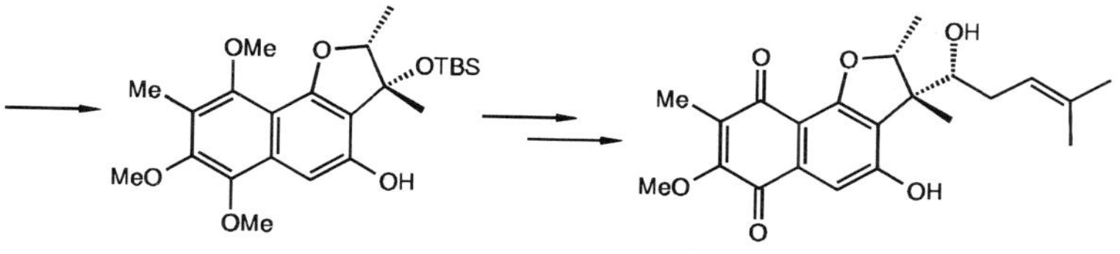

27 → **28**

The synthesis of the C16-C23 effector domain of FK-506 was accomplished via a copper-catalyzed metallate rearrangement of an α-alkenoxyalkenylcuprate starting with a lithiated dihydrofuran <95SYN195>. Irradiation of 3-acetyl-5,5-diaryl-2-methyl-4,5-dihydrofurans gave 2-acetyl-4-aryl-1-methylnaphthalenes <95TL5753>. The regioselective carbonyl insertion with α-substituted heterocycles using [Rh(cod)Cl]$_2$ as a catalyst was reported <95CC917>. Spirolactones can be obtained by a dirhodium(II)-catalyzed diazo decomposition of tetrahydrofurans <95JOC3035>. Spironaphthalenones are versatile starting materials for novel heterocyclic compounds <95T3051>. The cleavage of THF with acyl chlorides in the presence of zinc was reported <95JOC745>. An efficient access to 4,6-disubstituted dibenzofurans using two successive *ortho*-metallations was reported <95TL7657>. Bromination-dehydrobromination of 1,6-dioxaspiro[4.4]nonane **29** afforded the corresponding nonenes **30** and nonadienes **31**. The starting material is readily acquired by repetitive alkylation of acetone N,N-dimethylhydrazone with 2,2-dimethyloxirane followed by acidification of the dilithium diolate <95JCS(P1)1309>.

The reaction of phthalan **32** with an excess of lithium and a catalytic amount of DTBB followed by treatment with electrophiles leads, after hydrolysis, to the corresponding functionalized benzylic alcohols **33**. When the lithiation reaction is continued and a second electrophile is added, the disubstituted compounds **34** are obtained <95T3351>.

Li* = Li, DTBB cat.; E$^+$, E^1 $^+$, E^2 $^+$ = H$_2$O, D$_2$O, CO$_2$, RCHO, RCOR', PhCH=NPh

Patulin **36** has been synthesized in six steps (41.3% overall yield) starting with **35** and benzyloxyacetaldehyd <95TL7175>.

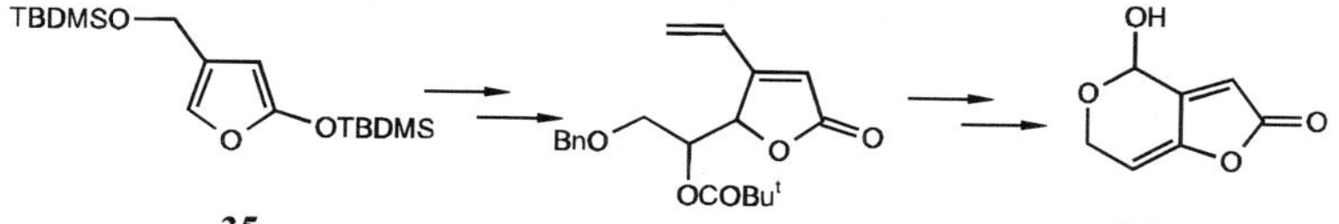

35   **36**

A reaction of furylbutenol **37** under Sharpless asymmetric oxidation conditions afforded the epoxide **38**, which was further converted into an antitumor antibiotic, asperlin **39** <95H425>.

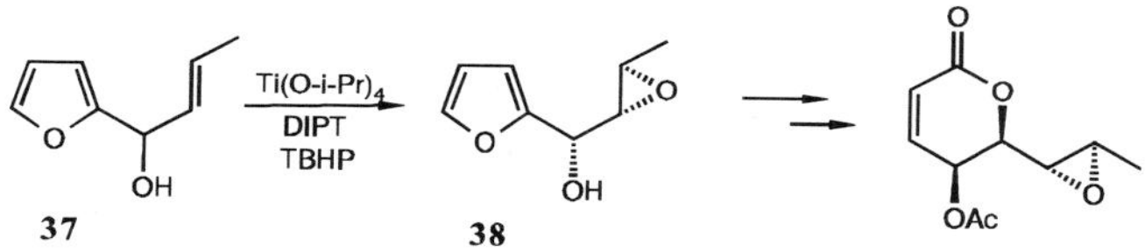

37   **38**   **39**

Condensation of amidines with 2-amino-3-cyanofurans gave in a one-step reaction 2-substituted-4-aminopyrrolo[2,3-d]pyrimidines <95JOC6684>. The first 6π 5-atom (and 6π 6-atom) heterocycle derivatives of methylidenecyclopropa[b]naphthalene were reported. The addition of furfural to the anion **40** produces **41** in 42% yield <95JCS(P1)2819>.

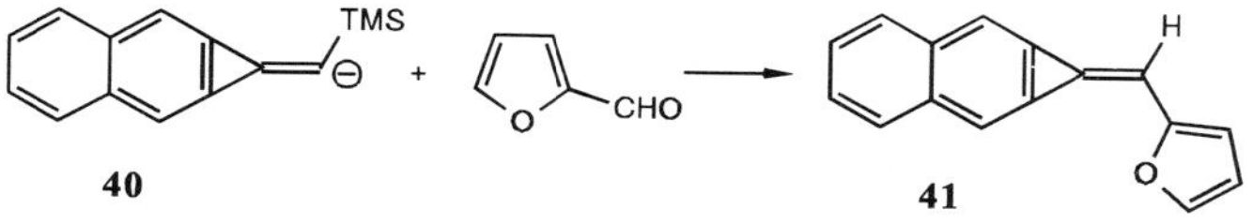

40   **41**

Cycloaddition reactions with furans remain a source of new compounds. On photochemical excitation of benzofuro-annulated oxanorbornadiene **42** in the presence of dipolarophiles 1:1-addition compounds are obtained. The formation of **43** constitutes one of the rare examples of the cycloaddition of a nitrile as a dipolarophile <95LA1503>.

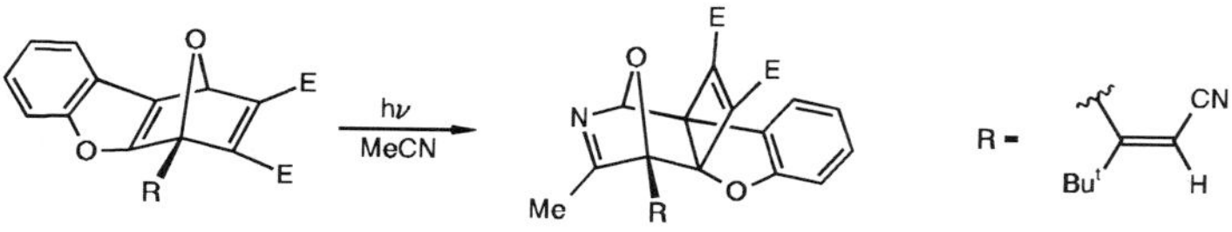

42   **43**

The oxa-2,3-dimethylenenorbornene derivatives **45** are available from **44**. Under the influence of Lewis acids they rearrange readily to give compounds of type **46** <95TL1865>.

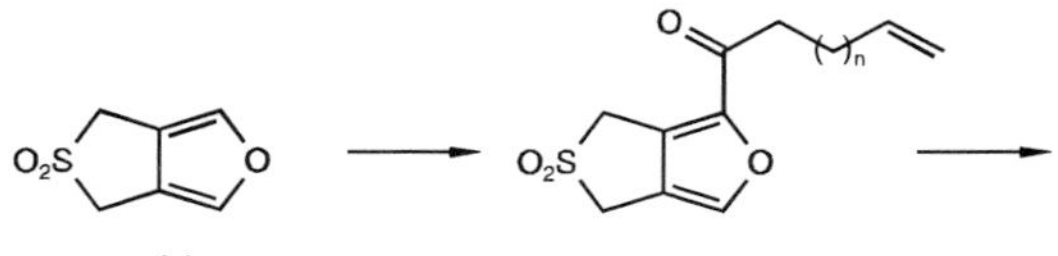

44

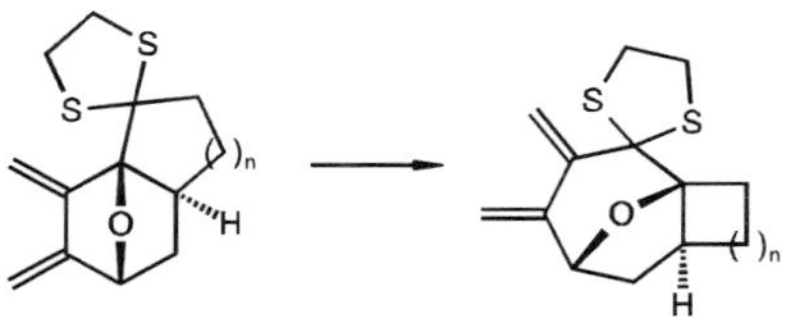

45   n = 1, 2   **46**

For further reactions of this type see <95CC2025>. The synthesis of 1,4-dihydrofurano[3,4-d]-3,2-oxathiine-2-oxides, precursors for nonclassical heteroaromatic *o*-quinodimethanes, and their application in the Diels-Alder reaction were reported <95CC2537>. The intramolecular Diels-Alder reaction with furans (e. g., **47**) offers a rapid access to highly functionalized isoquinolines <95JCS(P1)2393>.

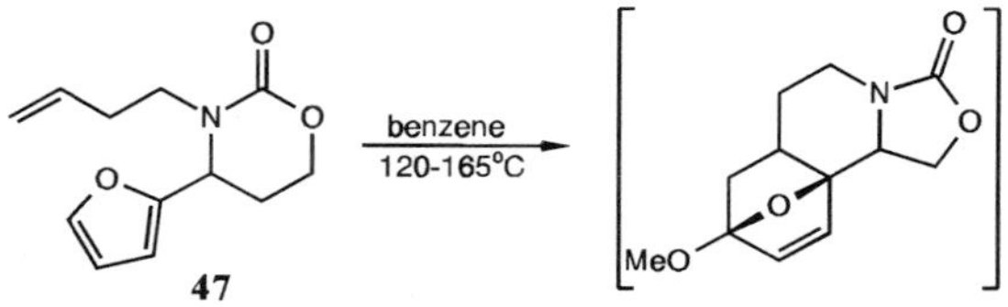

47   benzene
                120-165°C

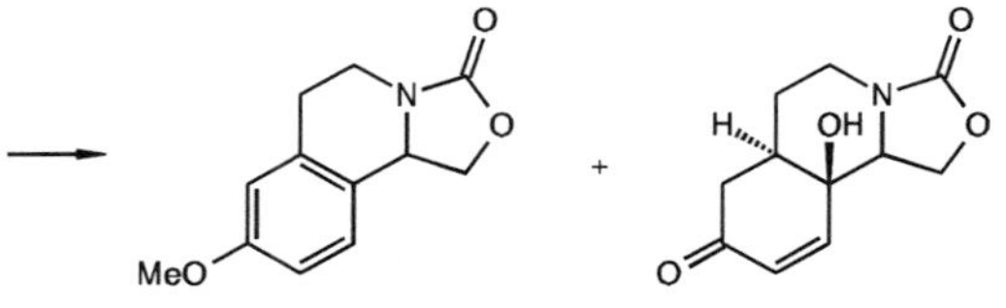

40%   50%

The total synthesis of gibberellins (+)-GA_1 and (+)-GA_3 was described by using intramolecular Diels-Alder reactions of furan-dienes <95SL105>. High pressure (>10kbar, 60-70°C) intramolecular Diels-Alder reactions of furans with unactivated methylenecyclopropane terminators are reported <95SL355>. The lithium dienolate of 2,5-dimethyl-3(2H)-furanone reacts with unsaturated compounds to give Diels-Alder adducts <95SL503>. For further Diels-Alder reactions of furans see <95JOC550, 95JOC6168, 95SL536, 95T193>, <95SL263> (total synthesis of angucycline using a regioselective benzyne-furan cycloaddition). Benzo[c]furan **48** (prepared from 1-methoxyphthalan with $NaNH_2$/THF), naphthofuran **49** and dihydropyrenofuran **50** were used as building blocks for the preparation of highly annulated dimethyldihydropyrenes (e. g., **51**, **52**; stereochemistry not known) <95JA1514>.

48 **49** **50**

51 **52**

Efficient inter- and intramolecular cycloadditions of furan with oxyallyl ([4+3]type) were reported <95JA1954, 95JOC5077, 95TL23, 95TL1397>. The photosensitized oxidation of furans (with $^1O_2$) has been used both for ring cleavage and ring transformation reactions <95SYN439, 95SYN303, 95SL1161, 95T4083>. Oxonanes can be readily prepared from phthalans (dihydrobenzo[c]furans) by a 3-step procedure involving Birch reduction, selective hydrogenation and oxidation <95JCS(P1)1137>. It is well known that 4-acyl substituted furan-2,3-dienes add heterocumulenes to give bicyclic products. Semiempirical calculations (AM1) have been performed on this reaction type <95JCS(P2)515>. The chemistry of 2,3-dimethylene-2,3-dihydrofuran has been studied extensively for many years. An influence of α-methyl groups on the rate of dimerisation and on the product ratio ([$\pi4+\pi4$]; [$\pi4+\pi2$]) has been reported <95JA841>.

5.3.3 SYNTHESIS

5.3.3.1 Furans, Dihydro- and Tetrahydrofurans

Substituted cycloprop-2-ene-1-carboxylates isomerize in refluxing benzene in the presence of dirhodium(II)tetrakis(perfluorobutyrate) (Rh$_2$(pbf)$_4$) to furans, dienoates, or cyclopentyliden-acetates. This reaction has been studied in detail <95HCA129>.

Substituted 2-(benzotriazol-1-ylmethyl)furans have been prepared in good yields from 1-propargylbenzotriazol and α-bromoketones via a one-pot process <95JOC638>. A novel synthesis of furans using the benzotriazol strategy was reported <95SYN1315>. Araldehydes react with stable 3-methyl-1-phenylbenzotriazolium ylide to give poly-substituted 4,5-dihydrofurans <95H765>. Depending on reaction conditions both butenolides and furans can be prepared by a tandem catalyzed reaction of terminal alkynes with γ-hydroxyalkynoates in the presence of Pd(OAc)$_2$/tris(2,6-dimethoxyphenyl)phosphine (TDMPP) in THF <95JA7255>.

The synthesis of 5-substituted 2-carbomethoxy-methylfurans can be achieved by base catalyzed cyclization of 4-pentynones <95TL4405>. It is well known that allenylketones **53** on treatment with Rh(I) or Ag(I) catalysts may yield furans **54**.

Depending on the catalyst ($Pd(OAc)_2$ and others) dimers of type **55** can also be formed in appreciable amounts <95AG1749, 95AG(E)1581>. $AgNO_3$ on silica gel is a very effective catalyst for the isomerization of allenones, alkynyl allylic alcohols, and allenylcarbinols to furans and dihydrofurans <95JOC5966>. Substituted furans **57** have been synthesized in the presence of ruthenium catalysts under neutral and mild conditions via cyclization of primary and secondary enynols of type **56** containing a terminal triple bond. The intramolecular addition of the hydroxy group to the triple bond of internal (Z)-enynols is also possible with Pd catalysts <95T13089>.

(Z)-R-C≡C-C(Me)=CH-CH(Y)OH

56

R = H, cat: (p-Cymene)RuCl₂(PPh₃)
R ≠ H, cat: Pd(OAc)₂ or Pd(PPh₃)₄

57

Y = H, Et, Ph, PhC≡C, TMS-C≡C, C≡N, allyl, 2-picolyl

Reaction of α-cyano-enamines and dibenzoylacetylene leads to dienes (via [2+2] cycloaddition followed by ring opening). α-Cyclization to oxygen produces cyano-imidoyl-substituted furans <95T13239>. A new strategy for the cyclization of enynes to tetrahydrofurans initiated by *in situ* generated electrophilic selenium species from PhSeSePh was reported <95T1483>. The synthesis of methylenetetrahydrofurans by an intramolecular carbocyclization of a β-bromo-propargyl ether was described <95SL923>. The reaction of 2,3-dichloropropene and carbonyl compounds with lithium and catalytic amounts of DTBB in THF leads, after hydrolysis, to the corresponding methylenic 1,4-diols in a Barbier-type process. The cyclization of diols under acidic conditions yields substituted methylenic tetrahydrofurans <95T3375>. Treatment of 1,3-dioxo compounds **58** with allyltrimethylsilane in the presence of $Mn(III)(OAc)_3$ and acetic acid gave silicon-containing dihydrofurans **59** in high yields <95JOC856>.

58

$\frac{Mn(OAc)_3}{AcOH, 80°C}$

59

6-Substituted 3-ethoxy-6-hydroxy-2,4-hexadienoates have been converted into 5-substituted 2-furylacetates by treating with 47% HBr in THF <95TL7685>. A facile synthesis of 2,4-disubstituted furans from β-hydroxy sulfones was reported <95TL923>. The total synthesis of spongia-13(16),14-diene **60** and spongiadiosphenol **61** was accomplished by stereoselective construction of the furanohydrophenanthrene ring system, which can be converted to spongiaterpenoids with a functionalized ring A <95T5771>.

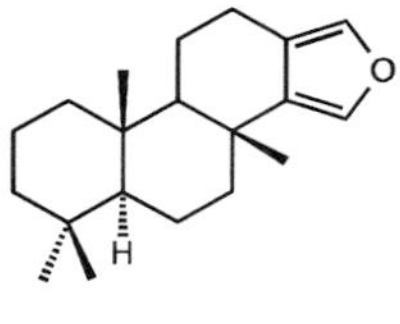

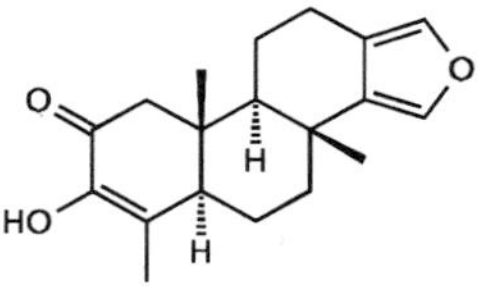

60   **61**

Furanoditerpenes have also been prepared by a biomimetic-like radical approach <95TL2925, 95TL2929>. A number of further furan syntheses using conventional techniques has been reported <95SL339, 95JOC4845, 95T7721>. The total synthesis of (±)-kallolide B was described <95JOC796>. An expeditious route to 3-formylfuran in 42% overall yield from *cis*-2-butene-1,4-diol has been developed <95SL175>. 4,7-Dihydro-4,7-methanoisobenzofuran **63** was prepared by the reduction of norbornadiene-monocarbaldehyde **62** with $NaBH_4$ and subsequent treatment with Amberlyst-15. In the reaction of **63** with N-phenylmaleimide a spontaneous oxidation of the Diels-Alder adduct **64** (not isolated) took place to give exclusively its epoxide **65** <95BCJ3269>.

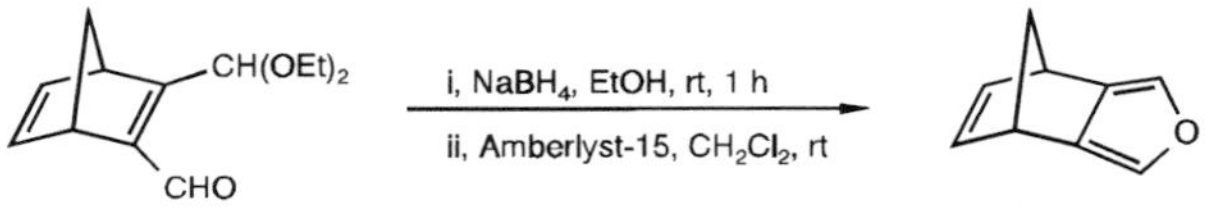

62   i, $NaBH_4$, EtOH, rt, 1 h   ii, Amberlyst-15, CH_2Cl_2, rt   **63**

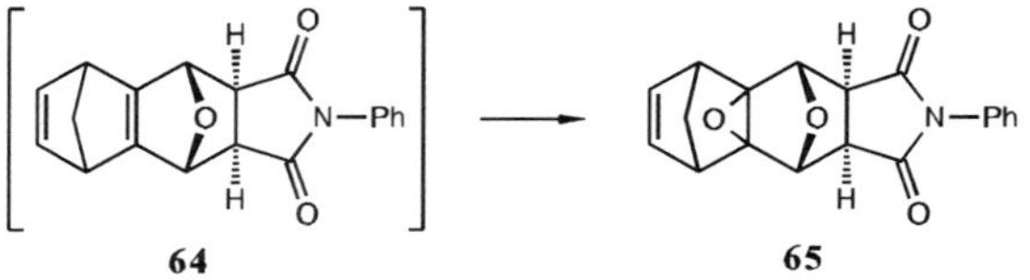

64   **65**

A bifuran-containing *p*-quaterphenoquinone **67** is accessible by oxidation of **66** with PbO_2. Contrary to expectations, the X-ray crystallographic analysis revealed that **67** exists in crystals in an O-*cis* conformation <95TL8055>.

Difullerenofuran" ($C_{120}O$) was prepared by reaction of C_{60} and $C_{60}O$. The compound has been characterized as a fullerene dimer, in which the 6,6-bonds in each cage form part of a furan-like brigde. A fullereno-dihydrofuran was also reported <95TL4971, 95TL5383>. Vögtle and coworkers reported the synthesis of amide-based furano-catenanes <95CC777>. The *bis*-Wittig reaction of **68** and **69** yields tetraoxa[26]annulene quinone **70**. This compound and its electrochemically prepared dianion seem to be the largest macrocyclic quinone/hydroquinone system known up to now <95TL4401>.

Again there are numerous reports on the synthesis of methylenefurans. The reaction of acetals with 2-(trimethylsilyloxymethyl)allyltrimethylsilane **71** under the influence of tin(II)halide and acetyl halide afforded 2-substituted 4-methylenetetrahydrofurans in good yields.

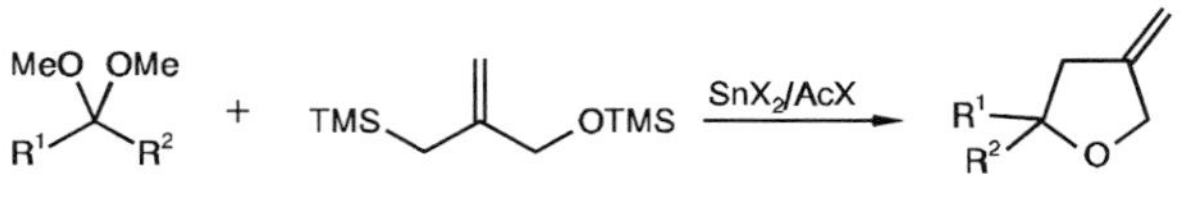

71

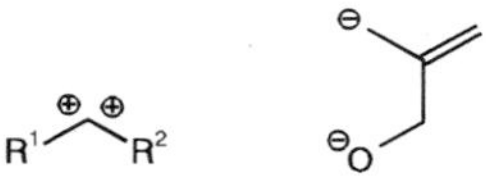

72   **73**

In this reaction, acetals are used as dication equivalent of one-carbon unit **72**, whereas **71** provides a dianion **73** <95TL5581>. A new stereocontrolled synthesis of substituted tetrahydrofurans starts with dioxalones **74**. A titanium-mediated methylenation using dimethyltitanocene (THF, 60°C) with subsequent treatment of **75** with trialkylaluminium reagents results in the formation of tetrahydrofurans **76** <95JA6394>.

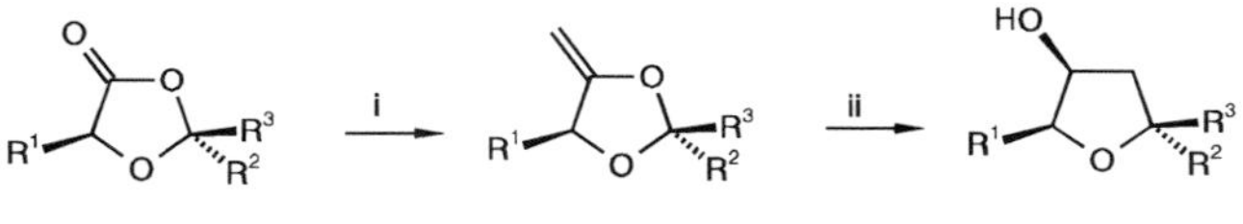

74   **75**   **76**

i, dimethyltitanocene; ii, ^{i}Bu$_3$Al, toluene.

Further work: <95JA9608 (stereocontrolled synthesis of (-)-arenaciolide), 95CC897 (allenylidene tetrahydrofuran), 95CC1893, 95LA689, 95SL1, 95SL705, 95TL241>. 4-Hydroxy-2-cyclo-butenones, which are readily available from diethylsquarate, react with Pb(OAc)$_4$ to give 5-acetoxy-2(5H)-furanones **77** and 5-alkylidene-2(5H)-furanones **78**. These reactions extend the synthetic utility of squaric acid considerably <95JA9653>.

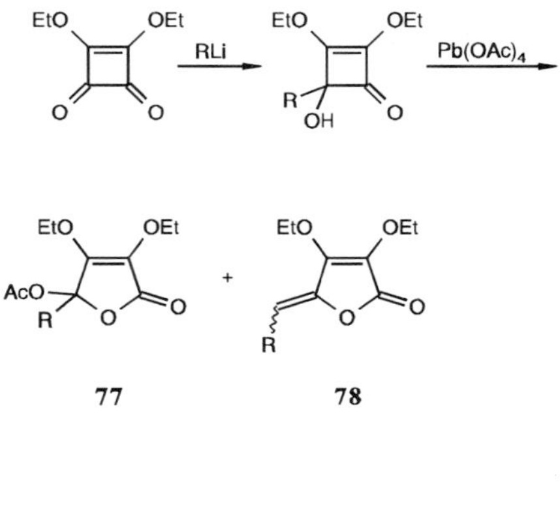

77   **78**

Reaction of cyclopropylacylsilanes with triflic acid results in the selective formation of dihydrofurans <95TL1667>. The synthesis of (-)-methylenolactocin <95TL231> and (R)-(-)-mevalonolactone <95CC321> was reported. Further syntheses of dihydrofurans and related compounds: <95JA1888 (butenolides), 95JCS(P1)187, 95JOC2668, 95MI1 (butanolides), 95SL742, 95T8507, 95TL4241>.

Tetrahydrofurans form a constituent part of a great number of biologically active products. In line with expectations there is a vast amount of synthetic work in this field, which will be presented only briefly. Stereoselective synthesis of tetrahydrofurans: <95CC295 (tetrahydrofuranyl ketones), 95JA8041, 95JOC3572, 95JOC5750, 95JOC6706, 95LA501, 95SL1191, 95SYN1171, 95T959 (a chiral furopiperidine), 95TL463, 95TL649, 95TL1127, 95TL1263, 95TL2587, 95TL2987, 95TL3805 (aryltetrahydrofuranylvinyl ketones), 95TL7531, 95T9995>; stereoselective synthesis of *cis*-2,5-disubstituted tetrahydrofuranones via an acyl radical cyclization: <95TL31>; (±)-dihydrosesamin: <95JCS(P1)927>; Ionomycin A (a polyether antibiotic): <95JA3448>; (+)-asimicin, (+)-bullatacin: <95JOC4419, 95TL1981, 95TL9257>; (±)-Ambrox®: <95T8333>; fluoroprostacyclines: <95T8771>; (-)-syringolides 1 and 2: <95T8809, 95TL3201>; (+)-nemorensic acid: <95CC1645> (the previously assigned stereochemistry of nemorensine must be revised); nonactin: <95TL3361>; dactyloxenes B, C: <95JOC191>; corossolone, corossoline: <95JOC1170>; cyclogoniodenins: <95H1743>; astribin, asiminenin A, B: <95H1731>; oligotetrahydrofurans: <95LA1415> (for reviews in this field see <95SYN115, 95SYN1447>); furosteroids (ring D): <95JCS(P1)569>; synthesis and structure of dioxapropellabiphenyl: <95LA1123>; synthesis of an epoxyeudesmanolide by an acid catalyzed cyclization of gallicin: <95LA1837>; fused 3a,4-dihydro-5a,H-benzofuro[3,3a-d]isoxazoles: <95H1051>; furofuran derivatives: <95JOC8179> (total synthesis of (+)-eremantholide A); (±)-fargesin: <95TL7271>; (+)-sasamin, (-)-asarinin: <95CL543>; (±)-samin: <95T8389>; furofuran bislactone: <95TL8225>; bis(tetrahydrofuran) subunit of asteltoxin: <95TL3095>; dioxatriquinanes: <95T7389>; (+)-goniotriol, (+)-goniofurfurone: <95T1429>; gracilins B, C: <95JA9616>. Furofurans have also been obtained by dipolar cycloaddition of diazocarbonyl compounds with vinyl ethers <95CC673> (see also <95HCA947>).

Thionolactons can be reduced with triphenyltin hydride/AIBN to give tetrahydrofurans in high yield <95CC1583>. Nafion-H is a catalyst for cyclodehydration of 1,4-diols to the corresponding tetrahydrofurans <95T3319>. Electrophilic cyclization of polymer-bound isoxazolines with iodine monochloride yields tetrahydrofurans and regenerates the initial polymer-bound functionality <95JOC4196, 95JOC4204>.

5.3.3.2 Benzo- and Dihydrobenzofurans

3-Benzyloxybenzaldehydes, -acetophenones and -benzophenones substituted in the benzyl part with electron-withdrawing groups cyclize easily to 2-arylbenzofurans by using a standardized KF- or CsF-Al$_2$O$_3$ base system <95SYN1135>. Under base conditions, the hydroxyl group of arylalkynes underwent smooth cyclization to the acetylenic group yielding benzofurans. Under the conditions of work-up rearrangement to benzopyrans may occur <95TL4717>. The synthesis of benzo[b]furans by Pd-catalyzed heteroannulation of internal alkynes was reported <95JOC3270>.

Tandem cyclization occurs in the vacuum pyrolysis of 2-methoxyphenyl and 2-methoxythiophenyl substituted phosphorous ylides. Benzothieno[3,2-b]benzofuran has been prepared for the first time <95SL53>. The well known Pd-catalyzed benzofuran synthesis has found application for the preparation of tricyclic systems of type **79** (benzofuran analogue of ILV) <95JA6666>.

Styryl-type geminal dihalides (e.g., **80**) containing a nucleophilic substituent in the *ortho*-position of the aromatic ring are used in the formation of carbenoids, which can undergo an intramolecular nucleophilic addition to give benzo[b]furans (e.g., **81**) <95JOC5588>.

Ailanthioidol, a 2-arylated benzofuran isolated from the tree *Zanthoxylum ailanthoides*, was prepared by base-catalyzed ring closure of an *o*-hydroxyarylalkyne <95SL1151>. Cu(II)-mediated photocyclization of methoxynaphthyl analogues of chalcone to naphthofurans via an electron-transfer process was reported <95CC957>. Cycloaddition of a furan analogue of *o*-quinodimethane with quinones and their bromo derivatives offers an access to benzofuranquinones <95T9595>. Compound **82** can be prepared by photoaddition of 2-hydroxy-1,4-naphthoquinone with β-naphthol <95T1377>.

82

The previously reported one-electron oxidations of mesityl-substituted enol acetates have been investigated in detail <95JOC2726>. A general and facile synthesis of heterocyclo[b]-fused carbazoles was reported by Katritzky and coworkers <95JOC3707>. The synthesis of dibenzofurans from diazotized *o*-(aryloxy)anilines has been improved by using Fe_2SO_4, hydroquinone, NaI etc. as electron donors, which promote a free-radical mechanism and shorten the reaction time from hours to minutes <95JOC4991>. A photochemical aromatic annulation strategy provides an efficient synthetic route to the linear furocoumarin bergapten <95SL573>. The photocyclization of 2,5-dibenzoylresorcinol dibenzyl ether yields substituted 2,3,5,6-tetraarylbenzo[1,2-b:5,4-b']difurans <95JOC1303>. An efficient synthesis of angular furocoumarins (angelicin, oroselenon, oroselol) has been carried out starting from dihydrobenzofuran derivatives. The key intermediates were prepared from diazocyclohexane-1,3-dione <95T3087>. Two norneolignans, egonol and (±)-machicendiol were synthesized by using a Pd-catalyzed cross-coupling reaction as a key step <95H1077>. An intramolecular Stetter reaction of methyl 3-(2-formylphenoxy)-prop-2-enoate and methyl 4-(2-formylphenoxy)-but-2-enoate catalyzed by a 1,3-thiazolium chloride gave methyl esters of 2,3-dihydro-3-oxobenzofuran-2-acetic acid and 3,4-dihydro-4-oxo-2H-1-benzopyran-3-acetic acid <95SYN1311>. [1]Benzofuro[6,7-d] or [5,4-d]isoxazoles were prepared by the thermal decomposition of diazo compounds through a tandem Wolff rearrangement-benzannulation sequence <95H175>. A convenient synthesis of benzofuran-3-acetic acids from phenols involving alkali-mediated rearrangement of 4-halomethylcoumarins via α,β-unsaturated acids was reported <95H647>. The intramolecular Meerwein reaction of 2-allyloxydiazonium salts in the presence of tetrathiafulvalene (TTF) yields dihydrobenzofurans <95JCS(P1)623>. The oxidative coupling of methyl ferulate in the presence of Ag_2O yields benzofurans. This methodology was used for the preparation of 3',4-O-methylcedrusin <95JCS(P1)1775>. A new approach to the synthesis of (±)-neorautenane was described using the chemoselective coupling of a benzodihydropyran and *o*-chloromercuriophenols as key step <95JCS(P1)949>. The Lewis-acid promoted reactions of 1,4-benzoquinone monoimides with various 2H-chromenes produced pterocarpans <95TL2713, 95TL7003>. Lewis-acid promoted reactions of substituted (E)-4-methoxystilbenes **83** with 2-methoxy-4-benzo-quinones **84** yield *trans*-2-(4'-methoxyphenyl)-3-aryl-2,3-dihydrobenzofuran-5-ols **85** stereo-selectively <95JOC3700>.

Thermal rearrangement of ethers generated in situ from hydroquinones and conjugated polyols affords 2,3-dihydrobenzofurans <95T9367>. A facile route to 3a,8a-dihydro[2,3-b]benzofurans **87** was explored. These compounds can be prepared conveniently from the corresponding 2-iodo-phenols **86** and 2,5-diacetoxy-2,5-dihydrofurans employing both Pd- and Sm-mediated reactions <95T8555>.

A novel oxidative cyclization of 2'-hydroxychalcones to 4,5-dialkoxyaurones by $Tl(III)(NO_3)_3$ was reported <95JOC6499>. Substituted dihydrobenzofurans have been prepared from α-methylene-γ-butyrolactone and 1,1-bis-(methylthio)-2-propanone (or butanone) via an 1,3-Michael-Claisen reaction <95T9559>. The alkylation of dihydroxynaphthalenes with 1,2-dihydronaphtho[2,1-b]furan-1,2-diol gave various benzofurofurans <95JOC5407>. 2-(β-Methylallyl)phenol and 2-isobutenylphenol were easily cyclized to 2,2-dimethyl-2,3-dihydrobenzofurans in the presence of a catalytic amount of iodine <95H219>. The reaction of tropones with the anions derived from methylmethoxycarbene complexes of chromium and tungsten gave pentacarbonyl(1-oxaazulene-2-ylidene)chromium and -tungsten complexes <95TL3699>. Thionolactones **88** can be transformed in a one-pot reaction to thioisobenzofurans **89** (trapped as Diels-Alder adducts). The starting

material is quite easily available from the corresponding lactone with Lawesson's reagent <95JCS(P1)589>. Thioisobenzofurans (generated in situ) have also been used as intermediates for the synthesis of arylnaphthalene lignans <95JOC3938, 95TL3495, 95TL9285>. Both isobenzofuran as well as 1,3-diphenylisobenzofuran (and related derivatives) have been employed in a number of cases as efficient trapping reagents for unsaturated compounds and for synthetic purposes <95JCS(P1)2819, 95LA1765, 95SYN236, 95T10979, 95TL939, 95TL4181, 95TL5195, 95TL5199, 95TL6141>. A novel synthesis of annulated hydroquinolines was reported using a benzo[c]furan **90** as an intermediate <95TL8581>.

90

The reaction of 1,3-diphenylisobenzofuran with cyclopropanone was studied in detail <95JOC4395>.

5.3.4 MISCELLANEOUS

A number of five-membered heterocycles including furan was investigated by theoretical methods (optimized geometries using MP2(fc)/6-31G*; IGLO calculations to obtain exaltations of the diamagnetic susceptibilities etc.). Using this techniques it was shown that in line with expectations in the series pyrrole-thiophene-furan the latter compound is least aromatic <95AG332, 95AG(E)337>. The cycloaddition of monofluoroallene with furan was studied computationally using *ab initio* methods with inclusion of electron correlation (MP3/6-31G*//3-21G) <95JA4967>. The Diels-Alder reaction of furan with cyclopropenone was examined at the MP4SDQ/6-31G*//MP2/6-31G* level. Optimized structures (reactants, transition states, products) indicate a stabilizing interaction between the ether oxygen and the carbonyl carbon and make the *exo* product thermodynamically and kinetically favoured <95JOC4395>. At 80°C 1a-acetyl-1-phthalimido-1a,6b-dihydrobenzofuro[2,3-b]aziridine **91** transfers phthalimidonitrene **92** to a series of traps (acetone, 2-methoxynaphthalene, indene etc.). Compound **91** can be obtained quite easily by oxidation of N-aminophthalimide with Pb(OAc)$_4$ in the presence of benzo[b]furan <95JCS(P1)809>.

91   **92**

Optically active dihydrobenzofurans (and dihydrofuropyridines) were shown to be good chiral dopants for ferroelectric liquid crystals <95CL537>. The stereochemistry of trilobacin and trilobin was determined by the Mosher (MTBA) method. Trilobin is selectively cytotoxic with over a billion times the potencies of adriamycin <95T7149>. The structure of glabrescol was shown to be a squalene-derived penta-tetrahydrofuranyl diol <95TL9137>. The absolute configuration of annonin has been determined by analysis of the CD spectrum <95T1921>. The biosynthesis of the fungal metabolite oudenone was investigated in cultures of *Oudemansiella radicata* <95JOC6922>. A comment on the radical reactions of 4-pentenyl tosylate was given <95TL1307>.

5.3.5. REFERENCES

95AG(E)337   P. v. R. Schleyer, P. K. Freeman, H. Jiao, B. Goldfuß, *Angew. Chem., Int. Ed. Engl.* **1995**, *34*, 337.
95AG(E)350   F. E. McDonald, M. M. Gleason, *Angew. Chem., Int. Ed. Engl.* **1995**, *34*, 350.
95AG(E)1581   A. S. K. Hashmi, *Angew. Chem., Int. Ed. Engl.* **1995**, *34*, 1581.
95AG332   P. v. R. Schleyer, P. K. Freeman, H. Jiao, B. Goldfuß, *Angew. Chem.* **1995**, *107*, 332.
95AG356   F. E. McDonald, M. M. Gleason, *Angew. Chem.* **1995**, *107*, 356.
95AG1749   A. S. K. Hashmi, *Angew. Chem.* **1995**, *107*, 1749.
95BCJ3269   T. Kobayashi, H. Suda, H. Takase, R. Iriye, H. Kato, *Bull. Chem. Soc. Jpn.* **1995**, *68*, 3269.
95CC295   T. Ishiyama, M. Murata, A. Suzuki, N. Miyaura, *J. Chem. Soc., Chem. Commun.* **1995**, 295.
95CC321   E. Lee, I. Choi, S. Y. Song, *J. Chem. Soc., Chem. Commun.* **1995**, 321.
95CC383   G. R. Pettit, Y. Ichihara, G. Wurzel, M. D. Williams, J. M. Schmidt, J.-C. Chapuis, *J. Chem. Soc., Chem. Commun.* **1995**, 383.
95CC673   M. C. Pirrung, Y. R. Lee, *J. Chem. Soc., Chem. Commun.* **1995**, 673.
95CC777   S. Ottens-Hildebrandt, M. Nieger, K. Rissanen, J. Rouvinen, S. Meier, G. Harder, F. Vögtle, *J. Chem. Soc., Chem. Commun.* **1995**, 777.
95CC897   J.-P. Dulcère, E. Dumez, R. Faure, *J. Chem. Soc., Chem. Commun.* **1995**, 897.
95CC917   K. Khumtaveeporn, H. Alper, *J. Chem. Soc., Chem. Commun.* **1995**, 917.
95CC957   S. Kar, S. Lahiri, *J. Chem. Soc., Chem. Commun.* **1995**, 957.
95CC1017   S. H. Kang, S. B. Lee, *J. Chem. Soc., Chem. Commun.* **1995**, 1017.
95CC1213   H. Ogawa, Y. Ohokubo, Y. Nogami, Y. Kato, T. Koga, T. Imoto, *J. Chem. Soc., Chem. Commun.* **1995**, 1213.
95CC1583   K. C. Nicolaou, M. Sato, E. A. Theodorakis, N. D. Miller, *J. Chem. Soc., Chem. Commun.* **1995**, 1583.
95CC1645   M. P. Dillon, N. C. Lee, F. Stappenbeck, J. D. White, *J. Chem. Soc., Chem. Commun.* **1995**, 1645.
95CC1893   J. F. Nguefack, V. Bolitt, D. Sinou, *J. Chem. Soc., Chem. Commun.* **1995**, 1893.
95CC2025   S. Maki, K. Konno, H. Takayama, *J. Chem. Soc., Chem. Commun.* **1995**, 2025.
95CC2159   T. Hu, J. M. Curtis, Y. Oshima, M. A. Quilliam, J. A. Walter, W. M. Wright, J. L. C. Wright, *J. Chem. Soc., Chem. Commun.* **1995**, 2159.
95CC2537   W.-S. Chung, W.-J. Lin, W.-D. Liu, L.-G. Chen, *J. Chem. Soc., Chem. Commun.* **1995**, 2537.
95CL537   T. Kusumoto, K. Sato, T. Hiyama, S. Takehara, K. Ito, *Chem. Lett.* **1995**, 537.
95CL543   K. Samizu, K. Ogasawara, *Chem. Lett.* **1995**, 543.
95H175   Y. P. Chen, B. Chantegrel, C. Deshayes, *Heterocycles* **1995**, *41*, 175.
95H187   Y. Takemura, Y. Matsushita, S. Onishi, T. Atarashi, J. Kunitomo, M. Ju-ichi, M. Omura, C. Ito, H. Furukawa, *Heterocycles* **1995**, *41*, 187.
95H219   K. Mahn Kim, E. K. Ryu, *Heterocycles* **1995**, *41*, 219.
95H279   M. Iinuma, H. Tosa, T. Tanaka, F. Asai, R. Shimano, *Heterocycles* **1995**, *40*, 279.
95H425   T. Honda, N. Sano, K. Kanai, *Heterocycles* **1995**, *41*, 425.
95H647   Y. Fall, L. Santana, M. Teijeira, E. Uriarte, *Heterocycles* **1995**, *41*, 647.
95H765   A. R. Katritzky, B. Yang, J. Jiang, P. J. Steel, *Heterocycles* **1995**, *41*, 765.
95H1035   Y. Hano, Y. Yamanaku, T. Nomura, Y. Momose, *Heterocycles* **1995**, *41*, 1035.
95H1051   K. Harada, E. Kaji, K. Sasaki, S. Zen, *Heterocycles* **1995**, *41*, 1051.
95H1077   Y. Aoyagi, T. Mizusaki, A. Hatori, T. Asakura, T. Aihara, S. Inaba, K. Hayatsu, A. Ohata, *Heterocycles* **1995**, *41*, 1077.
95H1731   M.-H. Woo, L. Zeng, J. L. McLaughlin, *Heterocycles* **1995**, *41*, 1731.
95H1743   Y. Zhang, L. Zeng, M.-H. Woo, Z.-M. Gu, Q. Ye, F.-E. Wu, J. L. McLaughlin, *Heterocycles* **1995**, *41*, 1743.
95HCA129   P. Müller, C. Gränicher, *Helv. Chim. Acta* **1995**, *78*, 129.
95HCA758   G. M. König, A. D. Wright, G. Bernardinelli, *Helv. Chim. Acta* **1995**, *78*, 758.
95HCA947   P. Müller, D. Fernandez, *Helv. Chim. Acta* **1995**, *78*, 947.

95HCA1437   P. Ubelhart, P. Mohler, R.-A. Fallahpour, H.-J. Hansen, *Helv. Chim. Acta* **1995**, *78*, 1437.
95JA841   M. Leung, W. S. Trahanovsky, *J. Am. Chem. Soc.* **1995**, *117*, 841.
95JA1514   R. H. Mitchell, V. S. Iyer, N. Khalifa, R. Mahadevan, S. Vanugopalan, S. A. Weerawarna, P. Zhou, *J. Am. Chem. Soc.* **1995**, *117*, 1514.
95JA1888   B. M. Trost, T. J. J. Müller, J. Martinez, *J. Am. Chem. Soc.* **1995**, *117*, 1888.
95JA1954   M. Lautens, S. Kumanovic, *J. Am. Chem. Soc.* **1995**, *117*, 1954.
95JA3448   D. A. Evans, A. M. Ratz, B. E. Huff, G. S. Sheppard, *J. Am. Chem. Soc.* **1995**, *117*, 3448.
95JA4967   A. Rastelli, H. Bagatti, R. Gandolfi, *J. Am. Chem. Soc.* **1995**, *117*, 4967.
95JA6394   N. A. Petasis, S.-P. Lu, *J. Am. Chem. Soc.* **1995**, *117*, 6394.
95JA6666   A. P. Kozikowski, D. Ma, L. Du, N. E. Lewin, P. M. Blumberg, *J. Am. Chem. Soc.* **1995**, *117*, 6666.
95JA7255   B. M. Trost, M. C. McIntosh, *J. Am. Chem. Soc.* **1995**, *117*, 7255.
95JA8041   S. R. Angle, G. P. Wei, Y. K. Ko, K. Kubo, *J. Am. Chem. Soc.* **1995**, *117*, 8041.
95JA9608   M. Suginome, Y. Yamamoto, K. Fujii, Y. Ito, *J. Am. Chem. Soc.* **1995**, *117*, 9608.
95JA9616   E. J. Corey, M. A. Letavic, *J. Am. Chem. Soc.* **1995**, *117*, 9616.
95JA9653   Y. Yamamoto, H. Ohno, S. Eguchi, *J. Am. Chem. Soc.* **1995**, *117*, 9653.
95JA10755   A. B. Smith, III, J. P. Sestelo, P. G. Dormer, *J. Am. Chem. Soc.* **1995**, *117*, 10755.
95JA10757   T. Saito, M. Morimoto, C. Akiyama, T. Matsumoto, K. Suzuki, *J. Am. Chem. Soc.* **1995**, *117*, 10757.
95JCS(P1)177   S. C. Gupta, A. Saini, D. Kumar, N. S. Yadav, K. Chand, S. Mor, S. N. Dehawar, *J. Chem. Soc., Perkin Trans. 1* **1995**, 177
95JCS(P1)187   V. Nair, J. Mathew, *J. Chem. Soc., Perkin Trans. 1* **1995**, 187.
95JCS(P1)569   M. B. Martín, A. F. Mateos, R. R. González, *J. Chem. Soc., Perkin Trans. 1* **1995**, 569.
95JCS(P1)589   J. H. Bailey, C. V. Coulter, A. J. Pratt, W. T. Robinson, *J. Chem. Soc., Perkin Trans. 1* **1995**, 589.
95JCS(P1)623   R. J. Fletcher, C. Lampard, J. A. Murphy, N. Lewis, *J. Chem. Soc., Perkin Trans. 1* **1995**, 623.
95JCS(P1)809   D. W. Jones, M. Thornton-Pett, *J. Chem. Soc., Perkin Trans. 1* **1995**, 809.
95JCS(P1)927   G. Maiti, S. Adhikari, S. C. Roy, *J. Chem. Soc., Perkin Trans. 1* **1995**, 927.
95JCS(P1)949   R. A. Lichtenfels, A. L. Coelho, P. R. R. Costa, *J. Chem. Soc., Perkin Trans. 1* **1995**, 949.
95JCS(P1)1085   P. J. Perry, V. H. Pavlidis, J. A. Hadfield, I. G. C. Coutts, *J. Chem. Soc., Perkin Trans. 1* **1995**, 1085.
95JCS(P1)1137   D. S. Brown, M. C. Elliott, C. J. Moody, T. J. Mowlem, *J. Chem. Soc., Perkin Trans. 1* **1995**, 1137.
95JCS(P1)1309   Y. Q. Tu, K. A. Byriel, C. H. L. Kennard, W. Kitching, *J. Chem. Soc., Perkin Trans. 1* **1995**, 1309.
95JCS(P1)1775   G. Lemière, M. Gao, A. de Groot, R. Dommisse, J. Lepoivre, L. Pieters, V. Buss, *J. Chem. Soc., Perkin Trans. 1* **1995**, 1775.
95JCS(P1)2393   T. Hudlicky, G. Butora, S. P. Fearnley, A. G. Gum, P. J. Persichini III, M. R. Stabile, J. S. Merola, *J. Chem. Soc., Perkin Trans. 1* **1995**, 2393.
95JCS(P1)2819   B. Halton, H. J. Cooney, T. W. Davey, G. S. Forman, Q. Lu, R. Boese, D. Bläser, A. H. Maulitz, *J. Chem. Soc., Perkin Trans. 1* **1995**, 2819.
95JCS(P1)2855   M. A. Brimble, S. J. Phythian, H. Prabaharan, *J. Chem. Soc., Perkin Trans. 1* **1995**, 2855.
95JCS(P1)2931   K. Oda, H. Tsujita, K. Ohno, M. Machida, *J. Chem. Soc., Perkin Trans. 1* **1995**, 2931.
95JCS(P2)515   W. M. F. Fabian, G. Kollenz, *J. Chem. Soc., Perkin Trans. 2* **1995**, 515.
95JOC8   M. J. Aurell, C. Einhorn, J. Einhorn, J. L. Luche, *J. Org. Chem.* **1995**, *60*, 8.
95JOC191   M. D. Lord, J. T. Negri, L. A. Paquette, *J. Org. Chem.* **1995**, *60*, 191.
95JOC550   M. Tada, N. Mutoh, T. Shimizu, *J. Org. Chem.* **1995**, *60*, 550.
95JOC638   A. R. Katritzky, J. Li., *J. Org. Chem.* **1995**, *60*, 638.
95JOC745   S. Bhar, B. C. Ranu, *J. Org. Chem.* **1995**, *60*, 745.
95JOC796   J. A. Marshall, E. M. Wallace, *J. Org. Chem.* **1995**, *60*, 796.
95JOC856   J. R. Hwu, C. N. Chen, S.-S. Shiao, *J. Org. Chem.* **1995**, *60*, 856.
95JOC1170   Z.-J. Yao, Y. L. Wu, *J. Org. Chem.* **1995**, *60*, 1170.
95JOC1303   M. Abdul-Aziz, *J. Org. Chem.* **1995**, *60*, 1303.
95JOC2668   T. Wang, J. Chen, K. Zhao, *J. Org. Chem.* **1995**, *60*, 2668.

95JOC2726   M. Schmittel, J. Heinze, H. Trenkle, *J. Org. Chem.* **1995**, *60*, 2726.
95JOC3035   M. P. Doyle, A. B. Dyatkin, *J. Org. Chem.* **1995**, *60*, 3035.
95JOC3270   R. C. Larock, E. K. Yan, M. J. Doty, K. K. C. Sham, *J. Org. Chem.* **1995**, *60*, 3270.
95JOC3572   B. H. Lipshutz, T. Gross, *J. Org. Chem.* **1995**, *60*, 3572.
95JOC3700   T. A. Engler, G. A. Gfesser, B. W. Draney, *J. Org. Chem.* **1995**, *60*, 3700.
95JOC3707   A. R. Katritzky, L. Xie, *J. Org. Chem.* **1995**, *60*, 3707.
95JOC3938   J. E. Cochran, A. Padwa, *J. Org. Chem.* **1995**, *60*, 3938.
95JOC3975   R. Sparrapan, C. Kascheres, M. T. P. Gambardella, *J. Org. Chem.* **1995**, *60*, 3975.
95JOC4196   X. Beebe, N. E. Schore, M. J. Kurth, *J. Org. Chem.* **1995**, *60*, 4196.
95JOC4204   X. Beebe, C. L. Chiappari, M. M. Olmstead, M. J. Kurth, N. E. Schore, *J. Org. Chem.* **1995**, *60*, 4204.
95JOC4395   S. M. Bachrach, *J. Org. Chem.* **1995**, *60*, 4395.
95JOC4419   H. Naito, E. Kawahara, K. Maruta, M. Maeda, S. Sasaki, *J. Org. Chem.* **1995**, *60*, 4419.
95JOC4845   G. A. Molander, J. S. Carey, *J. Org. Chem.* **1995**, *60*, 4845.
95JOC4991   F. W. Wassmundt, R. P. Pedemonte, *J. Org. Chem.* **1995**, *60*, 4991.
95JOC5077   M. Harmata, C. B. Gamlett, C. L. Barnes, D. E. Jones, *J. Org. Chem.* **1995**, *60*, 5077.
95JOC5407   X. Fan, T. Yanai, H. Okazaki, M. Yamaye, H. Mizobe, Y. Kosugi, T. Kito, *J. Org. Chem.* **1995**, *60*, 5407.
95JOC5588   M. Topolski, *J. Org. Chem.* **1995**, *60*, 5588.
95JOC5750   F. E. McDonald, T. B. Towne, *J. Org. Chem.* **1995**, *60*, 5750.
95JOC5966   J. A. Marshall, C. A. Sehon, *J. Org. Chem.* **1995**, *60*, 5966.
95JOC6168   H. J. Wu, F. H. Ying, W. D. Shao, *J. Org. Chem.* **1995**, *60*, 6168.
95JOC6499   K. Thakkar, M. Cushman, *J. Org. Chem.* **1995**, *60*, 6499.
95JOC6563   T. Umemoto, G. Tomizawa, *J. Org. Chem.* **1995**, *60*, 6563.
95JOC6684   E. C. Taylor, H. H. Patel, J. G. Jun, *J. Org. Chem.* **1995**, *60*, 6684.
95JOC6706   J. Hartung, F. Gallou, *J. Org. Chem.* **1995**, *60*, 6706.
95JOC6922   Y. S. Tsantrizos, F. Zhou, P. Famili, X. Yang, *J. Org. Chem.* **1995**, *60*, 6922.
95JOC7027   C. W. Lee, J. E. Hong, D. J. Oh, *J. Org. Chem.* **1995**, *60*, 7027.
95JOC7082   J. T. Kuethe, J. E. Cochran, A. Padwa, *J. Org. Chem.* **1995**, *60*, 7082.
95JOC7267   T. Satoh, T. Itaya, K. Okuro, M. Miura, M. Nomura, *J. Org. Chem.* **1995**, *60*, 7267.
95JOC8179   K. Takao, H. Ochiai, K. Yoshida, T. Hashizuka, H. Koschimura, K. Tadano, S. Ogawa, *J. Org. Chem.* **1995**, *60*, 8179.
95LA437   M. Yonemitsu, N. Fukuda, T. Kimura, R. Isobe, T. Komori, *Liebigs Ann. Chem.* **1995**, 437.
95LA501   G. Adiwidjaja, H. Flörke, A. Kirschning, E. Schaumann, *Liebigs Ann. Chem.* **1995**, 501.
95LA689   T. H. Al-Tel, M. Meisenbach, W. Voelter, *Liebigs Ann. Chem.* **1995**, 689.
95LA1039   P. Weyerstahl, C. Christiansen, H. Marschall, *Liebigs Ann. Chem.* **1995**, 1039.
95LA1123   J. Grochowski, J. Jamrozik, P. Serda, W. Zesławski, *Liebigs Ann. Chem.* **1995**, 1123.
95LA1415   U. Koert, M. Stein, H. Wagner, *Liebigs Ann. Chem.* **1995**, 1415.
95LA1503   J. Bussenius, M. Keller, W. Eberbach, *Liebigs Ann. Chem.* **1995**, 1503.
95LA1765   K. Rosendorfer, O. Jarosch, K. Polborn, G. Steinies, *Liebigs Ann. Chem.* **1995**, 1765.
95LA1837   J. A. Marco, J. F. Sanz-Cervera, V. García-Lliso, L. R. Domingo, M. Carda, S. Rodríguez, F. López-Ortiz, J. Lex, *Liebigs Ann. Chem.* **1995**, 1837.
95LA1849   P. Weyerstahl, A. Schenk, H. Marschall, *Liebigs Ann. Chem.* **1995**, 1849.
95MI1   V. S. Arutyunyan, T. V. Kochikyan, N. S. Egiazaryan, A. A. Avetisyan, *Russian Journal of Organic Chemistry* **1995**, *31*, 90.
95SL1   J. L. van der Baan, T. A. J. van der Heide, J. van der Louw, G. W. Klumpp, *Synlett* **1995**, 1.
95SL53   R. H. Aitken, C. K. Bradbury, G. Burns, J. J. Morrison, *Synlett* **1995**, 53.
95SL105   F. Nuyttens, J. Hoflack, G. Appendino, P. J. De Clerq, *Synlett* **1995**, 105.
95SL153   S. Hillers, O. Reiser, *Synlett* **1995**, 153
95SL175   K. Hiroga, K. Ogasawara, *Synlett* **1995**, 175.
95SL263   T. Matsumoto, T. Sohma, H. Yamaguchi, S. Kurata, K. Suzuki, *Synlett* **1995**, 263.
95SL339   C. Cinquin, I. Schaper, G. Mandville, R. Bloch, *Synlett* **1995**, 339.
95SL355   T. Heimer, S. Michalski, K. Gerke, G. Kuchta, M. Buback, A. De Meijere, *Synlett* **1995**, 355.
95SL503   D. Caine, R. F. Collison, *Synlett* **1995**, 503.

95SL536   R. H. Schlessinger, X.-H. Wu, T. R. R. Pettus, *Synlett* **1995**, 536.
95SL573   R. L. Danheiser, M. P. Trova, *Synlett* **1995**, 573.
95SL705   J.-P. Dulcère, N. Baret, J. Rodriguez, R. Faure, *Synlett* **1995**, 705.
95SL742   B. Jamart-Grégoire, S. Mercier-Girardot, S. Ianelli, M. Nardelli, P. Caubère, *Synlett* **1995**, 742.
95SL763   C. P. Chuang, S.-F. Wang, *Synlett*, **1995**, 763.
95SL923   J.-P. Dulcère, N. Baret, J. Rodriguez, *Synlett* **1995**, 923.
95SL1151   R. W. Bates, T. Rama-Devi, *Synlett* **1995**, 1151.
95SL1161   M. R. Iesce, F. Cermola, A. Guitto, R. Scarpati, M. L. Graziano, *Synlett* **1995**, 1161.
95SL1191   Y. Landais, D. Planchenault, *Synlett* **1995**, 1191.
95SYN115   U. Kort, *Synthesis* **1995**, 115.
95SYN195   K. Jarowicki, P. Kocienski, S. Norris, M. O'Shea, M. Stocks, *Synthesis* **1995**, 195.
95SYN236   T. Blitzke, D. Sicker, H. Wilde, *Synthesis* **1995**, 236.
95SYN248   M. D'Auria, G. Mauriello, *Synthesis* **1995**, 248.
95SYN303   L. Cottier, G. Descotes, L. Eynard, K. Rapp, *Synthesis* **1995**, 303.
95SYN439   M. R. Iesce, F. Cermola, A. Piazza, R. Scarpati, M. L. Graziano, *Synthesis* **1995**, 439.
95SYN607   G. Casiraghi, G. Rassu, *Synthesis* **1995**, 607.
95SYN1135 D. Hellwinkel, K. Göke, *Synthesis* **1995**, 1135.
95SYN1141 U. Lange, S. Blechert, *Synthesis* **1995**, 1141.
95SYN1171 H. G. Aurich, F. Biesemeier, *Synthesis* **1995**, 1171.
95SYN1311 E. Ciganek, *Synthesis* **1995**, 1311.
95SYN1315 A. R. Katritzky, H. Wu, L. Xie, S. Rachwal, B. Rachwal, J. Jiang, G. Zhang, H. Lang, *Synthesis* **1995**, 1315.
95SYN1447 R. Hoppe, H.-D. Scharf, *Synthesis* **1995**, 1447.
95T193   C. K. Sha, R. S. Lee, *Tetrahedron* **1995**, *51*, 193.
95T959   M. P. Vázquez-Tato, J. A. Seijas, G. W. J. Fleet, C. J. Mathews, P. R. Hemmings, D. Brown, *Tetrahedron* **1995**, *51*, 959.
95T1377   H. Suginome, A. Konishi, H. Sakurai, H. Minakawa, T. Takeda, H. Senboku, M. Tokuda, K. Kobayashi, *Tetrahedron* **1995**, *51*, 1377.
95T1429   Z. Yang, W. Zhou, *Tetrahedron* **1995**, *51*, 1429.
95T1483   G. Pandey, B. B. V. S. Sekhar, *Tetrahedron* **1995**, *51*, 1483.
95T1921   A. Gypser, C. Bülow, H.-D. Scharf, *Tetrahedron* **1995**, *51*, 1921.
95T2477   L. Zeng, Z. M. Gu, X. P. Fang, P. E. Fanwick, C. J. Chang, D. C. Smith, J. L. McLaughlin, *Tetrahedron* **1995**, *51*, 2477.
95T3051   T. R. Kasturi, I. A. Sattigeri, P. V. P. Pragnacharyulu, *Tetrahedron* **1995**, *51*, 3051.
95T3087   Y. R. Lee, *Tetrahedron* **1995**, *51*, 3087.
95T3319   I. Bucsi, Á. Molnár, M. Bartók, G. A. Olah, *Tetrahedron* **1995**, *51*, 3319.
95T3351   J. Almena, F. Foubelo, M. Yus, *Tetrahedron* **1995**, *51*, 3351.
95T3375   F. F. Huerta, C. Gómez, A. Guijarro, M. Yus, *Tetrahedron* **1995**, *51*, 3375.
95T4083   F. D'Onofrio, G. Piancatelli, M. Nicolai, *Tetrahedron* **1995**, *51*, 4083.
95T4383   M. S. Visser, A. H. Hoveyda, *Tetrahedron* **1995**, *51*, 4383.
95T5771   T. Sakamoto, K. Kanematsu, *Tetrahedron* **1995**, *51*, 5771.
95T5781   U. Lange, W. Plitzko, S. Blechert, *Tetrahedron* **1995**, *51*, 5781.
95T7149   G. X. Zhao, Z. M. Gu, L. Zeng, J. F. Chao, J. F. Kozlowski, K. V. Wood, J. L. McLaughlin, *Tetrahedron* **1995**, *51*, 7149.
95T7389   T. J. Woltering, H. M. R. Hoffmann, *Tetrahedron* **1995**, *51*, 7389.
95T7721   A. Barco, S. Benetti, C. De Risi, G. P. Pollini, V. Zanirato, *Tetrahedron* **1995**, *51*, 7721.
95T8333   A. Barco, S. Benetti, A. Bianchi, A. Casolari, M. Guarneri, G. P. Pollini, *Tetrahedron* **1995**, *51*, 8333.
95T8339   M. Mąkosza, E. Kwast, *Tetrahedron* **1995**, *51*, 8339.
95T8389   G. Maiti, S. Adhikari, S. C. Roy, *Tetrahedron* **1995**, *51*, 8389.
95T8507   J. C. Carretero, J. Rojo, N. Díaz, C. Hamdouchi, A. Poveda, *Tetrahedron* **1995**, *51*, 8507.
95T8555   C. W. Holzapfel, D. B. G. Williams, *Tetrahedron* **1995**, *51*, 8555.
95T8771   Y. Matsumura, T. Shimada, T. Nakayama, M. Urashihara, T. Asai, Y. Morizawa, A. Yasuda, *Tetrahedron* **1995**, *51*, 8771.

95T8809   S. Kuwahara, M. Moriguchi, K. Miyagawa, M. Konno, O. Kodama, *Tetrahedron* **1995**, *51*, 8809.
95T9367   L. Nowák, Gy. Pirok, P. Kovács, P. Kolonits, Cs. Szántag, *Tetrahedron* **1995**, *51*, 9367.
95T9559   G. Solladié, D. Boeffel, J. Maignan *Tetrahedron* **1995**, *51*, 9559.
95T9595   M. A. Hariri, F. Pautet, H. Fillion, M. Domard, B. Fenet, *Tetrahedron* **1995**, *51*, 9595.
95T9995   M. A. Brimble, M. K. Edmonds, *Tetrahedron* **1995**, *51*, 9995.
95T10979   N. Saracoglu, I. Durucasu, M. Balci, *Tetrahedron* **1995**, *51*, 10979.
95T11959   S. L. Miller, W. F. Tinto, S. McLean, W. F. Reynolds, M. Yu, C. A. G. Carter, *Tetrahedron* **1995**, *51*, 11959.
95T13089   B. Seiller, C. Bruneau, P. H. Dixneuf, *Tetrahedron* **1995**, *51*, 13089.
95T13239   B. De Boeck, Z. Janousek, H. G. Viehe, *Tetrahedron* **1995**, *51*, 13239.
95TL23   M. A. Walters, H. R. Arcand, D. J. Lawrie, *Tetrahedron Lett.* **1995**, *36*, 23.
95TL31   P. A. Evans, J. D. Roseman, *Tetrahedron Lett.* **1995**, *36*, 31.
95TL231   A. Vaupel, P. Knochel, *Tetrahedron Lett.* **1995**, *36*, 231.
95TL241   I. Matsuda, H. Ishibashi, N. Ii, *Tetrahedron Lett.* **1995**, *36*, 241.
95TL463   A. Garavelas, I. Mavropoulos, P. Perlmutter, G. Westman, *Tetrahedron Lett.* **1995**, *36*, 463.
95TL649   H. Zhang, P. Wilson, W. Shan. Z. Ruan, D. R. Mootoo, *Tetrahedron Lett.* **1995**, *36*, 649.
95TL923   J. H. Jung, J. W. Lee, D. Y. Oh, *Tetrahedron Lett.* **1995**, *36*, 923
95TL939   Y. Tobe, S. Saiki, K. Naemura, *Tetrahedron Lett.* **1995**, *36*, 939.
95TL1127   A. Srikrishna, R. Viswajanani, C. V. Yelamaggad, *Tetrahedron Lett.* **1995**, *36*, 1127.
95TL1263   E. Lorthiois, I. Marek, C. Meyer, J.-F. Normant, *Tetrahedron Lett.* **1995**, *36*, 1263.
95TL1307   D. C. Craig, A. Durie, G. L. Edwards, D. J. Sinclair, *Tetrahedron Lett.* **1995**, *36*, 1307.
95TL1397   M. Harmata, S. Elahmad, C. L. Barnes, *Tetrahedron Lett.* **1995**, *36*, 1397; Corrigendum: *Tetrahedron Lett.* **1995**, *36*, No. 40.
95TL1667   T. Nakajima, M. Segi, T. Mituoka, Y. Fukute, M. Honda, K. Naitou, *Tetrahedron Lett.* **1995**, *36*, 1667.
95TL1865   K. Konno, S. Maki, S. Sagara, H. Takayama, *Tetrahedron Lett.* **1995**, *36*, 1865.
95TL1981   T. R. Hoye, L. Tan, *Tetrahedron Lett.* **1995**, *36*, 1981.
95TL2117   A. K. Forrest, P. J. O'Hanlon, *Tetrahedron Lett.* **1995**, *36*, 2117.
95TL2587   D. F. Taber, Y. Song, *Tetrahedron Lett.* **1995**, *36*, 2587.
95TL2713   T. A. Engler, K. O. Lynch, jr., W. Chai, S. P. Meduna, *Tetrahedron Lett.* **1995**, *36*, 2713.
95TL2925   P. A. Zoretic, Z. Shen, M. Wang, A. A. Ribeiro, *Tetrahedron Lett.* **1995**, *36*, 2925.
95TL2929   P. A. Zoretic, Y. Zhang, A. A. Ribeiro, *Tetrahedron Lett.* **1995**, *36*, 2929.
95TL2987   Y. Landais, D. Planchenault, V. Weber, *Tetrahedron Lett.* **1995**, *36*, 2987.
95TL3095   J. V. Raman, H. K. Lee, R. Vleggar, J. K. Cha, *Tetrahedron Lett.* **1995**, *36*, 3095.
95TL3201   S. Kuwahara, M. Moriguchi, K. Miyagawa, M. Konno, O. Kodama, *Tetrahedron Lett.* **1995**, *36*, 3201.
95TL3361   J. Y. Lee, B. H. Kim, *Tetrahedron Lett.* **1995**, *36*, 3361.
95TL3495   J. E. Cochran, A. Padwa, *Tetrahedron Lett.* **1995**, *36*, 3495.
95TL3553   A. De Mico, R. Margarita, G. Piancatelli, *Tetrahedron Lett.* **1995**, *36*, 3553.
95TL3699   M. Iyoda, L. Zhao, H. Matsuyama, *Tetrahedron Lett.* **1995**, *36*, 3699.
95TL3805   R. D. Walkup, L. Guan, Y. S. Kim, S. W. Kim, *Tetrahedron Lett.* **1995**, *36*, 3805.
95TL4181   S. Leong-Neumann, S. D. Derrick, P. W. Dibble, *Tetrahedron Lett.* **1995**, *36*, 4181.
95TL4241   A. Tenaglia, J.-Y. Le Brazidec, F. Souchon, *Tetrahedron Lett.* **1995**, *36*, 4241.
95TL4401   G. Märkl, U. Striebl, P. Kreitmeier, A. Knorr, M. Porsch, J. Daub, *Tetrahedron Lett.* **1995**, *36*, 4401.
95TL4405   R. Vieser, W. Eberbach, *Tetrahedron Lett.* **1995**, *36*, 4405.
95TL4656   A. D'Annibale, A. Scettri, *Tetrahedron Lett.* **1995**, *36*, 4656.
95TL4717   M. D. Weingarten, A. Padwa, *Tetrahedron Lett.* **1995**, *36*, 4717.
95TL4971   S. Lebedkin, S. Ballenweg, J. Gross, R. Taylor, W. Krätschmer, *Tetrahedron Lett.* **1995**, *36*, 4971.
95TL4983   H.-J. Altenbach, R. Wischnat, *Tetrahedron Lett.* **1995**, *36*, 4983.
95TL5195   H. Takeshita, Y. Z. Yan, N. Kato, A. Mori, *Tetrahedron Lett.* **1995**, *36*, 5195.
95TL5199   H. Takeshita, Y. Z. Yan, N. Kato, A. Mori, H. Wakabayashi, T. Nozoe, *Tetrahedron Lett.* **1995**, *36*, 5199.

95TL5383   C. K. F. Shen, K.-M. Chien, T.-Y. Liu, T.-I Lin, G.-R. Her, T.-Y. Luh, *Tetrahedron Lett.* **1995**, *36*, 5383.
95TL5581   T. Oriyama, A. Ishiwata, T. Sano, T. Matsuda, M. Takahashi, G. Koga, *Tetrahedron Lett.* **1995**, *36*, 5581.
95TL5753   H. Nishino, S. Kajikawa, Y. Hamada, K. Kurosawa, *Tetrahedron Lett.* **1995**, *36*, 5753
95TL6141   R. N. Warrener, S. Wang, L. Maksimovic, P. M. Tepperman, D. N. Butler, *Tetrahedron Lett.* **1995**, *36*, 6141.
95TL7003   T. A. Engler, W. Chai, K. O. Lynch, jr., *Tetrahedron Lett.* **1995**, *36*, 7003.
95TL7175   J. Boukouvalas, F. Maltais, *Tetrahedron Lett.* **1995**, *36*, 7175.
95TL7271   S. Yoshida, T. Yamanaka, T. Miyake, Y. Moritani, H. Ohmizu, T. Iwazaki, *Tetrahedron Lett.* **1995**, *36*, 7271.
95TL7531   D. Craig, N. J. Ikin, N. Mathews, A. M. Smith, *Tetrahedron Lett.* **1995**, *36*, 7531.
95TL7657   F. Jean, O. Melnyk, A. Tartar, *Tetrahedron Lett.* **1995**, *36*, 7657.
95TL7685   T. Kawano, T. Ogawa, S. M. Islam, I. Ueda, *Tetrahedron Lett.* **1995**, *36*, 7685.
95TL8055   K. Takahashi, A. Gunji, K. Yanagi, M. Miki, *Tetrahedron Lett.* **1995**, *36*, 8055.
95TL8225   S. Yoshida, H. Ohmizu, T. Iwasaki, *Tetrahedron Lett.* **1995**, *36*, 8225.
95TL8581   O. Peters, W. Friedrichsen, *Tetrahedron Lett.* **1995**, *36*, 8581.
95TL9137   W. W. Harding, P. A. Lewis, H. Jacobs, S. McLean, W. F. Reynolds, L. Tay, J. Yang, *Tetrahedron Lett.* **1995**, *36*, 9137.
95TL9257   S. C. Sinha, A. Sinha-Bagchi, A. Yazbak, E. Keinan, *Tetrahedron Lett.* **1995**, *36*, 9257.
95TL9285   C. O. Kappe, J. E. Cochran, A. Padwa, *Tetrahedron Lett.* **1995**, *36*, 9285.

Chapter 5.4

Five-Membered Ring Systems: With More than One N Atom

S. A. Lang, Jr.
Wyeth-Ayerst Research, Pearl River, NY, USA

V. J. Lee
Microcide Pharmaceuticals Inc., Mountain View, CA, USA

5.4.1 INTRODUCTION

The heterocycles described in this review continue to find numerous uses in biological systems as potential pharmaceuticals, agricultural agents or mechanistic probes for drug action. During this period, key communications on a) AII receptor antagonists [96JMC323; 95BMC2617; 95JMC2938; 95JMC2925; 95JMC2357], b) H1 antagonists [95JMC1287], c) inhibitors of neuronal nitric oxide synthase [95MI2349], d) neuropeptide Y antagonists [95BMC2065], e) inhibitors of fungal myristoyl-CoA:protein N-myristoyl transferase [95JMC1837], and inhibitors of acyl CoA: cholesterol acyl transferase [95JMC1067] were reported. Molecular probes for a) RNA structure [95JMC2938] and b) diazepam-insensitive GABA-A receptors [95JMC1679] were also disclosed.

A comprehensive review of the synthesis and reactions of lithiated monocyclic azoles [Part IV], including triazoles and tetrazoles, appeared in 1995 [95H(41)1525]. Azoles continue to be well represented in the patent literature and, in particular, form the basic nucleus for antifungal agents for human use and a variety of herbicides. In a search for alternatives to sodium azide as a nitrogen source for automobile air bags, azoles have been investigated. A theoretical analysis of 4-nitro- and 4,5-dinitro-2H-1,2,4-triazoles and their explosive properties was published [95MI189] as was an article on explosive mixtures containing azoles [95EUP661252].

5.4.2 PYRAZOLES AND RING FUSED DERIVATIVES

During this period, various communications appeared describing the use of pyrazole-based ligands in asymmetric catalysis. Some are incorporated into ferrocenyl ligands [95OM5415;; 95AG(E)931], while others are peroxomolybdenum complexes [95AG(E)1737]. An impressive paper on the use of chiral pyrazole alcohols for the enantioselective addition of diethylzinc to benzaldehyde. Ligands **1** and **2** gave 83 and 93% *ee* of the (*R*)-alcohol, respectively; ligand **3** gave 87% *ee* of the (*S*)-alcohol [95TA2665]. However, the creation of new ligands and highly functionalized pyrazoles necessitates creative use of the hydrazine annulation methods with novel 1,3-dicarbonyl synthons. During this period there was a substantial number of citations on the synthesis of fluorinated pyrazoles by hydrazine annulation methods. The challenge is the design of appropriately fluorinated precursor 1,3-diketone synthons. Perfluorinated alkynes react readily with hydrazines to afford perfluoroalkyl pyrazoles (**4**) [95JFC129]. Alternatively, perfluoroalkyl halides undergo radical coupling to enamines and vinyl synthons to afford perfluorinated ketones which react identically with hydrazine (*cf.*, **9**) [95JCS(P1)1039]. The synthon **10** reacts with hydrazines to afford 3-(arylsulfonyl)-2-(trifluoromethyl)-5-hydrazinopyrazoles (**11**) [95JHC207]. Other creative hydrazine annulations include the interconvertive cyclization of α-(1,3,4-oxadiazoly)ketones (**12**) with hydrazine to afford 5-(acylhydrazino)pyrazoles (**13**) [95S805]. 1,3-Dithietane-2,4-diylidenebis(cyanoacetic acid esters) (**14**) are unique 1,3-dicarbonyl synthons and afford ready entry to 5H-pyrazolo[5,1-*b*] [1,3]thiazines (**15**) [95H1235]. Arylsulfonylvinamidinium salts (5) also participate as 1,3-dicarbonyl synthons with hydrazines to afford the 4-(aryl-sulfonyl)pyrazoles (6) which are easily functionalized at C-5 by metallation processes [95T9511]. Diazo cyclization approaches to pyrazoles are rarely used, except when diazo precursors are readily available. The synthesis of the highly electron-deficient pyrazole (16) was accomplished with dimethyl acetylenedicarboxylate and appropriate α-diazopyruvates [95KGS176].

Few new methods for direct functionalization of pyrazoles were reported. Notable is the N-hydroxylation of pyrazoles (cf., 17) with benzoyl peroxide [95LA1563]. These N-hydroxypyrazoles, after O-protection, undergo α-metallation and electrophile trapping processes to afford functionalized N-hydroxypyrazoles (19) [95JOC4998]. The O-stannylpyrazole (20), on metallation, undergoes an O-->C stannyl migration to stannylpyrazole (21). Direct sulfinylation of the 5-amino-3-cyanopyrazole (26) occured at C-4 [EUP668269].

Cine-substitution of 1,4-dinitro-5-methylpyrazoles with nucleophiles has been reported previously. However, substitution of 4-nitro substituent with 4-halogen is not detrimental to the outcome of the reaction [95JHC747]. These reactions occur by the initial formation of the diazafulvene intermediate (24).

5.4.3 IMIDAZOLES AND RING FUSED DERIVATIVES

Various cyclization procedures and variations of existing procedures continue to be communicated. An improved synthesis [C-C-N + C-N] of bis-(^{15}N)-hydroxymethylimidazole from formaldehyde, dihydroxyacetone, and ^{15}N-ammonia [95MI947] was reported. Syntheses of imidazole-1-oxides and 2,5-dihydroimidazole-1-oxyls by the [C-C-N + C-N] protocol were reported. Condensation of α-ketohydroxylamines (**29**) with ketones in the presence of ammonia affords the 2,5-dihydro-1-hydroxyimidazoles (**30**) [95LA2189]; subsequent oxidation affords the nitroxide radicals. Various 3-substituted imidazole-1-oxides (**31**) were obtained from α-ketoimines (or α,β-diimines) and oximes (95JCS(P1)2467). 4,4-Disubstituted 4H-imidazoles (**33**) are obtained from the reaction of 3-amino-3H-azirines (**32**) with amides catalyzed by boron trifluoride etherate [95HCA899]. An efficient synthesis of 4-perfluoroalkyl imidazoles (**35**) from mesoionic 1,3-oxazolium-5-olates (**34**) by a [C-N-C-C + N] cyclization was reported by Kawase and coworkers [95H(41)1617]. The acid-catalyzed cyclization [N-C-N-C-C] of 1-(1,1-dimethoxy-ethyl)chloroacetamidines [Cl$_2$CRC(=NH)NHCH$_2$CH(OMe)$_2$, R = H, Cl (**28**)] affords improved syntheses of imidazole-2-carboxaldehyde, imidazole-2-carboxylic acid and esters [95JOC1090].

Two types of [C-N-C-C-N] cyclizations were reported during this period. The first approach is the sequential conversion of ethyl cyano(acylamino)acetates with a) various alkyl (aryl) thiols and b) phosphorus pentachloride/4-dimethylaminopyridine to afford ethyl 4(5)-alkyl(aryl)thioimidazole-5(4)-carboxylates (38) [95S635]. The second variant is the cyclization of ortho-nitrotertiary anilines (39) [95MI408]. A one-pot synthesis of imidazolosugars by the [N-C-N + C-C] strategy is readily accomplished (30-50%) by the reaction of formamidine acetate with monosaccharides [95S944]. An analogous strategy is employed for the synthesis of α-(imidazolyl)-phenylacetic acids (or esters) (42) or α-(3-imidazo[1,2-a]pyridyl)phenylacetic ester (43) from α-phenyl-β-formyl-α,β-unsaturated acids (or esters) (41) [95H(41)1491].

Various strategies for direct functionalization of imidazoles continue to be reported, including direct metallation approaches. The versatility of these approaches is illustrated in the syntheses of several natural products. A double functionalization approach to kealiiquinone (45), a marine alkaloid from a sponge, commences with 1-methyl-2-(phenyllthio)imidazole [95TL8251]. Similarly, grossularine-1 (R = indol-3-yl, 49a) and grossularine-2 (R = 4-HOC$_6$H$_4$, 49b) were synthesized from ethyl 3-iodoindole-2-carboxylate and lithiated SEM-protected imidazoles [95JOC5899].

An enantiospecific synthesis of negstatin I (52) was accomplished efficiently with a sequence involving two C-imidazolide anion transformations. The first was coupling of a suitably protected carbohydrate intermediate with N-tritylimidazole. Direct monobromination of imidazole (51a, X = Y = H) was not feasible, except by selective halogen-metal exchange and reprotonation of dibromo intermediate (51b, X = Y = Br) [95TL6721]. Introduction of the pendant acetic acid function was accomplished by C-allylation of 51c.

Several stereoselective syntheses of 4-(ribofuranosyl)imidazole nucleosides were reported. Imidazole 53 was obtained from 50 by a Mitsunobu cyclization [95TL3165]. Treatment of a suitably protected ribofuranosyl chloride with two equivalents of a lithioimidazole afforded the 1-(5-imidazolyl)ribofuranoid glycal (54) directly which undergoes elimination to the furylimidazole (55) [95CPB152].

Palladium(0)-mediated couplings continue to show utility for iodoimidazole functionalizations, as illustrated in several reports of synthesis of (1R,2S,3R)-acetyl-4(5)-[(1,2,3,4)-tetrahydroxybutyl]imidazole (58) [95TL5969], and the trihydroxybutyl analogs [95JOC2378]. In contrast, 1,2-disubstituted imidazoles undergo palladium-mediated carbonylation, in the presence of alkenes, to afford 4-alkenoylimidazoles (59) [96JACS493].

N-Functionalization strategies continue to be reported, especially for unsymmetrically substituted imidazoles. Notably, the sequential dialkylation and selective dealkylation of unsymmetric 1,3-disubstituted imidazolium salts is compelling approach to polysubstituted imidazoles. The regioselective synthesis of an imidazole analog of prostaglandins (*cf.*, **61**) by N-alkylation of a N-trityl-4-alkenoylimidazole and detritylation of imidazolium salt (**60**) [95PJC259]. Similarly, 4- and 5-substituted-N-alkylimidazoles are obtained from N-(trimethylsilylethoxy-methyl)imidazoles by alkyl triflate quaternizations and removal of the SEM group [95H(41)215]. N-Aminoimidazoles and N-aminobenzimidazoles are similarly obtained by N-amination of 1-(methoxymethyl)- or 1-acetylimidazoles or benzimidazoles [94KGS1364].

N-Arylation of various azoles (or their anions) was readily accomplished with p-tolyllead triacetate in the presence of copper(II)acetate [95JOC5678]; however, the applicability of this procedure to other aryllead triacetates was not discussed. Solvent-dependent palladium-mediated allylations [95JHC1325] and Mitsunobu-based asymmetric alkylations [95JOC2008] of imidazoles and benzimidazoles have also been reported.

Oxidative functionalization of imidazoles is typically not preparatively useful. However, an optimized procedure for direct peracid oxidation of azoles to N-hydroxyazoles was reported [95JCS(P1)243], with imidazoles affording dioxygenated products. In contrast, imidazoles are conveniently converted to imidazole-2-thiones with phenyl chlorothionoformate [95SL239].

Several novel 10π bicyclic imidazoles (**63** or **65**), obtained from polysubstituted imidazoles, were reported during this period. The first synthesis of an imidazo[4′,5′:4,5]thieno[3,2-*d*]pyrimidine commences with 1-benzyl-2-(methylthio)-4-bromo-5-cyanoimidazole (**62**) [95TL12807]. Sequential metallation, sulfurization, S-alkylation, and Thorpe cyclization of **62** afforded the thienoimidazole intermediate **63**. Precursor **62** was obtained from 1-benzyl-2,4,5-tribromoimidazole in a series of metallation-electrophile trapping protocols. Nitroimidazo[1,5-*a*]imidazoles (**65**) were readily obtained from 1-(acylmethyl)-2-methyl-4-nitro-5-bromoimidazoles (**64**) by sequential amination and cyclization [94KGS490].

R^1 = H, Me, CH_2CH_2X (X = OH, NEt_2), CH_2CHMe_2, Ph, $(CH_2)_nCO_2H$ (n = 1-2), $CH_2C_6H_5$

5.4.4   1,2,3-TRIAZOLES AND RING FUSED DERIVATIVES

Nucleophilic substitution of a nitro group in a 2-alkyl-4,5-dinitro-1,2,3-triazole (66) was accomplished with a variety of oxygen and nitrogen nucleophiles in yields ≥77%. Replacement of the second nitro was inhibited when an electron-donating group was introduced into the 4-position [94ZOR915]. The parent and related 4,5-dinitro-2-aryl-1,2,3-triazole 1-oxide was prepared by the cyclization of HON:CHC(NO$_2$):NNHPh with K$_3$Fe(CN)$_6$ followed by stepwise nitration [94ZOR918].   The 5-siloxy-1,2,3-triazole (68) was prepared by cycloaddition of α-silyldiazo-ketone (67) with PhNCO at 50°C for 20 hr (yield 30-70%) [94ZOR1391].

Dinitrofuroxan oxide (70) was reacted with a variety of amines in CH$_2$Cl$_2$ at -20°C to generate the nitrofuroxan (71) which on further reaction with the same or different amine at 20°C generated 1,2,3-triazole 1-oxide (72) in an overall 20-40% yields. An x-ray structure determination was conducted and mechanistic considerations discussed [95MC194]. With excess ethylamine in CH$_2$Cl$_2$ at 20°C, 72 is quantitatively converted into nitrofuroxan (73). The highly fluorinated amino-1,2,3-triazole (69) was prepared by the SO$_2$Cl$_2$ oxidation of the requisite hydrazone [94MI1838].

1-Substituted benzotriazoles continue to be favorite intermediates for various transformations.   These include i) the alternative preparation of α-keto esters from acid chlorides [95OPP457], ii) the synthesis of α-acylaminophosphine oxides from aldehydes and acyl amines which proceeds *via* an N-α-acylaminobenzotriazole (74) [95SC1187] utilizing Amberlyst 15, iii) as alternatives to imidoyl chlorides in synthesis [95H(40)231], iv) as part of an improved peptide coupling reagent [95SC2185], and v) as a convenient N- or O- formylating agent as shown in the preparation of intermediate (76) [95S503] or a reagent to convert amines into guanidines [95SC1173]. N-Substitution into amides can also be achieved utilizing N-hydroxymethylbenzotriazole [95JOC4002].

N-Substituted benzotriazole intermediate (77) is an excellant synthon for the synthesis of 2-ethoxy-2-vinylcyclopropanecarboxylate esters (78) [95JOC6]. 1-Propargylbenzotriazole was reacted with bromoacetophenone to provide the novel 2-(benzotriazolomethyl)furan (80) in 60% yield [95JOC638]. Annelated N-aminotriazoles, on oxidation, are a good source of cyclic alkynes; as illustrated for the reaction of aminotriazolotropone (80) with 4-phenyloxazole to generate the furyl[3,4-*d*]tropone (82) from a Diels-Alder intermediate with facile loss of benzonitrile [94TL8421].

Additional examples of syntheses of polycyclic triazoles continue to be reported. 2-(2'-Hydroxyphenyl)benzotriazole (84) is prepared in >90% yield from azointermediate (83) by reaction with Raney nickel and DMSO, DMS or thiophene [95JAP07228577]. 2-Methylbenzo-triazole (85) is cyclized under acidic conditions and subsequently converted into the chloro analog (86) by treatment with $POCl_3$ [95FES47].

The 1,3-dipolar cycloaddition of azidoalkylphosphonates to enamines afforded Δ^2-1,2,3-triazoles which are further converted to the 1,2,3-triazoles [95H(40)543]; fused triazoles are similarly obtained when a cyclic enamine was employed. Fused 1,2,3-triazole (88), a xanthine oxidase inhibitor, was prepared by the reaction of an alkyl azide with cyanoacetamide with further elaboration of intermediate (87) by treatment with HMDS in xylene [95FES257]. The fused 4H-1,2,3-triazolo[1,5-*a*][1,4]benzodiazepin-6(5H)-one (90) was obtained from propargylamide (89) *via* an intermediate azide [95S647].

5.4.5   1,2,4-TRIAZOLES AND RING FUSED DERIVATIVES

Numerous references have appeared within the last year that highlight 1,2,4-triazole-based structures. Typically, the 1,2,4-triazole is usually an appended or occasionally a fused ring which has been designed and synthesized to impart a particular medicinal or agricultural. Uniquely, new synthesis are rare and many articles are based on the introduction of the triazole ring by displacement, manipulation of the moieties on the triazole or synthesis of fused triazoles. Triazoles are incorporated into peptidomimetics, along with a variety of other heterocycles [95JOC3112], or coupled with isoxazoles [95SC3219]. The triazole moiety [or pyrazole moiety] is incorporated by displacement with 4-nitrobenzyl bromide, subsequent reduction, elaboration into a hydrazine and Fisher indole synthesis, to generate indoles (*cf.*, **91**), which are potent agonists for the 5-HT_{1D} receptor [95JMC1799].

X = -NO$_2$, NH$_2$, NHNH$_2$ (91)

Michael adducts were employed in the regioselective functionalization of N-substituted azoles. 1,2,4-Triazole is reacted with acrylonitrile to generate the 1-adduct, subsequent reaction with an alkylating agent generates the triazolium salt (**92**) which on reverse Michael provides the 4-substituted product in a regiospecific fashion [95S1183]. Acetate salts are utilized to displace the Br in triazolylmethyl bromides (**93**) [95MI33].

(92)   (93)   (94)

The triazolines (**97**), were synthesized from the triazolinethione (**95**) by oxidation to the sulfonic acid and subsequent treatment with H$_2$O and HCl at 20-100° [95EUP657437]. The 1,2,4-triazole intermediate (**98**), prepared from the N-unsubstituted triazole by reaction with 4-MeOC$_6$H$_4$CH$_2$Cl and K$_2$CO$_3$ with tetrabutylammionium hydrosulfate for 3 h at 60°, was further elaborated to chiral crown ether macrocycles [94S1091].

(97)   (96)   (95)   (98)

The 1,4-diacyl-3-acylamino-5-phenyl-4,5-dihydro-1H-1,2,4-triazole (**99**) was generated by the ring-closure of a guanidinylhydrazone with acetic anhydride in *ca.* 80% yield. The structure of the triazole was confirmed by spectroscopy and x-ray analysis [95M733]. The N-benzyl triazoline (**100**) was prepared by reaction of N-benzylidenebenzylamine with a hydrazonyl halide with K$_2$CO$_3$ in benzene, followed by 2 eq of Et$_3$N for 1 h, in 75% yield [95ZOB308].

The alkylation of 5-amino-1H-1,2,4-triazole with chlorobenzenes activated by a nitro moiety generated the 1H-monosubstituted product (**101**). However, with excess reagent, a mixture of **102** and **103** was observed along with a number of fused analogs, particularly when the nitro group was ortho [95JHC1359]. Numerous 1,2,4-triazole-5-ylphosphonic acids (**104**), prepared as potential cyclic spatial mimics of glyphosate by low temperature lithiation/phosphorylation, were analyzed as ground state analogs of PEP [95JHC893].

Treatment of aromatic carboxaldehyde (diaminomethylene)hydrazones (**105**) with hot acetic anhydride or benzoyl chloride affords 1,4-diacyl-3-acylamino-5-aryl-4,5-dihydro-1H-1,2,4-traizoles (**106**) in 75-95% yields. In contrast, when the 4-pyridine analog of **105** was employed, the unusual hemianimal triazole derivative (**107**) was obtained. The structures of the novel compounds were determined by spectral methods and in several cases by x-ray structural analysis. Mechanistic considerations are discussed [95M733]. The oxazole-1,2,4-triazole (**108**) was prepared by cyclization of the corresponding oxazolecarbonyl-thiosemicarbazide with bicarbonate, alkylation at the sulfur and oxidation to the sulfoxide with MCPBA [95JHC1235].

In contrast to the alkylation with Meerwein salts of 4,5-dihydro-5,5-dimethyl-3-oxo-3H-1,2,4-triazole, the reaction of **109** produced the azoxy regional isomer at the 1-position rather than the 2-position. This observation was supported by *ab initio* calculations [94M1383]. The thermal rearrangement 4-methyl or 4-ethyl-4-H-1,2,4-triazole to the 1-substituted analog was observed. The observed results are in agreement with a nucleophilic group transfer mechanism [95ACS676]. The 2-oxazolin-5-one (**111**) reacts in a melt at 140° for 30 min. to form the 1,2,4-triazole (**112**) which undergoes the Fries rearrangement to (**113**) on treatment with anhydrous $ZnCl_2$ in AcOH at reflux for 5 h. Transformations into other triazole derivatives are also discussed [95MI113].

The 1,2,4-triazolium salt (114) react with activated olefins to afford triazolium N-allylidines (115). These undergo thermolysis to generate the betaine (116). Using different acceptors leads to the formation of several fused triazole systems and other fused heterocycles [95H(41)329]. A number of references to triazolophthalocyanines or triazolohemiporphyrazines and their metallo derivatives, related to the partial structure (117) were published in 1995. Several were directed to their synthesis and general characterization [95JOC1872; 95SM2289; 95ICA(230)153] and more specific characterization by FAB-MS [95LA495], electronic structure [95SM2291] and aggregation properties [95CC419].

A number of novel fused 1,2,4-triazole were reported and these include [1,2,4]-triazole[1,3]-thiazinoquinolines (118, 119) and their positional isomers [95MI297]. The electrocyclization of N-aziridinylimino carbodiimides generated by dehydration of urea (120), produces 5,6-dihydro-7H-imidazol[1,2-*b*][1,2,4]triazoles (121) and 5,6-dihydro[1,2,4]triazolo[5,1-*d*]-[1,3,5]oxadiaze-pines [95TL2815]. The mechanisms of each transformation is discussed.

5.4.6   TETRAZOLES AND RING FUSED DERIVATIVES

Aside from the numerous references on the use of tetrazoles for antifungal or agricultural uses, other uses of tetrazoles include corrosion inhibitors, agents with antiemetic activity, ACAT inhibitors, antiallergy agents, for the treatment of glaucoma disorders and growth hormone agonists to name a few. In most of these cases, a tetrazole moiety either as a monocyclic ring or fused ring, appears to impart essential activity. A theoretical study, based on *ab initio* calculations, was conducted to determine why tetrazoles are not a practical diene in the Diels-Alder reaction [95MI9]. An x-ray study of 2,3-diphenyltetrazolium salts containing a 5-amino group (122) or the bis-tetrazolium salt (123) indicates that there is minimal change in the ring geometries for free 2,3-diphenyl mesionic tetrazoles [95MI29]. 2-Methyl-5-aminotetrazole can be oxidized to the 5-nitro derivative (124) by dinitrogen peroxide along with some diazo products [95MC102].

1H-Tetrazol-5-thiol derivatives can be converted into suitable antifungal agents (125, 126) by reaction with cyanodithioimidocarbonic acid or formylation, conversion of the hemiaminal by SOCl₂ into a chloride analogs and subsequent reaction with the afford mentioned reagent [95MI035].

The radiolabelled angiotensin II receptor agonist (128) was prepared from the ^{14}C-labelled nitrile (127). The tetrazole ring was formed from 127 by reaction with Me_3SnN_3 in toluene at reflux [95MI915]. N-Phenyltetrazole has been employed as a protecting group in glycoside synthesis. The tetrazole can be removed with HF•Py to afford the fluoro glycoside. A large excess of HF•Py is required as, under acid conditions, epimerization can occur (yield 90% of a 3:2 mixture of 129) [95HCA959].

5-Aryltetrazoles (131) and 5-vinyltetrazoles are prepared by the palladium-catalyzed cross coupling reaction of bromotetrazole (130) with arylboronic acids in >90% yields [95TL1679]. The tetrazolium salt (133) was prepared by the NCBT closure of the formazan (132) [94H73].

1-Phenyltetrazoline-5-thiones can be easily converted into their 5-one counterparts in about 85% yields by treatment of the thione and NaOH in H_2O/EtOH at 0°C with propylene oxide. This may be a simple and easy for such a conversion in other systems [95EUP643049]. N-Substituted thioamides when treated with TMS-N_3 and $SnCl_4$ in CH_2Cl_2 generate 1,5-substituted tetrazoles (134) in high yields. Fused derivatives such as 135 can also be prepared from the corresponding amide to thioamide [95H(40)801]. 5-Halo-1-phenyltetrazoles (136) could be prepared in a general format by the reaction of N-halosuccinimide with azide, to generate the haloazide intermediate which is not isolated, and further reacts with phenylisocyanate to generate the products in 70-90% yields. This is a suitable alternative to the current literature routes and all 5-halo derivatives can be prepared [95JOC468].

Lithiation of tetrazoles substituted in the 1-position with an Bn or PMB and subsequent reaction with an electrophile, generates the 1,5-disubstituted tetrazole and subsequent removal of the protecting group yields the 5-substituted analogs free from other position isomers [95TL1759]. 1H-tetrazole reacts with methoxyarenes by a paired electrosynthesis to give aryltetrazoles of the type (137) [95TL7027].

A definitive reference on the thermolysis of the *gem*-diazide (138) in o-xylene to the ring expanded sugar tetrazole (139) has appeared. In contrast, when 138 was irradiated, positional tetrazole isomer (140) was isolated in 20% yield [95JCS(P1)1747].

Intramolecular cyclization of azide (141) was acheived by heating in toluene for 72 h (75% yield). Subsequent deprotection of the protecting groups with TFA afforded the fused tetrazole (142) [95TL7511]. The tetrazole (144) was formed from 143 by reaction with NaN_3 in HCl, AcOH and H_2O; compound possessed antiasthmatic activity [95CPB683].

5.4.7   REFERENCES

94H73   A. R. Katritzky, S. A. Belyakov, J. N. Lam, H. D. Durst and D. V. Karpenko, Heterocycles, 1994, **39**, 73.
94KGS490   P. M. Kochergin and V. A. Lifanov, *Khim. Geterotsikl. Soedin.*, 1994, 490.
94KGS1364   O. V. Vinogradova, O. V. Kryshtalyuk, M. I. Rudnev, A. F. Pozharsky and V. V. Kuzmenko, *Khim. Geterotsikl. Soedin.*, 1994, 1364.
94M1383   J. G. Schantl, J. Svetlik and V. Kettmann, *Monatsh. Chem.*, 1994, **125**, 1383.
94MI1838   G. G. Bargamov and M. D. Bargamova, *Nauk. Ser. Khim.*, 1994, 1838.
94S1091   M. V. Martinez-Diaz, J. Demendoza and T. Torres, *Synthesis*, 1994, 1091.
94TL8421   T. Nakazawa, M. Ishiharam M. Jinguji, R. Miyatake, Y. Sugihara and I. Muruta, *Tetrahedron Lett.*, 1994, **35**, 8421.
94ZOR915   M. A. Shafeev, V. I. Meshsheryakov, A. A. Almukhamedov, G. A. Gareev and L. I. Vereshchagin, *Zh. Org. Khim.*, 1994, **30**, 915; CA 123:198700.
94ZOR918   M. A. Shafeev, A. A. Almukhamedov, V. V. Shcherbakov, G. A. Gareev and L. I. Vereshchagin, *Zh. Org. Khim.*, 1994, **30**, 918: CA 122:290781.
94ZOR1391   D. Maier and G. Mass, *Zh. Org. Khim*, 1994, **30**, 1391.
94ZOR1560   N. M. Perova, L. G. Egorova, L. P. Sidorova, A. P. Novikova and O. N. Chupakhin, *Zh. Org. Khim.*, 1994, **30**, 1560.

95ACS676	Per H. J. Carlsen, K. B. Joergensen, O. R. Gautun, S. Jagner and M. Haakansson, *Acta. Chem. Scand.*, 1995, **49**, 676.
95AG(E)931	A, Schnyder, L. Hintermann and A. Togni, *Angew. Chem., Int. Ed. Engl.*, 1995, 34, 931.
95AG(E)1737	W. R. Thiel and T. Priermeier, *Angew. Chem., Int. Ed. Engl.*, 1995, 34, 1737.
95BMC2065	S. Knieps, M. Michel, S. Dove and A. Buschauer, *Bioorg. Med. Chem. Lett.*, 1995, **5**, 2065.
95BMC2617	P. Deprez, J. Guillaume, A. Corbier, J-P. Vevert, M. Fortin, B. Heckmann, *et al, Bioorg. Med. Chem. Lett.*, 1995, **5**, 2617.
95CC419	F. Fernando-Fernandez-Lazaro, A. Sastre and T. Torres, *J. Chem. Soc., Chem. Commun.*, 1995, 419.
95CPB152	S. Harusawa, M. Kawabata, Y. Murai, R. Yoneda and T. Kurihara, *Chem. Pharm. Bull.*, 1995, **43**, 152.
95CPB174	A. Miyashita, Y. Sato, S. Watanabe, K.-I. Tanji and T. Higashino, *Chem. Pharm. Bull.*, 1995, **43**, 174.
95CPB683	A. Sano, M. Ishihara, J. Yoshihara, M. Sumino and H. Nawa, *Chem. Pharm. Bull*, 1995, **43**, 683.
95EUP643049	Nihon Bayer, EUP643049. CA:95-088732.
95EUP661252	R. D. Taylor and T. M. Deppert, 95EUP661252: CA:123:87614
95EUP657437	W. Haas, K. H. Linker and K. Findeisen, EUP657437, 1995, CA: 123:286040.
95FES47	P. Sanna, P. A. Sequi and G. Paglietti, *Farmaco*, 1995, **50**, 47.
95FES257	G. Biaga. I. Giorai, O. Livi, V. Scartoni, I. Tonetti and L. Costantino, *Farmaco*, 1995, **50**, 257.
95H(40)231	A. R. Katritzky, C. V. Stevens, G. F. Zhang, J. L. Jiang and N. Dekimpe, *Heterocycles*, 1995, **40**, 231.
95H(40)543	F. Palacios, A. M. Ochoa de Retana and J. Pagalday, *Heterocycles*, 1995, **40**, 543.
95H(40)801	S. Lehnhoff and I Ugi, *Heterocycles,* 1995, **40**, 801.
95H(41)215	G. Shapiro and B. Gomez-Lor, *Heterocycles*, 1995, **41**, 215.
95H(41)329	Y. Matsuda, Y. Chiyomaru, C. Motokawa and T. Nishiyori, *Heterocycles*, 1995, **41**, 329.
95H(41)1235	M. Jochheim, H. G. Krug, R. Neidlein and C. Krieger, *Heterocycles*, 1995, **41**, 1235.
95H(41)1491	C. Saturnino, M. Abarghaz, M. Schmitt, C.-G. Wermuth and J.-J. Bourguignon, *Heterocycles*, 1995, **41**, 1491.
95H(41)1525	M . R. Grimmett and B. Iddon, *Heterocycles*, 1995, **41**, 1525.
95H(41)1617	M. Kawase, S. Saito and T. Kurihara, *Heterocycles*, 1995, **41**, 1617.
95HCA899	F. Arnhold, S. Chaloupka, A. Linden and H. Heimgartner, *Helv. Chim. Acta*, 1995, **78**, 899.
95HCA959	M. Palme and A. Vasella, *Helv. Chim. Acta*, 1995, **78**, 959.
95ICA(230)153	S. Rodriguez-Morgade and T. Torres, *Inorg. Chem. Acta.*, 1995, **230**, 153.
96JA493	N. Chatani, T. Fukuyama, F. Kakiuchi and S. Murai, *J. Am. Chem. Soc.*, 1996, **118**, 493.
95JAP0715999	G. Tamano, M. Takada and A. Yoshida, JAP 0715999, CA: 123:270825
95JCS(P1)243	M. Begtrup and P. Vedsoe, *J. Chem. Soc., Perkin Trans. 1*, 1995, 243.
95JCS(P1)1039	X.-Q. Tang and C.-M. Hu, *J. Chem. Soc., Perkin Trans. 1*, 1995, 1039.
95JCS(P1)1747	M. Yokoyama, S. Hirano, M. Matsushita, T. Hachiya, N. Kobayashi, M. Kubo, H. Togo and H. Seki, *J. Chem. Soc., Perkin Trans. 1*, 1995, 1747.
95JCS(P1)2467	J. Alcazar, M. Begrup and A. de la Hoz, *J. Chem. Soc., Perkin Trans. 1*, 1995, 2467.
95JFC129	X.-Q. Tang and C.-M. Hu, *J. Fluorine Chem.*, 1995, **73**, 129.
95JHC207	M. Takahashi and K. Chigira, *J. Heterocycl. Chem.*, 1995, **32**, 207.

95JHC747   H. Lammers, R. Vollinga, P. Zandbergen, P. Cohen-Fernandes and C. L. Habraken, *J. Heterocycl. Chem.*, 1995, **32**, 747.
95JHC893   D. K. Anderson, D. L. Deuwer and J. A. Sikorski, *J. Heterocycl. Chem.*, 1995, **32**, 893.
95JHC1235   A. Shafiee, E. Naimi, P. Mansobi, A. Foroumadi and M. Shekari, *J. Heterocycl. Chem.*, 1995, **32**, 1235.
95JHC1325   N. Arnau, Y. Arredondo, M. Moreno-Manas, R. Pleixats and M. Villarroya, *J. Heterocycl. Chem.*, 1995, **32**, 1325.
95JHC1359   P. Trinka and J. Reiter, *J. Heterocycl. Chem.*, 1995, **32**, 1359.
95JMC323   H. Yanagisawa, Y. Amemiya, T. Kanazaki, Y. Shimoji, K. Fujimoto, Y.Kitahara, T. Sada, M. Mizuno, M. Ikeda, *et al.*, *J. Med. Chem.*, 1996, **39**, 323.
95JMC1067   T. Maduskuie, R. Wilde, J. Billheimer, D. Cromley, S. Germain, P. Gillies, A. Higley, A. Johnson and P. Pennev., *J. Med. Chem.*, 1995, **38**, 1067.
95JMC1287   C. Leschke, S. Elz, M. Garbarg and W. Schunack, *J. Med. Chem.*, 1995, **38**, 1287.
95JMC1679   P. Zhang, W. Zhang, R. Liu, B. Harris, P. Skolnick and J. Cook, *J. Med. Chem.*, 1995, **38**, 1679.
95JMC1799   L. J. Street *et al.*, *J. Med. Chem.*, 1995, **38**, 1799.
95JMC1837   B. Devadas, M. Zupec, S. Freeman, D. Brown, S. Nagarajan, J. Sikorski, C. McWherter, D. Getman and J. Gordon, *J. Med. Chem.*, 1995, **38**, 1837.
95JMC2357   P. Deprez, J. Guillaume, R. Becker, A. Corbier, S. Didierlaurent, M. Fortin, D. Frechet, G. Hamon and B. Heckman, *J. Med. Chem.*, 1995, **38**, 2357.
95JMC2925   H. Nicholas, R. Giorgi, F. Bonaccorsi, G. Cerbai, S. Columbani, A. Renzetti, R. Cirillo, A. Subissi and G. Alagona, *J. Med. Chem.*, 1995, **38**, 2925.
95JMC2938   M. Quan, A. Chiu, C. Ellis, P. Wong, R. Wexler and P. Timmermans, *J. Med. Chem.*, 1995, **38**, 2938.
95JOC6   A. R. Katritzky and J. L. Jiang, *J. Org. Chem.*, 1995, **60**, 6.
95JOC468   W. L. Collibee, N. Nakajima and J-P. Anselme, *J. Org. Chem.*, 1995, **60**, 468.
95JOC638   A. R. Katritzky and J. Q. Li, *J. Org. Chem.*, 1995, **60**, 638.
95JOC1090   E. Galeazzi, A. Guzman, J. L. Nava, Y. Liu, M. L. Maddox and J. M. Muchowski, *J. Org. Chem.*, 1995, **60**, 1090.
95JOC1872   B. Cabezon, S. Rodriguez-Morgade and T. Torres, *J. Org. Chem.*, 1995, **60**, 1872.
95JOC2008   F. Corelli, V. Summa, A. Brogi, E. Monteagudo and M. Botta, *J. Org. Chem.*, 1995, **60**, 2008.
95JOC2378   M. D. Cliff and S. G. Pyne, *J. Org. Chem.*, 1995, **60**, 2378.
95JOC3112   S. Borg, G. Estenne-Bouhtou, K. Luthman, I. Csoregh, W. Hesselink and U. Hacksel, *J. Org. Chem.*, 1995, **60**, 3112.
95JOC4002   A. R. Katritzky, A. V. Ignatchenko and H. Y. Lang, *J. Org. Chem.*, 1995, **60**, 4002.
95JOC4995   P. Vedso and M. Begtrup, *J. Org. Chem.*, 1995, **60**, 4995.
95JOC5678   P. Lopez-Alvarado, C. Avendano and J. C. Menendez, *J. Org. Chem.*, 1995, **60**, 5678.
95JOC5899   T. Choshi, S. Yamada, E. Sugino, T. Kuwada and S. Hibino, *J. Org. Chem.*, 1995, **60**, 5899.
95KGS176   A. V. Sukhotin, V. G. Kartsev, K. I. Kobrakov and A. B. Serov, *Khim. Geterotsikl. Soedin.*, 1995, 176.
95LA495   F. Fernandez-Lazaro, W. Schaefer and T. Torres, *Liebigs Ann.*, 1995, 495.
95LA1563   W. Reuther and U. Baus, *Liebigs Ann.*, 1995, 1563.
95LA2189   F. Hintermaier, L. B. Volodarsky, K. Polborn, and W. Beck, *Liebigs Ann.*, 1995, 2189.
95M733   Z. Gyoergydeak, W. Holzer, R. W. Holzer , A. Linden and L. Kossuth,

Monatsh. Chem., 1995, **126**, 733.

95M1035 R. Foldenyi, *Monatsh. Chem.*, 1995, **126**, 1035.

95MC102 A. M. Churakov, S. Semenov, E. Sergei, S. L. Ioffe, Y. A. Strelenko and V. A. Tartakovskii, *Mendeleev Commun.*, 1995, 102.

95MC194 T. I. Godovikove, S. P. Golova, S. A. Vozchikova, E. L. Ignat'eva, M. V. Povorin, V. S. Kuz'min and L. I. Khmelnitskii, *Mendeleev Commun.*, 1995, 194.

95MI9 B. S. Jursic and Z. Zdravkovski, *Theochem*, 1995, **337**, 9.

95MI29 R. Luboradzki, J. Lipkowski, W. Kozminski and L. Stefaniak, *J. Chem. Crystallogr.*, 1995, **25**, 29.

95MI33 Y. Shi, J. Fang, J. Zhou and Y. Hua, *Huazue Tonhbao*, 1995, 33.

95MI63 B. Boduszek, *Phosphorus, Sulfur, Silicon Relat. Elem.*, 1995, **104**, 63.

95MI113 A. M. Radwan, E. E. Eslam, R. Kassab and M. H. El-Nagdy, *J. Chem. Soc. Pak.*, 1995, **17**, 113.

95MI189 V. N. Gamezo, S. Odiot, M. Blain, S. Fliszar and A. Delpuech, *Theochem*, 1995, **337**, 189.

95MI297 F. Korodi and Z. Szabo, *Heterocycl. Commun.*, 1995, **1**, 297.

95MI408 C.-H. Lee, H.-J. Baik, K.-J. Kim, K.-U. Cho and K. T. Oh, *J. Korean Chem. Soc.*, 1995, **9**, 408.

95MI915 N. Ueyama, T. Yanagisawa and T. Tomiyama, *J. Labelled Compd. Radiopharm*, 1995, **36**, 915.

95MI947 L. A. Silks III, E. Dunkle, C. J. Unkefer, J. L. Sudmeier, M. Butler and W. W. Bachovchin, *J. Labelled Compd. Radiopharm.*, 1995, **36**, 947.

95MI2349 R. Handy, P. Wallace, Z.A. Gaffen, K.J. Whitehead and P.K. Moore, *Br. J. Pharmacol.*, 1995, **116**, 2349.

95MI3161 V. Vlassov, G. Zuber, B. Felden, J-P Behr and R. Giege, *Nucleic Acids Res.*, 1995, **23**, 3161.

95OM5415 U. Burckhardt, L. Hintermann, A. Schnyder and A. Togni, *Organometallics*, 1995, 14, 5415.

95OPP457 A. R. Katritzky, Z. Q. Wang, A. P. Wells and P. J. Steel, *Org. Prep. Proc. Int.*, 1995, **27**, 457.

95PJC259 T. Filipiak, C. Seliga and A. Frankowski, *Pol. J. Chem.*, 1995, **69**, 259.

95S503 A. R. Katritzky, H. X. Chang and B. Z. Yang, *Synthesis*, 1995, 503.

95S635 J. C. Caille, S. Didierlaurent, D. Lefrancois, M. H. Lelievre, C. Sury and J. Aszodi, *Synthesis*, 1995, 635.

95S647 G. Broggini, G. Molteni and G. Zecchi, *Synthesis*, 1995, 647.

95S805 U. I. Jonsson, H. Kristinsson, H. Nussbaumer, V. Skulason and T. Winkler, *Synthesis*, 1995, 805.

95S926 B. Krassowska-Swiebocka, P. Lulinski and L. Skulski, *Synthesis*, 1995, 926.

95S944 J. Streith, A. Boiron, A. Frankowski, D. LeNouen, H. Rudyk and T. Tschamber, *Synthesis*, 1995, 944.

95S1183 A. Horvath, *Synthesis*, 1995, 1183.

95SC761 C. Subramanyam, *Synth. Commun.*, 1995, **25**, 761.

95SC1173 A. R. Katritzky, R. L. Parriss and S. M. Allin, *Synth. Commun.*, 1995, **25**, 1173.

95SC1187 A. R. Katritzky, H. Wu and L. Xie, *Synth. Commun.*, 1995, **25**, 1187.

95SC2185 I. A. Rivero, R. Somanathan and L. H. Hellberg, *Synth. Commun.*, 1995, **25**, 2185.

95SC3219 Z-N. Huang and Z-M. Li, *Synth. Commun.*, 1995, **25**, 3219.

95SL239 J. Xu and J. C. Yadan, *Synlett*, 1995, 239.

95SM2289 B. Cabezon, F. Fernandez-Lazaro, M. V. Martinex-Diaz, S. Rodriguez-Morgade, A. Sastre and T. Torres, *Synth. Met.*, 1995, **71**, 2289.

95SM2291   M. Boronat, R. Viruela and E. Orti, *Synth. Met.*, 1995, **71**, 2291.
95T9511   M. G. Hoffmann, *Tetrahedron*, 1995, **51**, 9511.
95T12807   D. W. Hawkins, B. Iddon and D. S. Longthorne, Tetrahedron, 1995, **51**, 12807.
95TA2665   H. Kotsuki, H. Hayakawa, M. Wakao, T. Shimanouchi and M. Ochi, *Tetrahedron: Asymmetry*, 1995, **6**, 2665.
95T12807   D. W. Hawkins, B. Iddon and D. S. Longthorne, *Tetrahedron*, 1995, **51**, 12807.
95TL1679   K. Y. Yi and S. E. Yoo, *Tetrahedron Lett*, 1995, **36**, 1679.
95TL1759   Y. Satoh and N. Marcopulos, *Tetrahedron Lett*, 1995, **36**, 1759.
95TL2815   K-J. Lee and S-U. Kang, *Tetrahedron Lett.*, 1995, **36**, 2815.
95TL3165   S. Harusawa, Y. Murai, H. Moriyama, H. Ohishi, R. Yoneda and T. Kurihara, *Tetrahedron Lett.*, 1995, **36**, 3165.
95TL5969   M. D. Cliff and S. G. Pyne, *Tetrahedron Lett.*, 1995, **36**, 5969.
95TL6721   K. Tatsuta and S. Miura, *Tetrahedron Lett.*, 1995, **36**, 6721.
95TL7027   K. Hu, M. E. Niyazymbetov and D. H. Evans, *Tetrahedron Lett.*, 1995, **36**, 7027.
95TL7511   T. W. Brandstetter, B. Davis, D. Hyett, C. Smith, L. Hackett, B. G. Winchester and G. W. Fleet, *Tetrahedron Lett.*, 1995, **36**, 7511.
95TL8251   I. Kawasaki, N. Taguchi, T. Yamamoto, M. Yamashita and S. Ohta, *Tetrahedron Lett.*, 1995, **36**, 8251.
95ZOB308   M. A. Abramov and M. L. Petrov, *Zh. Obshch. Khim.*, 1995, **65**, 308.

Chapter 5.5

Five-Membered Ring Systems: With N & S (Se) Atoms

Rie Tanaka
Suntory Institute for Biomedical Research, Shimamoto, Osaka, Japan

5.5.1 ISOTHIAZOLES

The reaction of zirconium metallacycles was used to produce a variety of main group heterocycles via metallacycle transfer of a carbon fragment. The scope and potential for this reaction for the synthesis of some different heterocycles, including heterocycles containing two heteroatoms, were delineated. An azazirconacycle (1) was prepared by reducing zirconocene dichloride in the presence of bis(trimethylsilyl)acetylene, which stabilized the low valent zirconium reagent but was itself too hindered to undergo coupling reaction, followed by addition of 1-cyano-5-heptyne. Also 3-hexyne reacted with ethyl magnesium chloride in the presence of zirconocene dichloride to afford the metallacyclopentene (3), which followed by addition of butyronitrile, formed an azazirconacycle (4). Reaction of the former or the later azazirconacycle with sulfur monochloride afforded the desired isothiazole (2, 5) in 22% and 51% yield, respectively. [94JA1880]

6-Fluoro benzisothiazoles (6) were synthesized via carbonyl directed nucleophilic aromatic substitution. Displacement of the ortho fluoro substituent in 2,4-difluorobenzaldehyde, 2'4'-difluoroacetophenone and 2,4-difluorobenzophenone with benzyl mercaptan and potassium t-butoxide in THF gave the desired benzylsulfides (ortho/para ratio about 10:1) in 50-70% yield. The solvent and counter-ion effects observed in this reaction supported a chelation controlled addition. Treatment of the benzylsulfides with sulfuryl chloride followed by ammonia provided 6-fluoro-1,2-benzisothiazoles in 55-70% yield. [93TL6525]

R = H, Me, Ph

Treatment of aryl and heteroaryl *o*-azidocarbaldehydes with bis(trimethylsilyl)sulfide and hydrochloric acid gave fused isothiazoles, via thionation of the formyl function followed by spontaneous decomposition at room temperature. Yield was dependent upon the nature of the heteroaromatic ring. [94CL1873, 94PS479]

As 1,3-dipolar reagents, 3-dialkylaminoisothiazole 1,1-dioxides (7) underwent cycloaddition with diazoalkanes. Reaction of isothiazole 1,1-dioxides with diazoalkanes below room temperature resulted in the highly site and regioselective formation of the corresponding cycloadducts, which were the more thermodynamically stable 2-pyrazolines (9) and/or less stable 1-tautomers (8). Cycloadducts underwent straightforward thermolysis reactions in satisfactory yield at elevated temperatures to give 2-thia-3-azabicyclo[3.1.0]hex-3-ene 2,2-dioxides (10) accompanyed by elimination of nitrogen. Having a methyl or phenyl group on the bridge carbon of cycloadducts, the relatively high stability of the pyrazoline ring should favor the alternative cleavage of the isothiazole 1,1-dioxide ring to give pyrazoles (11). [94JCS(P1)2553] Also similar reactions of isothiazole 1,1-dioxides with sodium azide, diaryl-oxazolones and münchnones were discussed. [93T9117, 95T2455]

R_1 = H, Me, Ph R_2 = p-MeO-Ph, Ph, p-Me-Ph
R_3 = H, Me, Ph, CO_2Et R_4 = H, Me

2,3-Dihydrobenzo-1,2-thiazole-1,1-dioxides (12) underwent a smooth photoisomerization into isomeric N-hydroxy sulfinamides (14). Initial homolytic cleavage of N-S bond and then formation of 13 and last rearrangement may occur. [94PS481]

12   R_1, R_2 = Me, Ph, H R_3 = H, CH_2OMe 13   14

A synthesis of substituted imidazo[4,5-*d*]isothiazoles (**15**), as novel purine analogs, via the ring annulation of isothiazole diamines was reported. The chemical and physical properties of the compounds were investigated. No desulfurization of the alkylthio/mercapto group at C-5 of imidazo[4,5-*d*]isothiazoles was observed with several reductants. The ring system was destroyed instead. Ring annulation with diethoxymethyl acetate provided the 5-unsubstituted ones only when a methyl group was present at C-3. Alkylation of 3-methyl-5-(methylthio)imidazo[4,5-*d*]isothiazole with NaH-MeI readily gave mixtures of the N-4- and N-6-substututed compounds (**16,17**). [95JOC6309]

15   R_1 = Me, H R_2 = Me, Bn, allyl

The formation of a carbon-carbon bond in the 4-position of an isothiazole was carried out in moderate yield using the 4-magnesioisothiazole, which was prepared via metal halogen exchange reaction. 4-Iodoisothiazole was reacted with ethylmagnesium bromide, then with electrophiles to give ethyl isothiazole-4-carboxylate and isothiazol-4-carbaldehyde. Secondary and tertiary alcohols were obtained from aromatic aldehydes and ketones. [95SC1383] A comparative study of reactions of 3-methyl-5-phenylisothiazole and 3-methyl-5-phenylisoxazole with electrophilic compounds was reported. In the presence of lithium isopropylcyclohexylamide (LICA)-N,N,N',N'-tetramethylethylenediamine, regioselective reaction of both compounds at the C-3 methyl group with different electrophiles was observed. In the case of isothiazole, treatment with LICA or n-BuLi gave the same result, except with the combination of n-BuLi-methyl iodide, in which case the dialkylated product at the C-4 and C-3 methyl groups was detected. [95JHC537]

Syntheses and reactions of lithiated isothiazoles and thiazoles were reviewed. [95H533] Phenylisothiazoles and phenylthiazoles are known to undergo a variety of phototranspositions upon irradiation in benzene solvent. These reactions were reinvestigated. [94JA2292]

5.5.2 THIAZOLES

A convenient quaternization and rearrangement procedure offered a simple route to different classes of N,S-heterocycles of medium and large sizes in moderate yield. The initial quaternizations of benzothiazole or thiazole with α,ω-dihaloalkanes in CH_3CN under reflux afforded the monoquaternary intermediates (**18**). In the subsequent rearrangement with NaOH in MeOH-H_2O the previously attached alkyl side chain was incorporated into in the newly formed hetero ring (**19**) with up to 12 membered ring sizes. [95JOC2597]

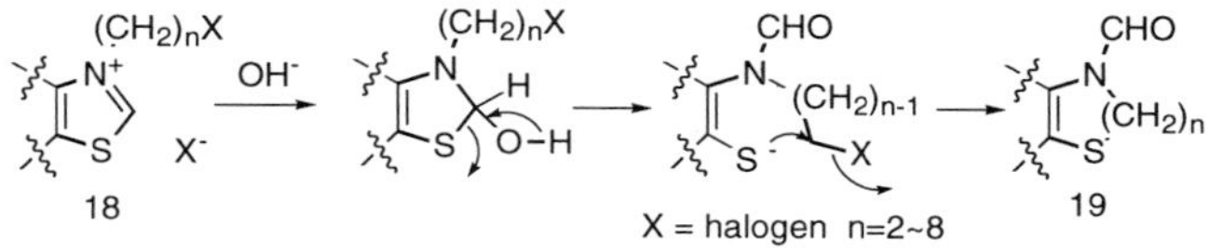

X = halogen n=2~8

Similarly, ring expansion of benzothiazole was described. Treatment of organolithiums (**21**), which were prepared by lithiation of heteroarylmethanes such as 2-benzothiazolyl methyllithium, with 2-chloromethylbenzothiazole (**20**) gave benzothiazines (**23**)in good yield by ring-enlargement of thiazoline intermediates (**22**) and tautomerization of unstable dihydro-benzothiazines. [95TL1913]

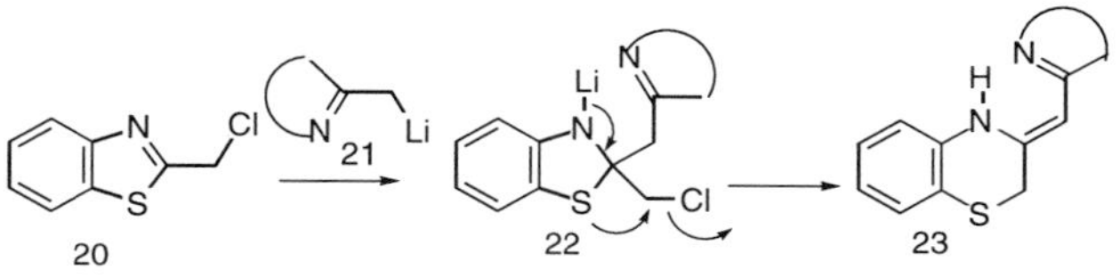

Treatment of α-bromolactams (**24**) with thioamides in EtOH under reflux gave 4-aminothiazolederivatives in moderate yield. From the intermediate (**25**) the reaction course may branch to two pathways depending on the structure, reactivity and stability of the intermediates. Although the reaction with acyclic α-bromoamides proceeds through the similar manner of path B to give 4-exothiazole after cleavage of the C-N bond, the reaction of cyclic lactams (**24**) prefers path A to give bicyclic derivatives (**26**). [94JHC1545]

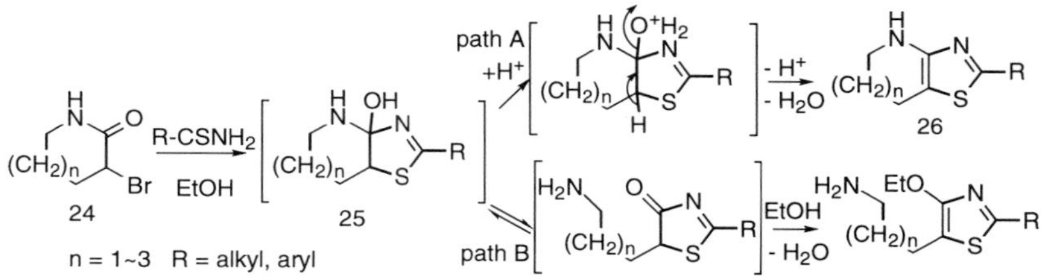

n = 1~3　R = alkyl, aryl

The instability of 1-azabuta-1,3-dienes arising from the imine moiety and the low reactivity as dienes in the Diels-Alder reaction are sometimes problems. Benzylidene(cyano)methyl-1,3-benzothia/oxazoles, featuring a stabilized imine moiety in the form of a heteroaromatic ring and having adequate reactivity arising from the electron-withdrawing cyano group, react with both electron-deficient and electron-rich dienophiles to give the corresponding cycloadducts regioselectively. The starting dienes (27), stable crystalline materials prepared from (1,3-benzothiazole-2-yl)acetonitrile and benzaldehydes, reacted with N-methylmaleimide, anethole, and 3,4-dihydro-$2H$-pyran to give *endo*-cycloadducts (28) of the first two compounds and *endo-exo* mixtures (28,29) of the latter. Cycloadditions of the intramolecular systems such as (E)-3-(2-allyloxyphenyl)-2-(benzothiazol-2-yl)acrylonitrile proceeded as well. [95JCS(P1)1759]

X = H, Cl, Me, OMe, NO_2,

The use of thiazole as a formyl group equivalent was applied to the total synthesis of the natural aza sugar (+)-galactostatin from D-serine and the synthesis of formyl C-glycosides. [95JOC4749, 94JOC6404] The approach of either *syn* or *anti* selective addition of 2-(trimethylsilyl)thiazole, controlling a singly or doubly protected nitrogen of α-amino aldehydes, was achieved in the preparation of the β-amino-α-hydroxy aldehyde intermediates of a HIV inhibitor. [95JOC8074]

The behavior of bis(heteroaryl)methanes in which the heterocycle was an electron-withdrawing group was similar to that typically exhibited by active methylene compounds. Bis(2-benzothiazolyl)methane and bis(2-(5-ethoxycarbonyl-4-methyl)thiazolyl)methane readily underwent azo-coupling with benzenediazonium chloride, nitrosation with nitrous acid and condensation with aromatic aldehydes under mildly basis conditions, such as in the Knoevenagel procedure. [94G301]

Most of previous work has implied that alkylation and acylation of 2-amino-2-thiazoline occurs on the ring nitrogen and the exocyclic nitrogen, respectively. However, both reactions gave initial attack on the more nucleophilic endocyclic nitrogen, and acyl groups readily rearranged to give the observed products. In the alkylation of the thiazoline (30) with α-bromo Michael acceptors yielded 2,3,5,6-tetrahydroimidazo[2,1-b]thiazoles (31). In the phosphorylation reaction of 30, in which the possible products should be differentiated by long-range C-P coupling in the ^{13}C nmr, with diphenyl chlorophosphate and triethylamine, the rearrangement occurred depending on the temperature. [94H2593] 5,6-Dihydrothiazolo[2,3-e][1,4,2] diazaphosphole were obtained regiospecifically by Hantzsch-type condensation, [3+2] cyclocondensation of 2-aminothiazoline with chloromethyldichlorophosphane in the presence of triethylamine.[95CB581]

EWG = CO_2Et, CN, COMe

The synthesis of various heterocyclic systems via 1,3-dipolar cycloaddition reactions of 1,3-oxazolium-5-oxides (**32**) with different dipolarophiles was reported. The cycloaddition reactions of mesoionic 5H,7H-thiazolo[3,4-*c*]oxazolium-1-oxides (**32**), which were prepared from *in situ* N-acyl-(*R*)-thiazolidine-4-carboxylic acids and N,N'-dicyclohexylcarbodiimide, with imines, such as N-(phenylmethylene)aniline and N-(phenylmethylene)benzenesulfonamide, gave 7-thia-2,5-diazaspiro[3,4]octan-1-one derivatives (**33**) and 1H,3H-imidazo[1,5-*c*]thiazole derivative (**35**). The nature of substituents on imines and on mesoionic compounds influenced the reaction. A spirocyclic β-lactam (**33**) may be derived from a two-step addition reaction. Alternatively, an imidazothiazole (**35**) may be obtained from a typical 1,3-dipolar cycloaddition via a tricyclic adduct (**34**) which loses carbon dioxide and benzenesulfinic acid. [95T9385]

An oxidative route to 1,3-thiazoles (**39**) and oxazoles, which bear the requisite functionality, such as amino groups and stereocenters, for incorporation into a variety of natural products was reported. Treatment of 1,3-thiazolines (**36**) with CuBr (1.1eq), Cu(OAc)$_2$ (1.1eq) and t-butyl perbenzoate (1.5eq) under benzene reflux gave 1,3-thiazoles (**39**) in about 80% yield. A plausible mechanism included generation of a Cu (III) species (**37**) via oxidative addition, reductive elimination to the acyloxy thiazoline (**38**), and syn elimination on warming to produce the thiazole (**39**). [94TL6803]

A novel and efficient synthesis of 5-(hydroxymethyl)thiazole starting from 2,4-thiazolidinedione was performed with phosphorus oxybromide and DMF to give 2,4-dibromo-5-thiazolecarboxaldehyde in 72 % yield. Reduction of the aldehyde with NaBH$_4$ and catalytic hydrogenation with Pd/C at room temperature afforded the desired product in excellent yield. [95SC2639]

Also, a novel synthesis of methyl 5-substituted thiazole-4-carboxylates (**43**) was reported. The reaction of methyl (*E*)- and/or (*Z*)-3-substituted 3-bromo-2-isocyanoacrylates (**40**) with hydrogen sulfide (1.2eq) and triethylamine at room temperature afforded the desired thiazoles (**43**) in good yield. The substitution reaction of the first sulfide with **40** may proceed with retention, and addition-elimination of the second sulfide to the β-thioacrylates (**42**) may cause isomerization of the double bond. The Z-isomers (**41**) cyclized to the thiazoles (**43**). [95TL257]

4,5-Dichloro-1,2,3-dithiazolium chloride, which was prepared from chloroacetonitrile and disulfur dichloride, reacted rapidly with fluoroanilines to give N-arylimines (**44**). Thermolysis of the imines (**44**) afforded 2-cyanobenzothiazoles (**45**) in modest yield together with cyanoimidoyl chlorides (**46**). [95JCS(P1)1659]

A convenient synthesis of 1*H*-indolyl-2-benzothiazoles in moderate yield by the direct conversion of indole-2- and 5-carboxylates with *in situ* generated trimethylaluminum-2-aminothiophenol was described. [95H1045] 2-Substituted 1,3-benzothiazoles having a variety of substituents can be prepared from 2-methylthio-N-triphenylphosphoranylideneaniline and acid chlorides by iminophosphorane-mediated cyclization. [95H455]

2,3-Dihydropyrazolo[5,1-*b*]thiazoles (**48**) were simply prepared from 3-aminorhodanines (**47**) and ethyl 2-bromo-3,3-diethoxypropionate under toluene reflux for 2 hr in fair yield, accompanying with tandem condensation, and sulfur extrusion reaction under mild condition. [94JHC1719]

The reaction of 5-phenyl-1,2,4-dithiazole-3-one (**49**) with the moderately stabilized Wittig reagents (R=OMe, OEt) and acetonylidenephosphorane gave a mixture of **50** and **51**. [93MI001]

A new method for the synthesis of 2-substituted-4-carbethoxythiazole derivatives was performed by Lewis acid (such as boron trifluoride etherate) promoted reaction of ethyl diazopyruvate with thioamides at 80 °C in moderate yield. [95JHC937] N-(Methylthioalkylidene) glycine ethyl esters, which can exist at equilibrium with the corresponding azomethine ylide, reacted with thionesters in the presence of DBU in THF to afford the corresponding ethyl 2,5-disubstituted-4-thiazolecarboxylates in fair yield. [94S1467, 94PS477] The highly reactive allenyl isothiocyanate, which can be easily obtained from propargyl thiocyanate by gas-phase thermolysis interpreted as a [3,3] sigmatropic rearrangement, reacted with various nucleophiles to give thiazoles in fair yield. [94PS323]

In a previously reported synthesis of 4,4-dimethyl-1,3-thiazole-5(4H)-thiones, 3-amino-2H-aziridines (**52**) were reacted with thiocarboxylic acids to yield thioamides which were heated with Lawesson's reagent to complete the cyclization. This method was applied to the synthesis of 2-alkylthio analogues (**53**) using trithiocarbonic acids instead of thiocarboxylic acids. The reactivity of the 2-alkylthio derivatives was also discussed. [94HCA1903] Reaction of 1,3-thiazole-5(4H)-thiones oxides (**54**), which were prepared from the corresponding thiones by oxidation with *m*-chloroperbenzoic acid in Et$_2$O, with organolithium followed by alkylation or protonation gave anti-adducts in fair yield via thiophilic attack. Also, reactivity with Grignard reagents and organocuprates was shown. [94HCA2133]

1-(Cyanomethyl)benzotriazole, the benzotriazole group of which has a combination of activating and leaving ability, can be used via a modified Hantzsch synthesis to prepare 2,4-di-, 2,5-di, and 2,4,5-trisubstituted thiazoles. 2-*tert*-Alkyl and other highly substituted thiazoles were obtained by the facile introduction of substituents either before or after thiazole ring formation. [95JOC5638] Thermal degradation of 2,4,6-chloromethyltrioxanes in the presence of a catalytic amount of commercially available montmorillonite clay at 110 °C for 0.5 hr without organic solvent generated α-chloroaldehydes, which are usually unstable and extremely labile polymerforming materials, with high purity. The generated aldehydes reacted with thioureato give 2-aminothiazole in good yield. [94CL2039]

Perfluoro-2-methyl-2-penten-3-yl isothiocyanate, which was prepared from perfluoro-2-methyl-2-pentene and KSCN in benzonitrile in high yield by direct substitution of fluorine, is a stable and versatile educt for heterocyclic synthesis. This α,β-unsaturated isothiocyanate reacted with enamines, such as 1-methylindole and 2-methyl-1-morpholino-1-propene, to yield 2-(1-methylindol-3-yl)-perfluro-4,5-dihydro-5,5-dimethyl-4-ethylidene-1,3-thiazole and its analogue in fair yield. [95H1015]

5.5.3 THIADIAZOLES

5.5.3.1 1,2,3-Thiadiazoles

One of the $6\alpha\lambda^4$-thiapentalenes, $6\alpha\lambda^4$-thia-1,2,3,5,6-pentaazapentalenes (56) having unusual bonding properties, was synthesized. Starting from chloropinacolone according to the method of Hurd and Mori, the thiadiazole (55), the phthalimido group of which was removed by hydrazinolysis was prepared. A bulky *tert*-butyl group at the 4-position was added in order to direct methylation exclusively at the N-2 atom. Treatment of 55 with Meerwein's reagent and then arenediazonium salts yielded the thiapentalene system (56). Of the two canonical forms (56A, 56B), the A form was considered to contribute most to the real structure by ^{13}CNMR data and X-ray analysis. [94JCS(P1)2895]

The phosphonium salts (58) were versatile reagents for the synthesis of 1,2,3-thiadiazoles (59) with unsaturated side chains. Ring closure of triphenylphosphonium chlorides (57) by the Hurd and Mori method gave these salts (58). Subsequent Wittig reactions did not occur stereoselectively. [95ZN(B)1121]

5.5.3.2 1,2,4-Thiadiazoles

Tellurium tetrachloride in combination with a strong amine base effected the mild dehydrosulfurization of thioamides to nitriles. Treatment of the thioamides (60) with tellurium tetrachloride and triethylamine in chloroform at room temperature formed nitriles (61) in excellent yield. Using selenium tetrachloride, a similar reaction also occurred in a little lower yield and accompanied by the formation of the 1,2,4-thiadiazole (63). In a plausible mechanism, some of the 1:1 adduct (61) undergoes a further addition reaction with another thioamide molecule prior to the degradation reaction to nitrile, leading to the formation of the 1,2,4-

thiadiazole (**63**). [95JCR(S)152]

Ring-transformations of suitably substituted azoles constitute widely used reactions for the synthesis of five-membered heterocycles. The sulfurization reaction of 3-acylamino-1,2,4-oxazoles (**64**,X=N) and isoxazoles (**64**,X=C)with the Lawesson reagent directly gave the rearranged 1,2,4-thiadiazoles (**65**) in moderate yield. In the case of 3-acylaminofurazans (**66**), owing to the lower reactivity of the ring towards rearrangements, thioamides could be detected. Treatment of the reaction mixture with aqueous sodium hydroxide as a work-up procedure gave rearranged 1,2,4-thiadiazole oximes (**67**). [94H2423]

5.5.3.3 1,2,5-Thiadiazoles

The synthesis of quinones (**69**) fused to a 1,2,5-thiadiazole ring has required a number of steps through diaminoquinones. However, treatment of 1,4-naphthoquinone (**68**) with trithiazyl trichloride, $(NSCl)_3$, in benzene containing pyridine at reflux for 2hr gave naphtho[2,3-c][1,2,5]thiadiazole-4,7-dione (**69**) in good yield in a simple one-step procedure. So do the thiazyl derivative related to $(NSCl)_3$, alkyl carbamates mixed with excess thionyl chloride, and pyridine under benzene reflux for a few hours. In a plausible mechanism, NSCl adds as a nucleophile to an unsaturated ketone incorporated first with pyridine. Use of $SeOCl_2$ yielded the selenium analogue. [95JOC1285]

A series of 4-substituted-1,2,5-thiadiazole-3-yl N-dialkylcarbamates was investigated as inhibitors of HIV-1. [95JMC2038]

5.5.3.4 1,3,4-Thiadiazoles

Partially and perfluorinated thioketones and thioaldehyde were stabilized as anthracene adducts (**70**). The adducts (**70**) were prepared in moderate yield from the corresponding carbonyl compounds with P_4S_{10} or Lawesson's reagent in the presence of anthracene under toluene reflux. The generated thiocarbonyl compounds are not accessible in bulk due to their tendency towards polymerization. By thermolysis of the anthracene adducts (**70**) in the presence of C,N-bis(triisopropylsilyl)nitrilimine (NI), 1,3,4-thiadiazole derivatives (**71**) were obtained. Also, 1,3-dipolar cycloaddition with bis(trimethylstannyl)diazomethane (BTSD) to give consecutive products (**72**) from a 1,2-metallotropic migration of primary adducts was discussed. [95LA95]

Reaction of N'-phenylthioformhydrazine (**73**) with ketones in the presence of trimethylsilyl chloride at room temperature gave 2,2-disubstituted-2,3-dihydro-3-phenyl-1,3,4-thiadiazoles (**74**) in good yield, except with benzophenone and α,β-unsaturated ketones. O-Trimethylsilyl phenylhydrazonomethylmonothioacetals were formed initially, intramolecular cyclization followed. [94CPB1912] Treatment of $ArCCl_3$ (Ar = Ph, 2,4-Me_2Ph) with thiosemicarbazide in MeOH-pyridine yielded 2-amino-5-aryl-1,3,4-thiadiazoles in moderate yield. [94PS469]

Formation of charge-transfer (CT) complexes between thiosemicarbazones (76) and 2,3-dichloro-5,6-dicyano-1,4-benzoquinone (75) yielded 3-amino-5-arylthiadiazoles (78) and hydroquinone (77) as a result of the irreversible chemical reactions. Mixing of quinone (75) (2eq) with thiosemicarbazones (76) (1eq) in ethyl acetate gave a blue color initially for the unstable CT complexes, and this color changed gradually to brown with the formation of a solid product by a chemical reaction. [94LA989]

A study of the 1,3-dipolar cycloaddition of pyrazines, pyrimidines and 1H-pyrimidinthiones with nitrilimines (80), generated *in situ* by dehydrohalogenation of the corresponding hydrazonoyl chlorides (79), was carried out. Reaction of pyrimidine-2(1H)-thiones (81) and -4(1H)-thiones with nitrilimines in benzene at reflux gave spiro[pyrimidine-2(1H), 2'(3'H)-[1,3,4]thiadiazoles (82) and spiro[pyrimidine-4(1H), 2'(3'H)-[1,3,4]thiadiazoles, respectively, in good yield. By using a large excess of nitrilimine (80) with pyrimidine-2(1H)-thiones (81), 2:1-cycloadducts (83) were formed. [94LA1005]

5.5.4 SELENAZOLES AND SELENADIAZOLES

An equilibrium of prop-2-yl selenocyanates (84) and allenes (85) was obtained on gas-phase thermolysis (0.1-0.01 Torr 350-400°C) of 84. This isomerization by [3,3]sigmatropic rearrangements provided access to the highly reactive allenyl isoselenocyanates (85). The isoselenocyanates (85) can only be handled in solution due to their pronounced tendency to polymerize. Although these are less reactive with nucleophiles than allenyl isothiocyanates, treatment with nucleophiles afforded selenazoles in moderate yield. [95AG(E)1627]

A one-pot synthesis of pyrroles (**90**) from 1,2,5-selenadiazoles (**88**) with 1,3-diketones in the presence of zinc powder and acetic acid was reported. Initial reductive elimination of selenium gave a diamine (**89**), then one amino group was condensed with a 1,3-diketone followed by intramolecular cyclization to afford a pyrrole (**90**). [94JCS(P1)2201]

N,N'-diarylglyoxaldihydrazonoyl dihalides (**91**), versatile intermediates for the synthesis of heterocyclic systems, reacted with KSeCN in ethanol at reflux to yield 2,2'-bi(4-aryl-4,5-dihydro-5-imino-1,3,4-selenadiazoles) (**92**) directly in good yield. Similarly, the reaction of the dihalides with selenourea and acylselenourea gave the biselenadiazoles in one step by elimination of ammonia or aniline. [94PS129]

Monocyclic selenazoles were obtained by the reaction of selenoamides with α-halocarbonyl compounds. Primary aryl and alkyl selenocarboxamides were prepared from nitriles and ethanolic sodium hydrogen selenide in the presence of pyridine and hydrochloric acid. [93S870] The reaction of 4,5,6,7,8,9-hexahydrocycloocta-1,2,3-selenadiazoles (**93**), which is synthon of selenaketocarbene derived by loss of dinitrogen, with tetrakis(triphenylphosphine)platinum under toluene reflux, yield two compounds, $[Pt(SeC_8H_{12})(PPh_3)_2]$ and $[Pt(Se_2C_8H_{12})(PPh_3)_2]_x$. [95JCR(S)64]

5.5.5 REFERENCES

93MI001	W. M. Abdou, E. M. A. Yakout and M. M. Said, *Sulfur Letters*, **1993**, *17(1)*, 33.
93S870	L-L Lai, D. H. Reid, *Synthesis*, **1992**, 870.
93T9117	O. Carugo, F. Clerici, D. Pocar, *Tetrahedron*, **1993**, *49(40)*, 9117.
93TL6525	D. M. Fink, J. T. Strupczewski, *Tetrahedron Letters*, **1993**, *34(41)*, 6525.
94CL1873	A. Degl'Innocenti, M. Funicello, P. Scafato, P. Spagnolo, *Chemistry Letters*, **1994**, 1873.
94CL2039	T. Wakasugi, T. Miyakawa, F. Suzuki, S. Itsuno, K. Ito, *Chemistry Letters,* **1994**, 2039.
94G301	A. Abbotto, S. Bradamante, G. A. Pagani, *Gazzetta Chimica Italiana*, **1994**, *124*, 301.
94H2423	S. Buscemi, N. Vivona, *Heterocycles*, **1994**, *38(11)*, 2423.
94H2593	G. Kaugars, S. E. Martin, S. J. Nelson, W. Watt, *Heterocycles*, **1994**, *38(12)*, 2593.
94HCA1903	J. Shi, A. Linden, H. Heimgartner, *Helvetica Chimica Acta*, **1994**, *77*, 1903.
94HCA2133	J. Shi, P. Tromm, H. Heimgartner, *Helvetica Chimica Acta*, **1994**, *77*, 2133.
94JA1880	P. J. Fagan, W. A. Nugent, J. C. Calabrese, *J. Am. Chem. Soc.*, **1994**, *116*, 1880.
94JA2292	J. W. Pavlik, P. Tongcharoensirikul, N. P. Bird, A. C. Day, J. A. Barltrop, *J. Am. Chem. Soc.*, **1994**, *116*, 2292.
94JCS(P1)2201	T. Ueda, C. Uchida, S. Nagai, J. Sakakibara, *J. Chem. Soc. Perkin Trans. 1*, **1994**, 2201.
94JCS(P1)2895	G. L'abbé, L. Bastin, W. Dehaen, L. V. Meervelt, *J. Chem. Soc. Perkin Trans. 1*, **1994**, 2895.
94JHC1545	O. Uchikawa, T. Aono, *J. Heterocyclic Chem.*, **1994**, *31*, 1545.
94JHC1719	W. Hanefeld, M. Schlitzer, *J. Heterocyclic Chem.*,**1994**, *31*, 1719.
94JOC6404	A. Dondoni, M-C Scherrmann, *J. Org. Chem.*, **1994**, *59*, 6404.
94LA989	A. A. Hassan, Y. R. Ibrahim, A. A. Semida, A-F E. Mourad, *Liebigs Ann. Chem.*, **1994**, 989.
94LA1005	L. Grubert, M. Pätzel, W. Jugelt, B. Riemer, . Liebscher, *Liebigs Ann. Chem.*, **1994**, 1005.
94PS129	A. M. Farag, Z. E. Kandeel, K. M. Dawood, *Phosphorus, Sulfur, and Silicon,* 1994, 91, 129.
94PS323	K. Banert, S. Groth, H. Hückstädt, K. Vrobel, *Phosphorus, Sulfur, and Silicon*, 1994, 95-96, 323.
94PS469	L. Belen'Kii, I. Poddubny, M. Krayushkin, *Phosphorus, Sulfur, and Silicon*, **1994**, *95-96*, 469.
94PS477	M. Yokoyama, *Phosphorus, Sulfur, and Silicon*, **1994**, *95-96*, 477.
94PS479	A. Capperucci, A. Degl'Innocenti, M. Funicello, P. Scafato, P. Spagnolo, *Phosphorus, Sulfur, and Silicon*, **1994**, *95-96*, 479.
94PS481	D. Döpp, P. Lauterfeld, M. Schneider, D. Schneider, U. Seidel, *Phosphorus, Sulfur, and Silicon*, **1994**, *95-96*, 481.
94S1467	M. Yokoyama, Y. Menjo, M. Watanabe, J. Togo, *Synthesis*, **1994**, 1467.
94TL6803	F. Tavares, A. I. Meyers, *Tetrahedron Letters*, **1994**, *35(37)*, 6803.
95AG(E)1627	K. Banert, C. Toth, *Angew. Chem. Int. Ed. Engl.*, **1995**, *34(15)*, 1627.

95CB581   K. Karaghiosoff, R. Mahnot, C. Cleve, N. Gandhi, R. K. Bansal, A. Schmidpeter, *Chem. Ber.*, **1995**, *128*, 581.

95H455   M. Takahashi, M. Ohba, *Heterocycles*, **1995**, *41(3)*, 455.

95H533   B. Iddon, *Heterocycles*, **1995**, *41(3)*, 533.

95H1015   V. Y. Popkova, F. M. Dolgushin, M. Y. Antipin, A. I. Yanovsky, Y. T. Struchkov, *Heterocycles*, **1995**, *40(2)*, 1015.

95H1045   R. L. Hudkins, *Heterocycles*, **1995**, *41(5)*, 1045.

95JCR(S)64   P. K. Khanna, C. R. Morley, *J. Chem. Research (S)*, **1995**, 64.

95JCR(S)152   Y. Aso, K. Omote, S. Takagi, T. Otsubo, F. Ogura, *J. Chem. Research (S)*, **1995**, 152.

95JCS(P1)1659   T. Besson, C. W. Rees, *J. Chem. Soc. Perkin Trans. 1*, **1995**, 1659.

95JCS(P1)1759   M. Sakamoto, A. Nozaka, M. Shimamoto, H. Ozaki, Y. Suzuki, S. Yoshioka, M. Nagano, K. Okamura, T. Date, O. Tamura, *J. Chem. Soc. Perkin Trans 1*, **1995**, 1759.

95JHC537   A. Alberola, L. Calvo, Mᵃ T. R. Rodríguez, Mᵃ C. Sanudo, *J. Heterocyclic Chem.*, **1995**, *32*, 537.

95JHC937   H-S Kim, I-C Kwon, O-H Kim, *J. Heterocyclic Chem.*, **1995**, *32*, 937.

95JMC2038   Y. Hanasaki, H. Watanabe, K. Katsuura, H. Takayama, S. Shirakawa, K. Yamaguchi, S. Sakai, K. Ijichi, M. Fujiwara, K. Jonno, T. Yokota, S. Shigeta, M. Baba, *J. Med. Chem.*, **1995**, *38*, 2038.

95JOC1285   S. Shi, T. J. Katz, B. V. Yang, L. Liu, *J. Org. Chem.*, **1995**, *60*, 1285.

95JOC2597   J-J Federsel, G. Glasare, C. Högström, J. Wiestål, B. Zinko, C. ödman, *J. Org. Chem.*, **1995**, *60*, 2597.

95JOC4749   A. Dondoni, D. Perrone, *J. Org. Chem.*, **1995**, *60*, 4749.

95JOC5638   A. R. Katritzky, J. Chen, Z. Yang, *J. Org. Chem.*, **1995**, *60*, 5638.

95JOC6309   E. E. Swayze, L. B. Townsend, *J. Org. Chem.*, **1995**, *60*, 6309.

95JOC8074   A. Dondoni, D. Perrone, P. Merino, *J. Org. Chem.*, **1995**, *60*, 8074.

95LA95   J. Hasserodt, H. Pritzkow, W. Sundermeyer, *Liebigs Ann.*, **1995**, 95.

95SC1383   F. Guilloteau, L. Miginiac, *Synthetic Communications*, **1995**, *25(9)*, 1383.

95SC2639   F. A. J. Kerdesky, L. S. Seif, *Synthetic Communications*, **1995**, *25(17)*, 2639.

95T2455   P. Baggi, F. Clerici, M. L. Gelmi, S. Mottadelli, *Tetrahedron*, **1995**, *51(8)*, 2455.

95T9385   P. D. Croce, R. Ferraccioli, C. La Rosa, *Tetrahedron*, **1995**, *51(34)*, 9385.

95TL257   M. Yamada, T. Fukui, K. Nunami, *Tetrahedron Letters*, **1995**, *36(2)*, 257.

95TL1913   S. Florio, L. Troisi, V. Capriati, *Tetrahedron Letters*, **1995**, *36(11)*, 1913.

95ZN(B)1121   N. Hanold, H. Kalbitz, M. Al-Smadi, H. Meier, *Z. Naturforsch*, **1995**, *50b*, 1121.

Chapter 5.6

Five-Membered Ring Systems: With O & S (Se, Te) Atoms

R. Alan Aitken and Lawrence Hill
University of St. Andrews, UK

5.6.1 1,3-DIOXOLES AND DIOXOLANES

The fragmentation of a range of 1,3-dioxolanes has been examined using positive-ion CI mass spectrometry [95RCM405] and nuclear Overhauser effects in the NMR spectra of 4-trimethylammoniomethyl-2,2-disubstituted-1,3-dioxolanes have been used to study their conformational properties [95MRC167].

Electrochemical reduction of substituted benzils, $Ar^1COCOAr^1$, in the presence of the imidoyl dichlorides $Ar^2N{=}CCl_2$ provides a high yielding synthesis of 2-imino-1,3-dioxoles (**1**) [95T3641]. The donor-acceptor spiro dioxolane (**2**) as well as its oxathiolane and dithiolane analogues have been prepared and their X-ray structures determined [94CB2215]. Cyclisation of the radicals derived from (**3**) under a variety of conditions proceeds with high selectivity to give the trans-dioxolanones (**4**) [94TL5193]. Electrochemical nickel-catalysed reaction of terminal epoxides with CO_2 proceeds at RT and atmospheric pressure to give the corresponding 4-substituted-1,3-dioxolan-2-ones (**5**) [95CC43], and carboxylation of trifluoroepoxypropane affords the dioxolanone (**6**) which has several applications [95JAP07165750]. Reaction of chiral styrene epoxide with carbonyl compounds catalysed by $TiCl_4$ affords the dioxolanes (**7**)

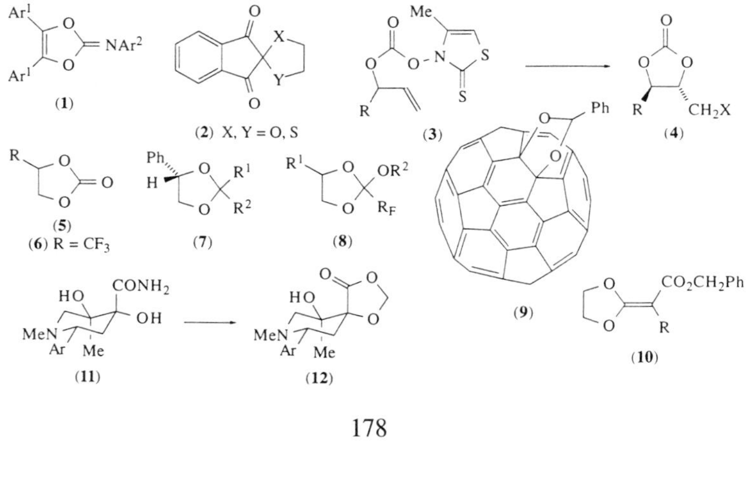

178

without loss of enantiomeric purity [94BCJ2614]. Various terminal epoxides react with alkyl perfluorocarboxylates to afford the cyclic orthoesters (8) [95TL2781]. The unusual formation of (9) by treatment of C_{60} with benzyl alcohol and its sodium salt in air appears to involve a radical mechanism [95CC1071]. New catalysts for the conversion of aldehydes and ketones into the corresponding dioxolanes with ethylene glycol include various forms of aluminium phosphate and $AlPO_4/Al_2O_3$ [95JCS(P2)815]. A direct synthesis of halogenated 2,2-difluoro-1,3-dioxolanes involves treatment of halo alkenes with $F_2C(OF)_2$ [95JFC(71)111]. The benzoxycarbonylalkylidene dioxolanes (10) are conveniently prepared by treating the enolate of a benzyl ester with 2-chloroethyl chloroformate and hydrogenation of these affords the corresponding unsaturated acids [95S512]. Treatment of the α-hydroxy amide (11) with CH_2O and H_2SO_4 gives (12) by an unusual mechanism involving the N-hydroxymethyl amide [94KGS1216]. Reliable syntheses have been described for both (S)-glyceraldehyde acetonide (13) [93OS1] and its (R)-enantiomer [93OS6], the two enantiomers of the corresponding acid (14) [95ACS297], and (15) [93OS48].

(13)   (14)   (15)   (16) X = H, CO_2Et

The deprotection of 2,2-disubstituted-1,3-dioxolanes to give the corresponding ketones can be achieved under mild conditions using NO_2 and silica and the mechanism has been elucidated [95CC1121]. Kinetic resolution has been reported in the hydrolysis of racemic 4-substituted-1,3-dioxolan-2-ones (5) using hydrolytic enzymes such as porcine pancreatic lipase to afford the (S)-diol in up to 82% e.e. and the unreacted (R)-carbonate in up to 95% e.e. [95TL6499]. The radicals (16) show excellent face selectivity in their addition to ethyl acrylate [95JPR113]. Chiral 1,3-dioxolanes have been used to direct a number of new asymmetric reactions. Thus, addition of an α-silylcuprate to the enantiomer of (13) gives (17) [95T9023] and conjugate addition of cuprates to (18) proceeds with 70-100% d.e. [94T13173]. Reaction of (19) with Bu^nLi followed by R^2CHO gives the alcohols (20) in 10-50% d.e. [94TL2063]. Direct lithiation of the β-chlorovinyldioxolane (21) at –90 °C affords the vinyllithium which can be reacted with a variety of electrophiles to give (22) [94TL7643].

Claisen rearrangement of the 2-vinyl-4-methylenedioxolanes (23) to afford the oxepinones (24) has been described [94TL3111]. Various cycloadditions involving chiral 1,3-dioxolanes have been reported including addition of dienes to (25) [95T8923], addition of nitrones or hetero-1,3-dienes to (26) with microwave irradiation in the absence of solvent [94JCS(P1)3595], addition of diazo compounds to (27) [95T1631], and addition of chiral cyclopentenone ketal (28) to C_{60} to afford a mixture of (29) and its diastereomer which can be separated [95CC1769].

The chiral tetraaryldioxolanediols ("TADDOLS") (30) have found a number of applications. The formation of crystalline host-guest complexes with (30) has allowed the resolution of aliphatic diols [94JAP06271481], sulfoxides [95CC639], 5-substituted-Δ^2-pyrazolines [95CC1453], and 2-substituted piperazines [94JAP06192236]. Photochemical cyclisation of phenylglyoxylic amides in an inclusion complex with (30) gives chiral β-lactams and oxazolidinones [95CC1719]. Titanium complexes such as (31) are effective chiral catalysts for Diels-Alder cycloaddition [95JOC1788], [2+2] cycloaddition [94T4529], and enantioselective alcoholysis of *meso*-anhydrides [95AG(E)2395].

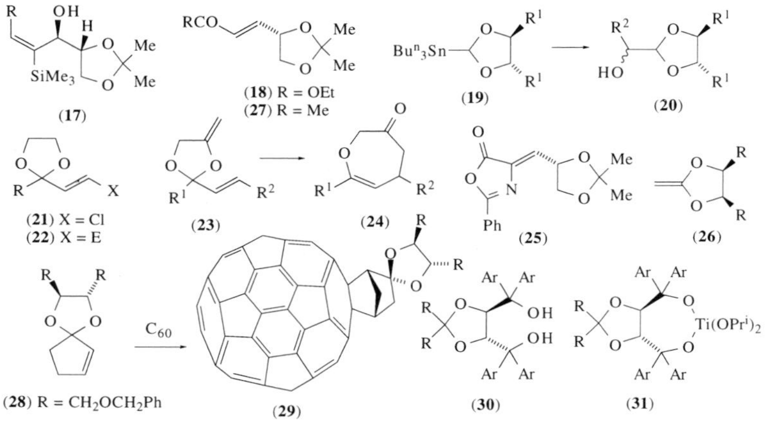

(17)

(18) R = OEt
(27) R = Me

(19)

(20)

(21) X = Cl
(22) X = E

(23)

(24)

(25)

(26)

(28) R = CH₂OCH₂Ph

(29)

(30)

(31)

Dioxolane bis-ammonium salts such as (32) are effective in inhibiting the biological activity of lipopolysaccharides [94BMC1691] and (33) has been used as a phase-transfer catalyst [93URP1833778]. The two enantiomers of the bicyclic dioxolane (34) have been tested for anticonvulsant activity [95BMC265]. A variety of benzodioxolylindoles such as (35) are effective steroid 5-α-reductase inhibitors with possible medical applications [94MIP27990, 95MIP05375]. The dioxolanes (36) have antifungal activity [95EJM617] and compounds such as (37) have been used as herbicides [95EUP643053, 95EUP661281]. Herbicidal activity has also been claimed for dioxolanones such as (38) [95GEP19510454] and difluorobenzodioxoles such as (39) [95EUP636622]. Perfluoroalkoxydioxoles such as (40) are useful as monomers for formation of tetrafluoroethylene copolymers [95EUP633257].

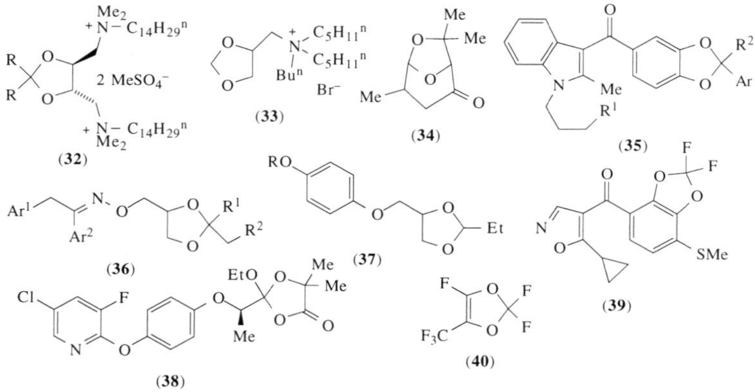

(32)

(33)

(34)

(35)

(36)

(37)

(38)

(39)

(40)

5.6.2 1,3-DITHIOLES AND DITHIOLANES

Reviews have appeared on benzo-1,3-dithioles, -diselenoles and -ditelluroles [93SR103], the organic chemistry of 1,3-dithiol-2-one-4,5-dithiolate ("DMIT") [95S215], and various aspects of tetrathiafulvalene (TTF) chemistry with an emphasis on molecular electronic applications [94MI367, 95MI235, 95MI1481]. Detailed mass spectrometric studies of 1,3-dithiole-2-thione- and TTF-fused thiophenes [95RCM276] and the three isomeric bis-dithiafulvenylbenzenes [94OMS571] have appeared.

New methods for the conversion of ketones into 2,2-disubstituted-1,3-dithiolanes include treatment with ethanedithiol and either $CoBr_2$ on silica [94TL5717] or an ion exchange resin in the absence of solvent [95JCR(S)108]. The reverse reaction: cleavage of 1,3-dithiolanes, may be achieved with $Cu(NO_3)_2$ on silica [95CL507] or SeO_2 in acetic acid [95S39], and reaction of 2,2-diaryl-1,3-dithiolanes with F_2/I_2 gives the geminal difluorides Ar_2CF_2 [95CC177]. An efficient synthesis of 2-alkylidene-1,3-benzodithioles (**41**) has been reported [94JHC1721] and the cycloaddition of mesoionic compound (**42**) to triphenylphosphirane has been described

[95H(40)311]. The 1,3-dithiol-2-ones (**43**) are formed in good yield by treatment of $RC\equiv CH$ with $(Pr^iOC(S)S-)_2$ under radical conditions [95CC1429] and related methods have been used to obtain (**44**) [95MI363] and (**45**) from 4-trifluoromethyltetrachloropyridine [94KGS1278]. A series of bicyclic dithiolanes (**46**) have been obtained from allyl dithioesters and TCNE and their X-ray structures determined [94KGS770]. Enzymatic oxidation of 1,3-dithiolane has been used to obtain (**47**) in >98% e.e. [95CC1123] and the disulfoxide (**48**) undergoes highly stereoselective Diels-Alder reaction [95JOC4962]. Acid catalysed cyclisation of allylthiosulfines gives the dithiolane S-oxides (**49**) [94JCS(P1)3299] whose relative configuration is confirmed by an X-ray structure [94MI793]. New synthetic routes have also been reported for the 1,3-thiaselenoles (**50**) [94TL8817], the spiro bisdiselenole (**51**) [94ZOR1009], and the benzoditellurolium salt (**52**) [93IZV387].

Syntheses and X-ray structures have been reported for (**53**) [94T11205] and (**54**) [95MI645]. The preparation and non-linear optical properties of 2-imino-1,3-dithioles (**55**) have been described [95MI35] and the dimeric derivatives ($R^3 = p$-phenylene) have also been reported [94BSF774]. The product (**56**), obtained from reaction of 4-methyl-5-phenyl-1,2-dithiol-3-thione with DMAD, undergoes cycloaddition with a further molecule of DMAD to afford the spiro compound (**57**) whose structure is confirmed by X-ray methods [94KGS908].

A great deal of work has once again been published in the area of TTF and its derivatives. The parent compound acts as an electron donating catalyst in the radical cyclisation of aromatic diazonium salts [95JCS(P1)623] and can undergo one-electron oxidation on treatment with oxoaminium salts [94CL1827]. The first evidence for formation of radicals and electrically conducting materials by protic doping of TTF with HBF_4 has been presented [94AM298]. The TTF allyl alcohol (58) has been prepared [95TL4319] and three different routes to diformyl TTF (59) have been described [94TL9243]. New tetrasubstituted TTFs which have been prepared and studied include (60) with Alk being a range of straight chain alkyl groups up to $C_{14}H_{29}$ [94JOC6519], (61) [95CC1201], the ferrocenyl compound (62) [95JCS(D)897] and the crown ether derivative (63) [95POL1327]. New routes have been developed to unsymmetrical TTFs (64) [94JCS(P1)2715], their selenium analogues, and the dihydro derivatives (65) which can act as donors despite the lack of full unsaturation [95JA1149]. The iodo compounds (66) [95CC1097] and (67) [95CC1667] form a variety of conducting complexes. The isomeric analogues (69) and (70) of the well known "ET" (68) containing three different chalcogens have been prepared [95CC2493]. Both $(68)_2$ $Au(CF_3)_4$ [95CC1311] and the tetraselenium analogue $(71)_2$ $GaBrCl_3$ [95CC1225] show

(58) (59) (60) R = CH$_2$OAlk
(61) R = SCH$_2$CH$_2$OH
(62) R = SCH$_2$Fc
(63) R = S-benzo-15-Crown-5

(64) X = S, Se (65) X = S, Se

(66) (67) (69) X = S, Y = Se
(70) X = Se, Y = S

(68) (71)

superconductivity. Reaction of 4,5-disubstituted TTFs with Bu^{n}Li followed by (PhC≡C)$_2$X gives (72) for X = Se [95AM644] but (73) for X = Te [94TL8489]. Both (74) [95CC475] and (75) [94KGS422] form stable Langmuir-Blodgett films. All six possible mono and dihalo ethylenedithioTTFs (76) and (77) have been prepared and the conductivity of their charge transfer salts measured [95CL183]. Improved syntheses of (78) have been described and the X-ray structure of the unsubstituted compound determined [95NJC161]. The uracil-fused TTFs (79) have been prepared and show hydrogen bonding in the solid state [95CC325, 94PS(95/96)511] and the bis-uracil compound (80) has also been reported [94KGS1285]. The pyrazine-fused bis-TTFs (81) have been prepared and studied by cyclic voltammetry [94JOC8030]. A pentakis-TTF with four units linked to the central one by S(CH$_2$)$_3$S tethers has been reported [95S521]. A variety of interesting compounds with multiple TTF units directly attached to an aromatic nucleus have been prepared including the benzene and pyridine systems (82-84) [94CL2369] and the naphthalene and 1,6-methano[10]annulene structures (85-87) [94CL2327].

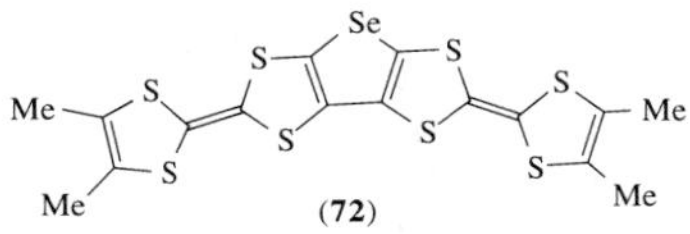

(72)

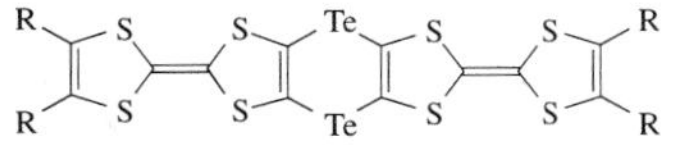

(73) R = Me, SMe

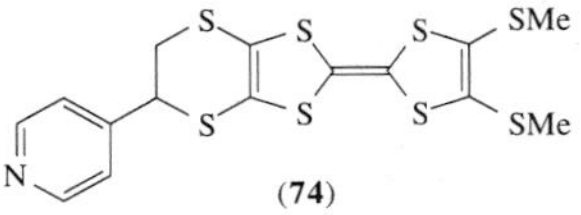

(74)

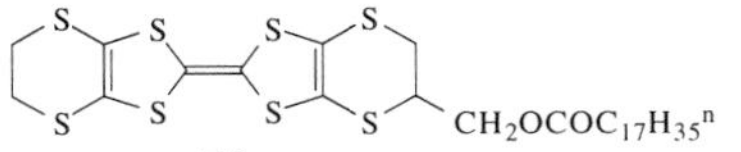

(75)

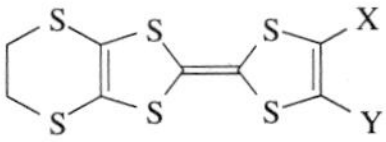

(76) X = Cl, Br, I Y = H
(77) X = Y = Cl, Br, I
(78) X = Y = H, Me

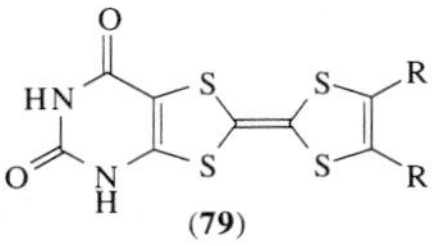

(79)

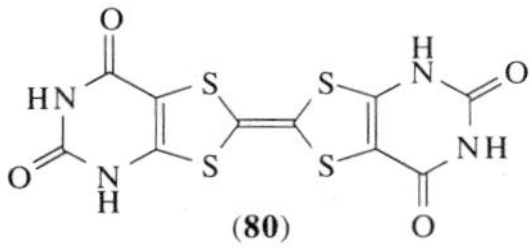

(80)

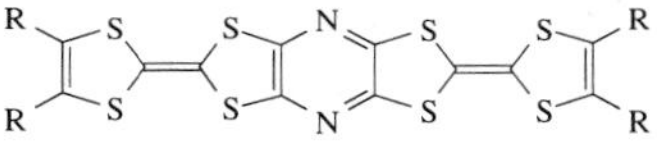

(81)

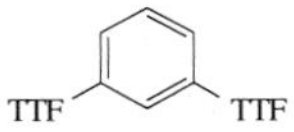

(82)

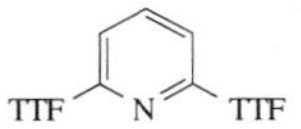

(83)

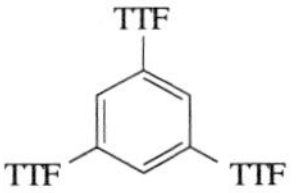

(84)

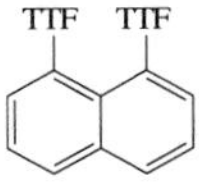

(85)

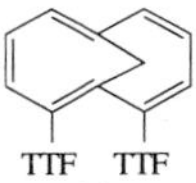

(86)

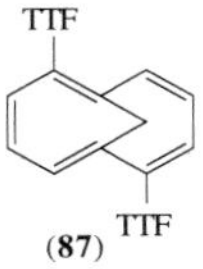

(87)

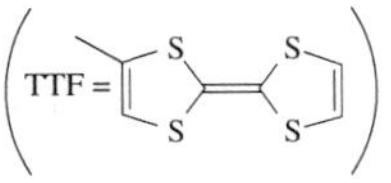

$$TTF = \text{(thiophene-TTF structure)}$$

A variety of vinylogous TTF derivatives (**88**) and (**89**) have been prepared and studied [95TL1645, 95JOC2443, 95BSF975]. The extended derivatives (**90**) [95CL77] and (**91**) [95CC821] have also been reported. More complex thiophene-containing extended derivatives have also been described [95TL2983, 95CC557, 95H(40)123] including the example (**92**) [95CC1761].

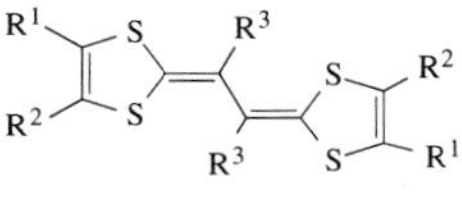

(88)

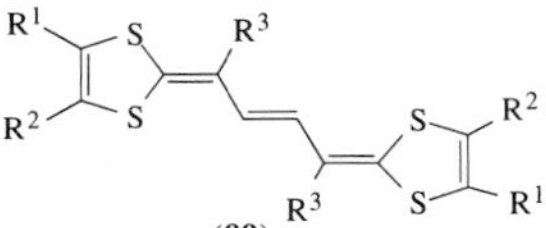

(89)

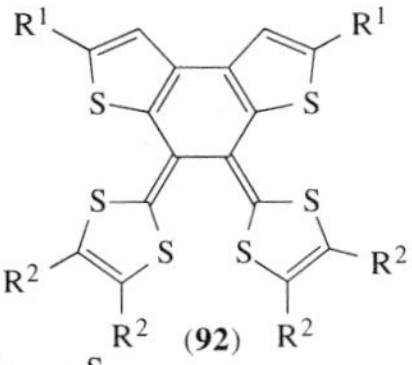

(92)

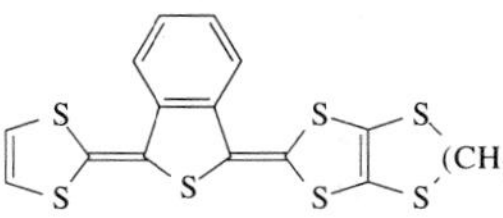

(90) n = 1, 2, 3

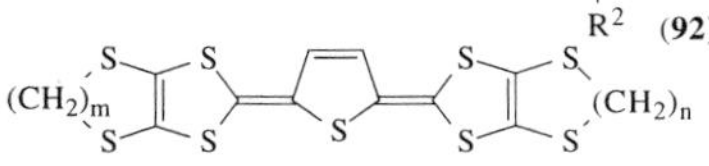

(91) m, n = 2, 3

5.6.3 1,3-OXATHIOLES AND OXATHIOLANES

Conversion of ketones into the corresponding 2,2-disubstituted-1,3-oxathiolanes with 2-mercaptoethanol is efficiently catalysed by Me_3SiOTf and this same catalyst is also effective in promoting the reverse reaction [95TL2285]. Treatment of α-mercaptoketones,

$R^1COCH(SH)R^2$ with $Et_2N–PCl_2$ results in dehydration to afford the bicyclic oxathiolanes (**93**) [94ZOB1778]. In an unusual reaction, electrochemical reduction of (**94**) in the presence of inorganic sulfur compounds gives (**95**) [94TL9623]. The chiral oxathiolane (**96**) of interest for synthesis of modified nucleosides has been obtained by enzymatic methods [95TA393], while (**97**) has been obtained by resolution [94TL4739]. Radical reduction of 1,3-oxathiolane-2-thiones (**98**) with Bu^n_3SnH gives the oxathiolanes (**99**) when the reducing agent is present in high concentration but the reduction otherwise proceeds with ring cleavage to give the alkene [95HAC325]. The oxathiolane (**100**) has found application as a fungicide for skin infections [94JAP06263757], while a variety of 1,3-benzoxathiole-2-thiones have been used for treatment of liver disorders [94JAP06239856].

5.6.4 1,2-DIOXOLANES

The hydroperoxyketones derived from alkene ozonolysis react with allyltrimethylsilane under the influence of a Lewis acid catalyst to afford the 1,2-dioxolanes (**101**) [95TL3655]. Addition of singlet oxygen to α-alkoxyallylstannanes (**102**) proceeds with migration of tin to give (**103**) [95TL2187]. Reaction of (**104**) with $^1O_2$ gives (**105**) as one of the products [94T9009] and the same reaction of substituted pentamethylcyclopentadienes gives mainly the *syn* isomer of (**106**) for R = H but the *anti* isomer for larger R groups [95CC839]. The synthesis and thermolysis of a range of 1,2-dioxolanes (**107**) has been described [94JOC6692].

5.6.5 1,2-DITHIOLES AND DITHIOLANES

A review on cyclic disulfides includes coverage of 1,2-dithioles and dithiolanes [94MI97]. Reaction of the 1,2-dithiolane (**108**) with $Me_2S=CHR$ results in ring expansion to give (**109**)

(108) (109) (110) (111) (112) (113) (114) (115) (116) (117) (118) (119) (120)

[95PS(106)227] and treatment of (110) with $R^3C\equiv CH$ and $KOBu^t/Bu^tOH$ gives the dithiepine (111) while in THF acyclic products are formed [95CC1763]. New syntheses have been described for (112) [95KGS420] and (113) [95JHC847]. The preparation and X-ray structures of (114) and (115) have been reported [94PS(91)53] and 1,2-diselenol-3-one (116) is formed in high yield by gas phase reaction of propargyl alcohol with dialkyl diselenides [94ZOR1012]. The reactivity of cyanodithiolethiones (117) towards trialkyl phosphites [95JCR(S)50] and stabilised phosphorus ylides [95PS(105)63] has been examined. The 1,2-dithiolium salts (118) react with CpLi or CpTl in a complex way to afford mixtures of tricyclic products [94H(40)85, 94PS(95/96)483]. The phenolic dithiolethione (119) has found use as an antioxidant and cardioprotective agent [95JAP07112978] while (120) acts as an antioxidant for hydrocarbons [94IZV814].

5.6.6 1,2-OXATHIOLES AND OXATHIOLANES

The spiro sulfurane (121) has been prepared and its thermal decomposition studied [94AG(E)2094]. Ring expansion of (122) affords (123) and the X-ray structures of both

(121) (122) (123) (124) (125) (126) (127) (128) (129) X = S, Se (130)

compounds have been reported [95CC1069]. Nucleophilic attack of active methylene compounds on the chiral selenurane (124) proceeds with retention of configuration at selenium [95CL379]. The 1,2-oxatelluroles (125) and their benzo derivatives (126) have been prepared and their reactivity examined [94KGS266].

5.6.7 THREE HETEROATOMS

The benzotrithioles (127) have been prepared for $R = Pr^i$ and OMe and the X-ray structure has been determined in the latter case [95CL321]. The hindered 1,2,4-trithiolane (128), a thiocarbonyl sulfide cycloaddition product, has been formed as a byproduct [95HCA1499]. The benzodithiatellurole and benzothiaselenatellurole (129) have been prepared and the former can be further converted into the spiro compound (130) [95TL587].

5.6.8 REFERENCES

93IZV387	I. D. Sadekov, B. B. Rivkin, P. I. Gadzhieva and V. I. Minkin; *Izv. Akad. Nauk, Ser. Khim.*, 1993, 387.
93OS1	C. Hubschwerlen, J.-L. Specklin and J. Higelin; *Org. Synth.*, 1993, **72**, 1.
93OS6	C. R. Schmid and J. D. Bryant; *Org. Synth.*, 1993, **72**, 6.
93OS48	R. C. Sun and M. Okabe; *Org. Synth.*, 1993, **72**, 48.
93SR103	I. D. Sadekov, B. B. Rivkin and V. I. Minkin; *Sulfur Reports*, 1993, **15**, 103.
93URP1833778	I. R. Khabibullin, L. Z. Rolnik, S. S. Zlotskii and D. L. Rakhmankulov; *Russ. Pat.* 1 833 778 (1993) [*Chem. Abstr.*, 1995, **123**, 198779].
94AG(E)2094	T. Kawashima, F. Ohno and R. Okazaki; *Angew. Chem., Int. Ed. Engl.*, 1994, **33**, 2094.
94AM298	M. Giffard, P. Alonso, J. Garín, A. Gorgues, T. P. Nguyen, P. Richomme, A. Robert, J. Roncali and S. Uriel; *Adv. Mater. (Weinheim, Ger.)*, 1994, **6**, 298.
94BCJ2614	T. Nagata, T. Takai, T. Yamada, K. Imagawa and T. Mukaiyama; *Bull. Chem. Soc. Jpn.*, 1994, **67**, 2614.
94BMC1691	K. I. Kim, D. A. Lill-Elghanian and R. I. Holingsworth; *Bioorg. Med. Chem. Lett.*, 1994, **4**, 1691
94BSF774	D. Lorcy, A. Robert, R. Carlier and A. Tallec; *Bull. Soc. Chim. Fr.*, 1994, **131**, 774.
94CB2215	R. Gleiter, H. Hoffmann, H. Irngartinger and M. Nixdorf; *Chem. Ber.*, 1994, **127**, 2215.
94CL1827	E. Yoshida, T. Takata, T. Endo, T. Ishizone, A. Hirao and S. Nakahama; *Chem. Lett.*, 1994, 1827.
94CL2327	U. Kux and M. Iyoda; *Chem. Lett.*, 1994, 2327.
94CL2369	M. Iyoda, M. Fukuda, M. Yoshida and S. Sasaki; *Chem. Lett.*, 1994, 2369.
94H(40)85	K. Hartke and X.-P. Popp; *Heterocycles*, 1994, **40**, 85.
94IZV814	O. T. Kasaikina, N. A. Golovina, Kh. S. Shihaliev and Zh. V. Shmyreva; *Izv. Akad. Nauk, Ser. Khim.*, 1994, 814.
94JAP06192236	K. Nishikawa and C. Takeuchi; *Jpn. Pat.* 06 192 236 (1994) [*Chem. Abstr.*, 1995, **122**, 31562].

94JAP06239856 T. Ueyama, K. Matsumoto, J. Hirase, Y. Oosugi, Y. Nishino, H. Ooshima, T. Sogawa, Y. Mizuno, Y. Okui *et al.*, *Jpn. Pat.* 06 239 856 [*Chem. Abstr.*, 1995, **123**, 143876].

94JAP06263757 S. Tamura, H. Ogura, H. Kobayashi, T. Aryoshi, M. Yokoo, S. Nakabashi and T. Naito; *Jpn. Pat.* 06 263 757 [*Chem. Abstr.*, 1995, **122**, 314558].

94JAP06271481 K. Nishikawa; *Jpn. Pat.* 06 271 481 (1994) [*Chem. Abstr.*, 1995, **122**, 132568].

94JCS(P1)2715 C. Gemmel, G. C. Janairo, J. D. Kilburn, H. Ueck and A. E. Underhill; *J. Chem. Soc., Perkin Trans. 1*, 1994, 2715.

94JCS(P1)3299 G. Mazzanti, E. van Helvoirt, L. A. van Vliet, R. Ruinaard, S. Masiero, B. F. Bonini and B. Zwanenburg; *J. Chem. Soc., Perkin Trans. 1*, 1994, 3299.

94JCS(P1)3595 A. Díaz-Ortiz, E. Díez-Barra, A. de la Hoz, P. Prieto and A. Moreno; *J. Chem. Soc., Perkin Trans. 1*, 1994, 3595.

94JHC1721 F. Bellesia, M. Boni, F. Ghelfi and U. M. Pagnoni; *J. Heterocycl. Chem.*, 1994, **31**, 1721.

94JOC6519 M. A. Fox and H.-l. Pan; *J. Org. Chem.*, 1994, **59**, 6519.

94JOC6692 A. L. Baumstark, P. C. Vasquez and Y.-X. Chen; *J. Org. Chem.*, 1994, **59**, 6692.

94JOC8030 K. Lahlil, A. Moradpour, C. Marienne and C. Bowlas; *J. Org. Chem.*, 1994, **59**, 8030.

94KGS266 I. D. Sadekov, A. A. Maksimenko, A. V. Zakharov and B. B. Rivkin; *Khim. Geterotsikl. Soedin.*, 1994, 266.

94KGS422 O. Ya. Neiland and Ya. Ya. Katsen; *Khim. Geterotsikl. Soedin.*, 1994, **30**, 422.

94KGS770 I. V. Magedov, S. Yu. Shapakin, V. N. Drozd, A. S. Batsanov, D. S. Yufit and Yu. T. Struchkov; *Khim. Geterotsikl. Soedin.*, 1994, **30**, 770.

94KGS908 V. N. Drozd, I. V. Magedov, D. S. Yufit and Yu. T. Struchkov; *Khim. Geterotsikl. Soedin.*, 1994, **30**, 908.

94KGS1216 F. F. Lakhvich and L. S. Stanishevsky; *Khim. Geterotsikl. Soedin.*, 1994, **30**, 1216.

94KGS1278 A. M. Sipyagin and Z. G. Aliev; *Khim. Geterotsikl. Soedin.*, 1994, **30**, 1278.

94KGS1285 O. Ya. Neiland, V. Zh. Tilika and A. S. Edzhinya; *Khim. Geterotsikl. Soedin.*, 1994, **30**, 1285.

94MI97 K. Steliou, P. L. Folkins and D. N. Harpp; *Adv. Sulfur Chem.*, 1994, **1**, 97 [*Chem. Abstr.*, 1995, **123**, 9344].

94MI367 M. C. Grossel and S. C. Weston; *Contemporary Org. Synth.*, 1994, **1**, 367.

94MI793 J. M. M. Smits, P. T. Beurskens, L. A. van Vliet, G. Mazzanti and B. Zwanenburg; *J. Chem. Crystallogr.*, 1994, **24**, 793 [*Chem. Abstr.*, 1995, **122**, 239581].

94MIP27990 G. N. Maw, J. Blagg and D. J. Rawson; *PCT Int. Appl. WO* 27 990 (1994) [*Chem. Abstr.*, 1995, **122**, 160689].

94OMS571 P. Frere, A. Gorgues, J. Garin and J. Orduna; *Org. Mass Spectrom.*, 1994, **29**, 571.

94PS(91)53 H. Bock, C. Näther, A. Rauschenbach, Z. Havlas, J. W. Bats, E. Fanghänel and T. Palmer; *Phosphorus, Sulfur and Silicon*, 1994, **91**, 53.

94PS(95/96)483 K. Hartke, X.-P. Popp and A. Kraska; *Phosphorus, Sulfur and Silicon*, 1994, **95/96**, 483.

94PS(95/96)511   O. Neilands, V. Tilika, Z. Celmina and A. Edzina; *Phosphorus, Sulfur and Silicon*, 1994, **95/96**, 511.

94T4529   K. Narasaka, K. Hayashi and Y. Hayashi; *Tetrahedron*, 1994, **50**, 4529.

94T9009   W. Adam, M. Balci, O. Çakmak, K. Peters, C. R. Saha-Möller and M. Schulz; *Tetrahedron*, 1994, **50**, 9009.

94T11205   T. Ozturk, D. C. Povey and J. D. Wallis; *Tetrahedron*, 1994, **50**, 11205.

94T13173   K. Nilsson and C. Ullenius; *Tetrahedron*, 1994, **50**, 13173.

94TL2063   L. Colombo, M. Di Giacomo, G. Brusotti and G. Delogu; *Tetrahedron Lett.*, 1994, **35**, 2063.

94TL3111   J.-i. Sugiyama, K. Tanikawa, T. Okada, K. Noguchi, M. Ueda and T. Endo; *Tetrahedron Lett.*, 1994, **35**, 3111.

94TL4739   W. Wang, H. Jin and T. S. Mansour; *Tetrahedron Lett.*, 1994, **35**, 4739.

94TL5193   M. Newcomb and B. Dhanabalasingam; *Tetrahedron Lett.*, 1994, **35**, 5193.

94TL5717   H. K. Patney; *Tetrahedron Lett.*, 1994, **35**, 5717.

94TL7643   A. Bachki, F. Foubelo and M. Yus; *Tetrahedron Lett.*, 1994, **35**, 7643.

94TL8489   C. Wang, A. Ellern, J. Y. Becker and J. Bernstein; *Tetrahedron Lett.*, 1994, **35**, 8489.

94TL8817   T. Murai, H. Takada, T. Kanda and S. Kato; *Tetrahedron Lett.*, 1994, **35**, 8817.

94TL9243   R. Andreu, J. Garín, J. Orduna, M. Savirón, J. Cousseau, A. Gorgues, V. Morisson, T. Nozdryn, J. Becher, R. P. Clausen, M. R. Bryce, P. J. Skabara and W. Dehaen; *Tetrahedron Lett.*, 1994, **35**, 9243.

94TL9623   J. I. Lozano and F. Barba; *Tetrahedron Lett.*, 1994, **35**, 9623.

94ZOB1778   A. R. Burilov, I. L. Nikolaeve and M. A. Pudovik; *Zh. Obshch. Khim.*, 1994, **64**, 1778.

94ZOR1009   M. L. Petrov and I. K. Rubtsova; *Zh. Org. Khim.*, 1994, **30**, 1009.

94ZOR1012   E. N. Deryagina, N. A. Korchevin and M. G. Voronkov; *Zh. Org. Khim.*, 1994, **30**, 1012.

95ACS297   P. H. Carlsen, K. Misund and J. Roe; *Acta Chem. Scand.*, 1995, **49**, 297.

95AG(E)2395   D. Seebach, G. Jaeschke and Y. M. Wang; *Angew. Chem., Int. Ed. Engl.*, 1995, **34**, 2395.

95AM644   C. Wang, A. Ellern, J. Y. Becker and J. Bernstein; *Adv. Mater. (Weinheim, Ger.)*, 1995, **7**, 644.

95BMC265   L. V. Tinao-Wooldridge, B. C. H. Hsiang, T. M. Latifi, J. A. Ferrendelli and D. F. Covey; *Bioorg. Med. Chem. Lett.*, 1995, **5**, 265.

95BSF975   P. Frère, A. Belyasmine, Y. Gouriou, M. Jubault, A. Gorgues, G. Duguay, S. Wood, C. D. Reynolds and M. R. Bryce; *Bull. Soc. Chim. Fr.*, 1995, **132**, 975.

95CC43   P. Tascedda and E. Dunãch; *J. Chem. Soc., Chem. Commun.*, 1995, 43.

95CC177   R. D. Chambers, G. Sandford and M. Atherton; *J. Chem. Soc., Chem. Commun.*, 1995, 177.

95CC325   O. Neilands, S. Belyakov, V. Tilika and A. Edzina; *J. Chem. Soc., Chem. Commun.*, 1995, 325.

95CC475   L. M. Goldenberg, J. Y. Becker, O. P.-T Levi, V. Yu. Khodorkovsky, M. R. Bryce and M. C. Petty; *J. Chem. Soc., Chem. Commun.*, 1995, 475.

95CC557   A. Ohta and Y. Yamashita; *J. Chem. Soc., Chem. Commun.*, 1995, 557.

95CC639   F. Toda, K. Tanaka and T. Okada; *J. Chem. Soc., Chem. Commun.*, 1995, 639.

95CC821   K. Takahashi and K. Tomitani; *J. Chem. Soc., Chem. Commun.*, 1995, 821.

95CC839   W. Adam, U. Jacob and M. Prein; *J. Chem. Soc., Chem. Commun.*, 1995, 839.

95CC1069   J. Rábai, I. Kapovits, G. Argay, T. Koritsánszky and A. Kálmán; *J. Chem. Soc., Chem. Commun.*, 1995, 1069.

95CC1071   G.-W. Wang, L.-H. Shu, S.-H. Wu, H.-M. Wu and X.-F. Lao; *J. Chem. Soc., Chem. Commun.*, 1995, 1071.

95CC1097   T. Imakubo, H. Sawa and R. Kato; *J. Chem. Soc., Chem. Commun.*, 1995, 1097.

95CC1121   T. Nishiguchi, T. Ohosima, A. Nishida and S. Fujisaki; *J. Chem. Soc., Chem. Commun.*, 1995, 1121.

95CC1123   S. Colonna, N. Gaggero, A. Bertinotti, G. Carrea, P. Pasta and A. Bernardi; *J. Chem. Soc., Chem. Commun.*, 1995, 1123.

95CC1201   A. S. Batsanov, N. Svenstrup, J. Lau, J. Becher, M. R. Bryce and J. A. K. Howard; *J. Chem. Soc., Chem. Commun.*, 1995, 1201.

95CC1225   H. Kobayashi, H. Tomita, T. Naito, H. Tanaka, A. Kobayashi and T. Saito; *J. Chem. Soc., Chem. Commun.*, 1995, 1225.

95CC1311   J. A. Schlueter, J. M. Williams, U. Geiser, J. D. Dudek, S. A. Sirchio, M. E. Kelly, J. S. Gregar, W. H. Kwok, J. A. Fendrich, J. E. Schirber, W. R. Bayless, D. Naumann and T. Roy; *J. Chem. Soc., Chem. Commun.*, 1995, 1311.

95CC1429   Y. Gareau; *J. Chem. Soc., Chem. Commun.*, 1995, 1429.

95CC1453   F. Toda, K. Tanaka, L. Infantes, C. Foces-Foces, R. M. Claramunt and J. Elguero; *J. Chem. Soc., Chem. Commun.*, 1995, 1453.

95CC1667   T. Imakubo, H. Sawa and R. Kato; *J. Chem. Soc., Chem. Commun.*, 1995, 1667.

95CC1719   F. Toda, H. Miyamoto and K. Kanemoto; *J. Chem. Soc., Chem. Commun.*, 1995, 1719.

95CC1761   A. Ohta and Y. Yamashita; *J. Chem. Soc., Chem. Commun.*, 1995, 1761.

95CC1763   M. Tazaki, M. Kumakura, S. Nagahama and M. Takagi; *J. Chem. Soc., Chem. Commun.*, 1995, 1763.

95CC1769   M. Ohkita, K. Ishigami and T. Tsuji; *J. Chem. Soc., Chem. Commun.*, 1995, 1769.

95CC2493   T. Imakubo, Y. Okano, H. Sawa and R. Kato; *J. Chem. Soc., Chem. Commun.*, 1995, 2493.

95CL77   K. Takahashi and T. Ise; *Chem. Lett.*, 1995, 77.

95CL183   U. Kux, H. Suzuki, S. Sasaki and M. Iyoda; *Chem. Lett.*, 1995, 183.

95CL321   S. Ogawa, S. Saito, T. Kikuchi, Y. Kawai, S. Niizuma and R. Sato; *Chem. Lett.*, 1995, 321.

95CL379   T. Takahashi, N. Kurose, S. Kawanami, A. Nojiri, Y. Arai, T. Koizumi and M. Shiro; *Chem. Lett.*, 1995, 379.

95CL507   J. G. Lee and J. P. Hwang; *Chem. Lett.*, 1995, 507.

95EJM617   H. Baji, M. Flammang, T. Kimny, F. Gasquez, P. L. Compagnon and A. Delcourt; *Eur. J. Med. Chem.*, 1995, **30**, 617.

95EUP633257   W. Navarrini, V. Tortelli, P. Colaianna and J. A. Abusleme; *Eur. Pat.* 633 257 (1995) [*Chem. Abstr.*, 1995, **122**, 187563].

95EUP636622   N. Geach, D. W. Hawkins, C. J. Pearson, P. H. G. Smith and N. White; *Eur. Pat.* 636 622 (1995) [*Chem. Abstr.*, 1995, **122**, 290845].

95EUP643053   M. Barz and F. Karrer; *Eur. Pat.* 643 053 (1995) [*Chem. Abstr.*, 1995, **122**, 265360].

95EUP661281   F. Karrer; *Eur. Pat.* 661 281 (1995) [*Chem. Abstr.*, 1995, **123**, 256688].

95GEP19510454   J. Wegner and R. Schyrter; *Ger. Pat.* 19 510 454 (1995) [*Chem. Abstr.*, 1996, **124**, 55941].

95H(40)123   A. Ohta and Y. Yamashita; *Heterocycles*, 1995, **40**, 123.

95H(40)311   T. Kobayashi, H. Minemura and H. Kato; *Heterocycles*, 1995, **40**, 311.

95HAC325   J. Uenishi, T. Kunugi and Y. Kubo; *Heteroatom Chem.*, 1995, **6**, 325.

95HCA1499   G. Mloston, J. Romanski, A. Linden and H. Heimgartner; *Helv. Chim. Acta*, 1995, **78**, 1499.

95JA1149   J.-i. Yamada, Y. Amano, S. Takasaki, R. Nakanishi, K. Matsumoto, S. Satoki and H. Anzai; *J. Am. Chem. Soc.*, 1995, **117**, 1149.

95JAP07112978   S. Mita, H. Mori, Y. Aoki, A. Kanematsu, K. Sakasai, M. Mori, T. Sugawara, S. Yuasa and K. Kawai; *Jpn. Pat.* 07 112 978 (1995) [*Chem. Abstr.*, 1995, **123**, 198805].

95JAP07165750   T. Endo, N. Kihara and J. Umezawa; *Jpn. Pat.* 07 165 750 (1995) [*Chem. Abstr.*, 1995, **123**, 198777].

95JCR(S)50   W. M. Abdou, I. T. Hennawy and Y. O. ElKhoshnieh; *J. Chem. Res. (S)*, 1995, 50.

95JCR(S)108   A. K. Maiti, K. Basu and P. Bhattacharyya; *J. Chem. Res. (S)*, 1995, 108.

95JCS(D)897   S. B. Wilkes, I. R. Butler, A. E. Underhill, M. B. Hursthouse, D. E. Hibbs and K. M. Abdul Malik; *J. Chem. Soc., Dalton Trans.*, 1995, 897.

95JCS(P1)623   R. J. Fletcher, C. Lampard, J. A. Murphy and N. Lewis; *J. Chem. Soc., Perkin Trans. 1*, 1995, 623.

95JCS(P2)815   F. M. Bautista, J. M. Campelo, A. Garcia, J. Leon, D. Luna and J. M. Marinas; *J. Chem. Soc., Perkin Trans. 2*, 1995, 815.

95JFC(71)111   W. Navarrini, L. Bragante, S. Fontana, V. Tortelli and A. Zedda; *J. Fluorine Chem.*, 1995, **71**, 111.

95JHC847   M. Pregnolato, P. Borgnan and M. Terreni; *J. Heterocycl. Chem.*, 1995, **32**, 847.

95JOC1788   D. Seebach, R. Dahinden, R. E. Marti, A. K. Beck, D. A. Plattner and F. N. M. Kühnle; *J. Org. Chem.*, 1995, **60**, 1788.

95JOC2443   D. Lorcy, R. Carlier, A. Robert, A. Tallec, P. Le Maguerès and L. Ouahab; *J. Org. Chem.*, 1995, **60**, 2443.

95JOC4962   V. K. Aggarwal, J. Drabowicz, R. S. Grainger, Z. Gültekin, M. Lightowler and P. L. Spargo; *J. Org. Chem.*, 1995, **60**, 4962.

95JPR113   G. Kneer, J. Mattay, A. Heidbreder, G. Raabe, B. Krebs and M. Laege; *J. Prakt. Chem.–Chem. Ztg.*, 1995, **337**, 113.

95KGS420   K. A. Balodis, I. A. Meirovits and R. B. Kampare; *Khim. Geterotsikl. Soedin.*, 1995, 420.

95MI35   M. Guillemet, J. M. Raoul, F. Pelle, A. Robert and M. Baudy-Floc'h; *J. Mater. Chem.*, 1995, **5**, 35.

95MI235   (various authors); *NATO ASI Ser., Ser. C*, 1995, **456**, 235-325.

95MI363   S. G. Liu, P. J. Wu, Y. Q. Liu and D. B. Zhu; *Chin. Chem. Lett.*, 1995, **6**, 363 [*Chem. Abstr.*, 1995, **123**, 228029].

95MI645   Q. Fang, J.-H. Xu, W.-T. Yu, S.-Y. Guo, D. Xu and M.-H. Jiang; *Huaxue Xuebao*, 1995, **53**, 645 [*Chem. Abstr.*, 1995, **123**, 313853].

95MI1481   M. R. Bryce; *J. Mater. Chem.*, 1995, **5**, 1481.

95MIP05375   J. Blagg, G. N. Maw and D. J. Rawson; *PCT Int. Appl. WO* 05 375 (1995) [*Chem. Abstr.*, 1995, **123**, 256687].

95MRC167   A. Mucci, L. Schenetti, L. Brasili and L. Malmusi; *Magn. Reson. Chem.*, 1995, **33**, 167.

95NJC161 B. Garreau, D. de Montauzon, P. Cassoux, J.-P. Legros, J.-M. Fabre, K. Saoud and S. Chakroune; *New J. Chem.*, 1995, **19**, 161.

95POL1327 P. D. Beer, J. P. Danks and D. Hesek; *Polyhedron*, 1995, **14**, 1327.

95PS(105)63 W. M. Abdou and N. A. F. Ganoub; *Phosphorus, Sulfur and Silicon*, 1995, **105**, 63.

95PS(106)227 M. Tazaki, M. Kumakura, S. Nagahama and M. Takagi; *Phosphorus, Sulfur and Silicon*, 1995, **106**, 227.

95RCM276 C. Rovira, J. Tarres, M. Dias, J. Garin and J. Orduna; *Rapid Commun. Mass Spectrom.*, 1995, **9**, 276.

95RCM405 C. Aubert and J. F. Rontani; *Rapid Commun. Mass Spectrom.*, 1995, **9**, 405.

95S39 S. A. Haroutounian; *Synthesis*, 1995, 39.

95S215 N. Svenstrup and J. Becher; *Synthesis*, 1995, 215.

95S512 A. Rutar, F. Tratar and D. Kikelj; *Synthesis*, 1995, 512.

95S521 J. Lau, O. Simonsen and J. Becher; *Synthesis*, 1995, 521.

95T1631 G. Galley, M. Pätzel and P. G. Jones; *Tetrahedron*, 1995, **51**, 1631.

95T3641 A. Guirado, A. Zapata and P. G. Jones; *Tetrahedron*, 1995, **51**, 3641.

95T8923 E. Buñuel, C. Cativiela and M. D. Diaz-de-Villegas; *Tetrahedron*, 1995, **51**, 8923.

95T9023 P. Metz and A. Schoop; *Tetrahedron*, 1995, **51**, 9023.

95TA393 R. P. C. Cousins, M. Mahmoudian and P. M. Youds; *Tetrahedron Asymmetry*, 1995, **6**, 393.

95TL587 S. Ogawa, M. Yamashita and R. Sato; *Tetrahedron Lett.*, 1995, **36**, 587.

95TL1645 C. Guillot, P. Hudhomme, P. Blanchard, A. Gorgues, M. Jubault and G. Duguay; *Tetrahedron Lett.*, 1995, **36**, 1645.

95TL2187 P. H. Dussault and U. R. Zope; *Tetrahedron Lett.*, 1995, **36**, 2187.

95TL2285 T. Ravindranathan, S. P. Chavan and S. W. Dantale; *Tetrahedron Lett.*, 1995, **36**, 2285.

95TL2781 A. Kameyama, Y. Hatakeyama and T. Nishikubo; *Tetrahedron Lett.*, 1995, **36**, 2781.

95TL2983 A. Benahmed-Gasmi, P. Frère, J. Roncali, E. Elandaloussi, J. Orduna, J. Garin, M. Jubault and A. Gorgues; *Tetrahedron Lett.*, 1995, **36**, 2983.

95TL3655 P. H. Dussault and U. Zope; *Tetrahedron Lett.*, 1995, **36**, 3655.

95TL4319 R. Andreu, J. Garín, J. Orduna, M. Savirón and S. Uriel; *Tetrahedron Lett.*, 1995, **36**, 4319.

95TL6499 K. Matsumoto, S. Fuwa and H. Kitajima; *Tetrahedron Lett.*, 1995, **36**, 6499.

Chapter 5.7

Five-Membered Ring Systems: With O & N Atoms

G. V. Boyd
The Hebrew University, Jerusalem, Israel

5.7.1 ISOXAZOLES

A new synthesis of isoxazoles is by successive treatment of a ketoxime with butyllithium, the ester of a carboxylic acid and sulfuric acid, e.g. 1 -> 2 (94S989). Nitrovinyl
oximes 3 (R^1, R^2 = alkyl or aryl) undergo
oxidative cyclization to isoxazoles 4 by the
action of DDQ or iodine/potassium iodide
(94JHC861). Flash-vacuum pyrolysis of the
1,3-dipolar cycloadduct 5 of acrylonitrile
oxide to norbornadiene results in a retro-
Diels-Alder reaction to give cyclopentadiene
and 3-vinylisoxazole 6 (94CC2661).

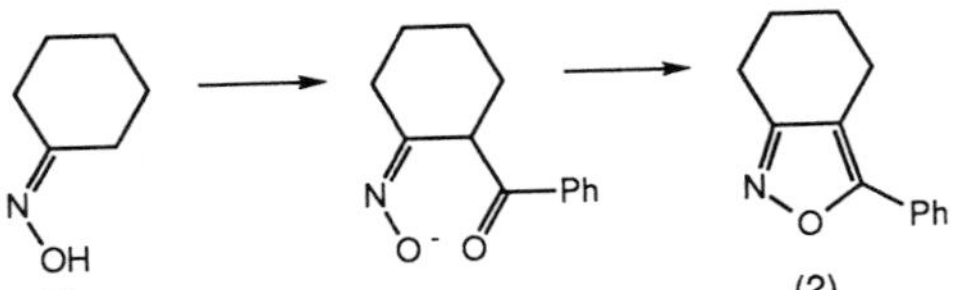

192

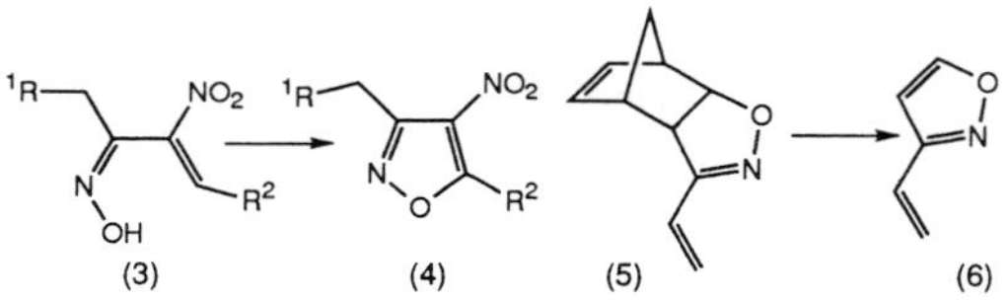

(3) (4) (5) (6)

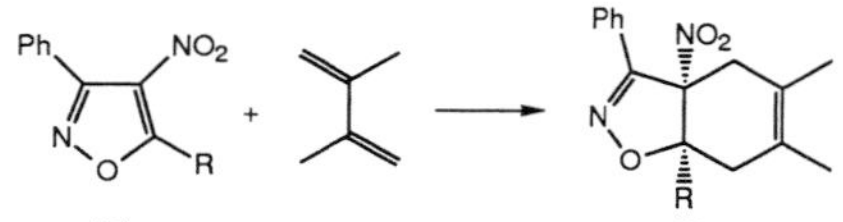

(7) (8)

4-Nitro-3-phenylisoxazoles 7 (R = H or CO_2Et) function as dienophiles towards 2,3-dimethyl-butadiene, yielding 8 (94JOC6840, 95T7085).

5.7.2 ISOXAZOLINES

The chemistry of 3,4-disubstituted 5-isoxazo-linones has been reviewed (94MI213). The cycloadducts of vinylboronic esters 9 (R = Pr, Bu, Ph etc) to benzonitrile oxide are oxidized to trans-4-hydroxy-2-isoxazolines 10 by t-butyl hydroperoxide (94TL7493). A rever-sal of regiochemistry was observed in the reaction of aromatic nitrile oxides with deri-vatives of cinnamic acid: the methyl ester gave a mixture of the esters 11 and 12 (R = OMe), in which the former predominated, while in the case of N,N-diethylcinnamide the amide 12 (R = NEt_2) was the main product (94TL6473).

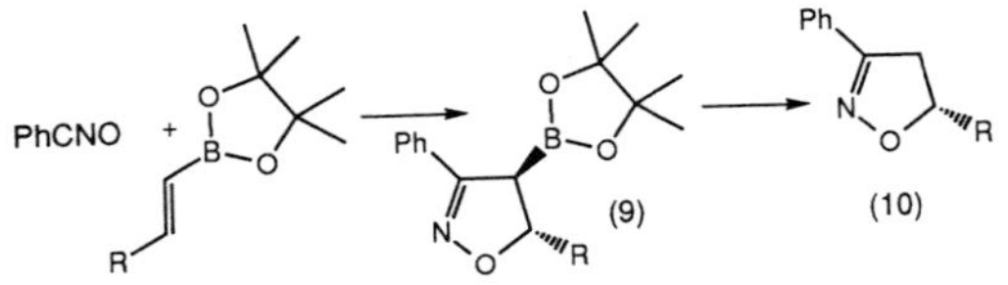

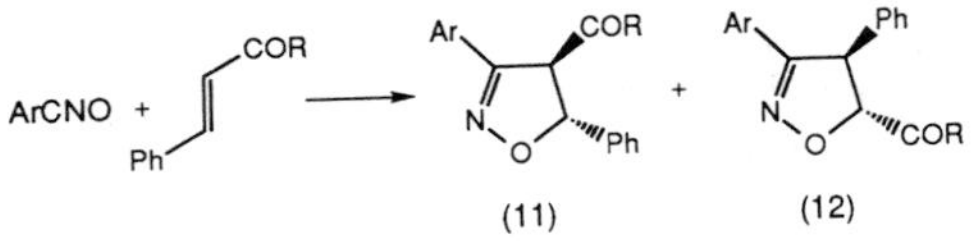

(9) (10)

(11) (12)

5.7.3 ISOXAZOLIDINES

Bu_2SnO catalyzes the formation of the nitrone 14 from benzaldehyde and the oxime 13. Addition of an olefin, followed by hydrolysis, gives a <u>N</u>-unsubstituted isoxazolidine (95CL357). The enolate ion derived from the nitrone 15 undergoes an unusual intramolecular dipolar cycloaddition reaction involving the enol double bond to yield 16 (95T6285).

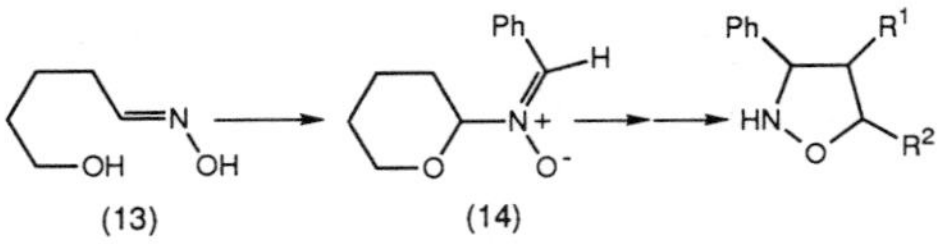

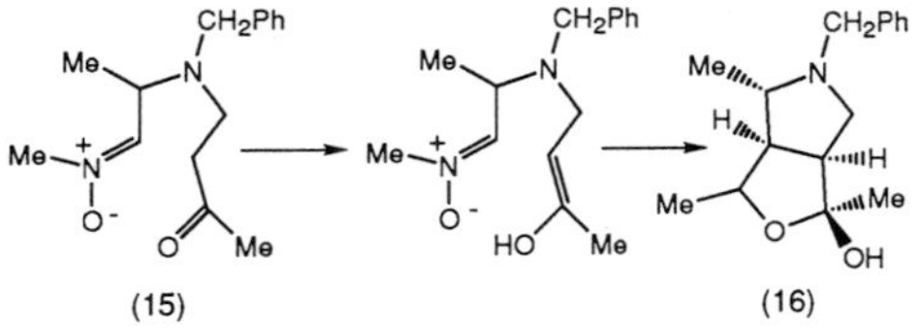

(13) (14)

(15) (16)

5.7.4 OXAZOLES

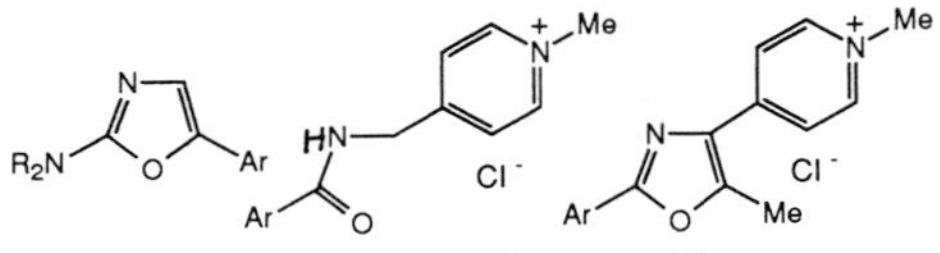

(17)　　　(18)　　(19)

N,**N**-Dialkylcyanamides react with diazo-
acetophenones under Rh$_2$(OAc)$_4$-catalysis to
yield 2-dialkylamino-5-aryloxazoles 17
(95H149). The pyridinium salts 18 are converted into the oxazoles 19 by hot acetic anhydride (94T10061).

Oxazolyl ethers 20 (R = H, Me, Ph etc)
undergo a formal [3+2] cycloaddition reaction
with diethyl mesoxalate to afford the oxazolines 21 (94CL1673). The mesoionic oxazolium
5-oxide 22 is transformed into imidazolines
24 by the action of amidines 23 (R = H, Me
or Ph) (94CC2101). Rhodium(II) perfluorobutyrate catalyses the decomposition of the
diazoimides 25 (**n** = 1 or 2) to the mesoionic
oxazolium 4-oxides 26, which undergo a spontaneous intramolecular reaction to give the
bridged dipolar cycloadducts 27 (94TL7159). A
tandem cycloaddition of dimethyl acetylenedicarboxylate to the 3-(furylpropyl)-substituted
oxazolium 4-oxide 28 results in the endo-com-
pound 30 via the intermediate cycloadduct 29
(E = CO$_2$Me) (94JOC7072).

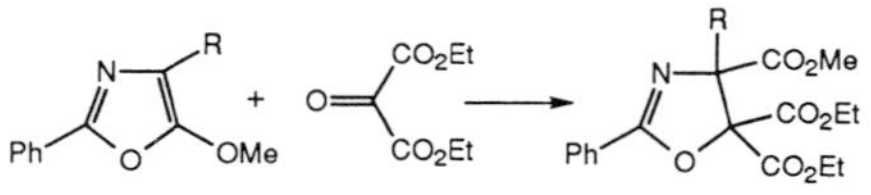

(20)　　　　　　　　　(21)

(22)   (23)   (24)

(25)   (26)   (27)

(28)   (29)   (30)

5.7.5 OXAZOLINES

Aldehydes or ketones R^1R^2CO react with the
dimer of α,α'-dihydroxyacetone and ammonia
to yield 4-hydroxymethyl-3-oxazolines 31
(95T755). 2-Oxazolines, e.g. 32, are obtained from amino alcohols and imino ether
hydrochlorides in the presence of potassium
fluoride supported on alumina under microwave
irradiation (95SC659). 4-Iodomethyl-5-methyl-
2-dimethylamino-2-oxazoline 34 is produced by
the action of N-iodosuccinimide on the allylic
1,1-dimethylisourea 33 (95SC1145). Aliphatic
and aromatic aldehydes RCHO add to N-methoxy-
N-methyl-α-isocyanoacetamide $CNCH_2CON(OMe)Me$ in
the presence of a gold catalyst containing a
chiral ferrocenylphosphine ligand to give

2-oxazolines 35 with high enantio- and dia-
stereoselectivities (95JOC1727). The chiral
Lewis acid 36 catalyzes the Diels-Alder addition of cyclopentadiene to the aldehydes 37
(R = Me or Br) with high exo/endo selectivity
(95AG798). The diastereoselective oxidation
of the optically active aryl sulfide 38 with
m-chlorobenzoic acid affords the enantiomerically pure corresponding sulfoxide by
1,6-asymmetric induction (94TL7111).

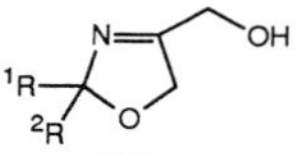

(31) 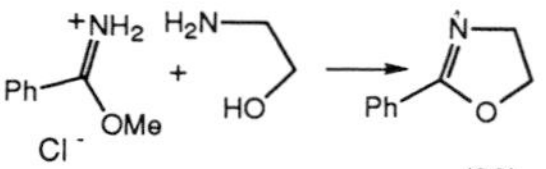 (32)

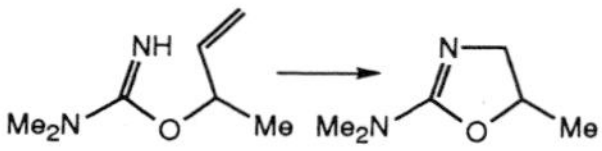

(33) (34) 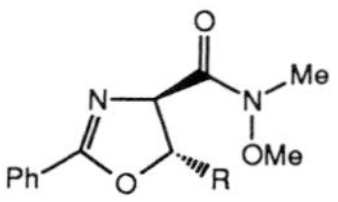 (35)

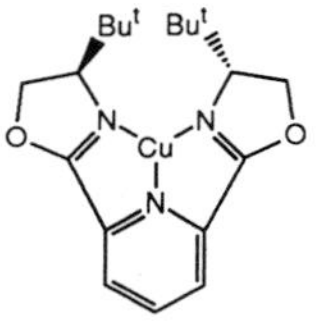

(36)

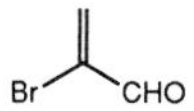

(37)

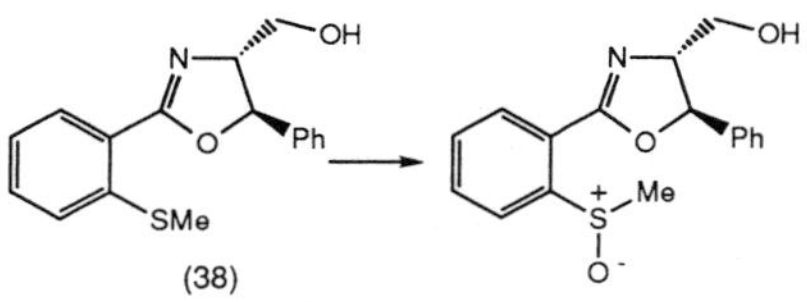

(38)

5.7.6 OXAZOLIDINES

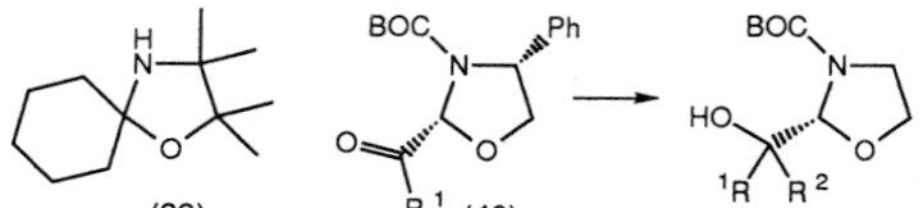

(39)　　(40)　　

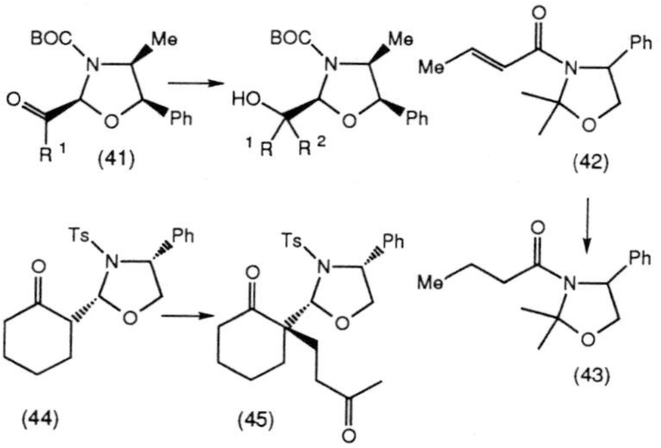

(41)　　(42)

(44)　　(45)　　(43)

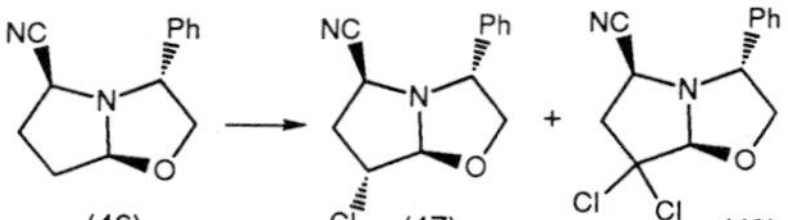

(46)　　(47)　　(48)

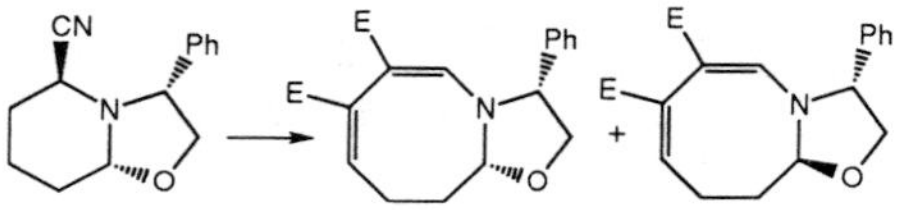

(49)　　(50)　　(51)

The oxazolidine 39 is formed by the action of di-t-butyl peroxide on a mixture of $\underline{N}$-isopropylidenecyclohexylamine and i-propyl alcohol (94KGS846). Protected 2-acyloxazolidines 40 and 41 react with Grignard compounds R^2MgBr to give tertiary alcohols with high diastereoselectivity (95T4043). Conjugate addition of organometallic compounds MeLi.CuI, PhLi.CuI or PhMgBr.CuI in the presence of chlorotrimethylsilane to the $\underline{N}$-crotonyloxazolidine 42 to yield acyloxazolidines 43 proceeds with effective enantiocontrol (94JOC6949). In the presence of cesium carbonate, the oxazolidine 44 undergoes a diastereoselective Michael reaction with 3-buten-2-one to give the adduct 45 (94SYN1313). Anodic oxidation of the bicyclic oxazolidine 46 in acetonitrile at a platinum electrode in the presence of chloride and bromide ions gives a mixture of epimeric monochloro derivatives 47, together with the dichloro compound 48 (94TL6879). A mixture of geometrically isomeric ring-expansion products 50 and 51 ($E = CO_2Et$) is produced on treatment of the oxazolidine 49 with diethyl acetylenedicarboxylate (95TL2053).

5.7.7 OXAZOLIDIN-2-ONES

The oxazolidin-2-ones 53 ($R = H_2CCH=CH_2$ or COEt) are obtained in a one-pot reaction of amino alcohol carbamates 52 with sodium hydroxide, followed by allyl bromide or propionyl chloride (94TL9533). A modified procedure for the preparation of chiral oxazolidin-2-ones 56 from α-amino acids 54, which avoids the hazardous reduction of the acids with borane and the intermediacy of water-soluble amino alcohols, is treatment of the methyl ester of the amino acid with ethyl chloroformate to give 55, followed by reduction with sodium borohydride and thermal ring-closure of the resulting carbamate (95SC561). The 2-propynylcarbamates 57 ($R = Ts$, Ac, Bz, Ph or allyl) cyclize to the methyleneoxazolidinones 58 under the influence of silver cyanate or copper(I) chloride/triethylamine (94BCJ2838).

$PdCl_2(PhCN)_2/NEt_3$ catalyses the formation of the trans-substituted oxazolidinones 60 in the condensation of the allenes 59 (R^1, R^2 = H or alkyl) with allyl chloride (95JOC3764). A new route to oxazolidin-2-ones is exemplified by the reaction of the proline derivative 61 with ethylmagnesium bromide and subsequent hydrolysis - cyclization by means of potassium hydroxide at room temperature (94JCS3041). N-(Ethoxycarbonyl)aziridinofullerene-C_{60} 62, in which the three-membered ring is located at the junction of two six-membered rings, reacts with boron tribromide to give the corresponding fused oxazolidinone 63 (94JCS3355).

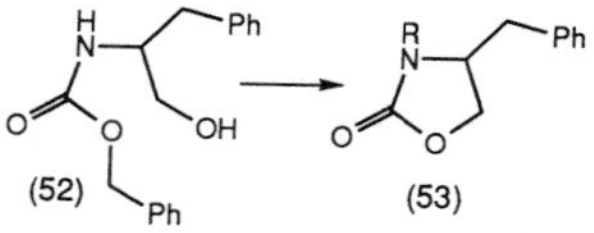

(52) (53)

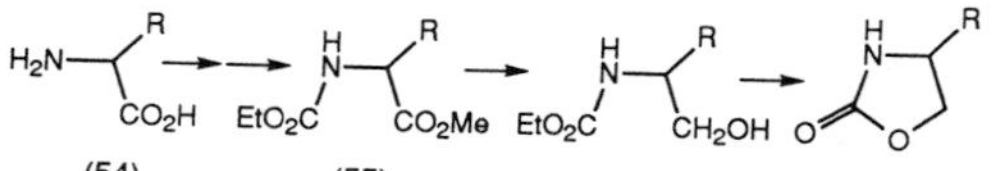

(54) (55) (56)

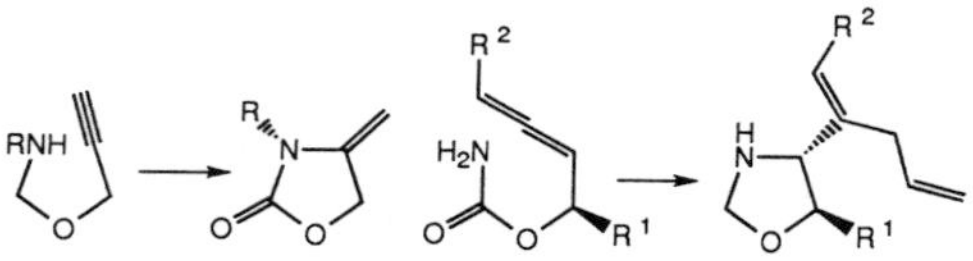

(57) (58) (59) (60)

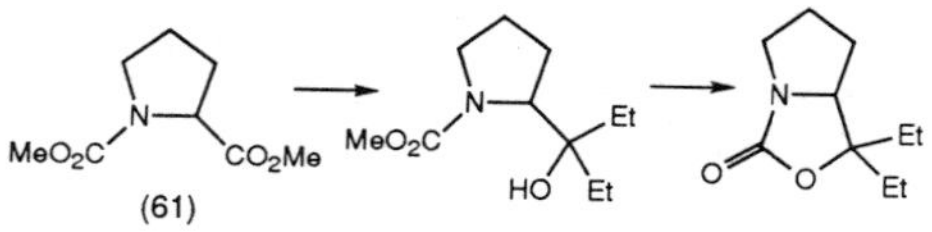

(61)

(62) (63)

Diastereoselective substitutions of 4-methoxy-oxazolidin-2-ones have been described. The trans-$\underline{N}$-methyl derivative 64 reacts with Bu_3Cu_2Li by the S_N2 mechanism to give the cis-product 65 with 76% diastereoselectivity; on the other hand, treatment of the $\underline{N}$-unsubstituted analogue 66 with the same reagent affords the trans-compound 67 by a S_N1 process (94JOC5658). Chiral $\underline{N}$-acyloxazolidin-2-ones 68 (R^1 = i-Pr or $PhCH_2$, R^2 = Me, Bu or t-Bu) are converted into 69 in good diastereomeric excess by ethyl difluoroiodoacetate in the presence of triethylborane (94TL7399). An electrosynthesis of the oxazolidin-2,4-dione 70 is by controlled-potential electrolysis of $\underline{N}$-benzylchloroacetamide in the presence of tetraethyl ethylenetetracarboxylate and carbon dioxide (95T5891).

(64)   (65)   (66)   (67)

(68)   (69)   (70)

5.7.8 1,2,4-DIOXAZOLES

Ozonolysis of the cyclic vinyl ethers 71 ($\underline{n}$ = 2, 3 or 4) in the presence of $\underline{N}$-benzylidene-benzylamine affords the dioxazoles 73 by dipolar cycloaddition to transient carbonyl oxides 72. The dioxazoles fragment to mixtures of phenylcycloalkenes, benzaldehyde and $\underline{N}$-formyl-benzylamine by the action of silica gel (94JCS2449). Carbonyl oxides 75 (E = CO_2Me), generated by thermolysis of the peroxides 74, add to phenyl isocyanate to yield 1,2,4-dioxa-zolidin-3-ones 76 (94JCS3295).

5.7.9 OXADIAZOLES

Sydnones 78 (R^1 = Ph, Ar or 3-pyridyl, R^2 = H
or Me) are obtained from the nitrosoamino
acids 77 and acetic anhydride under ultrasound
(94MI153). Three examples of the formation of
oxadiazoles by microwave irradiation are from
O-acyl amide oximes 79 in the presence of aluminium oxide, from amide oximes 80 and isoprop-
enyl acetate in the presence of KSF-clay and
from $\underline{N},\underline{N}'$-diacylhydrazines 81 and thionyl
chloride (95SC1451).

Arenecarbonitrile oxides add to the dicyano-
ketene ethylene acetal 82 to yield 1,2,4-
oxadiazoles 83 (95SC2379). The formation of
the oxadiazole 86 by the action of nitronium
tetrafluoroborate in acetonitrile on the
ester 84 is thought to proceed by way of the
α-carbonyl cation 85, which undergoes a 1,2-
shift of a methyl group (95TL3039). The high-
pressure reaction of nitrones with cyanides
to yield 1,2,4-oxadiazolines, e.g. 87 and 88,
has been reported (95SYN498).

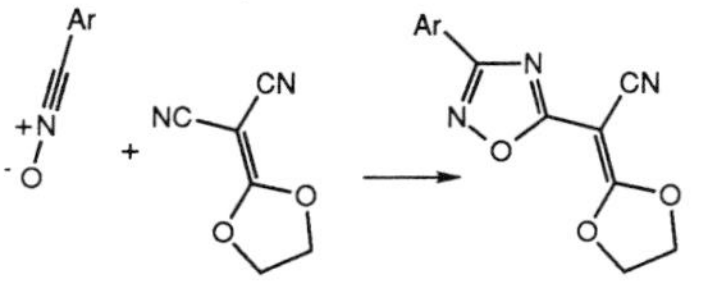

(82)   (83)

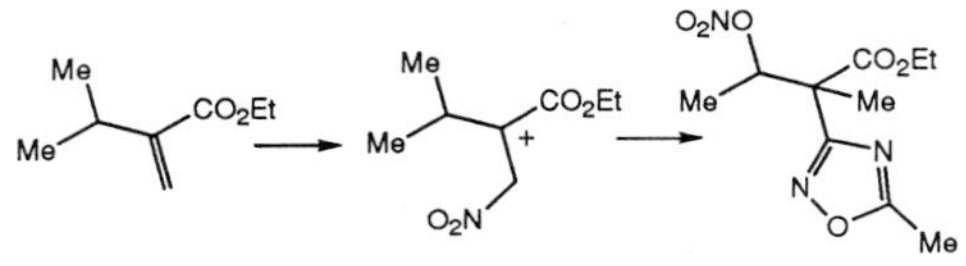

(84)   (85)   (86)

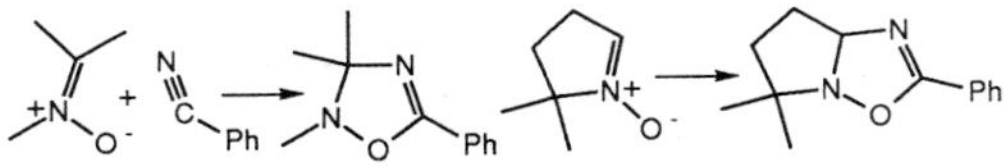

(87)   (88)

The chemistry of cyclopentafurazans (cyclopen-
ta-1,2,5-oxadiazoles) and furazans fused to
five-membered heterocycles with one to four
heteroatoms has been reviewed (95JHC371).
Treatment of 3-amino-4-nitro-1,2,5-oxadiazole
with dinitrogen pentoxide yields dinitro-1,2,5-
oxadiazole 89 (95MC102). The latter reacts normally with benzenethiol to give the sulfide 90,

while potassium thiocyanate affords a mixture of compounds 91 and 92 (95MC25). 4-Dialkylamino-3-chloro-1,2,5-oxadiazole 2-oxides 94 (R = NMe$_2$, NEt$_2$, piperidin-1-yl etc) are formed by the action of trimethylsilylamines Me$_3$SiR on the chloronitrooxadiazole oxide 94 (R = NO$_2$) (94KGS1133). Treatment of benzofurazan 95 with isopropyl alcohol and sulfuric acid produces a mixture of the dihydrobenzimidazole N-oxide 96 and o-nitroso-N-isopropylaniline 97 (95KGS395). A mixture of the benzofurazan 99 and the benzotriazole 100 results from the action of benzenediazonium chloride on the aminobenzofurazan 98. Both products were oxidized to the triazolobenzofurazan 101 (94KGS1432). Benzofuroxan 102 is converted into the 2H-benzimidazole 1,3-dioxides 103 (R$_2$ = Me$_2$, Ph$_2$, (CH$_2$)$_4$ or (CH$_2$)$_5$) by the action of an alcohol R$_2$CHOH under acidic conditions (94KGS524).

The synthesis of 1,3,4-oxadiazoles from tetrazoles has been reviewed (94ZOB1698). 1,3,4-oxadiazolylacetones 104 (R = H, Me, Ph etc) undergo ring-transformation to the isoxazoles 105 by reaction with hydroxylamine (95SYN805).

5.7.10 REFERENCES

94BCJ2838   Y.Tamura, M.Kimura, S.Tanaka, S. Kure and Z.Yoshida, Bull. Chem. Soc. Jpn., 1994, <u>67</u>, 838.

94CC2101   M.Kawase, J. Chem. Soc., Chem. Commun., 1994, 2101.

94CC2661   P.W.Ambler, R.M.Paton and J.M.Tout, J. Chem. Soc., Chem. Commun., 1994, 2661.

94CL1673   H.Suga, X.Shi and T.Ibata, Chem. Lett., 1994, 1673.

94JCS2449 R.Fukagawa and M.Nojima, J. Chem. Soc., Perkin Trans. 1, 1994, 2449.

94JCS3041 D.Delaunay and M.Le Corre, J. Chem. Soc., Perkin Trans. 1, 1994, 3041.

94JCS3295 M.R.Iesce, F.Cermola, F.Giordano, R. Scarpati and M.L.Graziano, J. Chem. Soc., Perkin Trans. 1, 1994, 3295.

94JCS3355 L.-L.Shiu, K.-M.Chien, T.-Y.Liu, T.-I.Lin, G.-R.Her, S.-L.Huang and T.-Y.Luh, J. Chem. Soc., Perkin Trans. 1, 1994, 3355.

94JHC861 C.Dell'Erba, M.Novi, G.Petrillo and P.Stagnaro, J. Heterocycl. Chem., 1994, 31, 861.

94JOC5658 A.Zietlow and E.Steckhan, J. Org. Chem., 1994, 59, 5658.

94JOC6840 D.Giomi, R.Nesi, S.Turchi and T. Fabriani, J. Org. Chem., 1994, 59, 6840.

94JOC6949 S.Kanemasa and K.Onimura, J. Org. Chem., 1994, 59, 6949.

94JOC7072 A.Padwa, D.L.Hertzog and W.R.Nadler, J. Org. Chem., 1994, 59, 7072.

94KGS524 V.A.Samsonov, L.B.Volodarsky and O. V.Shamirzaeva, Khim. Geterotsikl. Soedin., 1994, 524; Chem. Abstr., 1995, 122, 290776j.

94KGS846 E.V.Pastushenko and G.I.Safuilova, Khim. Geterotsikl. Soedin., 1994, 846; Chem. Abstr., 1995, 122, 31386x.

94KGS1133 O.V.Zavarzina, O.A.Rakitin and L.I. Khmelnitsky, Khim. Geterotsikl. Soedin., 1994, 1133; Chem. Abstr., 1995, 122, 214012s.

94KGS1432 V.A.Samsonov, L.V.Volodarskii, V.L. Korolev and G.Kh.Khisamutdinov, Khim. Geterotsikl. Soedin., 1994, 1432; Chem. Abstr., 1995, 123, 143747t.

94MI153 H.-J.Tien, M.-J.Tien and W.-J.Hung, Huaxue, 1994, 52, 153; Chem. Abstr., 1995, 122, 265312x.

94MI213 S.Batra and A.P.Bhaduri, J. Indian Inst. Sci., 1994, 74, 213.

94SYN989 Y.He and N.-H.Lin, Synthesis, 1994, 989.

94SYN1313 O.Prien, H.Hoffmann, K.Conde-Frieboes, T.Krettek, B.Berger, K.Wagner, M.Bolte and D.Hoppe, Synthesis, 1994 (Spec. Issue), 1313.

94T10061 M.F.Brana, J.M.Castellano, P.de Miguel, P.Posada, C.Sanz and A.S.Migallon, Tetrahedron, 1994, $\underline{50}$, 10061.

94TL6473 M.A.Weidner-Wells, S.A.Fraga and J.P.Demers, Tetrahedron Lett., 1994, $\underline{35}$, 6473.

94TL6879 T.Martens, F.Souquet and J.Royer, Tetrahedron Lett., 1994, $\underline{35}$, 6879.

94TL7111 J.F.Bower and J.M.J.Williams, trahedron Lett., 1994, $\underline{35}$, 7111.

94TL7159 A.Padwa, D.J.Austin and A.T.Price, Tetrahedron Lett., 1994, $\underline{35}$, 7159.

94TL7399 K.Iseki, D.Asada, M.Takahashi, T.Nagai and Y.Kobayashi, Tetrahedron Lett., 1994, $\underline{35}$, 7399.

94TL7493 R.H.Wallace and J.Liu, Tetrahedron Lett., 1994, $\underline{35}$, 7493.

94TL9533 C.M.Huwe and S.Blechert, Tetrahedron Lett., 1994, $\underline{35}$, 9533.

94ZOB1698 G.I.Koldobskii and S.E.Ivanova, Zh. Obshch. Khim., 1994, $\underline{64}$, 1698; Chem. Abstr., 1995, $\underline{122}$, 265270g.

95AG798 D.A.Evans, J.A.Murry, P.von Matt, R.D.Norcross and S.J.Miller, Angew. Chem., Int. Ed. Engl., 1995, $\underline{34}$, 798.

95CL357 A.Abiko, Chem. Lett., 1995, 357.

95H149 K.Fukushima and T.Ibata, Heterocycles, 1995, $\underline{40}$, 149.

95JHC371 A.B.Sheremetev, J. Heterocycl. Chem., 1995, $\underline{32}$, 371.

95JOC1727 M.Sawamura, Y.Nakayama, T.Kato and Y.Ito, J. Org. Chem., 1995, $\underline{60}$, 1727.

95JOC3764 M.Kimura, S.Tanaka and Y.Tamaru, J. Org. Chem., 1995, $\underline{60}$, 3764.

95KGS395 V.A.Samsonov, L.B.Volodarsky, I.Yu. Bagryanskaya, Yu.V.Gatilov and M.M. Shakirov, Khim. Geterotsikl. Soedin., 1995, 395; Chem. Abstr., 1995, $\underline{123}$, 285354m.

95MC25 A.B.Sheremetev, E.V.Mantseva, N.S. Aleksandrova, V.S.Kuzmin and L.I. Khmelnitskii, Mendeleev Commun., 1995, 25.

95MC102   A.M.Churukov, S.E.Semenov, S.L.
            Ioffe, Y.A.Strelenko and V.A.
            Tartakovskii, Mendeleev Commun.,
            1995, 102.
95MI871   C.E.Song, E.J.Roh, S.Lee and I.O.
            Kim, Tetrahedron: Asymmetry, 1995,
            6, 871.
95SC561   N.Lewis, A.McKillop, R.J.K.Taylor
            and R.I.Watson, Synth. Commun., 1995.
            25, 561.
95SC659   B.Oussaid, J.Berlan, M.Soufiaoui
            and B.Garrigues, Synth. Commun.,
            1995, 25, 659.
95SC1145   R.M.Giuliano and C.Bigos, Synth.
            Commun., 1995, 25, 1145.
95SC1451   B.Oussaid, L.Moeini, B.Martin, D.
            Villemin and B.Garrigues, Synth.
            Commun., 1995, 25, 1451.
95SC2379   R.Neidlein and S.Li, Synth. Commun.,
            1995, 25, 2379.
95SYN498   Y.Yu, H.Fujita, M.Ohno and S.Eguchi,
            Synthesis, 1995, 498.
95SYN805   U.I.Jonsson, H.Kristinsson, H.
            Nussbaumer, V.Skulason and T.
            Winkler, Synthesis, 1995, 805.
95T755   A.Doemling, A.Bayler and I.Ugi,
            Tetrahedron, 1995, 51, 755.
95T4043   C.Agami, F.Couty and C.Lequesne,
            Tetrahedron, 1955, 51, 4043.
95T5891   M.A.Casadei, S.Cesa and A.Inesi,
            Tetrahedron, 1995, 51, 5891.
95T6285   H.G.Aurich and H.Koester,
            Tetrahedron, 1995, 51, 6285.
95T7085   S.Turchi, D.Giomi, R.Nesi and P.
            Paoli, Tetrahedron, 1995, 51, 7085.
95TL2053   M.-C.Lallemand, M.Chiadmi, A.Tomas,
            N.Kunesch and H.-P.Husson,
            Tetrahedron Lett., 1995, 36, 2053.
95TL3039   S.A.Hewlins, J.A.Murphy and J.Lin,
            Tetrahedron Lett., 1995, 36, 3039.

Chapter 6.1

Six-Membered Ring Systems: Pyridine and Benzo Derivatives

Joseph E. Toomey, Jr. and Ramiah Murugan
Reilly Industries, Inc., Indianapolis, IN, USA

6.1.1 SYNTHESIS

6.1.1.1 Reviews

Use of aliphatic nitro compounds to prepare a variety of pyridines, 1,4-dihydropyridines, and 2-pyridiones has been reviewed <94CHE(30)1125>. Syntheses of pyridines by catalysis and subsequent derivatization reactions were reviewed <94CHE(30)1284>. A review of cyclotrimerization of alkynes and chiral nitriles to give chiral-substituted pyridines using Co(I) catalysis was reported <95T(A)(6)811>. Nekrasov reviewed the heterodiene approach to pyridines using cyanamides <94CHE(30)997>. Synthesis of 1,4-dihydropyridines having sulfur substituents was reviewed <94CHE(30)1386>. New directions for the Pictet-Spengler condensation were also reviewed <95CR(95)1797>. Harrison reviewed the syntheses of saturated nitrogen heterocycles <95COS(2)209>. Use of amino acid esters to form asymmetric nitrogen heterocycles using heterodiene syntheses, Mannich reactions, Pictet-Spengler reactions, 1,3-diploar cycloadditions, aza Diels-Alder reactions, and radical additions to carbonyl functionality was reviewed <95SL133>.

6.1.1.2 Pyridines

Selective cyclotrimerization of alkynes with nitriles produced pentasubstituted pyridines (**1**) with little formation of benzenoid products (**Scheme 1**) <94CB(127)2535>.

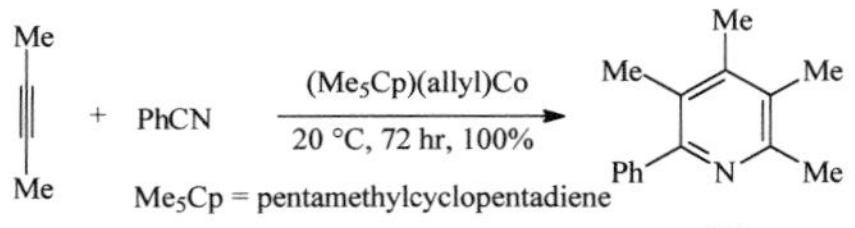

Scheme 1

209

Similar cyclotrimerizations were accomplished with irradiation in 3 hours, but in lower yield <95CC(2)179>. Rhodium catalysis yielded pyridines without irradiation in slightly longer times, but the unsymmetrical alkynes used led to isomeric products, such as (2) and (3), (**Scheme 2**) <95JO(488)47>.

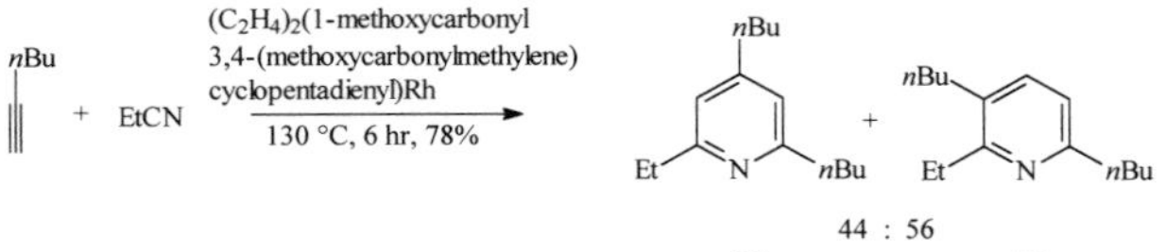

Scheme 2

2-Pyridones with 5-phosphonate ester substituents, (4), can be made from alkynes and enamine derivative (5) (**Scheme 3**) <95H(41)1915>.

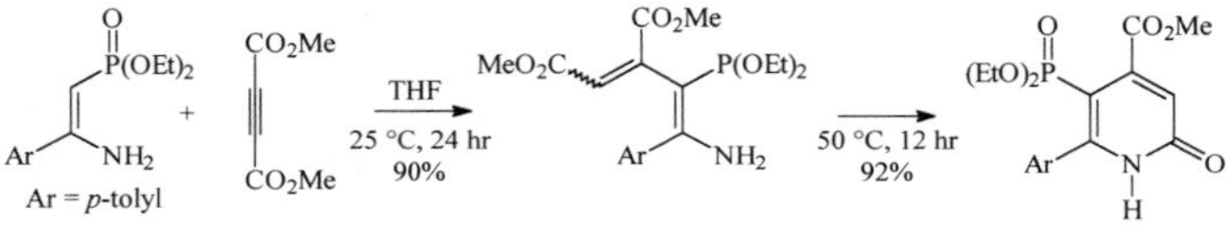

Scheme 3

Malononitrile condenses with 3-pyridinecarboxaldehyde and a ketone to form substituted bipyridine (6) (**Scheme 4**) <95JCR(S)(4)146>.

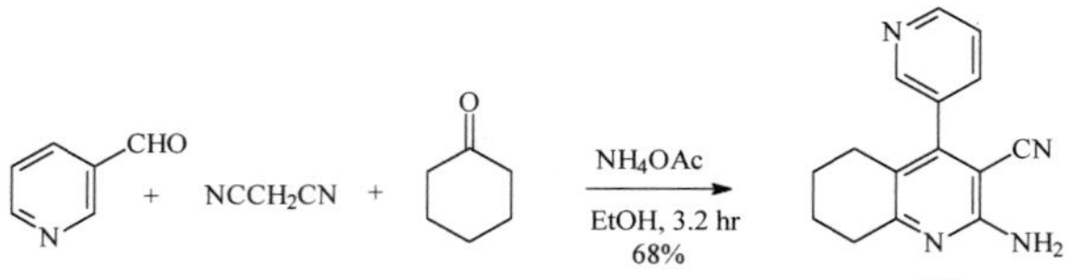

Scheme 4

Vinylogous iminium salts, *e.g.* (7), cyclize with β-aminocrotonitriles to form trisubstituted pyridines, *e.g.* (8), (**Scheme 5**) <95T(51)1575>.

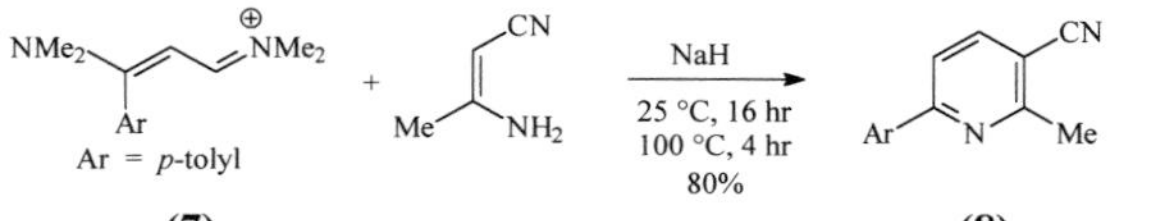

Scheme 5

2-Chloro-3-aryl- (**9**) and 2-amino-3-arylpyridine (**10**) can be formed by cyclization of enamine (**11**) under acidic or basic conditions respectively (**Scheme 6**) <95JOC(60)3750>.

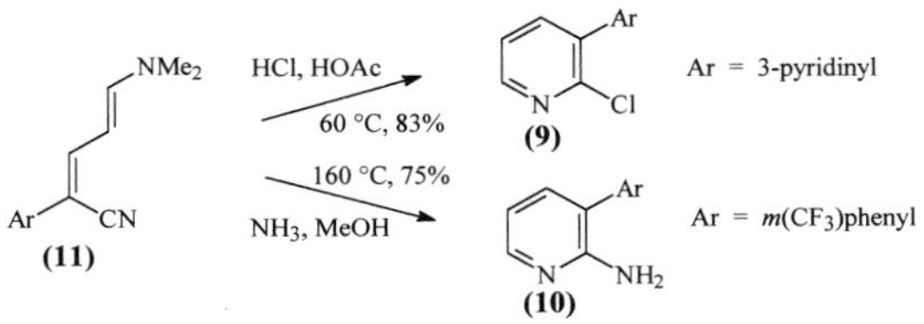

Ar = 3-pyridinyl

Ar = m(CF$_3$)phenyl

Scheme 6

3-Cyano-2-pyridones can be prepared in a single step using cyanoacetamide and an unsaturated ketone <95TL(36)3307>.

An unusual cadmium-promoted cyclization to form a pyridine ring, as part of a tricyclic system, was reported (**Scheme 7**) <95JOC(60)5243>. Zinc and copper (I) salts can replace the cadmium salt. Organocadmium promoters allow room temperature cyclization.

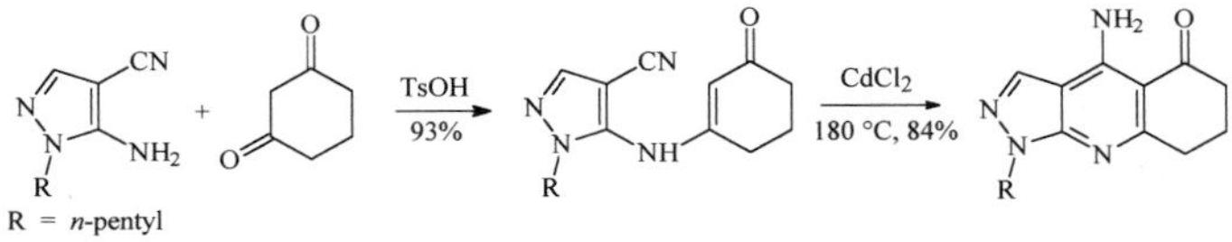

R = n-pentyl

Scheme 7

Chloride anion has been used to effect dehydrochlorination of pyridone (**12**) (**Scheme 8**) <94JOC(59)6783>. The product is an important intermediate for agricultural compounds.

(**12**)

Scheme 8

4-Trifluoromethyl-2-pyridone derivative (**13**) can be prepared in modest yield using polyphosphoric acid (PPA) (**Scheme 9**) <95JCR(S)476>.

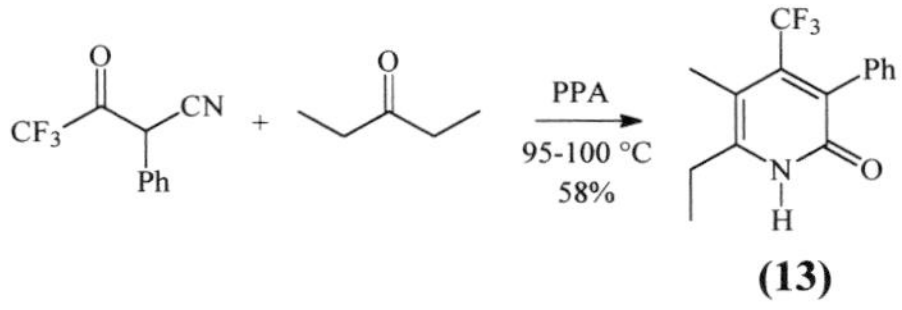

(**13**)

Scheme 9

Bentonite K10 clay has been utilized as catalyst in both forming Hantzsch 1,4-dihydropyridines and in mild oxidation of those Hantzsch dihydropyridnes to pyridines <95BCB(104)387> <94AMC(131)383>. Chiral 1,4-dihydropyridines have been made <95T(A)(6)877>. Modified Hantzsch ester synthesis, employing nitroacetone, has been used to prepare a series of calcium-channel blocking agents <95JMC(38)2851>. Very rapid, solventless Hantzsch ester synthesis was accomplished with microwaves <95SC(25)857>; use of aqueous hydrotrope solution was claimed to be safer <95TL(36)8083>.

Substituted β-aminocinnamic acid esters, such as (**14**), condense with 3-chloro-2-methoxycrotonaldehyde (**15**) to form nicotinic esters, such as (**16**), (**Scheme 10**) <94AP(327)755>.

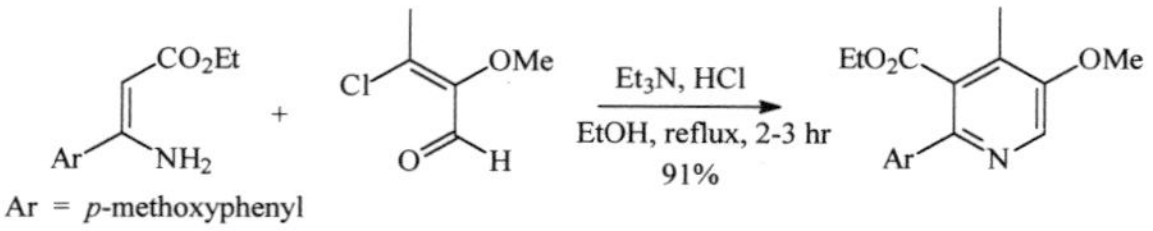
CO2Et
Ar
NH2
Ar = p-methoxyphenyl
+
Cl
OMe
O
H
Et3N, HCl
EtOH, reflux, 2-3 hr
91%
EtO2C
OMe
Ar
N

(14) **(15)** **(16)**

Scheme 10

Condensation of α,β-*cis*-dienals with primary amines was reported to be a general method for synthesizing 1,2-dihydropyridines (**Scheme 11**); mechanism was studied and indicated unprecedented steric acceleration of a 6π-electrocyclization <95JOC(60)1763> [see also <89JA(111)4051>].

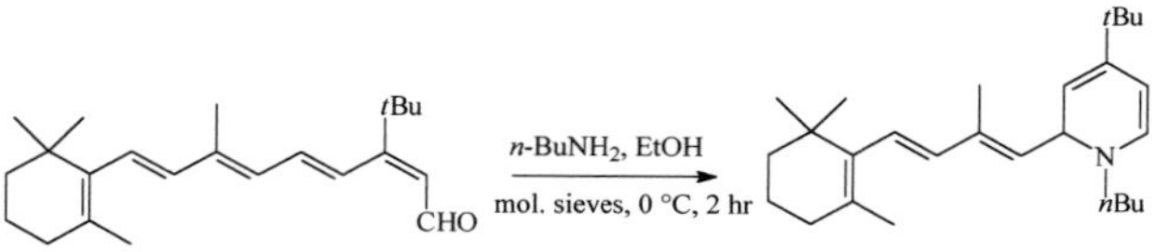
tBu
CHO
n-BuNH2, EtOH
mol. sieves, 0 °C, 2 hr
tBu
N
nBu

Scheme 11

Ring closure of (**17**) under Vilsmeier conditions led to pyridine compound (**18**) (**Scheme 12**) <95JHC(32)505>.

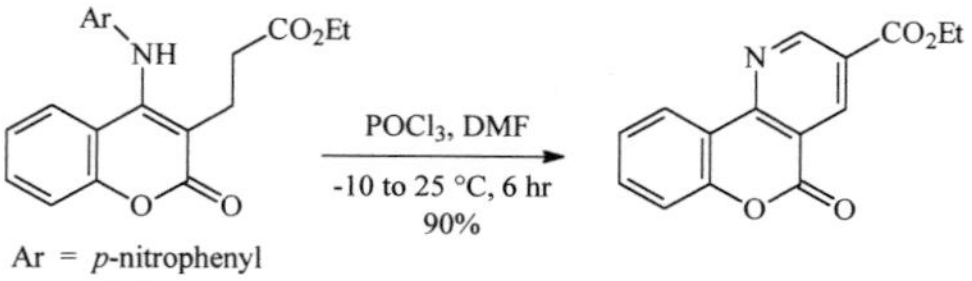
Ar
NH
CO2Et
O
O
Ar = p-nitrophenyl
POCl3, DMF
-10 to 25 °C, 6 hr
90%
N
CO2Et
O
O

(17) **(18)**

Scheme 12

Malononitrile adds to α,β-unsaturated ketones to make isomeric pyridines (**Scheme 13**) <95JCR(S)392>.

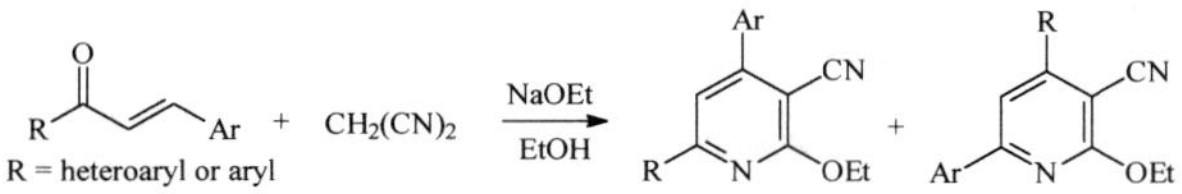

Scheme 13

Either dimethyl maleate or dimethyl fumarate participated with 2-cyano-1-azabutadiene derivative (19) in the heterodiene synthesis to stereospecifically form pyridines (20) and (21) (**Scheme 14**) <95TL(36)8977>. Large rate enhancements were noted using 2.5 $\underline{M}$ LiNTf$_2$ in acetonitrile.

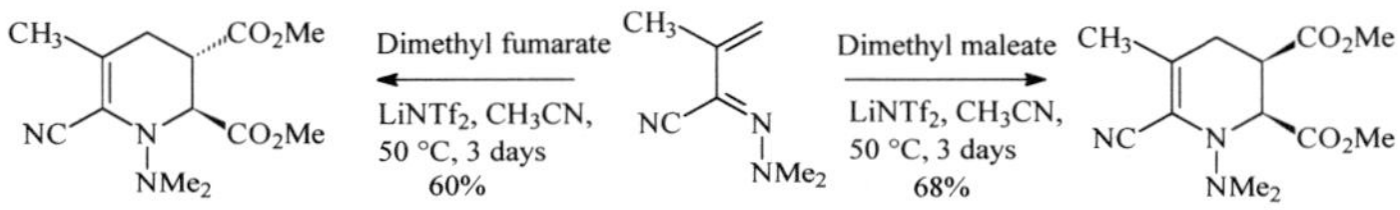

(21)   **(19)**   **(20)**

Scheme 14

Intramolecular heterodiene synthesis used alkyne (22) (**Scheme 15**) <95B(ECTOC-1)>.

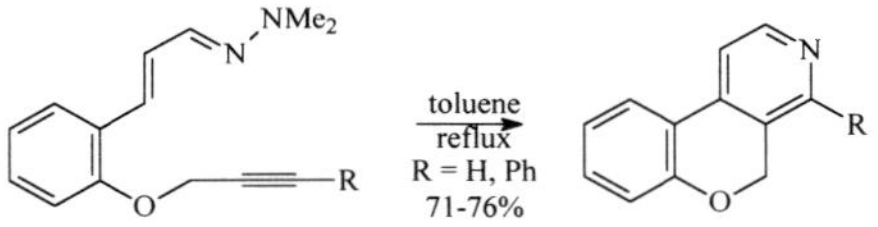

(22)

Scheme 15

A pair of papers describe the use of lanthanide triflates, in preference to unstable lithium perchlorate, as catalysts in heterodiene synthesis <95SL233> <95SYN1195>, as was also noted in <95TL(36)8977> and **Scheme 14**.

Thermolysis of 2H-aziridines having cyclopropyl ring substitution yielded pyridines <95H(40)511>. Steric inhibition of pyridine ring formation was noted for some aziridines. Aza-Wittig reaction on aziridines yields tetrahydropyridines <95TL(36)3557>.

Azapyrylium (23) reacts with a variety of alkynes under Lewis-acid catalysis to form pyridines, such as the 2,6-diphenylpyridine shown in (**Scheme 16**) <95H(40)531>.

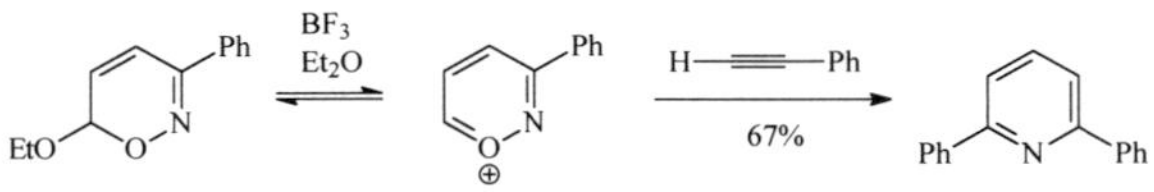

(23)

Scheme 16

Indigo (24) can be pyrolysed in good yield, with double ring expansion, to form tetracycle (25) (**Scheme 17**) <95AG(34)67>.

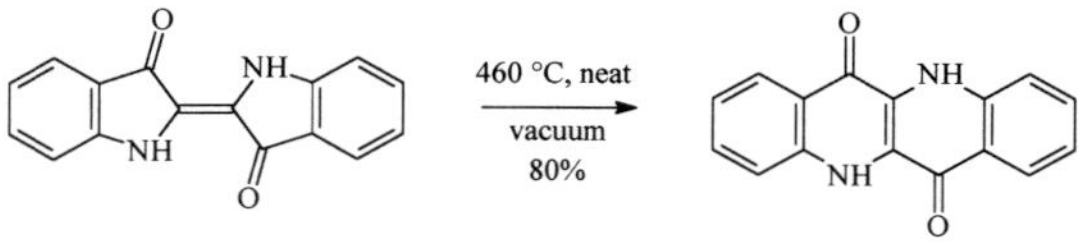

(24)   **(25)**

Scheme 17

Anhydrobases can act as carbon nucleophiles in reactions with pyryliums <95JHC(32)563>.

6.1.1.3 Quinolines and Isoquinolines

Aza-Wittig ring closure proved effective in making both quinoline derivative (**26**) <94TL(35)9229> and isoquinoline derivative (**27**) (**Scheme 18**) <95TL(36)59>.

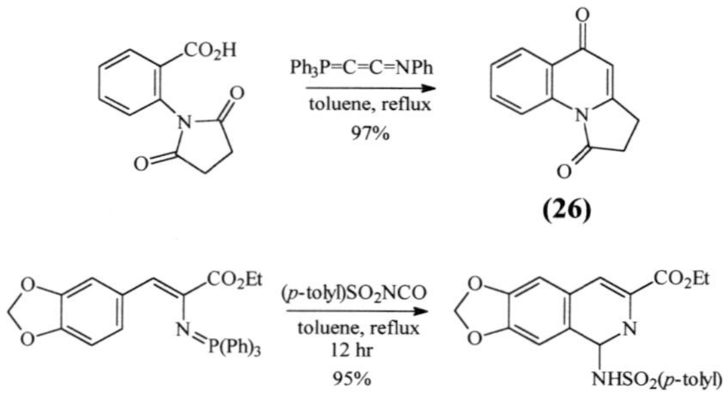

(26)

(27)

Scheme 18

Irradiation of azadiene (**28**) in the presence of fluoroboric acid gave a 4-aminoquinoline compound, (**29**), in excellent yield (**Scheme 19**) <94SYN1155>.

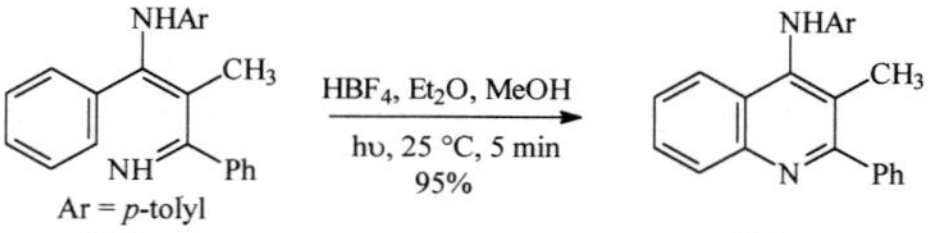

(28)   **(29)**

Scheme 19

2,4-Dimethylpyrroloquinoline (**30**) is the product of reaction of 7-aminoindoles with acetylacetone (**Scheme 20**) <95SC(25)1601> <95CHE(31)50>, not the pyrrolobenzodiazepine originally reported <57PCS354>.

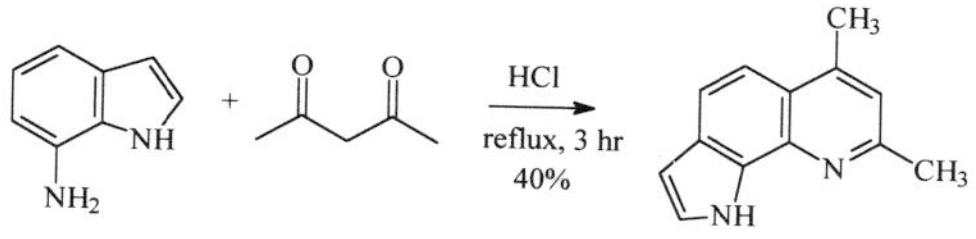

(30)

Scheme 20

Sterospecific synthesis of tetrahydroquinoline compound (**31**) was achieved from simple starting materials in high yield (**Scheme 21**) <95JOC(60)2588> <95JOC(60)3993>.

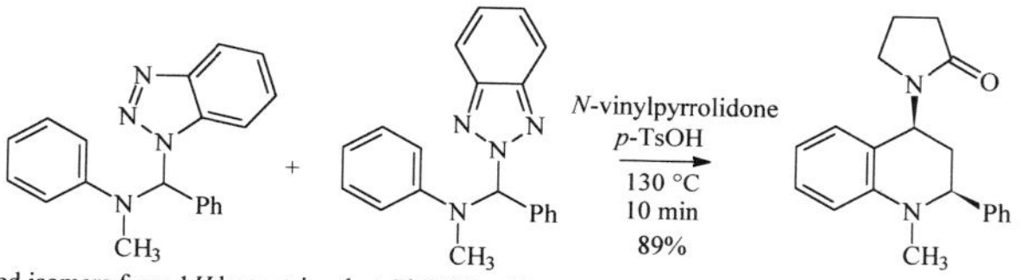

{Mixed isomers from 1*H*-benzotriazole + PhCHO + N-methylaniline}

(31)

Scheme 21

Oxime derivative (**32**) can be cyclized to quinoline compound (**33**) under Lewis-acid catalysis (**Scheme22**) <95CL5>.

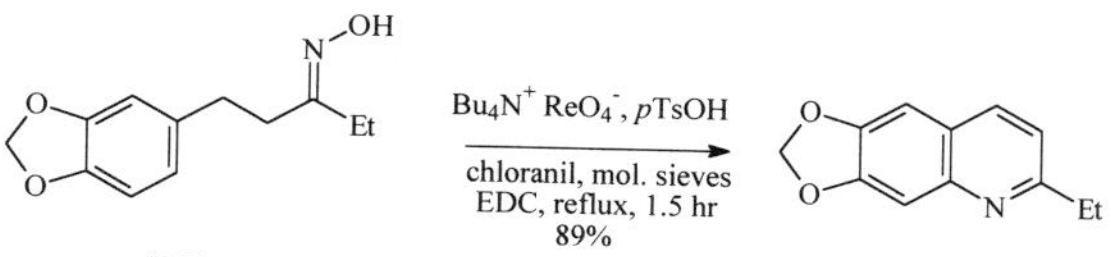

(32)

(33)

Scheme 22

Substituted phenylisocyanide (**34**) can be used to make a dihydroquinoline compound, (**35**), (**Scheme 23**) <95CL575>.

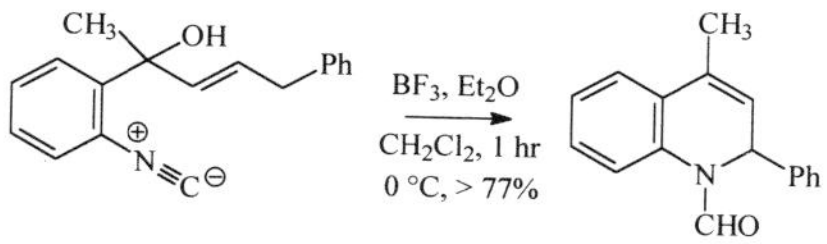

(34)

(35)

Scheme 23

Isoquinoline derivative (**36**) can be prepared from substituted benzocyclobutenoxide (**37**) and 2-cyanopyridine in fair yield (**Scheme 24**) <94TL(35)9177>.

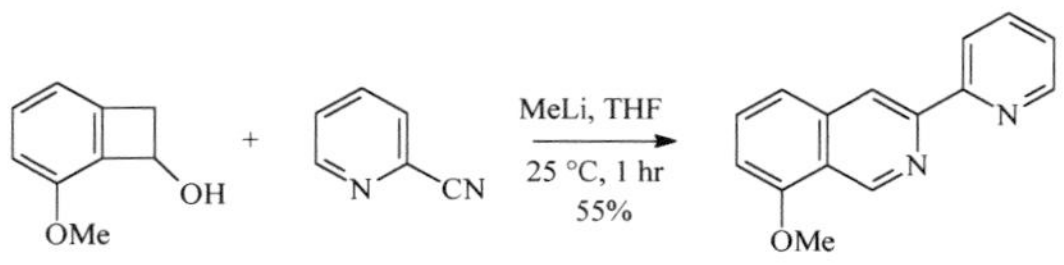

(37) **(36)**

Scheme 24

6.1.1.4 Piperidines

The indolizidine alkaloid skeleton can be easily synthesized using the Barton-Ester method (**Scheme 25**) <94TL(35)9157>.

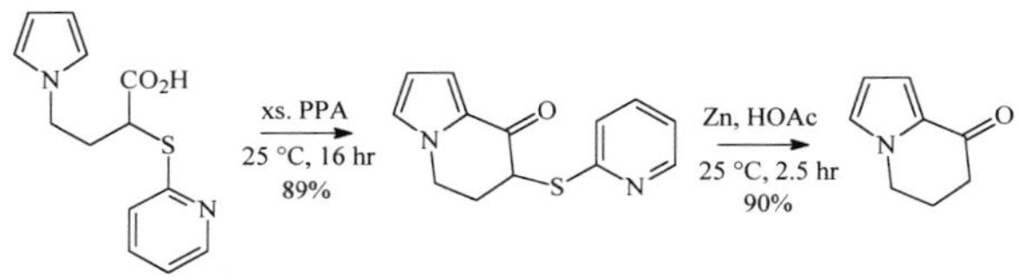

Scheme 25

Irradiation of 2,6-diaminopimelic acid in a CdS suspension gave *trans*-2,6-piperidinedicarboxylic acid, as a pair of enantiomers, along with the single *cis*-diastereomer (**Scheme 26**) <95TL(36)3189>.

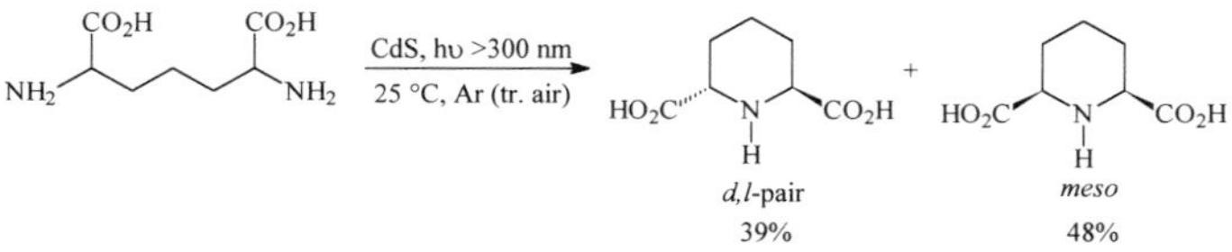

d,l-pair 39%   *meso* 48%

Scheme 26

Ti(IV) mediated Diekmann condensation of diester precursor (**38**) gave good yield of substituted 4-piperidone derivative, (**39**), (**Scheme 27**) <95SC(25)177>.

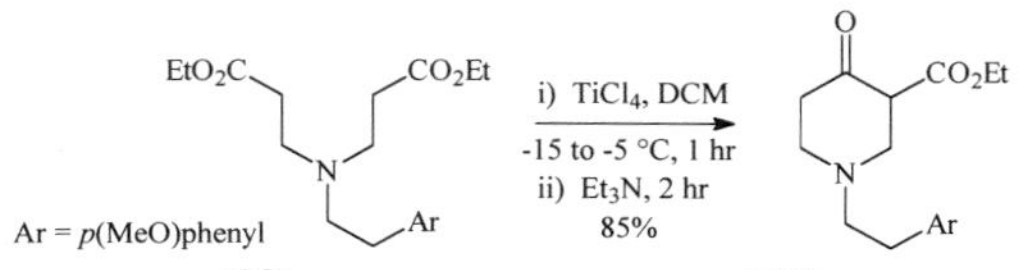

Ar = *p*(MeO)phenyl

(38) **(39)**

Scheme 27

β-Aminoacrylates were transformed into piperidines by radical cyclization using Bu_3SnH and AIBN in good yield, product being formed as two sets of d,l-enantiomers related to each other as diastereomers (one *cis*-pair and one *trans*-pair) <95TL(36)417>.

6.1.2 REACTIONS

6.1.2.1 Reviews

A comprehensive review on functionalization of the pyridine ring with carbon-carbon bond formation covering the past fifteen years was published <94CHC(30)1331>. Reviews on the syntheses of *N*-substituted amino-2-pyridones <94OPPI(26)465>, chemistry of pyrido[c]coumarins (94CHC(30)867>, stereoselective syntheses of chiral piperidin-4-ones <94KGS1619>, pyridinium betaines <94AHC(60)198>, cyclopenta- and indenopyridine anhydrobases <95CHC(31)1>, and on pyridine and piperidine alkaloids <94NPR(11)581> were written. A general method for the synthesis of bridged indole alkaloids based on addition of carbon nucleophiles to *N*-alkylpyridinium salts was reviewed <95SL587>.

Reviews of the chemistry of heterocycles containing pyridine rings appeared in the following areas: transformations of nitrogen-containing heterocycles <94KGS1482>; chemistry of aromatic *N*-oxides <95H(40)1035>; lithiations promoted by heteroaromatic substituents <95OR(47)1>; aromatic heterocycles as intermediates in the synthesis of natural products <95COS(2)1>; synthesis of nitrogen-containing heterocyclic compounds based on α-haloketones <94CHC(30)745>; and microbiological transformation in a series of nitrogen-containing heterocycles <94CHC(30)1308>.

6.1.2.2 Pyridines

An interesting reaction leading to 5-substitution of 2-aminopyridines has been reported (**Scheme 28**) <95JCS(P1)3129>.

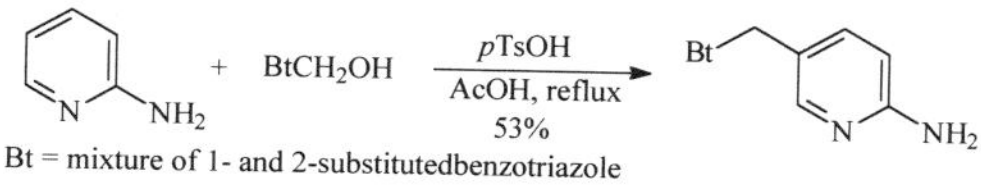

$$+ \quad BtCH_2OH \xrightarrow[\substack{AcOH, reflux \\ 53\%}]{pTsOH}$$

Bt = mixture of 1- and 2-substitutedbenzotriazole

Scheme 28

Similar to last year's reported reaction <94H(37)1489> between 4-cyanopyridine, benzophenone, and metals to give diphenyl(4-pyridyl)carbinol, this year the reaction between 4-cyanopyridine, alkali metal, and ketones or aldehydes was reported to give 4-pyridinemethanols in good yield <95TL(36)7275>.

A novel, one-pot synthesis of 6,6"-dibromo-2,2':6',2"-terpyridine (**40**) from 2,6-dibromopyridine and butyllithium is reported (**Scheme 29**) <95S939>.

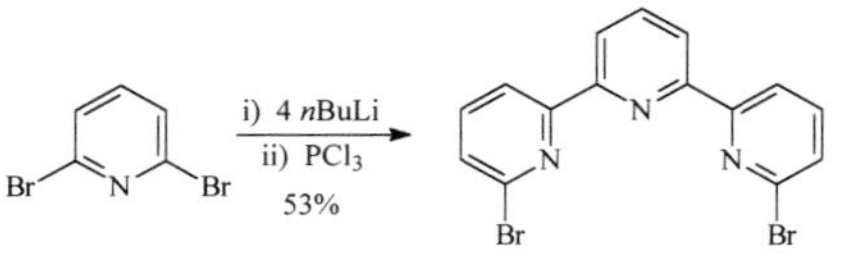

(40)

Scheme 29

A redox reaction of trichloromethylarenes with pyridines results in N-(α-chloroarylmethyl)substituted pyridinium chlorides, which on hydrolysis give aromatic aldehydes and 4-chloropyridines or 1,4'-bipyridinium salts <95TL(36)5075>.

On nitration, aminopyridines, such as (**41**), gave dinitro-derivative (**42**) (**Scheme 30**) <95JHC(32)585>.

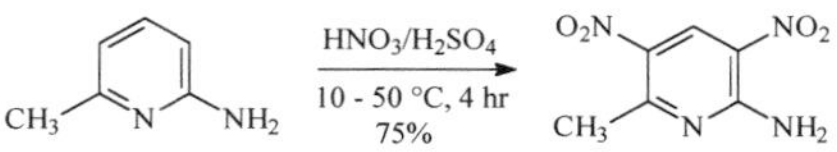

(41)   **(42)**

Scheme 30

Synthesis of (S)-6-hydroxymethylcotinine for use in radioimmunoassay analysis of nicotine metabolites was achieved by reacting (S)-cotinine with a carbon-centered radical derived from methanol <95JCR(S)246>.

Smiles-type rearrangement followed by cyclization has been described in the formation of thieno[2,3-h][1,6]-naphthryridine skeleton (**43**) from 2-(3-cyanopropylthio)pyridine-3-carbonitrile (**44**) (**Scheme 31**) <95H(41)1307>.

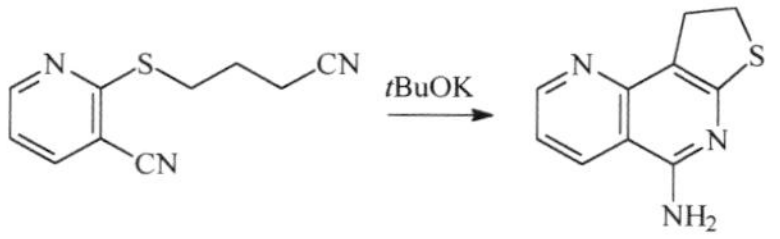

(44)   **(43)**

Scheme 31

The alkylation of 2-pyridone was effected under mild conditions by use of cesium fluoride. Benzyl and allyl chlorides furnished the N-alkylated product selectively, while secondary alkyl iodides gave O-alkylation selectively <95SL845>.

The first persubstitution of perfluorobenzene with 4-dimethylaminopyridine has been achieved using trifluoromethane sulfonate as the counterion <95AG(34)1319>.

A novel method for chlorination of 2-acetamidopyridines using chlorine and sodium hydrogen sulfate was reported to give 5-chloro derivatives <94NKK1036>.

An electrochemical approach was feasible for selective monosubstitution of dichloropyridines (**Scheme 32**) <95JOC(60)18>.

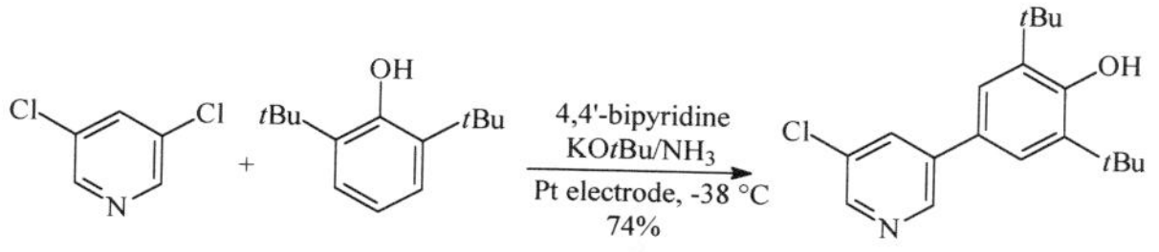

Scheme 32

On refluxing in benzene with excess pyridine, the monocycloadduct of diphenylnitrile imine and pyridine smoothly underwent a [1,5]-sigmatropic shift and subsequent electrocyclic ring opening to afford 1,2,4-triazole derivative (**44**) (**Scheme 33**) <95H(40)515>.

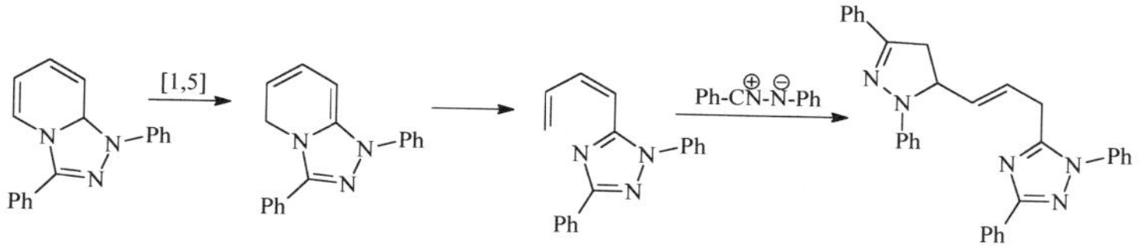

(44)

Scheme 33

In the presence of alkylchloroformate esters, *bis*(tributylstannyl)acetylene has been used in the 2-ethynylation of pyridines <94T(50)13089>. An unexpected regioselectivity has been observed in the rearrangement of 3-pyridyl thiophosphates to 2- and 4-pyridyl thiophosphonates <94ZOK(64)610>. A method for introduction of acyl carbon functional groups using trimethylstannyl pyridine (**45**) was explored and applied to making fusaric acid (**46**) (**Scheme 34**) <95H(41)817>.

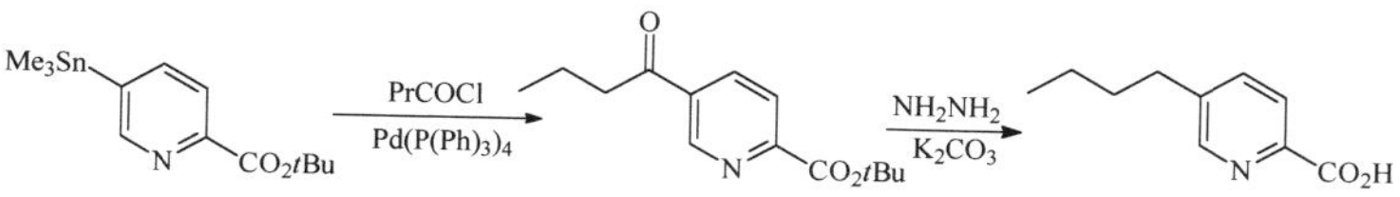

(45) **(46)**

Scheme 34

The DE ring of camptothecin has been prepared enantioselectively in six steps from 2-fluoropyridine using a "halogen dance" reaction <95TL(36)7995>. The first total synthesis of dimethyl sulfomycinamate (**47**) was reported starting from 3-hydroxy-6-methylpyridine (**48**) <95TL(36)5319>.

(47)   **(48)**

Convenient new syntheses of 4-azaphenothiazine <95LA591> and pyridobenzothiazine <95H(41)461> have been achieved by oxidative ring closure. Oxidative ring closure was achieved by heating in the presence of diethyl azodicarboxylate, NBS, or iodine.

A practical synthesis of furopyridine (**49**), a fragment of a HIV-protease inhibitor, was accomplished starting with 6-hydroxynicotinic acid <95TL(36)4571>. Nevirapine (**50**), and its derivatives, have received much attention because of their inhibition of reverse transcriptase in HIV-type 1 <95JMC(38)4830> <95JMC(38)4839>. (**50**) has been synthesized using a directed metallation approach <95JOC(60)1875> <95H(41)753>.

(49)   **(50)**

Metallation of chloropyridines <95H(41)289> <95H(41)1431> and methoxypyridines <95H(41)675> <94JOC(59)5120> <95TL(36)4791> has been used to put substituents on the pyridine ring. Directed *ortho*-metallation using amide functionality has also been utilized to put substituents on the pyridine ring <95T(51)1259> <95JOC(60)5721> <95S321> <95LA1441>.

Palladium-catalyzed cross-coupling has been used extensively for substitution on the pyridine ring. Cross-coupling has been done on the following starting pyridine derivatives: pyridyl boranes <95JOC(60)264> <94TL(35)9063>, pyridyl stannanes <95JOC(60)3487> <95TL(36)5247> <95TL(36)6261>, pyridyl triflates <95SL157> <95P(50)182> <95TL(36)5015>, and halopyridines <95H(41)2405> <94TL(35)9355> <95LA645> <95JHC(32)467> <95JOC(60)2640> <95SL153> <95T(51)1941> <95SC(25)2901> <95MC(126)805>.

6.1.2.2 Pyridiniums

An intermolecular condensation of 4-(ω-cyclopentadienyl)-1-methylpyridinium salts leads to synthesis of [*n*](1,6)- and [*n*](2,6)azulenophanes (*n* = 11, 12, 13) <95TL(36)2603>.

An enamine rearrangement has been proposed for the formation of indole rings from pyridinium salt (**51**) (**Scheme 35**) <95IJC(B)(34)285>.

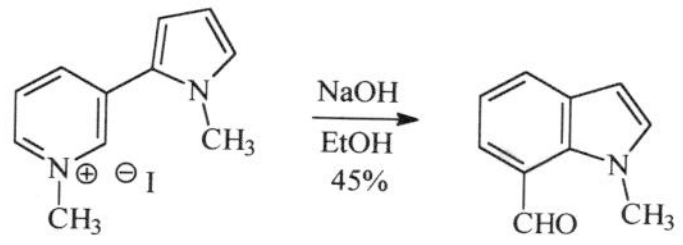

Scheme 35

6.1.2.4 *N*-Oxides

A rapid, mild, and efficient method for the preparation of pyridine *N*-oxides has been reported using *m*-CPBA in DMF/MeOH solvent in the presence of HF <95H(41)323>. Metallation of pyridine *N*-oxides at the 2- or 6-position has been used in the preparation of α-substituted pyridine *N*-oxides <95H(40)809> <95JCS(P1)2503>.

Deoxygenation of pyridine *N*-oxides has been achieved using dimethyldioxiran <95CC1831> and palladium with sodium hypophosphite <95GCI(124)385>. Pyridine *N*-oxides, with ruthenium porphyrin catalysts, have been used as an oxidant of aromatic compounds <95JA(117)8879> or olefins, alcohols, sulfides and alkanes <95H(40)867>.

6.1.2.5 Quinolines

Quinoline, on treatment with zinc and acetic anhydride in THF, readily gives the pentacyclic quinobenzazepine skeleton (**52**) (**Scheme 36**) <95SL603>.

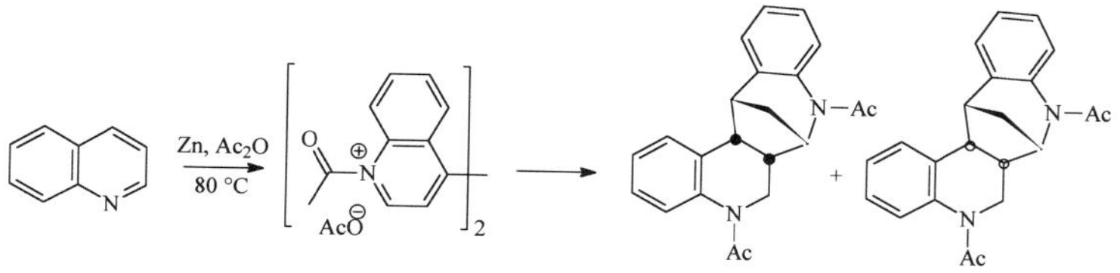

Scheme 36

However, quinaldine gives a high yield of Heller's dimer (**53**) on treatment with Zn in HOAc (**Scheme 37**) <95JCR(S)242>.

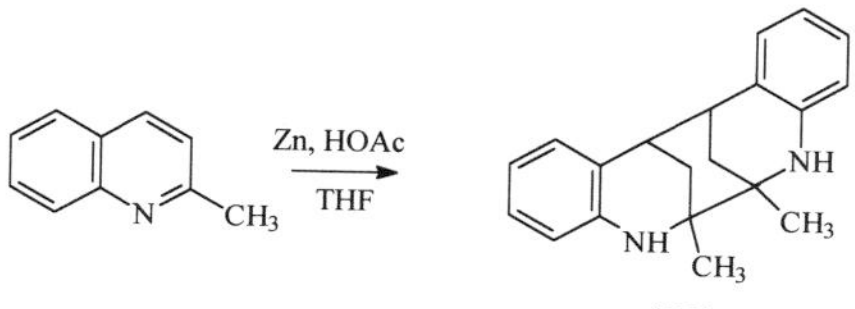

Scheme 37

Hydroxyquinolines have been alkylated with methyliodide <94CHC(30)1061> or with various other methylating agents <94H(38)2615>. They have also been brominated <94CHC(31)176>.

Quinolinium salts have been used in the synthesis of hydroxyquinoline derivatives with KO*t*Bu in the presence of ultrasound <95SC(25)2999>. Quinolinium salts have been used in cycloaddition reaction with butadiene derivatives to give acridine compounds (**Scheme 38**) <95SL938>.

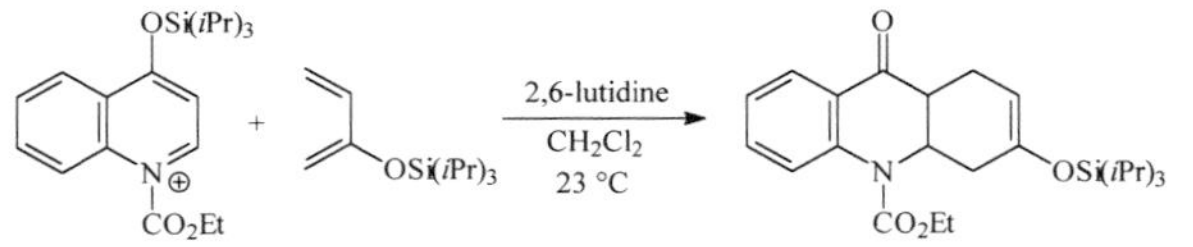

Scheme 38

A facile synthesis of 3-hydroxythieno[3,2-c]quinolin-4(5H)-ones has been done starting with a nucleophilic displacement with mercaptoacetic acid on 4-chloroquinolin-2(1H)-ones <95IJC(B)(34)432>. Selective dehalogenations of 2,4-dichloroquinolines have been done using lithium metal and ultrasound <94MC(125)1407>. Lithium exchange for bromine, followed by electrophile quenching, has been used in the preparation of substituted quinolines <95TL(36)8415> <95S1159>.

Quinoline derivatives have been substituted by nucleosides <94JCS(P1)2931> and by *tert*-butyl groups <95JOC(60)5390> *via* radical substitution reactions. Palladium-catalyzed cross coupling method has been used to couple quinoline triflates with acetylene <95T(51)3737>. 4-Quinolones, in contrast to 2-quinolones, react with peroxodisulfate anions in aqueous base to form 3-hydroxyquinolines *via* the 3-sulfate ester <95JCR(S)164>.

Sodium cyanide in DMF at 120 °C has been used for the decarboxylation of 1-substituted-4-oxoquinoline-3-carboxylic acids <94TL(35)8303>. Quinoline Reissert adducts have been epoxidized at the 3,4-bond. Its reaction with amine nucleophiles gave regiospecifically substituted 1,2,3,4-tetrahydroquinolines <95H(41)897>. Successive Claisen rearrangements of 2-(8-quinolinoxymethyl)-3-(8-quinolinoxy)-1-propene gave a product which shows excellent ability to extract heavy metal ions <95TL(36)5567>. An Eschenmoser approach has been used in a facile synthesis of monofunctional and difunctional N-substituted-4-alkylidenequinolines (**54**) (**Scheme 39**) <95S(St)56>.

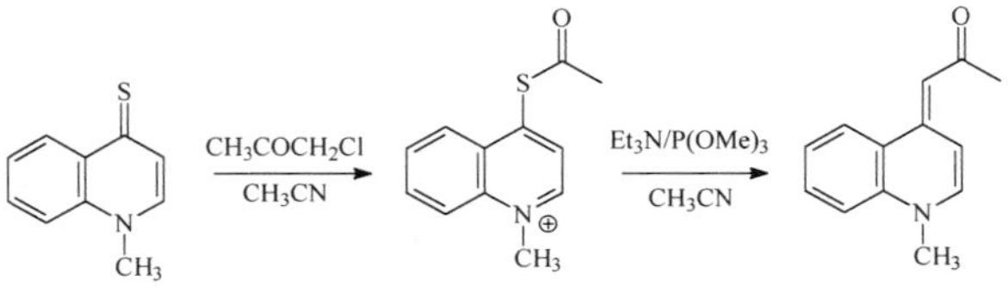

(**54**)

Scheme 39

6.1.2.6 Isoquinolines

Isoquinoline has been used, as shown in **Scheme 40,** to make (±)-[4aα, 4bβ, 12aβ]-9-halegeno-2-methyl-1,2,3,4,4a,4b,5,6,10b,11,12,12a-dodecahydronaphtho[2,1-f]isoquinolines (**55**) <95JCS(P1)1273>.

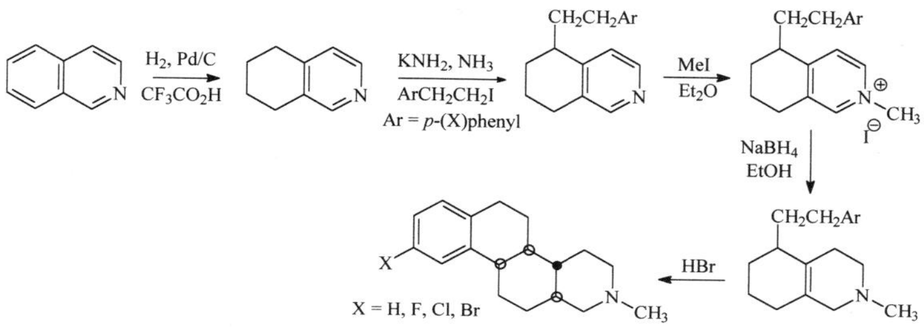

(55)

Scheme 40

1,2,3,4-Tetrahydroisoquinolines have been oxidized to 3,4-dihydroisoquinolines using cerric ammonium nitrate <95SC(25)2591>, as well as by using molecular oxygen catalyzed by cuprous chloride <95H(41)773>. 3,4-dihydroisoquinolines have been used in the synthesis of 1-substituted-2-aryltetrahydroisoquinolines <95SC(25)1817>, and in the synthesis of 11-*N*-arylaminomethylene derivatives of 8-azasteroids (**Scheme 41**) <95KGS266>.

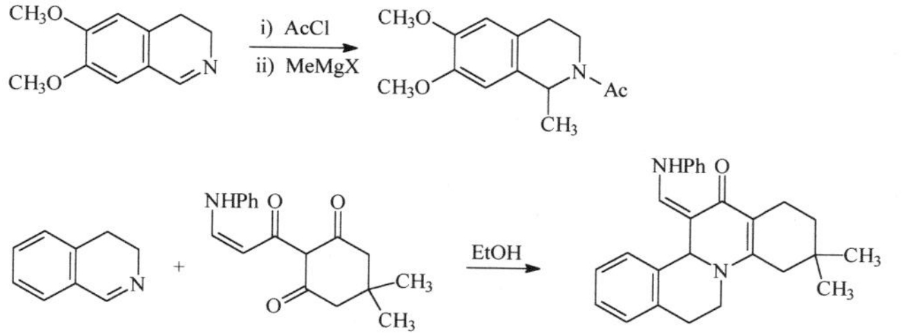

Scheme 41

1,2,3,4-Tetrahydroisoquinoline derivative has been substituted at 1-position using formamidine ancillary group developed by Meyers in the enantioselective synthesis of a homologue of the alkaloid (-)-protoemitinol <95TL(36)2941>. Ring enlargement and rearrangement of *cis*- and *trans*-2-methyl-3-(substituted phenyl)-1,2,3,4-tetrahydrosioquinolineium-2-methylides have been investigated <95JOC(60)4272>. Photochemical intramolecular hydroxylation in papaverine *N*-oxide has been observed and studied in detail <95TL(36)2653>.

6.1.2.7 Acridines

The mechanism of photochemical coupling of hindered phenols in the presence of acridine has been probed using Chemically Induced Dynamic Electron Polarization (CIDEP) <95CL845>. Reduction of 10-methylacridinium iodide was achieved photochemically using diphenylphosphinons aid in aqueous acetonitrile solvent under argon atmosphere to give 10-methylacridan <95JOC(60)2099>. Using potassium cyanide displacement, catalyzed by p-toluene sulfinate or methane sulfinate, a quantitative yield of 9-acridinecarbonitrile was obtained from 9-chloroacridine <94H(39)345>.

6.1.2.8 Piperidines

The scope and limitations of the alkylation of racemic and achiral 2-lithiopiperidines, obtained by transmetallation of the corresponding stannes, is reported <95JOC(60)5763>. Anthraquinone photocatalyzed addition of piperidines to α,β-unsaturated esters led to a novel route to indolizidone (56) (Scheme 42) <95JCS(P1)1797>.

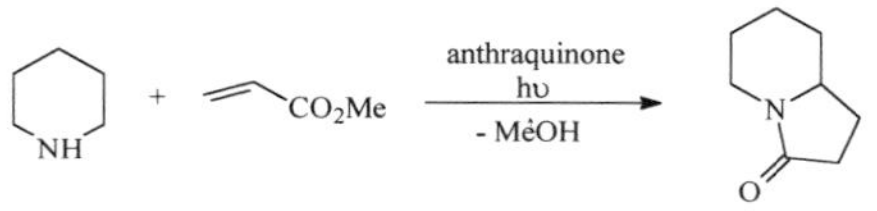

(56)

Scheme 42

A general method was described for the synthesis of 3-aminopiperidines from 4-piperidones on treatment of the tosylate of the corresponding oxime with KOEt (Neber rearrangement) <95T(51)5143>. 2-Oxopiperidines have been used in the synthesis of tricyclic compounds <95JOC(60)2952>, and in synthesis of β-substituted piperidines <95TL(36)1035>. 4-Oxopiperidines have been used in the synthesis of 4,4'-diacetylaminobipiperidines <95CHC(31)66>, and in the study of Favorskii rearrangements <95JOC(60)3414>.

6.1.3 THEORETICAL ASPECTS OF SYNTHETIC IMPORTANCE

Kurasawa, *et. al.*, have updated previous reviews of the very important area of isomerization, epimerization, and tautomerization in heterocyclic systems <95H(41)1805> <95H(41)2057>. Menshutkin reactions of pyridines with methyl halides were studied with regard to transition state structure and steric effects <95JOC(60)1975> <95JOC(60)5037>. A related paper describes evidence for SET mechanisms in displacement reactions <95ACR(28)313>. 4-Carboxypyridinyl radicals are important intermediates; proton reactivity and structure, bonding, and vibrational modes were studied <95JA(117)5540>. Having a basis set of structures and physical properties, physical properties of unknown pyridines and piperidines can be predicted by calculation from structure without the necessity of resorting to synthesis <94CT(24)17>.

REFERENCES

57PCS354   P.M. Maitlis, *Proc. Chem. Soc.* **1957**, 354.

89JA(111)4051   A.R. de Lera, W. Reischl and W.H. Okamura, *J. Am. Chem. Soc.* **1989**, *111*, 4051.

94AHC(60)198   E. Alcalde, *Adv. Heterocycl. Chem.* **1994**, *60*, 198.

94AMC(131)383 M. Balogh, E. Gacsbaitz, K. Simon and I. Hermecz, *ACH-Models Chem.* **1994**, *131*, 383.

94AP(327)755   H. Achenbach and A. Schwinn, *Arch. Pharm.* **1994**, *327*, 755.

94CB(127)2535   H. Nehl, *Chem. Ber.* **1994**, *127*, 2535.

94CHC(30)745   I.K. Moiseer, M.N. Zemtsova and N.V. Makarova, *Chem. Heterocycl. Compds.* **1994**, *30*, 745.

94CHC(30)867   T.K. Mandal, V.V. Kuznetsov and A.T. Soldatenkov, *Chem. Heterocycl. Compds.* **1994**, *30*, 867.

94CHC(30)1061 E. Lukevits, I Segal, I. Birgele and A. Zablstskaya, *Chem. Heterocycl. Compds.* **1994**, *30*, 1061.

94CHC(30)1308 I.A. Parshikov, P.B. Terentev and L.V. Modyanova, *Chem. Heterocycl. Compds.* **1994**, *30*, 1308.

94CHC(30)1331 M.A. Yurovskaya and A.V. Karchava, *Chem. Heterocycl. Compds.* **1994**, *30*, 1331.

94CHC(31)176   I.V. Ukrainets, S.G. Taran, O.A. Evtifeeva, O.V. Gorokhova, N.I. Filimonova and A.V. Turov, *Chem. Heterocycl. Compds.* **1994**, *31*, 176.

94CHE(30)997   D.D. Nekrasov, *Chem. Heterocycl. Compd. (English Transl.)* **1994**, *30*, 997.

94CHE(30)1125 G.A. Shvekhgeimer, *Chem. Heterocycl. Compd. (English Transl.)* **1994**, *30*, 1125.

94CHE(30)1284 É. Lukevits, M. Shimanska, L. Leitis and I. Iovel, *Chem. Heterocycl. Compd. (English Transl.)* **1994**, *30*, 1284.

94CHE(30)1386 Ya. Ozols, B. Vigante and G. Duburs, *Chem. Heterocycl. Compd. (English Transl.)* **1994**, *30*, 1386.

94CT(24)17   R. Murugan, M.P. Grendze, J.E. Toomey, Jr., A.R. Katritzky, M. Karelson, V. Lobanov and P. Rachwal, *CHEMTECH* **1994**, *24*, 17.

94H(37)1489   G.L. Goe, G.F. Hillstrom, R. Murugan, E.F.V. Scriven and A.R. Sherman, *Heterocycles* **1994**, *37*, 1489.

94H(38)2615   M. Fernandez, E. de la Cresta and C. Avendano, *Heterocycles* **1994**, *38*, 2615.

94H(39)345   A. Miyashita, Y. Suzuki, K. Ohta and T. Higashino, *Heterocycles* **1994**, *39*, 345.

94JOC(59)5120 D.L. Comins, H. Hong, J.K. Saha and J.H. Gao, *J. Org. Chem.* **1994**, *59*, 5120.

94JOC(59)6783 R.G. Pews and J.A. Gall, *J. Org. Chem.* **1994**, *59*, 6783.

94JCS(P1)2931 H. Togo, S. Ishigami, M. Fujii, T. Ikuma and M. Yokoyama, *J. Chem. Soc., Perkins 1* **1994**, 2931.

94KGS1482   E. Lukevics, M. Shimamska, L. Leitis and I. Iovel, *Khim. Getero. Soedin.* **1994**, 1482.

94KGS1619   G.V. Grishina, E.L. Gaidarova and N.C. Zefirov, *Khim. Getero. Soedin.* **1994**, 1619.

94MC(125)1407 A.G. Osborne and J.F. Warmsley, *Monatsch Chem.* **1994**, *125*, 1407.

94NKK1036 Y. Igarashi, H. Asano, K. Yagami and S. Watanabe, *Nippon Kag. Kaishi* **1994**, 1036.

94NPR(11)581 A.O. Plunkett, *Nat. Product Rep.* **1994**, *11*, 581.

94OPPI(26)465 G.E.H. Elgmeie, S.R. Elizbarry, H.A. Ali and A.K. Mansour, *Org. Prep. Proc. Intl.* **1994**, *26*, 465.

94SYN1155 P.J. Campos, C.-Q. Tan, J.M. Gonzalez, M.A. Rodriguez, *Synthesis* **1994**, 1155.

94T(50)13089 T. Itoh, H. Hasegawa, K. Nagata, M. Okada and A. Oshawa, *Tetrahedron* **1995**, *50*, 13089.

94TL(35)8303 M. Reuiman, M.A. Eissenstat and J.D. Weaver, *Tet. Lett.* **1994**, *35*, 8303.

94TL(35)9063 C. Sonesson and J. Lindborg, *Tet. Lett.* **1994**, *35*, 9063.

94TL(35)9157 D.H.R. Barton, M.M.M. Araújo Pereira and D.K. Taylor, *Tet. Lett.* **1994**, *35*, 9157.

94TL(35)9177 J.J. Fitzgerald, F.E. Michael, R.A. Olofson, *Tet. Lett.* **1994**, *35*, 9177.

94TL(35)9229 P. Kumar, C.U. Dinesh and B. Pandey, *Tet. Lett.* **1994**, *35*, 9229.

94TL(35)9355 I.N. Houpis, W.B. Choi, P.J. Reider, A. Molina, H. Churchill, J. Lynch and R.P. Volante, *Tet. Lett.* **1994**, *35*, 9355.

94ZOK(64)610 P.P. Onysko, E.A. Suralova, T.I. Chudakova and A.D. Sinitsa, *Zh. Obshch. Khim.* **1994**, *64*, 610.

95ACR(28)313 H. Lund, K. Daasbjerb, T. Lund and S.U. Pedersen, *Acc. Chem. Res.* **1995**, *28*, 313.

95AG(34)67 G. Haucke and G. Graness, *Angew. Chem. Int. Ed.* **1995**, *34*, 67.

95AG(34)1319 R. Weiss, B. Pomrehn, F. Hampel and W. Bauer, *Angew. Chem. Int. Ed.* **1995**, *34*, 1319.

95B(ECTOC-1) C.J. Moody and D.A. Riddick, *in* "Electronic Conference on Trends in Organic Chemistry (ECTOC-1)," H.S. Rzepa and J.G. Goodman, eds., (CD-ROM), Royal Soc. of Chem. Publications, **1995**.

95BCB(104)387 J.J. Vanden Eynde, A. Mayence, P. Lor, Y. Van Haverbeke, *Bull. Soc. Chim. Belg.* **1995**, *104*, 387.

95CC179 B. Heller and G. Oehme, *J. Chem. Soc., Chem. Commun.* **1995**, 179.

95CC1831 W. Adam, K. Briviba, F. Duschek, D. Golsch, W. Kiefer and H. Sies, *J. Chem. Soc., Chem. Commun.* **1995**, 1831.

95CHC(31)1 A.T. Soldatenkov, N.S. Prostakov and A.A. Obynschnyi, *Chem. Heterocycl. Compd.* **1995**, *31*, 1.

95CHC(31)66 T.D. Sokolova, I.P. Boiko, G.V. Cherkaev, A.S. Moskovkin and N.V. Dubrovina, *Chem. Heterocycl. Compd.* **1995**, *31*, 66.

95CHE(31)50 S.A. Yamashkin and I.A. Batanov, *Chem. Heterocycl. Compd. (English Transl.)* **1995**, *31*, 50.

95CL5 H. Kusama, Y. Yamashita and K. Narasaka, *Chem. Lett.* **1995**, 5.

95CL575 K. Kobayashi, S. Nagato, M. Kawakita, O. Morikawa and H. Konishi, *Chem. Lett.* **1995**, 575.

95CL845 K. Okada, K. Okuba, M. Oda and H. Murai, *Chem. Lett.* **1995**, 845.

95COS(2)1 M. Shipman, *Contemp. Org. Synth.* **1995**, *2*, 1.

95COS(2)209 T. Harrison, *Contemp. Org. Synth.* **1995**, *2*, 209.

95CR(95)1797 E.D. Cox and J.M. Cook, *Chem. Rev.* **1995**, *95*, 1797.

95GCI(124)385 R. Balicki and L. Kaczmarek, *Gazz. Chim. Ital.* **1995**, *124*, 385.

95H(40)511 K. Isomura, H. Kawasaki, K. Takehara and H. Taniguchi, *Heterocyles* **1995**, *40*, 511.

95H(40)515   P. Caramelle, A.G. Imcernizzi, E. Pastormerlo, P. Quadrelli and A. Corsano, *Heterocyles* **1995**, *40*, 515.

95H(40)531   K. Homann, R. Zimer and H.-U. Reissig, *Heterocycles* **1995**, *40*, 531.

95H(40)809   Y. Tagawa, K. Hama, Y. Goto and M. Hamana, *Heterocycles* **1995**, *40*, 809.

95H(40)867   H. Ohtake, T. Higuchi and M. Hirobe, *Heterocycles* **1995**, *40*, 867.

95H(40)1035   L.L. Rodina and A.V. Ryzhakov, *Heterocycles* **1995**, *40*, 1035.

95H(41)289   E.R. Biehl, H.M. Refat and A.A. Fadda, *Heterocycles* **1995**, *41*, 289.

95H(41)323   S.Y. Rhie and E.K. Ryu, *Heterocycles* **1995**, *41*, 323.

95H(41)461   J.W. Chern and K.R. Wu, *Heterocycles* **1995**, *41*, 461.

95H(41)675   V. Bertini, F. Lucchesini, M. Pocci and A. De Munno, *Heterocycles* **1995**, *41*, 675.

95H(41)753   G. Viti, D. Giannotti, R. Nannicini, G. Balacco, V. Pestellini, P. Pasli and P. Dapporto, *Heterocycles* **1995**, *41*, 753.

95H(41)773   M. Shimizu, H. Orita, T. Hayakawa, K. Suzuki and K. Takehira, *Heterocycles* **1995**, *41*, 773.

95H(41)817   Y. Yamamoto, T. Tanaka, H. Ouchi, M. Miyakawa and Y. Morita, *Heterocycles* **1995**, *41*, 817.

95H(41)897   M. Kratzel and R. Hiessbock, *Heterocycles* **1995**, *41*, 897.

95H(41)1307   K. Sasaki, A.S.S. Rouf, S. Kashino and T. Hirota, *Heterocycles* **1995**, *41*, 1307.

95H(41)1431   E.R. Biehl, H.M. Refat and A.A. Fadda, *Heterocycles* **1995**, *41*, 1431.

95H(41)1805   Y. Kurasawa, A. Takada and H.S. Kim, *Heterocycles* **1995**, *41*, 1805.

95H(41)1915   F. Palacios, J. García, A.Mª. Ochoa de Retana and J. Oyarzabal, *Heterocycles* **1995**, *41*, 1915.

95H(41)2057   Y. Kurasawa, A. Takada and H.S. Kim, *Heterocycles* **1995**, *41*, 2057.

95H(41)2405   T. Takahashi, H. Koeya, H. Sato, T. Ishizawa and N. Taka, *Heterocycles* **1995**, *41*, 2405.

95IJC(B)(34)285 H.A. Etman, *Indian J. Chem. (B)* **1995**, *34*, 285.

95IJC(B)(34)432 M.C.L.N. Gupta and M. Darbarwar, *Indian J. Chem. (B)* **1995**, *34*, 432.

95JA(117)5540 G.N.R. Tripathi, Y. Su and J. Bentley, *J. Am. Chem. Soc.* **1995**, *117*, 5540.

95JA(117)8879 T. Higuchi, C. Sasake and M. Hirobe, *J. Am. Chem. Soc.* **1995**, *117*, 8879.

95JCR(S)146   F.F. Abdel-Latif and R.M. Shaker, *J. Chem. Res. (S)* **1995**, 146.

95JCR(S)164   E.J. Behrman, R.L. Kiser, W.F. Garas, E.C. Behrman and B.M. Pitt, *J. Chem. Res. (S)* **1995**, 164.

95JCR(S)242   J.C. Gauffre and M.G. Dubois, *J. Chem. Res. (S)* **1995**, 242.

95JCR(S)246   A.T. Hewson and R.F. Smith, *J. Chem. Res. (S)* **1995**, 246.

95JCR(S)392   F. Al-Omran and N. Al-Awadi, *J. Chem. Res. (S)* **1995**, 392.

95JCR(S)476   H. Kikukawa and T. Nishiwaki, *J. Chem. Res. (S)* **1995**, 476.

95JCS(P1)1273 G.L. Patrick, *J. Chem. Soc., Perkin Trans. 1* **1995**, 1273.

95JCS(P1)1797 S. Das, J.S.D. Kumar, K. Shivaramayya and M.V. George, *J. Chem. Soc., Perkin Trans. 1* **1995**, 1797.

95JCS(P1)2503 O. Mongin, P. Rocca, L. Thomas-dit-Dumont, F. Trecourt, F. Marsais, A. Godard and G. Queguiner, *J. Chem. Soc., Perkin Trans. 1* **1995**, 2503.

95JCS(P1)3129 A.R. Katritzky, S. El-Zemity and H. Lang, *J. Chem. Soc., Perkin Trans. 1* **1995**, 3129.

95JHC(32)467 S. Griras and S. Lindstrom, *J. Heterocycl. Chem.* **1995**, *32*, 467.

95JHC(32)505 D. Heber, I.C. Ivanov and S.K. Karagiosov, *J. Heterocycl. Chem.* **1995**, *32*, 505.

95JHC(32)563   T. Zimmermann, *J. Heterocycl. Chem.* **1995**, *32*, 563.
95JHC(32)585   H. Ritter and H.H. Licht, *J. Heterocycl. Chem.* **1995**, *32*, 585.
95JMC(38)2851 D. Vo, W.C. Matowe, M. Ramesh, N. Iqbal, M.W. Wolowyk, S.E. Howlett and E.E. Knaus, *J. Med. Chem.* **1995**, *38*, 2851.
95JMC(38)4830 J.R. Proudfoot, *et. al.*, *J. Med. Chem.* **1995**, *38*, 4830.
95JMC(38)4839 T.A. Kelly, *et. al.*, *J. Med. Chem.* **1995**, *38*, 4839.
95JO(488)47   M. Costa, F.S. Dias, G.P. Chiusoli and G.L. Gazzola, *J. Organomet. Chem.* **1995**, *488*, 47.
95JOC(60)18   C. Amatore, C. Combellas, N.E. Lebbar, A. Thiebault and J.N. Verpeaux, *J. Org. Chem.* **1995**, *60*, 18.
95JOC(60)264   J.A. Zoltewicz, M.P. Cruskie and C.D. Dill, *J. Org. Chem.* **1995**, *60*, 264.
95JOC(60)1763 D.F. Maynard and W.H. Okamura, *J. Org. Chem.* **1995**, *60*, 1763.
95JOC(60)1875 T.A. Kelly and U.R. Patel, *J. Org. Chem.* **1995**, *60*, 1875.
95JOC(60)1975 U. Berg, M. Chanon, R. Gallo and M. Rajzmann, *J. Org. Chem.* **1995**, *60*, 1975.
95JOC(60)2099 S. Yasui, K. Shiaji, A. Ohno and M. Yoshihara, *J. Org. Chem.* **1995**, *60*, 2099.
95JOC(60)2588 A.R. Katritzky, B. Rachwal and S. Rachwal, *J. Org. Chem.* **1995**, *60*, 2588.
95JOC(60)2640 B. Ye and T.R. Burke, *J. Org. Chem.* **1995**, *60*, 2640.
95JOC(60)2952 A. Padwa, S.R. Harring and M.A. Semones, *J. Org. Chem.* **1995**, *60*, 2952.
95JOC(60)3414 G. Sasnovsky and Z.W. Cai, *J. Org. Chem.* **1995**, *60*, 3414.
95JOC(60)3487 J.A. Zoltewicz and M.P. Cruskie, *J. Org. Chem.* **1995**, *60*, 3487.
95JOC(60)3750 R. Church, R. Trust, J.D. Albright and D.W. Powell, *J. Org. Chem.* **1995**, *60*, 3750.
95JOC(60)3993 A.R. Katritzky, B. Rachwal and S. Rachwal, *J. Org. Chem.* **1995**, *60*, 3993.
95JOC(60)4272 N. Kawanishi, N. Shirai, Y. Sato, K. Hatano and Y. Kurono, *J. Org. Chem.* **1995**, *60*, 4272.
95JOC(60)5037 J. Persson, U. Berg and O. Matsson, *J. Org. Chem.* **1995**, *60*, 5037.
95JOC(60)5243 J.B. Campbell and J.W. Firor, *J. Org. Chem.* **1995**, *60*, 5243.
95JOC(60)5390 G.A. Russell, L. Wang and C.F. Yao, *J. Org. Chem.* **1995**, *60*, 5390.
95JOC(60)5721 M.Y. Chu-Moyer and R. Berger, *J. Org. Chem.* **1995**, *60*, 5721.
95JOC(60)5763 R.E. Gawley and Q. Zhang, *J. Org. Chem.* **1995**, *60*, 5763.
95KGS266   O.V. Gulyakevitch, A.L. Mikhalchuk and A.A. Akhrem, *Khim. Getero. Soedin* **1995**, 266.
95LA591   B. Kutscher, H.R. Dieter, H.G. Tromer, B. Bartz, J. Engel and A. Kleemann, *Liebigs Ann.* **1995**, 591.
95LA645   F. Bracher and K. Mink, *Liebigs Ann.* **1995**, 645.
95LA1441   W. Schlecker, A. Huth, E. Ottow and J. Mulzer, *Liebigs Ann.* **1995**, 1441.
95MC(126)805   F. Bracher and T. Papke, *Monatsh Chem.* **1995**, *126*, 805.
95OR(47)1   R.D. Clark and A. Jahangir *in* "Organic Reactions," Vol. 47, L.A. Paquette, ed.-in-chief, John Wiley & Sons, Inc., New York, 1995, p. 1.
95P(50)182   F. Bracher and D. Hildebrand, *Pharmazie* 1995, *50*, 182.
95S321   C. Cochennec, P. Rocca, F. Marsais, A. Godard and G. Queguiner, *Synthesis* **1995**, 321.
95S939   Y. Uchida, H. Okabe, H. Kobayashi and S. Oae, *Synthesis* **1995**, 939.
95S1159   F. Trecourt, M. Mallet, F. Mongin and G. Queguiner, *Synthesis* **1995**, 1159.
95S(St)56   J. Levillain and M. Vazeux, *Syntheisis-Stuttgart* **1995**, 56.
95SC(25)177   M.N. Deshmukh, U.S. Kumar and A.V.R. Rao, *Synth. Commun.* **1995**, *25*, 177.

95SC(25)857   Y.W. Zhang, Z.X. Shen, B. Pan, S.H. Lu and M.H. Chen, *Synth. Commun.* **1995**, *25*, 857.

95SC(25)1601   M. El ouar, N. Knouzi, A. El kihel, E.M. Essassi, M. Benchidimi, J. Hamelin, R. Carrié and R. Danion-Bougot, *Synth. Commun.* **1995**, *25*, 1601.

95SC(25)1817   A.P. Venkov and S.M. Statkova-Abeghe, *Synth. Commun.* **1995**, *25*, 1817.

95SC(25)2591   I. Bedea, P. Cotelle and J.P. Catteau, *Synth. Commun.* **1995**, *25*, 2591.

95SC(25)2901   P. Rocca, F. Marsais, A. Godard and G. Queguiner, *Synth. Commun.* **1995**, *25*, 2901.

95SC(25)2999   M.G. Dubois and A. Meola, *Synth. Commun.* **1995**, *25*, 2999.

95SL133   H. Waldmann, *Synlett* **1995**, 133.

95SL153   S. Hillers and O. Reiser, *Synlett* **1995**, 153.

95SL157   T.L. Draper and T.R. Bailey, *Synlett* **1995**, 157.

95SL233   S. Kobayashi, M. Araki, H. Ishitani, S. Nagayama and I. Hachiya, *Synlett* **1995**, 233.

95SL603   M.G. Dubois and J.C. Gauffre, *Synlett* **1995**, 603.

95SL845   T. Sato, K. Yoshimatsu and J. Otera, *Synlett* **1995**, 845.

95SL938   U. Beifuiss and S. Ledderhose, *Synlett* **1995**, 938.

95SL1587   J. Bosch and M.L. Bennasar, *Synlett* **1995**, 587.

95SYN1195   S. Kobayashi, H. Ishitani and S. Nagayama, *Synth.* **1995**, 1195.

95T(51)1259   M. Villacampa, E. Delacu iesta and C. Avendano, *Tetrahedron* **1995**, *51*, 1259.

95T(51)1575   S.A. Petrich, F.A. Hicks, D.R. Wilkinson, J.G. Tarrant, S.M. Bruno, M. Vargas, K.N. Hosein, J.T. Gupton and J.A. Sikorski, *Tetrahedron* **1995**, *51*, 1575.

95T(51)1941   P. Melnyk, B. Legrand, J. Gasche, P. Ducrot and C. Thal, *Tetrahedron* **1995**, *51*, 1941.

95T(51)3737   T. Okita and M. Isobe, *Tetrahedron* **1995**, *51*, 3737.

95T(51)5143   A. Diez, A. Voldoire, I. Lopez, M. Rubiralta, V. Segarra, L. Pages and J.M. Palacios, *Tetrahedron* **1995**, *51*, 5143.

95T(A)(6)811   G. Chelucci, *Tetrahedron: Asymm.* **1995**, *6*, 811.

95T(A)(6)877   N. Martin, A. Martinezgrau, C. Seoane, J.L. Marco, A. Albert and F.H. Cano, *Tetrahedron: Asymm.* **1995**, *6*, 877.

95TL(36)59   J.A.R. Rodrigues, G.C. Leiva and J.D.F. Desousa, *Tet. Lett.* **1995**, *36*, 59.

95TL(36)417   E. Lee, T.S. Kang, B.J. Joo, J.S. Tae, K.S. Li and C.K. Chung, *Tet. Lett.* **1995**, *36*, 417.

95TL(36)1035   T. Varea, M. Dufour, L.Micouin, C. Riche, A. Chiaroni, J.C. Quirion and H.P. Husson, *Tet. Lett.* **1995**, *36*, 1035.

95TL(36)2603   P. Schuchmann and K. Hafner, *Tet. Lett.* **1995**, *36*, 2603.

95TL(36)2653   R. Suau, R. Rico-Gomez, F.A. Souto-Bachiller, L.R. Rodriguez and M.L. Ruiz, *Tet. Lett.* **1995**, *36*, 2653.

95TL(36)2941   J.M. Takacs and S.C. Boito, *Tet. Lett.* **1995**, *36*, 2941.

95TL(36)3189   B. Ohtani, S. Kusakabe, K. Okada, S. Tsuru, K. Izawa, Y. Amino and S.-I. Nishimoto, *Tet. Lett.* **1995**, *36*, 3189.

95TL(36)3307   R. Jain, F. Roschangar and M.A. Ciufolini, *Tet. Lett.* **1995**, *36*, 3307.

95TL(36)3557   I. Coldham, A.J. Collis, R.L. Mould and R.E. Rathmell, *Tet. Lett.* **1995**, *36*, 3557.

95TL(36)4571   W.B Choi, I.N. Houpis, H.P.O. Churchill, A. Molina, J.E. Lynch, R.P. Volante, P.J. Reider and A.O. King, *Tet. Lett.* **1995**, *36*, 4571.

95TL(36)4791   P. Gros, Y. Fort, G. Quieguiner and P. Caubere, *Tet. Lett.* **1995**, *36*, 4791.

95TL(36)5015   N. Vicart, B. Cazes and J. Goye, *Tet. Lett.* **1995**, *36*, 5015.
95TL(36)5075   L.I. Belenkii, I.S. Poddubnyi and M.M. Krayushkin, *Tet. Lett.* **1995**, *36*, 5075.
95TL(36)5247   M. Fujita, H. Oka and K. Ogura, *Tet. Lett.* **1995**, *36*, 5247.
95TL(36)5319   T.R. Kelly and F. Lang, *Tet. Lett.* **1995**, *36*, 5319.
95TL(36)5567   K. Hiratani, T. Takahashi, K. Kasuga, H. Sugihara, K. Fujiwara and K. Ohashi, *Tet. Lett.* **1995**, *36*, 5567.
95TL(36)6261   F. Lam, K.S. Chan and B.J. Liu, *Tet. Lett.* **1995**, *36*, 6261.
95TL(36)7275   X. Zeng, J. Cai and Y. Gu, *Tet. Lett.* **1995**, *36*, 7275.
95TL(36)7995   D.L. Comins and J.K. Saha, *Tet. Lett.* **1995**, *36*, 7995.
95TL(36)8083   B.M. Khadilkar, V.G. Gaikar and A.A. Chitnavis, *Tet. Lett.* **1995**, *36*, 8083.
95TL(36)8415   F. Mongin, J.M. Fourquez, S. Rault, V. Levacher, A. Godard, F. Trecourt and G. Queguiner, *Tet. Lett.* **1995**, *36*, 8415.
95TL(36)8977   R. Tamion, C. Mineur and L. Ghosez, *Tet. Lett.* **1995**, *36*, 8977.

Chapter 6.2

Six-Membered Ring Systems: Diazines and Benzo Derivatives

Michael P. Groziak
Southern Illinois University, Carbondale, IL, USA

6.2.1 INTRODUCTION

Isolated and benzo-fused diazine rings are key structural elements in many natural and synthetic compounds of current, active interest. This contribution relates highlights from many of the studies on the diazines pyridazine, pyrimidine, pyrazine, and their benzo-fused derivatives cinnoline, phthalazine, quinazoline, quinoxaline, and phenazine published in English in the journal literature during 1995, as covered by *Chem. Abstr.* through volume 124, issue 9. Review articles published in 1994 and not cited in *Prog. Heterocycl. Chem.* have been included.

6.2.2 REVIEWS AND GENERAL STUDIES

Pyrimidines and their derivatives were included in a general survey of heterocycle synthetic methods [95COS337]. Intra- and intermolecular inverse electron-demand Diels-Alder reactions and ANRORC-processes of the pyrimidines have been reviewed [94KGS1649], as have routes to pyrimidines from aminoamide oximes involving ring-chain tautomerism [94H(37)2051]. Cycloaddition approaches to certain pyridazines and dihydropyridazines have been summarized [94MI235], as have the syntheses of saturated thiazolo- and thiazino[2,3-*b*]quinazolines [94BSB509]. The general reactivity of quinoxaline oxides and 1,4-dioxides [95JHC1085], the nucleophilic and electrophilic substitution reactivity of pyridazines [94MI219], the ring transformations initiated by addition of carbon nucleophiles to 5-nitropyrimidines [95H(40)441], and condensed pyridazines as azadienes in [4+2]-cycloaddition reactions [94MI205] have served as the focus of reactivity-oriented reviews. A critical evaluation of the chemistry of the pyrimidine ring portion of thiamin has been published [94BOC1], and the chemistry of copper complexes of heterocyclic thioamides including those of quinazolinethionates have been summarized [94CCR91]. Fused pyrazine oxide bioreductive drugs [95MI167], 3-hydrazinopyridazine-based drugs [94F683], phenazine-based antibiotics [94PAC2083], and 4,5-functionalized-3(2*H*)-pyridazinones [94MI189] are among those bioactive heterocycles serving as the focus of synthetically-oriented reviews.

More biologically-oriented reviews include those on the quinoline, quinazoline, and acridone alkaloids [94NPR163, 95NPR77, and 95NPR465], quinazolinones as AT_1/AT_2-balanced nonpeptide angiotensin II receptor antagonists [95EJM255s], quinoxalines as non-nucleoside anti-HIV-1 agents [94MI145], tricyclic pyridazines [94MI173], quinoxalines that act at the glycine site on the NMDA receptor [94JMC4053, see also 95JOC5838], and anticancer quinazoline inhibitors of thymidylate synthase (TS) [94JHC603]. Reviews of the drugs Oltipraz [4-methyl-5-(2-pyrazinyl)-1,2-dithiole-3-thione, 1], an inhibitor of HIV-1 replication [95MI117, 95MI101], and Brodimoprim [2,4-diamino-5-(4-bromo-3,5-dimethoxybenzyl)pyrimidine, 2], an inhibitor of bacterial dihydrofolate reductase (DHFR) [95MI221], have appeared.

The regio-, site-, and stereospecificity of benzonitrile oxide cycloaddition to the diazines and their benzo-fused derivatives has been explored [95T11855]. Trichloromethyldiazines 3-5 are readily prepared from the corresponding methyldiazines [95JCS(P1)2595]. Perfluoroalkyl- and perfluorooxaalkyl-pyridazines, pyrimidines, and pyrazines are obtained *via* copper-mediated cross-coupling of chlorodiazines to perfluoroalkyl and perfluorooxaalkyl iodides [95JFC113]. Together with the preparation of diazine-substituted *tert*-butylureas and thioureas, a convenient access to the diazine-based carbodiimides has been offered [95JHC13]. Ring lithiation of pyrimidine, pyridazine, and pyrazine *sans* directing group has been accomplished by exposure of these diazines to a 4-fold excess of LTMP at -75 °C for a short period of time [95JOC3781]. Mono- and disubstituted diazines were obtained upon introduction of an electrophilic reagent.

Along similar lines, a study of the LDA- or LTMP-mediated ring lithiation of 3- or 4-, chloro- or methoxycinnolines has been conducted [95T13045]. Synthetic methodologies of the tandem ring metalation/transition metal-catalyzed cross-coupling variety as applied to the synthesis of biologically-derived or -active diazines have served as the topic for a recent discussion [95H(40)1055]. The diazines were among the several heteroaromatic ring systems used as substitutes for the imidazole ring of known histamine H_3-receptor antagonists in a structure-activity relationship (SAR) study [95AP445]. A number of 4-diazinylimidazoles were also synthesized and tested for interaction at the AT_1 receptors in another SAR study [95JMC2925].

6.2.3 PYRIDAZINES AND BENZODERIVATIVES

A combination EIMS and X-ray study of [1,2,4]triazolo[1,2-*b*]- and [1,3,4]thiadiazolo[3,4-*b*]phthalazines was undertaken [95JHC283], and X-ray crystal structure determinations of 5-(2-chlorobenzyl)-6-methyl-3(2*H*)-pyridazinone [95AX(C)1834], and on 6-benzyloxy-7,8-dihydro-8-phenyl-3-trifluoromethyl-*s*-triazolo[4,3-*b*]pyridazine and its 5,6-dihydro-6-one derivative [95AX(C)1829] have been performed. Structures of some pharmacologically-active pyridazines previously reported as arylidene-4,5-dihydropyridazines need to be revised to those of aromatic pyridazine tautomers 6-8 based on a combination ^1H NMR nOe and X-ray study [95AJC1601].

6.2.3.1 Syntheses

A new, general synthesis of pyridazines begins with the reaction of dichlorohydrazones and i-Pr_2NEt, followed by inverse electron-demand Diels-Alder condensation of the resultant 4-chloroazodienes and electron-rich dienophiles [95TL5703]. Pyridazine and fused pyridazines have been obtained by the reaction of benzil monohydrazone and active keto methylene reagents, followed by base treatment of the chloro-substituted tetrahydropyridazine adducts thus formed [95PJC685]. A new route to thiazolo[4',5':2,3]pyridino[4,3-d]pyridazines has been developed from pyridino[2,3-d]thiazole intermediates, in turn obtained by reaction of Knoevenagel condensation adducts and $PhNCS/S_8$ [95PS179]. Pyridazino[3,2-b]quinazolin-6-imine (readily converted to the 6-one) was obtained *via* coupling of 3-dicyanomethylene-3-phenylpropionitrile to diazotized 2-cyanoaniline, and cyclization of the resultant hydrazono species [95HC281]. An efficient synthesis of pyrrolo[1',2':2,3]pyridazino[6,1-a]isoindole diones **9** has been developed *via* the sequence of 1-phthalimidopyrrole reduction, $EtO_2CCH=PPh_3$ Wittig reaction, and $BF_3 \cdot Et_2O$-mediated cyclization [95H(41)689]. 1-Substituted 3,6-diarylimidazo[1,5-b]pyridazines **10** have been prepared in three steps from aryl methyl ketones and 1-amino-2-substituted-4-arylimidazoles [95SC3271]. 6-Hydrazino- and 6-chloro-2-phenyl-3(2H)-pyridazinone have been shown undergo cyclization affording s-triazolo[4,3-b]pyridazinones and to imidazo[1,2-b]pyridazinones [95CPJ123].

$R = Me, Ph, Ar = Ph, 4-X-C_6H_4, 4-pyridyl, 2-thienyl$

Pyridyl- and thienyl-substituted pyridazines, pyridazin-3(2H)-ones and quinoxalin-2(1H)-ones have been accessed by Pd(0)-catalyzed coupling of organotin reagents and aryl, acyl, and heteroaryl halides [95JCR402]. The synthesis of 5-[(aryloxy or arylthio)methyl]-4-pyridazinecarboxylic acid and derivatives **11** by radical reactions in a two-phase system has been reported [95H(41)1461]. A new route to trifluoromethylpyridazines has been developed *via* the Ph_3P-assisted reductive cyclization of vinyldiazomethanes derived from ethyl 2-diazo-4,4,4-trifluoroacetoacetate and Wittig or Horner-Emmons-Wadsworth reagents [95S920]. Pyridazines with 2- and 3-thienyl substituents have been made from precursor 4-oxobutanoic acids *via* their 4,5-dihydro derivatives [95JCR306]. SeO_2-mediated oxidation of the latter (or base-catalyzed condensation of methanal or aryl aldehydes at their 4-position) led to the pyridazin-3(2H)-ones. A new route to antihypertensive 5,6-diarylpyridazin-3-ones has been developed from 3,6-dichloropyridazine [95JHC1057]. It involves regioselective metalation and silylation to 6-chloro-2-methoxy-3-(trimethylsilyl)pyridazine, and then introduction of iodine by another metalation to permit subsequent Pd(0)-mediated cross-coupling with arylboronic acids. Hydrolytic removal of the 6-methoxy group then affords the pyridazinones. Rearrangement of 3-acetyl-4-aryl-2-pyrazolines at 0 °C was shown to afford 3-methyl-5-aryl-4(1H)-pyridazinones in moderate yields [95IJC(B)342]. Treatment of 4-(1-piperazinyl)-1H-pyrrolo[3,4-c]pyridine-1,3(2H)-diones and 1H-pyrrolo[3,4-c]pyridine-1,3,4(2H,5H)-trione with $MeNHNH_2$ has been shown to afford pyrido[3,4-d]pyridazine-1,4-diones and pyrido[3,4-d]pyridazine-1,4,5(6H)-triones, some of which could be transformed into pharmacologically-active N-arylpiperazinylalkyl derivatives [95F37]. Unsymmetrically 3,6-disubstituted pyridazines **12** not readily accessible by other methods have been synthesized from 3,6-diiodopyridazines *via* Pd(0)-catalyzed cross couplings of 6-substituted-3-iodopyridazines [95JOC748].

$R_1 = R_2 = H, X = O;$
$R_1 = Et, R_2 = H, X = O;$
$R_1 = H$ or $Et, R_2 = Br, X = O;$
$R_1 = H$ or $Et, R_2 = H, X = S$

11

12

$R_1 = OMe, F, NMe_2,$ or $SMe;$
$R_2 = Ph, 2-thienyl,$ or $2-furanyl$

Cyclooctatetraene reacts as a dienophile with 3,6-bis(trifluoromethyl)-1,2,4,5-tetrazine to form, upon loss of N_2, a cycloocta[d]pyridazine and a tetracyclic bis-Diels-Alder cycloadduct [95LA661]. In a nonpolar solvent, the former produced a dihydrobarreleno[d]pyridazine that could be oxidized (with 4-phenyltriazolinedione) to the barreleno[d]pyridazine, but in a polar solvent it gave a dihydrocycloocta[d]pyridazine in a multistep process. X-ray crystal structures of some of these compounds have been obtained. The attempted dehydrogenation of 4,4a-dihydro-5H[1]benzopyrano[4,3-c]pyridazin-3(2H)-ones with m-$C_6H_4(NO_2)SO_3Na$ unexpectedly led to new 5-hydroxy[1]benzopyrano[4,3-c]pyridazin-3(2H)-ones [95JHC79].

The synthesis of cinnolines and phthalazines has also received attention. Cinnolines were among the products obtained by acid-catalyzed ring closure of adducts derived from a ring-lithiated phenylacetaldehyde dimethyl acetal [95LA1303]. As part of a synthesis of the pyrido[3,2,1-i,j]cinnoline ring system of certain potent DNA gyrase inhibitors, 4,5-difluoro-2,3-dihydro-1-methyl-6-nitro-7-oxo-1H,7H-pyrido[3,2,1-i,j]cinnoline-8-carboxylic acid (**13**) was shown to be obtained from the reaction of ethyl 6,7,8-trifluoro-1,4-dihydro-1-(methylamino)-4-oxo-3-quinolinecarboxylate and di-t-butyl methylenemalonate [95JOC3928]. Some cyclic (aryl ether phthalazine)s related to poly(aryl ether) high performance polymers have been prepared by high dilution transformation of the 1,2-dibenzoylbenzene moiety of the corresponding (aryl ether ketone)s [95MI6705]. The synthesis of 1-amino-[1,2,3]oxadiazolo[4,3-a]phthalazin-4-ium chloride and some of its substituted dihydro derivatives has been reported in a study of the preparation of annelated sydnonimines [95JHC643]. Pyrolysis of N-(1-phthalazinyl)-N'-cycloalkylidenehydrazines has been shown to afford s-triazolo[3,4-a]phthalazines **14** and triazolylbenzonitriles, among other products [95JOC1908].

13   **14**, n = 3, 5, or 10

6.2.3.2 Reactions

The participation of pyridazines and their benzo-fused derivatives in pericyclic reactions has been the subject of several studies. Due to the exceptional facility of its [4+2] cycloaddition reactions with unactivated dienophiles, 4,5-dicyanopyridazine (**15**) has earned the moniker "superheterodiene" [95CC2201]. Inverse electron-demand Diels-Alder reaction of 1,4-bis(trifluoromethyl)pyrido[3,4-d]pyridazine (**16**) and electron-rich indole-type dienophiles has been shown to lead to tetracycles structurally related to the alkaloids ellipticine and isoellipticine, upon Pd/C-mediated dehydrogenation [95H(41)1445]. X-ray structural analyses of some of these products were conducted. A synthesis of g-annelated quinolines has been developed via an inverse electron-demand Diels-Alder approach which involves the condensation of pyrido[2,3-d]pyridazine and enamines or ketene N,S-acetals [95M211]. The dipolar cycloaddition of 3-arylphthalazinium-1-olates to olefins and acetylenes has been shown to afford ethano- and ethenophthalazines, respectively [95BSB595]. The regio- and stereochemistry of 8-azabicyclo[3.2.1]oct-3-en-2-one synthesis via dipolar cycloaddition across the 2- and 6-positions of 1-(phthalazin-1-yl)pyridinium-3-olate have been investigated [95JCR298]. The high yield thermal (360 °C, 30 min) rearrangement of polyphenylated phthalazines **17** to the corresponding quinazoline structural isomers has been reported [95JOC3131]. One product, 2,4,5,8-tetraphenylquinazoline, was subjected to X-ray crystallographic analysis.

15   **16**   **17**

R_1, R_2 = H or Ph, Ar = Ph or 4-F-C_6H_4

Pyridazines bearing *ortho*-directing groups at the C-4 position have been metalated (LTMP) and treated with aldehydes to provide an access to various 4,5-disubstituted pyridazines [95JHC841]. Vicarious nucleophilic substitution of 3-substituted pyridazinium 4-dicyanomethylides **18** has been used to effect the regiospecific introduction of a 4-arylsulfonylmethyl group [95CC2067]. The reaction of 3-(*p*-halophenyl)pyridazinium ylides **19** and an aryl isocyanate has been shown not to give dipolar cycloaddition adducts, but instead simply effects *C*-acylation [95ACS778]. The effect of the phthalazinyl substituent on the dimerization tendency of 1-phthalazin-3-yl-3-oxidopyridinium betaines has been explored experimentally, and FMO analyses were used to explain the structural and configurational assignments deduced from spectral evidence [95PJC33].

New insight into the synthetic and mechanistic aspects of the Richter reaction has been offered, and from this a modification of the conditions of the 2-alkynylbenzenediazonium salt thermal cyclization has led to 4-Br- or Cl-substituted cinnolines and 4-Br- or Cl-substituted pyrazolopyridazines for the first time [95LA775]. The factors that influence the mode of ring transformation (addition-cyclization-denitrogenation giving naphthalenes, addition-cyclization-ring expansion giving benzodiazocines, and pyridazine N-N bond cleavage giving penta-substituted pyridines) occurring in the reaction of 1-substituted phthalazines and ynamines has been the subject of investigation [95CPB679].

6.2.3.3 Applications

Biological SAR studies have included those on 5*H*-indeno[1,2-*c*]pyridazines as MAO-B inhibitors [95JMC3874], alkane-bridged [4-(phenoxyethyl)-1-piperazinyl]-3(2*H*)-pyridazinones as selective postsynaptic *a*-adrenoreceptor antagonists [95EJM71], imidazo[1,2-*b*]pyridazine-2-acetic acids as analgesics [95F349], 4-amino-1,2,3-triazolo[4,5-*d*]pyridazines as A_1 and A_2 receptor ligands [95F99], *N*-(ω-carboxyalkyl)pyridazinecarboxamide analogs of pyridazomycin as antifungals [95AP307], imidazo[1,2-*b*]pyridazines analogs as CNS agents [95AJC1031], and 1,4-bis[(aminoalkyl)amino]benzo[*g*]phthalazine-5,10-diones as chromophore-modified antitumor anthracenediones [95JMC526].

6.2.4 PYRIMIDINES AND BENZODERIVATIVES

X-ray crystal structures of 3,3-diethyl-2,4,6-[1*H*,3*H*,5*H*]pyrimidinetrione [95CRT817], methyl 4-diethylamino-2-(formamido)thieno[2,3-*d*]pyrimidine-6-carboxylate [95AX(C)1607], 4-amino-*N*-(2-pyrimidinyl)benzenesulfonamide [95AX(C)333], 5-(3-cyclopropyl-1,2,4-oxadiazol-5-yl)-2,3-dihydrodiimidazo[1,5-*a*:1',2'-*c*]quinazoline [95AX(C)318], 9,9'-thiobis(1,2,3,4,7,8-hexahydro-7-methyl-6*H*-pyrimido[1,6-*a*]pyrimidine-6,8-dione) [95AX(C)1861], (Z)-1-ethyl-3-(4-chlorobenzylidene)-1,2,3,5-tetrahydroimidazo[2,1-*b*]quinazoline-2,5-dione [95AX(C)1833], benz[4,5]isoquino[1,2-*b*]quinazoline-7,9-dione [95AX(C)2157], 4-phenyl-6,7,8,9-tetrahydro-[1]benzothieno[3,2-*e*][1,2,4]triazolo[4,3-*a*]pyrimidin-5(4*H*)-one [95AX(C)2092], and 3-{2-[4-(4-fluorobenzoyl)piperidino]ethyl}-2-methyl-4*H*-pyrido[1,2-*a*]pyrimidin-4-one (pirenperone) [95AX(C)533] have been obtained.

A combination $^{13}C/^{15}N$ NMR and PM3 quantum-mechanical study of 7-OH-, SH-, and NH_2-substituted 1,2,4-triazolo[1,5-*a*]pyrimidines **20** has provided evidence that the former two exist as a 4*H* and 3*H* prototropic mixture in rapid equilibrium on the NMR time scale [95JMS273]. In a combination X-ray and PM3 computational study, the reaction of 5-(alkylaminomethylene)-6-methyleneperhydropyrimidine-2,4-diones and tropone has been shown to afford 2,5-ethanopyrido[2,3-*f*]quinazoles and 6,10a-methanopyrimido[4',5':4,5]cyclohepta[1,2-*b*]azocines [95JCS(P1)1453]. In related studies, the same research group has reported the isolation and characterization of diastereoisomeric cyclohepta[*g*]quinazolines **21** from *endo* or *exo* [4+2] cyclocondensative approach of tropone and 8,8-dicyanoheptafulvene to 5-(arylaminomethylene)-1,3-dimethyl-6-methyleneperhydropyrimidine-2,4(1*H*,3*H*)-diones [95S51895, JCS(P1)1445].

20, X = OH, SH, NH_2 X = O, $C(CN)_2$ **21** X

By determining one- and multiple-bond heteronuclear coupling constants, unambiguous ^1H and ^{13}C NMR spectral assignments for some 4(3*H*)-quinazolinones and (3*H*)-quinazolinethiones has been accomplished, revealing a need for the revision of assignments made previously for the C-5 and C-8 resonances of four of the quinazolinones [95M789]. The IR, electronic absorption, and ^1H NMR spectra of solid nitrobenzene CT complexes of pyrimidine, pyrazine, and their 2-amino derivatives have been obtained [95EJC269]. Spectroscopic structure elucidation of charine, a new pyrimidine arabinopyranoside from the unripe fruit of *M. charantia*, has been reported [95P361]. Vicine, a known pyrimidine glucopyranoside, was found in the same plant.

6.2.4.1 Syntheses

Advances have been made in the synthesis of compounds featuring an isolated, substituted pyrimidine ring. For example, cinnamoyl isothiocyanate has been found to condense with enaminones, anilines, and cyano(thio)acetamides to produce pyrimidines [95PJC1018]. Condensation adducts of *N*-nucleophiles and ketene dithioacetals or alkoxymethylene reagents undergo regioselective cyclization to afford pyrimidines **22** and **23**, a process thought to be governed by the stereoelectronic factors or geometry about the C=C bond [95H(41)71]. A convenient synthesis of polyfunctionally-substituted 5-(thiazol-2'-yl)pyrimidines *via* immediate cyclization of the adducts formed from active methylene agents, PhNCS, and 4-bromo-2-phenylhydrazono-3-oxo-butyronitrile, has been reported [95PS57]. 2,4-Bis[4-(5-imidazolin-2-yl-, amidino-, and *N*-isopropylamidino-2-benzimidazolyl)phenyl]pyrimidines have been prepared from 2,4-bis(4-cyanophenyl)pyrimidine [95HC225]. Synthesis of the osmoprotector amino acid 2,4,5,6-tetrahydro-2-methyl-4-pyrimidinecarboxylic acid (ecotine, **24**) was achieved by thermal cyclization of *N*-acetyl-2,4-diaminobutyric acid [95SC2223]. A multistep synthesis of 5-hydroxy-6-methyl-4-pyrimidinemethanol, a potential pyridoxine antagonist, from 5-acetyl-4-methyloxazole has been reported together with the ring transformative synthesis of 4-(benzyloxymethyl)-5-hydroxy-6-methylpyrimidine from 5-(benzyloxyacetyl)-4-methyloxazole (NH_3, MeOH, 170 °C) [95IJC(B)112]. An *O*-alkylated derivative of methyl 3-hydroxyindole-2-carboxylate was used to prepare a pyrimidine in a study of the regioselectivity (O *vs.* C2 *vs.* N) of alkylation of the former [95HC181]. A one-pot, phase-transfer catalyzed (PTC) condensation of $PhNHCH=C(CN)_2$ or $1,4-C_6H_4[NHCH=C(CN)_2]_2$ and EtO_2CCOCl has afforded esters which undergo cyclization with amines to give pyrimidinones **25** [95SC1119].

22, R_1 = Ph, OMe, H, SMe,   **23**   **24**   **25**, R = NH_2, NHPh,
R_2 = CO_2Me or CN,   Ph, $C(=NH)NH_2$
X = S or O

Heterocycle-fused pyrimidines have been the focus of a large number of synthetic efforts. Some of these have given rise to papers describing the synthesis of furo- or pyranopyrimidines. For example, condensation of 2-amino-3-cyano-4,5-bis(3,4,5-trimethoxyphenyl)furan and RNCS, H_2NCONH_2 or H_2NCSNH_2, or CS_2 has furnished furo[2,3-d]pyrimidines [95IJC(B)191]. 4-Amino-substituted products obtained in this fashion led to 4-imide, diacetyl, and benzamide analogs. A synthesis of furo[2,3-d]pyrimidine nucleosides based on intramolecular cyclocondensation of 5-(2-bromovinyl)uracil has been reported [95JHC211]. A one-pot synthesis of pyrano[2,3-d]pyrimidines **26** from pyrans and phosgeniminium chloride has been reported [95T5901].

Others have described the pyrrolo-, pyrazolo-, or imidazopyrimidines. For example, a one-step ring transformative approach to 2-substituted 4-aminopyrrolo[2,3-d]pyrimidines **27** has been demonstrated by the condensation of amidines and 2-amino-3-cyanofurans [95JOC6684]. An efficient synthesis of 2'-deoxycadeguomycin (**28**), a 2'-deoxy-β-D-ribofuranosylated, 5-substituted pyrrolo[2,3-d]pyrimidine, has been developed based on pyrrole ring annelation of a 6-chlorouracil via condensation with sodium N-(4-nitrophenethyl)glycinate followed by thermal cyclization in Ac_2O [95JOC5069]. A nitrile-condensative, one-step synthesis of pyrazolo- and 1,2,4-triazolo[1,5-a]pyrimidines has been developed [95JCR290]. Condensation of 5-chloro-3-methyl-1-phenylpyrazole-4-carbaldehyde and active methylene reagents gave unsaturated precursors to certain pyrazolo[3,4-d]pyrimidinones [95JIC641]. 5-Amino-4-cyanopyrazole has served as a starting material for the synthesis of new 3-cyano-2-(3-tolylamino)pyrazolo[1,5-a]pyrimidines [95JCR324]. α-, β-Naphthylhydroximidoyl chlorides have been shown to condense with 2-aminopyrimidine to give 3-nitrosoimidazo[1,2-a]pyrimidines [95JCC83]. o-Acetyl(bromoacetyl)benzene monoketal has been used in a racemic synthesis of an (imidazo[1,2-a]pyrimidin-2-yl)phenylethanol-based sulmazole-pronethalol hybrid model [95JCR56].

26, R = N-morpholino or piperidino   **27**   **28**, R = 1-(2-deoxy-β-D-ribofuranosyl)

Still others have related the synthesis of isoxazolo- or triazolopyrimidines. For example, a one-step synthesis of isoxazolo[4,5-d]pyrimidines from pyrimidines has been developed [95PJC70]. Symmetrical 2-substituted vinamidinium salts have been found to condense with 3-amino-1,2,4-triazole in base, thereby affording 6-substituted triazolo[1,5-a]pyrimidines [95H(40)729]. 2-Oxo-3-phenylisoxazolo[2,3-a]pyrimidines **29** have been synthesized by treatment of 3-amino-4-phenyl-5-isoxazolone with malonaldehyde tetraacetal, 3-oxobutyraldehyde diacetal, 2,4-pentanedione, and 1-phenyl-1,3-butanedione [95JOC5250]. The products, two of which were analyzed by X-ray, underwent thermal ring opening followed by decarboxylation in H_2O or EtOH, giving phenylpyrimidylmethanols or phenylpyrimidyl ethyl ethers, respectively.

$R_1 = R_2 = H;$
$R_1 = Me, R_2 = H;$
$R_1 = H, R_2 = Me;$
$R_1 = Me, R_2 = Ph$

Some have described the synthesis of sulfur-containing heterocycle-fused pyrimidines such as thieno-, thiopyrano-, or thiazolopyrimidines. For example, thieno[2,3-d]pyrimidines, thieno[2,3-d]pyrimidine 7,7-dioxides, and thiopyrano[2,3-d]pyrimidines have been accessed from 5-acetyl-4-mercaptopyrimidines [95PJC887]. 2-Styrylthiopyranopyrimidines and cinnamoylpyrimidines have been obtained by the reaction of pyrimidines and aldehydes [95PJC892]. 3-Benzyl-5-phenyl-7-alkylaminothiazolo[4,5-d]pyrimidine-2(3H)-thiones have been synthesized by a sequence involving condensation of 3-benzyl-4-amino-5-carboxyamidothiazole-2($3H$)-thione and an alkyl orthobenzoate, then treatment with HBr in HOAc, then reaction with $POCl_3$, and finally halide displacement with amines [95F579].

In a few instances, the product of synthesis bears a pyrimidine ring that is fused to a seven-membered ring or to a large polycyclic framework. Pyrimidino[4,5-*b*][1,4]diazepines and -thiazepines **30** have been prepared by reaction of polyfunctionalized pyrimidines and carbon suboxide (O=C=C=C=O) [95H(41)303]. Cholesteno[4,3-*d*]- and [7,6-*d*]pyrimidines for use in a CD study have been prepared *via* $HC(NHCHO)_3$-derived hydroxymethylene cholestanones [95LA1871]. Upon exposure to Vilsmeier-Haack conditions ($POCl_3$, DMF) and subsequent treatment of the α-chloro-substituted carbaldehyde with urea or guanidine hydrochloride, 3β-acetoxyandost-5-en-17-one has afforded 5-androsteno[17,16-*e*]pyrimidines [95JHC353].

$$X = S, Y = W = NH, Z = SH;$$
$$X = Y = NH, W = O, Z = SH \text{ or } H$$

30

In others, a new synthetic strategy proved to be useful for the preparation of different types of heterocycle-fused pyrimidines. For example, condensation of (hetero)aromatic *ortho*-amino carbonyl-based compounds and [bis(methylthio)methylene]amino (BMMA) esters such as $(MeS)_2C=NCH_2CO_2Et$, $(MeS)_2C=NCH_2CH_2CO_2Et$, and $(MeS)_2C=NNHCO_2Et$ has been shown to be a viable annelation route to benzo- and thieno-fused pyrimidines, pyrrolo[1,2-*c*]pyrimidines, imidazo[1,2-*c*]pyrimidines, and 1,2,4-triazolo[1,5-*c*]pyrimidines [95H(40)851]. The reaction of β-naphthylidenylmalonitrile and thiourea, followed by annelation with cyclohexanone, $HCONH_2$, NH_2NH_2, BzNCO, CS_2, or HCO_2H has also been shown to afford condensed pyrimidines [95JHC265]. 2-(*p*-Nitrobenzylideneamino)benzoxazole, -benzothiazole, and -benzimidazole gave normal Diels-Alder pyrimidine adducts upon treatment with electron-deficient dienophiles and inverse electron-demand Diels-Alder pyrimidine adducts with electron-rich dienophiles such as styrene [95RRC165].

Advances in the construction of the pyridopyrimidine ring systems have been made as well. 6-Oxo-2,3,4,6,7,8-hexahydro-1*H*-pyrido[1,2-*a*]pyrimidine-9-carbonitriles have been prepared by an apparent ring opening-ring closure sequence that ensues upon treatment of methoxytetrahydropyridinonecarbonitriles with $H_2N(CH_2)_3NH_2$ [95H(41)2173]. Condensation of aroyl ketenes or diketene and cyclic *N*-cyanoamidines has been shown to afford 4,7-dioxo-6-acyl-2,3-polymethylenepyrido[2,3-*d*]pyrimidines [95MC193]. A facile synthesis of 9-methyl-3-(1*H*-tetrazol-5-yl)-4*H*-pyrido[1,2-*a*]pyrimidin-4-one, the conjugate acid of a clinical anti-asthma agent, has been developed in which use of the explosive aluminum azide is avoided [95CPB683]. A two-step approach to pyrido[2,3-*d*]pyrimidines from acyclic precursors has been developed, and involves an HX-mediated cyclization of 2-cyanamino-4,6-diphenylpyridine-3-carbonitrile to the 4-amino-2-halo-substituted pyrido[2,3-*d*]pyrimidines **31** [95T10253]. The preparation and characterization of new pyrido-fused versions **32** of the previously known 1,2,4-benzothiadiazine 1,1-dioxides have been reported [95T3221]. An earlier study had described the somewhat structurally-related, readily 1,4-hydrating 2,4,1-benzodiazaborines **33** [94JA7597].

31   **32**   **33**

In the benzo-fused series, synthetic efforts have given rise not only to new quinazolines, but also to new methods of preparing them. Quinazoline **34** has been obtained via deprotonation of *N*-phenyldiethylketenimine with excess strong base (LTMP/KO*t*Bu) in *tert*-BuOMe followed by addition of another equivalent of the ketenimine and subsequent introduction of *t*BuCOCl [95T9031]. Semiempirical computational analyses were conducted to provide support for the suggested reaction pathway characteristics, and the X-ray crystal structure of **34** was obtained. A mixture of $PdCl_2(PPh_3)_2$ and $MoCl_5$ has been found to catalyze the intermolecular reductive *N*-heterocyclization of 2-nitrobenzaldehyde or 2-nitrophenyl ketones by formamide under CO, a process that affords quinazolines **35** in moderate (19-46%) yield [95JOM229]. A nitrene intermediate generated *via* NO_2 deoxygenation by CO is suspected to be on the reaction pathway. A single heteroannulation study describes the reaction of cyclohexane-1,3-diones and EtOC(Me)=NCSNHPh to give quinazolines, 3-(phenylamino)-2-cyclohexen-1-one and PhCONCS to give a quinazolinethione, and the synthesis and transformation of (1,3-dioxocyclohex-2-yl)CSNHCOPh into quinazolines, isoquinolines, and/or oxazines [95PJC873]. Quinazolinium salts **36** have been obtained from the $POCl_3$-mediated Vilsmeier formylation of 4-$MeC_6H_4NMe_2$ with *N*-formylated dialkyl amines [95CC1463].

35, R = H, Me, Et, OMe   **36**

Quinazolines with specific substitution patterns can be synthesized by employing methods described in some of the other reports. In a study detailing the synthesis of the 4-aza papaverine analog **37**, an azolium salt-catalyzed aroylation reaction was shown to be a useful route to 4-aroyl-6,7-dimethoxyquinazolines [95H(40)653]. 1-(2-Benzazolylaminosulfonyl)-4-[4-oxo-2-thioxo(oxo)-1,2,3,4-tetrahydro-3-quinazolinyl]benzenes have been shown to be readily synthesized from dithiocarbamic acid derivative precursors [95JHC1181]. 2-(Benzotriazol-1-yl)enamines, readily available *via* condensation of lithiated 1-(arylmethyl)benzotriazoles and aryl nitriles, have been shown to undergo a regiospecific thermal rearrangement (110 °C, PhMe) to afford 2,4-diarylquinazolines **38** [95JOC246], whereas lithiated versions of the *N*-(α-alkoxyalkyl)benzotriazoles **39** have been found to undergo ring opening and concomitant N_2 extrusion at -78 °C to give *o*-iminophenyl anions, useful for the synthesis of a variety of heterocycles including 2,3,4-triaryl-3*H*,4*H*-dihydroquinazolines, 2-phenyl-4-arylquinazolines, and 2-aryl-3-phenyl-3*H*,4*H*-quinazoline-4-thiones [95JOC7625].

37

1. BuLi, THF, -78 °C
2. R_1CN, -78 °C - rt
3. PhMe, Δ

R_1 = Ar, R_2 = Ar, R_3 = R_4 = H;
R_1 = R_2 = Ph, R_3 = R_4 = Me;   **38**

39
R_1 = Ph, R_2 = Me or
Et; R_1 = Ar, R_2 = *i*Pr

The synthesis of quinazolin-2- and/or 4-ones or their thione analogs has been of importance to several studies. The cardiotonic bemarinone, 5,6-dimethoxy-4-methyl-2(1*H*)-quinazolinone, has been synthesized by a route involving the directed metalation of *N*-(3,4-dimethoxyphenyl)-2,2-dimethylpropanamide [95JHC761]. A more convenient synthesis of 1-(2-deoxy-β-D-erythropentofuranosyl)quinazoline-2,4(3*H*)-dione has been reported, together with an analysis of its solution conformation and its incorporation into a G-rich, triplex-forming oligodeoxyribonucleotide segment by the solid-support, phosphoramidite method [95MI45]. 8-Aminomethyl- and 8-azolylmethyl-2-phenyl-3*H*-quinazoline-4-thiones have been prepared by the reaction of secondary amines or azoles and 8-chloromethyl-2-phenyl-3*H*-quinazoline-4-thione, in turn derived *via* intramolecular cyclization of *N*-(2-chloromethylphenyl)benzimidoyl isothiocyanate [95CCC705].

Developments have also been seen in the synthesis of fused quinazolines. Preparation of the linear 3*a*-(*p*-chlorophenyl)perhydropyrrolo[2,1-*b*]quinazolin-1-one (**40a**) and the angular 3*a*-(*p*-chlorophenyl)perhydropyrrolo[2,1-*a*]quinazolin-1-one (**40b**) from 3-(*p*-chlorobenzoyl)propanoic acid and *cis*-2-aminocyclohexylmethanamine has been achieved, and these tricyclics and have been characterized by NMR and X-ray methods [95ACS751]. The condensation of 3-methyl-1-phenacylbenzotriazolium ylides and acetylenic esters has been shown to be a viable route to the pyrazoloquinazoline tricyclics **41** in a study supported by X-ray analyses [95H(41)765]. Condensation of 2-amino-5-bromovanillin and 4-aminobutyraldehyde in pH 5.8 phosphate buffer followed by catalytic hydrogenation (H_2, Pd/BaSO$_4$, 65 °C) of the resulting quinazolinium complex gave 1,2,3,9-tetrahydro-7-bromo-6-hydroxy-5-methoxypyrrolo[2,1-*b*]quinazoline (**42**), a new deoxyvasicine analog [95SC569]. The condensation of 2-carbethoxy-3-ethoxymethyleneiminoquinazolin-4[3*H*]-one and alkyl-, aryl-, or aralkylamines or hydrazines has led to the development of a high yield, one-pot synthesis of new 3-substituted-3*H*-[1,2,4]triazino[6,1-*b*]quinazoline-4,10-diones possessing analgesic activity [95IJC(B)617]. 6-Trifluoroacetyl-4-trifluoromethylbenzo[*h*]quinazolines **43** have been readily prepared by the reaction of 2,4-bis(trifluoroacetyl)-1-naphthylamine and aldehydes in aqueous NH$_3$ (73-100%), and DDQ-mediated dehydrogenation (80-100%) of the 1,2-dihydrobenzo[*h*]quinazolines thus obtained [95H(40)905].

40a   **40b**

R = 4-ClC$_6$H$_4$

41

R$_1$ = H, R$_2$ = Et;
R$_1$ = CO$_2$Me, R$_2$ = Me

42

43

R = H, alkyl, aryl

6.2.4.2 Reactions

Pyrimidines bearing Me$_3$Sn substituents at the 2- and/or 4-positions were reported to undergo acylation better with acylformyl chlorides than with acyl chlorides [95H(41)1275]. The use of EtO$_2$CCOCl gave (ethoxycarbonyl)pyrimidines, and stepwise acylation and ethoxycarbonylation of bis(trimethylstannyl)pyrimidines was employed to access diacylpyrimidines.

Some interesting reactions involving pyrimidinediones have been described. 1-Methyl-2-(*N*-methylthiocarbamoylimino)-4,6(1*H*,3*H*,5*H*)-pyrimidinediones bearing two C5 substituents have been found to give the corresponding 2-(2'-ethyl-methyl-3'-isoureido)-1-methyltetrahydro-4,6(1*H*,5*H*)-pyrimidinediones upon oxidation [95PJC235]. An unusual ring-opening reaction has been observed to occur when 6,7-dihydrothieno[3,2-*d*]pyrimidine-2,4-diones are treated with BnBr in the presence of dilute NaOH [95JOC1461]. A β-sulfonium elimination reaction occurs, and 6-vinyl-5-(alkylthio)pyrimidines **44** are obtained. Facile intramolecular Schiff base condensation in 2'-substituted 2-amino-6-[(aminoethyl)amino]-4,5-pyrimidinediones **45** provided an access to the labile 4a-hydroxytetrahydropterins **46** for a study of the mechanism of their nonenzymatic dehydration to quinoid dihydropterins [95JA10203].

R$_1$ = R$_3$ = H, R$_2$ = Me;
R$_1$ = R$_2$ = H, R$_3$ = Ph;
R$_1$ = R$_3$ = Ph, R$_2$ = H

44

45

R = Me, Pr

46

Advances have been made in our understanding of the reactivity of the pyrimidine ring in compounds related to nucleosides and their aglycons. A 5-Me group to C-4 pyrone photoadduct obtained by reaction of thymidine and 5-methoxypsoralen in the dry state has been characterized by a wide array of spectroscopic methods [95JPP167]. The *cis-syn* cytosine-cytosine and cytosine-thymine cyclobutane photodimers have been prepared, and were shown to revert back to monomeric form upon UV irradiation or photochemically-mediated electron transfer in the presence of *N,N*-dimethylaniline, *N,N,N,N*-tetramethylbenzidine, 2-anthraquinonesulfonate, or 9,10-dicyanoanthracene [95JOC624]. Upon photolysis in TFA-containing *p*-xylene, the 5-H, F, Cl, Me, and *p*-xylyl-substituted 1,3-dimethyluracils have been found to afford 5,6-dihydro-1,3-dimethyl-6-*p*-methylbenzyluracils, 5,6-dihydro-1,3-dimethyl-5-*p*-methylbenzyluracils, and 5,6-dihydro-1,3-dimethyluracils [95CPB1024]. The 1,3-diphenylation of uracil (37%) or 3-phenylation of pyrimidine nucleosides (42-52%), respectively, has been effected under the conditions of PhI, CuI, 2,4,6-trimethylpyridine, 20 h [95JCS(P1)733]. A high yield C5-phenylselenenylation of pyrimidine nucleosides has been reported to be effected by $(PhSe)_2$ in HOAc the presence of Mn(III) acetate [95SL349]. The spectrum of reactivity (substitution *vs.* X-philic *vs.* SET) exhibited by 5-bromo-1,3,6-trimethyluracil upon treatment with alkyl-, aryl, and heteroarylthiolate ions has been investigated [95BMC891]. Adducts formed by condensation of 5-formyl-6-methyluracil and active methylene acid derivatives have been characterized by IR, UV, NMR, and mass spectral methods [95CCC605]. In what amounts to an S_N(ANRORC) transformation, *N*-nitrouridines **47** have been shown to undergo ring opening at the N3-C4 bond upon treatment with two equivalents of a primary amine, giving an isolable *N*-nitroamidate salt that undergoes cyclization to the 3-substituted pyrimidine-2,4-diones **48** upon treatment with TFA [95JA3665]. A similar ring transformation was documented for *N*-nitroinosines, wherein transient purine N1-C2 bond heterolysis occurs. Covalent hydration of a uridine-6,5'-dicarboxaldehyde has been found to proceed along a diastereospecific three-step tandem hydration/1,2-addition/conjugate addition pathway, affording the unusual C6 spiro-fused cyclouridine derivative **49** [95AX(C)1204].

R = tri-*O*-protected 1-β-D-ribofuranosyl
R' = H, $PhCH_2$, NH_2, 2-carboethoxyalkyl

The 1,4-cycloaddition reaction of 2-(methylthio)-3,6-dihydro-3,5-dimethyl-6-oxo-1-aryl(or alkyl)-1-pyrimidinium-4-olates and electron-deficient alkenes has been shown to proceed regio- and diastereoselectively [95CPB705]. Whereas bicyclic pyrido-pyrimidine mesoions were found to react with TCNE to produce tricyanovinyl derivatives, monocyclic pyrimidine betaines **50** were found to give 1,4-dipolar cycloaddition products [95H(40)681]. Two of these products were found to rearrange to cyclopenta[*d*]pyrimidines **51** when heated at >200 °C, a reaction accelerated in the presence of $AlCl_3$. An X-ray crystal structure of **51**, R = Me, was obtained. 3-Acetyl-4-phenylaminopyrido[1,2-*a*]pyrimidin-2-one, prepared from acetoacetic *N*-(pyrid-2-yl)amide and PhNCS, has been shown to undergo thermal equilibration to the isomeric 3-acetyl-2-phenylaminopyrido[1,2-*a*]pyrimidin-4-one [95MC106]. Condensation of 5-ureidomethylene-2-thiobarbituric acids and ethyl cyanoacetate gave 6-ethoxycarbonyl-4-oxo-1,2,3,4-tetrahydro-7*H*-pyrano[2,3-*d*]pyrimidin-7-ones, while that of 1,3-diaryl-2-thiobarbituric acids and thiourea and $(EtO)_3CH$ gave the corresponding 1,3-diaryl-2-thioxo analogs [95IJC(B)51].

50, $R_1 = R_2$ = H, Me;
R_1 = Ph, R_2 = Et or Bn

220 °C
(R_1 = Ph, R_2=Et or Bn)

51, R = Me, Ph

Treatment of 2-mercapto-4(3H)-quinazolinone (**52**) with hydrazonoyl halides affords 1,3-disubstituted 1,2,4-triazolo[4,3-a]quinazolin-5-ones **53** [95H(41)1999]. Hydrazones derived from [(2-methyl-4-quinazolinyl)oxy]acetic acid hydrazide and aldehydes or ketones were shown to give 4-thiazolidinones and pyrazoles under cyclization conditions [95IJC(B)537].

52, R = alkyl, Ar = Ph or 4-NO$_2$C$_6$H$_4$ **53**

6.2.4.3 Applications

3-(Acetoxyamino)quinazolinones **54** have been known to be effective aziridinating agents for electron-rich and electron-poor allylic alcohols. Now, structures of the transition states thought to be responsible for the differing diastereoselectivity of these reactions have been proposed [95TL3241]. A new chiral pyrimidino-18-crown-6 ligand has been found to exhibit recognition for the enantiomers of α-(1-naphthylethyl)ammonium perchlorate [95PAC691]. Under oxidative desulfurization-fluorination conditions, ethyl N-pyrimidyl-N-alkyldithiocarbamates afford trifluoromethylamino-substituted pyrimidine precursors **55** for the cross-coupling synthesis of liquid crystalline materials [95TL563]. 2,2'-Dimethyl-6,6'-diphenyl-4,4'-bipyrimidine and 6,6'-dimethyl-2,2'-bipyrazine were found to form 2:1 complexes with Cu(I) (like **56**), and an infinite-chain Cu(I) polymer was obtained by using 2,2'-dimethyl-4,4'-bipyrimidine [95IC5205]. All of the ring nitrogen atoms were found to be involved in metal coordination in this polymer.

54, R = H, tBu   **55** R = Me, n-propyl, n-octyl, n-dodecyl   **56**

Perhaps not surprisingly, a very large number of biological SAR studies have been conducted on pyrimidine- or quinazoline-based compounds. Subjects of these include 7-amino-4-(phenylamino)- and 7-amino-4-(benzylamino)pyrido[4,3-d]pyrimidines as tyrosine kinase inhibitors [95JMC3780], 3-N-substituted pyrimidine-4(3H)-ones and 4-O,N,S-substituted pyrimidines as C-linked biphenyl tetrazole AT$_2$ antagonists [95EJM365], 4,6-di-(heteroaryl)-2-(N-methylpiperazino)pyrimidines as 5-HT$_{1\alpha}$ and 5-HT$_{2\alpha}$ receptor ligands [95AP659], heterocycle-to-p-aminobenzoyl-L-glutamate-bridged 5-substituted 2,4-diaminofuro[2,3-d]pyrimidines as both DHFR and TS inhibitors [95JMC3798], 2,4-diamino-5-substituted-pyrrolo[2,3-d]pyrimidines [95JMC2158], 2,4-diaminopyrido[3,2-d]pyrimidines [95JMC2615], 6-substituted 2,4-diamino-5-methylpyrido[2,3-d]pyrimidines [95JMC1778], 2,4-diamino-6,7-dihydro-5-H-cyclopenta[d]pyrimidine analogs [95CPB820], 2,4-diamino-5,6,7,8-tetrahydropyrido[4,3-d]pyrimidine analogs of trimetrexate and piritrexim [95JHC335], and 2,4-diamino-5-substituted quinazolines as DHFR inhibitors [95JMC745], 3-(dialkylamino)-1H-pyrimido[1,2-a]quinolin-1-ones and 2-(dialkylamino)-4H-pyrimido[2,1-a]isoquinolin-4-ones as antiplatelet compounds [95EJM27], and 2-(pyrimidin-4-yl)estradiols as uterotrophics and antifertility compounds [95EJM423].

Others include tetramethylene-substituted thieno[2,3-d]pyrimidines [95F611], 4H-pyrido[1,2-a]pyrimidin-4-ones [95F69], 4-triazolo-, tetrazolo-, and (3,5-dimethylpyrazolo)pyrrolo[2,3-d]pyrimidines [95JCR314], and 6,7-annelated pyrido[2,3-d]pyrimidines [95JPS661] as antimicrobials, 2 and 3-substituted imidazolo[1,2-a]pyrimidines [95MI551], imidazo[1,2-a]pyrimidine-5(1H)-ones [95JHC1003], 2,4(1H,3H)-quinazolinediones and thieno[2,3-d]pyrimidine-2,4(1H,3H)-diones [95LA1371], and 3-alkyl-substituted 5-aminothiazolo[4,5-

d]pyrimidine-2,7($3H,6H$)-diones [95JHC547] as antivirals, ethyl 2-[(1H-benzimidazol-2-yl)sulfinylmethyl]-4-dimethylamino-5-pyrimidinecarboxylate [95CPB166] and 2-benzylthio-5,6,7,8-tetrahydro-4($3H$)-quinazolinones [95CPB2021] as antiulcer agents, 6-(4-pyridinyl)-1H-1,2,3-triazolo[4,5-d]pyrimidin-4($5H$)-one as an AMPA receptor antagonist [95JMC587], 3-N-substituted pyrimidinones as AT_1-selective receptor antagonists [95JMC4806], isoxazolo[4,3-d]pyrimidines as anticonvulsant, anxiolytic, and antiserotonin agents [95F183], 5-substituted 6-methyl-2-phenylpyrimidines as immunomodulatory agents [95F131], 1,3,4-triazolo[1,5-a]pyrimidines as antiparasitics [95IJC(B)209], 5H-[1,3]thiazolo[3,2-a]pyrido[3,2-e]pyrimidin-5-ones as diuretics [95AF306], pyrimidine analogs of the 2,6-di-$tert$-butylphenol as antiinflammatory agents [95JHC1197], 6-acet(benz)amido-2,7-diaryl-6,7-dihydro-5H-1,3,4-oxa(thia)diazolo[3,2-a]pyrimidin-5-ones as fungicides [95IJC(B)500], and pyrrolo[3,2-d]pyrimidines [95JOC7947] and quinazolines [95JMC994] as antifolates.

Still others include quinazoline-based C-nucleosides [95MI397] and 6-substituted 2-aryl-3-[N-acetyl-N-(D-gluco- or galactopyranosyl)amino]-4-($3H$)-quinazolinones and their aglycons [95PJC583] as antitumor agents, 4-[(phenylmethyl)amino]- and 4-(phenylamino)quinazolines as ATP binding site inhibitors of the tyrosine kinase domain of the epidermal growth factor receptor [95JMC3482], 2,3-disubstituted quinazolin-4($3H$)-ones as antibacterial, antitubercular, anticancer, or anti-HIV agents [95IJC(B)201], and 6-(N-alkyl-N-acyl)-2-propyl-3-[(2'-(tetrazol-5-yl)biphen-4-yl)methyl]quinazolinones as balanced AT_1 and AT_2 antagonists [95BMCL1359].

6.2.5 PYRAZINES AND BENZODERIVATIVES

A combination semiempirical MO and X-ray study of pyrrolo[1,2-a]quinoxalines has been conducted [95JHC1317], and X-ray crystal structure reports of 1,2,3,5,6,8a-hexahydro-8,8a-diphenylimidazo[1,2-a]pyrazine [95AX(C)482], adducts of pyrazine-2,3-dicarboxylic acid and 2-aminobenzoic acid (1:2) and 3-aminobenzoic acid (1:1 dihydrate) [95AX(C)2629], and of pair-stacked 10-(4-nitrophenyl)-5(10H)phenazinyl radicals [95AX(C)1420] have appeared. The unambiguous structure determination of 2-phenacylidene-1,2-dihydro-4H-pyrido[2,3-b]pyrazin-3-one and 3-phenacylidene-3,4-dihydro-1H-pyrido[2,3-b]pyrazin-2-one, isomeric products of the condensation of 2,3-diaminopyridine and ethyl benzoylpyruvate appearing to exist in enamine tautomeric form [95JHC347], have been determined via hydrolysis followed by hydrogenation to 2-methyl-1,2-dihydro-4H-pyrido[2,3-b]pyrazin-3-one and 3-methyl-3,4-dihydro-1H-pyrido[2,3-b]pyrazin-2-one, the latter of which was shown to be identical to that obtained by an alternative route [95JHC703]. Structures of two new phenazine antibiotic metabolites isolated from a *Streptomyces* have been determined [95MI1081].

A tautomeric equilibrium between enamine and methylene imine forms has been demonstrated to exist in 2-(3,4-dihydro-3-oxo-2(1H)-quinoxalinylidene)-N-phenylacetamides and 3,4-dihydro-3-oxo-N-phenyl-2-quinoxaline acetamides when these are in DMSO solution either in the absence or presence of TFA [95JHC671]. The reduction potentials of some pyrazines and their benzo-fused analogs have been summarized as part of an EPR study of the electron transfer interaction between nitrogen heterocycles and n-Bu$_4$N$^+$BH$_4^-$ [95JOM123].

6.2.5.1 Syntheses

Pyrazine and its 2-methyl derivative have been prepared *via* cyclization of N-(2,3-dihydroxypropyl)ethylenediamine over chromite catalysts [95IJC(B)573]. New fused pyrazines in the form of pyrrolo[1'',2'':1',6']pyrazino[2',3':4,5]thieno[2,3-b]quinolines have been accessed from thieno[2,3-b]quinoline-2-carboxylates [95PS143]. Condensation of 1,3-disubstituted-5-amino-4-nitrosopyrazoles **57** and dimethylphenacylsulfonium bromides in C$_5$H$_5$N solution was shown to give pyrazolopyrazine oxides **58** and/or pyrazolopyrazinones **59** [95H(41)1667]. 5-Methyl-2(1H)-pyrazinones **60** have been obtained from dipeptidyl chloromethyl ketones [95T7361]. A facile, non-racemizing synthesis of 2(1H)-pyrazinones from dipeptidyl aldehydes applicable to the construction of naturally-occurring products like deoxyaspergillic acid, flavacol, and deoxymutaaspergilic acid, has been developed [95PC169]. The atropisomeric pyrazinone ($\alpha S,S$)-6-(2-α-iodophenyl)-3,5-dichloro-1-(1-phenylethyl)-2(1H)-pyrazinone (**61**) has been prepared (57%) *via* chirality transfer cyclization of (S,S)-α-[(1-

phenylethyl)amino]-α-(2-iodophenyl)acetonitrile upon treatment with (COCl)$_2$ in PhMe or PhCl solution at 70 °C [95TL2017]. Mixtures of atropisomers were obtained when an *ortho* substituent smaller than an iodo was employed. Stereochemistry was assigned from X-ray and nOe NMR spectral analyses. Equilibration of *cis*-dimethyl piperidine-2,6-dicarboxylate followed by alkylation with phthalimidoethyl triflate has led to an efficient synthesis of *trans*-2-(1,2-benzisoxazol-3-yl)octahydro-2*H*-pyrido[1,2-*a*]pyrazine-7-methanol [95JHC857]. The optically-active 2,7-disubstituted octahydro-2*H*-pyrido[1,2-*a*]pyrazine CNS agent **62** related to the serotonergic anxiolytics buspirone and tiospirone has been synthesized according to an approach involving equilibration of an optically-active *cis*-aldehyde to the *trans*-isomer prior to treatment with the anion derived from CH$_3$NO$_2$ [95TAS321]. (Z)- and (E)-7-Benzylidene-substituted octahydro-2*H*-pyrido[1,2-*a*]pyrazines **63**, bicyclic analogs of the calcium antagonist flunarizine, have been prepared in four steps from 2-benzyloctahydro-2*H*-pyrido[1,2-*a*]pyrazin-7-one [95JCS(P1)369]. Intramolecular reductive (H$_2$, Pd/C) amination of methyl 5-[(*N*-benzyloxycarbonyl)-L-alanyl]amino-2-methoxycarbonyl-4-oxopentanoate gave 79% (4*S*,7*R*,8a*R*)- and 15% (4*S*,7*S*,8a*S*)-7-methoxycarbonyl-4-methyl-3,6-dioxoperhydropyrrolo[1,2-*a*]-pyrazine (**64a,b**), members of a series of 4,7-di- and 4,7,7-trisubstituted products useful as peptidomimetic templates [95T10361].

The synthesis of quinoxalines has been the focus of several reports. For example, solvent-less condensation of α-dicarbonyl compounds and *o*-diaminobenzenes under focused microwave irradiation has been shown to be a viable synthetic route to quinoxalines **65** [95SC2319]. The reaction of 1,2-benzenediamine and alloxan under these conditions gave benzo[*g*]pteridine-2,4(1*H*,3*H*)-dione (isoalloxazine, **66**). A method for the regiospecific oxidative nitration of asymmetrically-6,7-disubstituted 3,4-dihydroquinoxalin-2(1*H*)-ones **67** to the corresponding 1,4-dihydro-5-nitroquinoxalin-2,3-diones, antagonists acting on the glycine site of the NMDA receptor, has been developed [95JOC5838]. Highly reactive *o*-quinonoid thieno[3,4-*b*]quinoxalines **68** have been prepared by a base-catalyzed Pummerer reaction performed on the corresponding 1,3-dihydro 2-oxides [95JOC8283]. 3,5-Dimethyl-1-(5-substituted-2-nitrenophenyl)pyrazoles (derived from thermal or photochemical decomposition of the corresponding azides **69**) have been shown to undergo efficient singlet state cyclization to dimethylpyrazolo[1,2-*a*]benzotriazoles, but inefficient triplet state cyclization to methyl pyrazolo[1,2-*a*]quinoxalines **70** due to a competitive dimerization to azo products and reduction to aminophenylpyrazoles [95H(40)597]. The asymmetric synthesis of the urothion models 2-[(1*R*)- and (1*S*)-1,2-dihydroxyethyl]thieno[2,3-*b*]quinoxaline has been achieved [95HC451]. 1-Isopropyl-1*H*-azepine-4,5-diones have been shown to condense with pyridinediamines to afford 8-isopropylpyridopyrazino[2,3-*d*]azepines, and with substituted *o*-phenylenediamines and 3,3',4,4'-tetraaminobiphenyl to afford 3*H*-3-alkylazepino[4,5-*b*]quinoxalines [95JHC57]. A two-step synthesis of substituted indolo[1,2-*a*]quinoxalin-6(5*H*)-ones **71** has been developed based on the reaction (NaH, NMP) of indole-2-carboxylates and 2-fluoronitrobenzenes, and the reduction (Fe(0), HOAc) of the resulting 1-(2-nitrophenyl)indole-2-carboxylates [95SC2165]. A simple method for the preparation of 3-carbamoylfuro[2,3-*b*]quinoxalin-2-ones **72** based on a base-mediated (NaH, DMSO) condensation of 3-methoxycarbonylmethylene-2-oxoquinoxalines and isocyanates has been developed [95H(41)1951]. Structure determination was supported by X-ray analysis of **72**, R$_1$ = H, R$_2$ = Ph.

65
R$_1$ = R$_2$ = Me, Ph, OEt, OH;
R$_1$ = Me, R$_2$ = OH or OMe

66

67
R$_1$, R$_2$ = F, Br, Cl, or Me
(R$_1$ ≠ R$_2$)

68
R = H, Me

69
R$_1$ = H, R$_2$ = H, Me, OMe,
NMe$_2$, Cl, CF$_3$, NO$_2$;
R$_1$ = R$_2$ = NO$_2$

70

71, X, Y = various

72
R$_1$ = H or Me,
R$_2$ = Et, Bu, Ph, or 3-MeC$_6$H$_4$

New phenazine syntheses have been developed. 1-Formyl-, 2-formyl-, and 2,7-dibenzoylphenazine were prepared from the corresponding substituted 5,10-dimethyl-5,10-dihydrophenazines along a redox route involving HBr-mediated demethylation prior to aromatization [95HC177]. Instead of the expected azo or azoxy compounds, the reaction of 1-naphthyliminodimagnesium dibromide and 1-nitronaphthalene was found to give dibenzo[*a*,*h*]phenazine (**73**) [95JOC5690]. The isomeric dibenzo[*a*,*j*]phenazine was obtained *via* autoxidation of a 1:1 mixture of 1- and 2-aminonaphthalenes in the presence of KO*t*Bu. Finally, a triflate-mediated, one-step synthesis of *N*-alkylated phenazinones from trialkylsiloxyphenazines was described in the course of a synthesis of lavanducyanin [95SL186].

73

6.2.5.2 Reactions

Our knowledge of the pericyclic reactivity of these heterocycles has increased. Quinoxalino-2,3-quinodimethane (**74**) generated *in situ* from 2,3-bis(bromomethyl)quinoxaline has been found to give Diels-Alder adducts upon exposure to dienophiles [95TL6777]. Semiempirical computational analyses supported this study. Photo-induced reactions of benzo[*b*]phenazine (**75**) are governed by the presence of low-lying π-π^* states, and include both [4+4] dimerization and self- or exogenously-sensitized photooxygenation [95H(40)577]. The endoperoxide generated in the latter undergoes O-O bond homolysis to give a quinone and a diol. Fused 7-aza-indolizines **76** have been accessed *via* thermal intramolecular [3+2] dipolar cycloaddition of substituted pyrazinium dicyanomethylides bearing side chain terminal alkynes [95H(40)69].

6.2.5.3 Applications

Poly-η-(pyrazine)-Zn(BH$_4$)$_2$ has been developed as a shelf-stable reductant for aldehydes, ketones, acid chlorides, and azides [95SC3089]. Functionalities unaffected by this reagent include nitrile, epoxide, oxime, ester, amide, and nitro. A chemoenzymatic method has been developed for the preparation of L-amino acid-derived quinoxalinols **77** for the sensitive determination of ^{13}C- or ^{2}H-label content by GCMS [95MI153]. The luminol-related compound 3-propyl-7,8-dihydropyridazino-[4,5-*g*]quinoxaline-2,6,9(1*H*)-trione (PDIQ, **78**) has been found useful in the chemiluminescent detection of H$_2$O$_2$ in the presence of microperoxidase in base, and of glucose in human serum by manual- and flow-injection methods [95MI1083]. The kinetics of uptake of superoxide radical anion by 2-methyl-6-phenylimidazo[1,2-*a*]pyrazin-3(7*H*)-one, the Cypridina luciferin analog (CLA, **79**), have been investigated [95JCS(P2)1699]. *N*-(Benzyloxy)-3-(2-carboxyethyl)-2(1*H*)-pyrazinone (**80**), synthesized in five steps from L-glutamic acid, was coupled first with alanine or leucine and tris(2-aminoethyl)amine, and then was debenzylated to give hexadentate ligands as Fe(III) chelators [95JOC1583]. Fluorescent pyrido[1',2':1,2]imidazo[4,5-*b*]pyrazines **81** with crown ether side-chains have been prepared and were shown to complex alkali earth metal cations and thiocyanate anions simultaneously, thereby functioning as an "AND" logic gate with fluorescence quenching output [95CC1491].

Biological SAR studies have included those on known quinoxaline-based kainate/α-amino-3-hydroxy-5-methyl-4-isoxazolepropionic acid receptor antagonists as selective blockers of the directional-selectivity mechanism in ganglion cells [95PNA1127], pyrazinecarboxylate esters as antimycobacterials [95JMC3902], thioamido-substituted pyrazinecarboxamidrazones [95P565] and 3-arylamino-5-cyano-2-pyrazinecarboxamides [95CCC1236] as antituberculotic agents, 8-amino-3-benzyl-1,2,4-triazolo[4,3-*a*]pyrazines as anticonvulsants [95JMC3676], quinoxaline-2-carbonitrile 1,4-dioxides [95JMC4488], fused pyrazine oxides [95MI259], and quinoxaline 1,4-

dioxides related to the benzotriazine tirapazamine as hypoxia-selective cytotoxins, 2,3,6,7-tetrahydro-2,3-dioxo-$1H,5H$-pyrido[1,2,3-de]quinoxaline-5-acetamides and acetic acids [95BMCL1533] and their Me-substituted derivatives [95BMCL1527] as antagonists for the glycine binding site of the NMDA receptor, 1,4,7,8,9,10-hexahydro-9-methyl-6-nitropyrido[3,4- f]quinoxaline-2,3-dione and related quinoxalinediones as NMDA receptor ligands and anticonvulsants [95JMC3720], N-(ω-carboxyalkyl)pyrazine-carboxamide analogs of pyridazomycin [95AP307] and 2-substituted 5,8-diethylimidazo[4,5-g]quinoxaline-6,7-diones and pyrazinoquinoxalines [95PJC61] as antifungals, 10-substituted 2,3-dimethyl- or diphenylpyrido[3,2-f]quinoxalines and their oxides as antimalarials [95IJC(B)778], and 1-aryl-$1H$-imidazo[4,5-b]quinoxalines as A_1 and $A_{2\alpha}$ adenosine receptor ligands [95JMC1330].

6.2.6 REFERENCES

94BOC1	J. A. Zoltewicz, G. Uray, *Bioorg. Chem.*, **1994**, *22*, 1.
94BSB509	G. Bernath, *Bull. Soc. Chim. Belg.*, **1994**, *103*, 509.
94CCR91	E. S. Raper, *Coord. Chem. Rev.*, **1994**, *129*, 91.
94F683	M. Pinza, G. Pifferi, *Farmaco*, **1994**, *49*, 683.
94H(37)2051	D. Korbonits, K. Horvath, *Heterocycles*, **1994**, *37*, 2051.
94JA7597	M. P. Groziak, A. D. Ganguly, P. D. Robinson, *J. Am. Chem. Soc.*, **1994**, *116*, 7597.
94JHC603	P. R. Marsham, *J. Heterocycl. Chem.*, **1994**, *31*, 603.
94JMC4053	P. D. Leeson, L. L. Iversen, *J. Med. Chem.*, **1994**, *37*, 4053.
94KGS1649	H. C. van der Plas, *Khim. Geterotsikl. Soedin.*, **1994**, 1649.
94MI145	E. De Clercq, *Int. J. Immunother.*, **1994**, *10*, 145.
94MI173	G. Cignarella, D. Barlocco, G. A. Pinna, M. M. Curzu, *Acta Chim. Slov.*, **1994**, *41*, 173.
94MI189	V. Dal Piaz, G. Ciciani, M. P. Giovannoni, *Acta Chim. Slov.*, **1994**, *41*, 189.
94MI205	N. Haider, *Acta Chim. Slov.*, **1994**, *41*, 205.
94MI219	T. Kappe, *Acta Chim. Slov.*, **1994**, *41*, 219.
94MI235	J. Sauer, *Acta Chim. Slov.*, **1994**, *41*, 235.
94NPR163	J. P. Michael, *Nat. Prod. Rep.*, **1994**, *11*, 163.
94PAC2083	T. Kitahara, Y. Kinoshita, S. Aono, M. Miyake, T. Hasegawa, H. Watanabe, K. Mori, *Pure Appl. Chem.*, **1994**, *66*, 2083.
95ACS751	A. E. Szabó, G. Stájer, P. Sohár, R. Silanpää, G. Bernáth, *Acta Chem. Scand.*, **1995**, *49*, 751.
95ACS778	I. Mangalagiu, *Acta Chem. Scand.*, **1995**, *49*, 778.
95AF306	A. Monge, V. Martinez-Merino, M. A. Simon, C. Sanmartin, *Arzneim.-Forsch.*, **1995**, *45*, 306.
95AJC1031	G. B. Barlin, L. P. Davies, P. W. Harrison, *Aust. J. Chem.*, **1995**, *48*, 1031.
95AJC1601	J. A. M. Guard, P. J. Steel, *Aust. J. Chem.*, **1995**, *48*, 1601.
95AP307	J. Easmon, G. Heinisch, W. Holzer, B. Matuszczak, *Arch. Pharm. (Weinheim, Ger.)*, **1995**, *328*, 307.
95AP445	K. Kiec-Kononowicz, X. Ligneau, H. Stark, J.-C. Schwartz, W. Schunack, *Arch. Pharm. (Weinheim, Ger.)*, **1995**, *328*, 445.
95AP659	M. J. Mokrosz, L. Strekowski, W. X. Kozak, B. Duszynska, A. J. Bojarski, A. Klodzinska, A. Czarny, M. T. Cegla, A. Deren-Wesolek, *et al.*, *Arch. Pharm. (Weinheim, Ger.)*, **1995**, *328*, 659.
95AX(C)1204	M. P. Groziak, R. Lin, P. D. Robinson, *Acta Cryst.*, **1995**, *C51*, 1204.
95AX(C)1420	C. Krieger, G. Peraus, F. A. Neugebauer, *Acta Cryst.*, **1995**, *C51*, 1420.
95AX(C)1607	P. Tsiveriotis, N. Hadjiliadis, F. Dahan, J.-P. Laussac, *Acta Cryst.*, **1995**, *C51*, 1607.
95AX(C)1829	J. Karolak-Wojciechowska, H. B. Trzezwinska, J. Lange, M. Wieczorek, *Acta Cryst.*, **1995**, *C51*, 1829.
95AX(C)1833	J. Karolak-Wojciechowska, K. Kiec-Kononowicz, *Acta Cryst.*, **1995**, *C51*, 1833.

95AX(C)1834   S. Moreau, J. Metin, P. Coudert, J. Couquelet, *Acta Cryst.*, **1995**, *C51*, 1834.

95AX(C)1861   V. Kettmann, A. Bozoova, A. Rybar, *Acta Cryst.*, **1995**, *C51*, 1861.

95AX(C)2092   R. Velavan, K. Sivakumar, U. S. Pathak, K. S. Jain, S. Singh, H.-K. Fun, *Acta Cryst.*, **1995**, *C51*, 2092.

95AX(C)2157   S. V. Lindeman, I. I. Ponomarev, A. L. Rusanov, *Acta Cryst.*, **1995**, *C51*, 2157.

95AX(C)2629   G. Smith, D. E. Lynch, K. A. Byriel, C. H. L. Kennard, *Acta Cryst.*, **1995**, *C51*, 2629.

95AX(C)318   R. A. Palmer, R. W. Janes, A. L. Corper, J. N. Lisgarten, H. C. Hansen, *Acta Cryst.*, **1995**, *C51*, 318.

95AX(C)333   M. K. Kokila, Puttaraja, M. V. Kulkarni, S. Thampi, *Acta Cryst.*, **1995**, *C51*, 333.

95AX(C)482   D. S. Parihar, R. Bohra, R. N. Prasad, P. N. Nagar, *Acta Cryst.*, **1995**, *C51*, 482.

95AX(C)533   N. M. Blaton, O. M. Peeters, C. J. De Ranter, *Acta Cryst.*, **1995**, *C51*, 533.

95BMC891   S. Kumar, S. S. Chimni, D. Cannoo, J. S. Arora, *Bioorg. Med. Chem.*, **1995**, *3*, 891.

95BMCL1359   S. E. de Laszlo, R. S. Chang, T.-B. Chen, K. A. Faust, W. J. Greenlee, S. D. Kivlighn, V. J. Lotti, S. S. O'Malley, T. W. Schorn,; *et al.*, *Bioorg. Med. Chem. Lett.*, **1995**, *5*, 1359.

95BMCL1527   R. Nagata, N. Ae, N. Tanno, *Bioorg. Med. Chem. Lett.*, **1995**, *5*, 1527.

95BMCL1533   R. Nagata, T. Kodo, H. Yamaguchi, N. Tanno, *Bioorg. Med. Chem. Lett.*, **1995**, *5*, 1533.

95BSB595   N. Celebi, I. Kayalidere, L. Turker, *Bull. Soc. Chim. Belg.*, **1995**, *104*, 595.

95CC1463   O. Meth-Cohn, D. L. Taylor, *J. Chem. Soc., Chem. Commun.*, **1995**, 1463.

95CC1491   S. Iwata, K. Tanaka, *J. Chem. Soc., Chem. Commun.*, **1995**, 1491.

95CC2067   T. Itoh, Y. Matsuya, K. Nagata, M. Okada, A. Ohsawa, *J. Chem. Soc., Chem. Commun.*, **1995**, 2067.

95CC2201   R. Nesi, D. Giomi, S. Turchi, A. Falai, *J. Chem. Soc., Chem. Commun.*, **1995**, 2201.

95CCC1236   M. Dolezal, J. Hartl, A. Lycka, V. Buchta, Z. Odlerova, *Collect. Czech. Chem. Commun.*, **1995**, *60*, 1236.

95CCC605   P. Bobal, R. Gazo, R. Kada, D. Ilavsky, N. Pronayova, L. Zalibera, *Collect. Czech. Chem. Commun.*, **1995**, *60*, 605.

95CCC705   S. Stankovsky, K. Spirkova, *Collect. Czech. Chem. Commun.*, **1995**, *60*, 705.

95COS337   T. L. Gilchrist, *Contemp. Org. Synth.*, **1995**, *2*, 337.

95CPB1024   K. Ohkura, K.-i. Seki, *Chem. Pharm. Bull.*, **1995**, *43*, 1024.

95CPB166   K. Terashima, H. Shimamura, A. Kawase, Y. Tanaka, K. Uenishi, I. Kimura, Y. Ishzuka, M. Sato, *Chem. Pharm. Bull.*, **1995**, *43*, 166.

95CPB2021   K. Terashima, H. Shimamura, A. Kawase, Y. Tanaka, T. Tanimura, T. Kamisaki, Y. Ishizuka, M. Sato, *Chem. Pharm. Bull.*, **1995**, *43*, 2021.

95CPB679   K.-i. Iwamoto, S. Suzuki, E. Oishi, K.-i. Tanji, A. Miyashita, T. Higashino, *Chem. Pharm. Bull.*, **1995**, *43*, 679.

95CPB683   A. Sano, M. Ishihara, J. Yoshihara, M. Sumino, H. Nawa, *Chem. Pharm. Bull.*, **1995**, *43*, 683.

95CPB705   A. Ohta, F. Okazaki, Y. Yamanoi, M. Maeda, Y. Aoyagi, T. Kurihara, G.-L. Pang, *Chem. Pharm. Bull.*, **1995**, *43*, 705.

95CPB820   H. Kotake, T. Okauchi, A. Iijima, K. Yoshimatsu, H. Nomura, *Chem. Pharm. Bull.*, **1995**, *43*, 820.

95CPJ123   S. A. H. El-Feky, *Chin. Pharm. J. (Taipei)*, **1995**, *47*, 123.

95CRT817   V. S. Sambyal, K. N. Goswami, R. K. Khajuria, *Cryst. Res. Technol.*, **1995**, *30*, 817.

95EJC269   Y. M. Issa, A. L. El-Ansary, N. A. Darwish, H. B. Hassib, *Egypt. J. Chem.*, **1995**, *36*, 269.

95EJM255s W. T. Ashton, L. L. Chang, K. L. Flanagan, N. B. Mantlo, D. L. Ondeyka, D. Kim, S. E. de Laszlo, T. W. Glinka, R. A. Rivero, *et al.*, *Eur. J. Med. Chem.*, **1995**, *30*, 255s.

95EJM27 M. Di Braccio, G. Roma, G. Leoncini, *Eur. J. Med. Chem.*, **1995**, *30*, 27.

95EJM365 E. Nicolaie, G. Cure, J. Goyard, M. Kirchner, J. M. Teulon, A. Versigny, M. Cazes, A. Virone-Oddos, F. Caussade, A. Cloarec, *Eur. J. Med. Chem.*, **1995**, *30*, 365.

95EJM423 K. A. Ismail, A. A. El-Tombary, A. M. M. E. Omar, O. M. Abouwafa, N. I. Madi, *Eur. J. Med. Chem.*, **1995**, *30*, 423.

95EJM71 S. Corsano, R. Scapicchi, G. Strappeghetti, G. Marucci, F. Paparelli, *Eur. J. Med. Chem.*, **1995**, *30*, 71.

95F131 J. Cieplik, Z. Machon, M. Zimecki, Z. Wieczorek, *Farmaco*, **1995**, *50*, 131.

95F183 E. Wagner, K. Poreba, I. Jackowicz, D. Balicka, M. Rutkowska, L. Kedzierska-Gozdzik, A. Szelag, *Farmaco*, **1995**, *50*, 183.

95F349 E. Luraschi, F. Arena, A. Sacchi, S. Laneri, E. Abignente, M. D'Amico, L. Berrino, F. Rossi, *Farmaco*, **1995**, *50*, 349.

95F37 H. Sladowska, J. Potoczek, M. Sieklucka-Dziuba, G. Rajtar, M. Mlynarczyk, Z. Kleinrok, *Farmaco*, **1995**, *50*, 37.

95F579 G. Biagi, I. Giorgi, O. Livi, V. Scartoni, *Farmaco*, **1995**, *50*, 579.

95F611 K .A. Ismail, O. M. Aboulwafa, E. Koreish, *Farmaco*, **1995**, *50*, 611.

95F69 P. L. Ferrarini, C. Mori, G. Armani, L. Rossi, *Farmaco*, **1995**, *50*, 69.

95F99 G. Biagi, I. Giorgi, O. Livi, V. Scartoni, S. Velo, C. Martini, G. Senatore, P. L. Barili, *Farmaco*, **1995**, *50*, 99.

95H(40)1055 A. Godard, F. Marsais, N. Plé, F. Trecourt, A. Turck, G. Quéguiner, *Heterocycles*, **1995**, *40*, 1055.

95H(40)441 V. L. Rusinov, O. N. Chupakhin, H. van der Plas, *Heterocycles*, **1995**, *40*, 441.

95H(40)577 E. Fasani, M. Mella, A. Albini, *Heterocycles*, **1995**, *40*, 577.

95H(40)597 A. Albini, G. Bettinetti, G. Minoli, *Heterocycles*, **1995**, *40*, 597.

95H(40)653 A. Miyashita, H. Matsuda, Y. Matsuoka, K.-i. Iwamoto, T. Higashino, *Heterocycles*, **1995**, *40*, 653.

95H(40)681 T. Kappe, W. Lube, K. Thonhofer, C. Kratky, U. G. Wagner, *Heterocycles*, **1995**, *40*, 681.

95H(40)69 M. Engelbach, P. Imming, G. Seitz, R. Tegethoff, *Heterocycles*, **1995**, *40*, 69.

95H(40)729 S. A. Petrich, Z. Qian, L. M. Santiago, J. T. Gupton, J. A. Sikorski, *Heterocycles*, **1995**, *40*, 729.

95H(40)851 Sauter, F. Fröhlich, J. Blasl, K. Gewald, K., *Heterocycles*, **1995**, *40*, 851.

95H(40)905 E. Okada, R. Masuda, M. Hojo, H. Tone, N. Gotch, T.-K. Huang, *Heterocycles*, **1995**, *40*, 905.

95H(41)1275 Y. Yamamoto, H. Ouchi, T. Tanaka, Y. Morita, *Heterocycles*, **1995**, *41*, 1275.

95H(41)1445 N. Haider, K. Mereiter, R. Wanko, *Heterocycles*, **1995**, *41*, 1445.

95H(41)1461 G. Heinisch, B. Matuszczak, K. Mereiter, J. Soder, *Heterocycles*, **1995**, *41*, 1461.

95H(41)1667 M. Takahashi, M. Hatazaki, *Heterocycles*, **1995**, *41*, 1667.

95H(41)1951 T. Okawara, S. Matsumoto, M. Eto, K. Harano, M. Furukawa, *Heterocycles*, **1995**, *41*, 1951.

95H(41)1999 H. A. Abdelhadi, T. A. Abdallah, H. M. Hassaneen, *Heterocycles*, **1995**, *41*, 1999.

95H(41)2173 P. Victory, N. Busquets, J. I. Borrell, J. Teixido, C. de Alvaro, A. Arenas, A. Alvarez-Larena, J. F. Piniella, *Heterocycles*, **1995**, *41*, 2173.

95H(41)303 L. Bonsignore, F. Cottiglia, G. Loy, D. Secci, *Heterocycles*, **1995**, *41*, 303.

95H(41)689 S. Marchalin, B. Decroix, *Heterocycles*, **1995**, *41*, 689.

95H(41)71 A. Lorente, L. Vaquerizo, A. Martin, P. Gómez-Sal, *Heterocycles*, **1995**, *41*, 71.

95H(41)765   A. R. Katritzky, B. Yang, J. Jiang, P. J. Steel, *Heterocycles*, **1995**, *41*, 765.

95HC177   A. Sugimoto, H. Jin, K. Uehara, T. Adachi, H. Inoue, *Heterocycl. Commun.*, **1995**, *1*, 177.

95HC181   A. S. Bourlot, J. Y. Merour, *Heterocycl. Commun.*, **1995**, *1*, 181.

95HC225   M. Bajic, D. W. Boykin, *Heterocycl. Commun.*, **1995**, *1*, 225.

95HC281   Z. E. Kandeel, A. M. Farag, F. M. Abdelrazek, *Heteroat. Chem.*, **1995**, *6*, 281.

95HC451   N. Kuboyama, A. Sakurai, Y. Hashimoto, Y. Okumura, *Heterocycl. Commun.*, **1995**, *1*, 451.

95IC5205   F. Bodar-Houillon, T. Humbert, A. Marsura, J.-B. R. de Vains, O. Dusausoy, N. Bouhmaida, N. E. Ghermani, Y. Dusausoy, *Inorg. Chem.*, **1995**, *34*, 5205.

95IJC(B)112   S. Ray, S. K. Pal, C. K. Saha, *Indian J. Chem.*, **1995**, *34B*, 112.

95IJC(B)191   M. M. Ali, M. A. Zahran, Y. A. Ammar, Y. A. Mohamed, A. T. Seleim, *Indian J. Heterocycl. Chem.*, **1995**, *4*, 191.

95IJC(B)201   B. R. Shah, J. J. Bhatt, H. H. Patel, N. K. Undavia, P. B. Trivedi, N. C. Desai, *Indian J. Chem.*, **1995**, *34B*, 201.

95IJC(B)209   R. P. Srivastava, V. V. Kumar, S. Bhatia, S. Sharma, *Indian J. Chem.*, **1995**, *34B*, 209.

95IJC(B)342   G. Subbaraju, K. S. Rao, G. S. Reddy, Z. Urbanczyk-Lipkowska, *Indian J. Chem.*, **1995**, *34B*, 342.

95IJC(B)500   L. D. S. Yadav, S. Saigal, *Indian J. Chem.*, **1995**, *34B*, 500.

95IJC(B)51   V. K. Ahluwalia, V. K. Garg, A. Dahiya, M. D. Alauddin, *Indian J. Chem.*, **1995**, *34B*, 51.

95IJC(B)537   A. A. F. Wasfy, F. A. Yassin, A. M. F. Eissa, *Indian J. Chem.*, **1995**, *34B*, 537.

95IJC(B)573   M. Subrahmanyam, A. R. Prasad, S. J. Kulkarni, A. V. R. Rao, *Indian J. Chem.*, **1995**, *34B*, 573.

95IJC(B)617   U. S. Pathak, I. S. Rathod, M. B. Patel, V. S. Shirsath, K. S. Jain, *Indian J. Chem.*, **1995**, *34B*, 617.

95IJC(B)778   B. Venugopalan, E. Pinto de Souza, K. M. Sathe, D. K. Chatterjee, N. Iyer, *Indian J. Chem.*, **1995**, *34B*, 778.

95JA10203   S. W. Bailey, I. Rebrin, S. R. Boerth, J. E. Ayling, *J. Am. Chem. Soc.*, **1995**, *117*, 10203.

95JA3665   X. Ariza, V. Bou, J. Vilarrasa, *J. Am. Chem. Soc.*, **1995**, *117*, 3665.

95JCC83   A. O. Abdelhamid, A. A. Al-Hamidi, *J. Chin. Chem. Soc. (Taipei)*, **1995**, *42*, 83.

95JCR290   Z. E.-S. Kandeel, *J. Chem. Res., Synop.*, **1995**, 290.

95JCR298   S. A. El-Abbady, A. H. Moustafa, *J. Chem. Res., Synop.*, **1995**, 298.

95JCR306   P. Powell, M. H. Sosabowski, *J. Chem. Res., Synop.*, **1995**, 306.

95JCR314   K. A. M. El-Bayouki, W. M. Basyouni, H. Hosni, A. S. El-Deen, *J. Chem. Res., Synop.*, **1995**, 314.

95JCR324   Y. A. Ammar, A. M. Sh. Ei-Sharief, M. A. Zahran, M. Z. El-Said, U. H. El-Said, *J. Chem. Res., Synop.*, **1995**, 324.

95JCR402   M. Sosabowski, P. Powell, *J. Chem. Res., Synop.*, **1995**, 402.

95JCR56   P. Barraclough, S. Smith, *J. Chem. Res., Synop.*, **1995**, 56.

95JCS(P1)1445   K. Ikuno, T. Kobayashi, T. Harada, M. Noguchi, A. Kakehi, *J. Chem. Soc., Perkin Trans. 1*, **1995**, 1445.

95JCS(P1)1453   T. Kobayashi, K. Ikuno, M. Noguchi, A. Kakehi, *J. Chem. Soc., Perkin Trans. 1*, **1995**, 1453.

95JCS(P1)2595   D. Cartwright, J. R. Ferguson, T. Giannopoulos, G. Varvounis, B. J. Wakefield, *J. Chem. Soc., Perkin Trans. 1*, **1995**, 2595.

95JCS(P1)369   M. A. Saleh, F. Compernolle, S. Toppet, G. J. Hoornaert, *J. Chem. Soc., Perkin Trans. 1*, **1995**, 369.

95JCS(P1)733   T. Maruyama, K. Fujiwara, M. Fukuhara, *J. Chem. Soc., Perkin Trans. 1*, **1995**, 733.

95JCS(P2)1699 K. Akutsu, H. Nakajima, T. Katoh, S. Kino, K. Fujimori, *J. Chem. Soc., Perkin Trans.* 2, **1995**, 1699.
95JFC113   G. J. Chen, L. S. Chen, *J. Fluorine Chem.*, **1995**, *73*, 113.
95JHC1003   E.-S. Badawey, T. Kappe, *J. Heterocycl. Chem.*, **1995**, *32*, 1003.
95JHC1057   F. Trecourt, A. Turck, N. Plé, A. Paris, G. Quéguiner, *J. Heterocycl. Chem.*, **1995**, *32*, 1057.
95JHC1085   Y. Kurasawa, A. Takada, H. S. Kim, *J. Heterocycl. Chem.*, **1995**, *32*, 1085.
95JHC1181   S. Franco, E. Melendez, F. L. Merchan, *J. Heterocycl. Chem.*, **1995**, *32*, 1181.
95JHC1197   P. C. Unangst, D. T. Connor, C. R. Kostlan, G. P. Shrum, S. R. Miller, G. Kanter, *J. Heterocycl. Chem.*, **1995**, *32*, 1197.
95JHC1213   A. Monge, J. A. Palop, M. Gonzalez, F. J. Martinez-Crespo, A. Lopez de Cerain, Y. Sainz, S. Narro; A. J. Barker, E. Hamilton, *J. Heterocycl. Chem.*, **1995**, *32*, 1213.
95JHC13   G. Heinisch, B. Matuszczak, G. Puerstinger, D. Rakowitz, *J. Heterocycl. Chem.*, **1995**, *32*, 13.
95JHC1317   Y. Blache, A. Gueiffier, A. Elhakmaoui, H. Viols, J.-P. Chapat, O. Chavignon, J.-C. Teulade, G. Grassy, G. Dauphin, A. Carpy, *J. Heterocycl. Chem.*, **1995**, *32*, 1317.
95JHC211   K. Eger, M. Jalalian, M. Schmidt, J. Heterocycl. Chem., **1995**, 32, 211.
95JHC265   R. M. Fikry, *Indian J. Heterocycl. Chem.*, **1995**, *4*, 265.
95JHC283   K. Joutsiniemi, M. Ahlgren, P. Vainiotalo, O. Morgenstern, M. Meusel, *J. Heterocycl. Chem.*, **1995**, *32*, 283.
95JHC335   A. Rosowsky, C. E. Mota, S. F. Queener, *J. Heterocycl. Chem.*, **1995**, *32*, 335.
95JHC347   T. Seki, H. Sakata, Y. Iwanami, *J. Heterocycl. Chem.*, **1995**, *32*, 347.
95JHC353   A. U. Siddiqui, V. U. M. Rao, M. Maimirani, A. H. Siddiqui, J. Heterocycl. Chem., **1995**, 32, 353.
95JHC547   A. F. Lewis, G. R. Revankar, S. M. Fennewald, J. H. Huffman, R. F. Rando, *J. Heterocycl. Chem.*, **1995**, *32*, 547.
95JHC57   H. G. Bonacorso, K.-E. Mack, F. Effenberger, *J. Heterocycl. Chem.*, **1995**, *32*, 57.
95JHC643   J. M. Ruxer, J. Mauger, D. Benard, C. Lachoux, *J. Heterocycl. Chem.*, **1995**, *32*, 643.
95JHC671   Y. Kurasawa, R. Miyashita, A. Takada, H. S. Kim, Y. Okamoto, *J. Heterocycl. Chem.*, **1995**, *32*, 671.
95JHC703   T. Seki, H. Sakata, Y. Iwanami, *J. Heterocycl. Chem.*, **1995**, *32*, 703.
95JHC761   R. A. Conley, D. L. Barton, S. M. Stefanick, M. M. Lam, G. C. Lindabery, C. F. Kasulanis, S. Cesco-Cancian, S. Currey, A. C. Fabian, S. D. Levine, *J. Heterocycl. Chem.*, **1995**, *32*, 761.
95JHC79   G. Cignarella, D. Barlocco, *J. Heterocycl. Chem.*, **1995**, *32*, 79.
95JHC841   A. Turck, N. Plé, L. Mojovic, B. Ndzi, G. Quéguiner, N. Haider, H. Schuller, G. Heinisch, *J. Heterocycl. Chem.*,**1995**, *32*, 841.
95JHC857   F. J. Urban, *J. Heterocycl. Chem.*, **1995**, *32*, 857.
95JIC641   F. M. A. El-Latif, M. A. Barsi, A. S. Maghraby, M. Z. A. Badr, D. Doepp, *J. Indian Chem. Soc.*, **1995**, *72*, 641.
95JMC1330   D. Catarzi, L. Cecchi, V. Colotta, G. Filacchioni, C. Martini, P. Tacchi, A. Lucacchini, *J. Med. Chem.*, **1995**, *38*, 1330.
95JMC1778   A. Gangjee, A. Vasudevan, S. F. Queener, R. L. Kisliuk, *J. Med. Chem.*, **1995**, *38*, 1778.
95JMC2158   A. Gangjee, F. Mavandadi, S. F. Queener, J. J. McGuire, *J. Med. Chem.*, **1995**, *38*, 2158.
95JMC2615   A. Rosowsky, R. A. Forsch, S. F. Queener, *J. Med. Chem.*, **1995**, *38*, 2615.
95JMC2925   J. S. H. Nicholas, R. Giorgi, F. Bonaccorsi, G. Cerbai, S. M. Colombani, A. R. Renzetti, R. Cirillo, A. Subissi, G. Alagona, *et al.*, *J. Med. Chem.*, **1995**, *38*, 2925.

95JMC3482　　G. W. Rewcastle, W. A. Denny, A. J. Bridges, H. Zhou, D. R. Cody, A. McMichael, D. W. Fry, *J. Med. Chem.*, **1995**, *38*, 3482.

95JMC3676　　J. L. Kelley, J. A. Linn, D. D. Bankston, C. J. Burchall, F. E. Soroko, B. R. Cooper, *J. Med. Chem.*, **1995**, *38*, 3676.

95JMC3720　　C. F. Bigge, T. C. Malone, P. A. Boxer, C. B. Nelson, D. F. Ortwine, R. M. Schelkun, D. M. Retz, L. J. Lescosky, S. A. Borosky, *et al.*, *J. Med. Chem.*, **1995**, *38*, 3720.

95JMC3780　　A. M. Thompson, A. J. Bridges, D. W. Fry, A. J. Kraker, W. A. Denny, *J. Med. Chem.*, **1995**, *38*, 3780.

95JMC3798　　A. Gangjee, R. Devraj, J. J. McGuire, R. L. Kisliuk, *J. Med. Chem.*, **1995**, *38*, 3798.

95JMC3874　　S. Kneubuehler, U. Thull, C. Altomare, V. Carta, P. Gaillard, P.-A. Carrupt, A. Carotti, B. Testa, *J. Med. Chem.*, **1995**, *38*, 3874.

95JMC3902　　M. H. Cynamon, R. Gimi, F. Gyenes, C. A. Sharpe, K. E. Bergmann, H. J. Han, L. B. Gregor, R. Rapolu, G. Luciano, J. T. Welch, *J. Med. Chem.*, **1995**, *38*, 3902.

95JMC4488　　A. Monge, F. J. Martinez-Crespo, A. Lopez de Cerain, J. A. Palop, S. Narro, V. Senador, A. Marin, Y. Sainz, M. Gonzalez, *et al.*, *J. Med. Chem.*, **1995**, *38*, 4488.

95JMC4806　　A. Salimbeni, R. Canevotti, F. Paleari, D. Poma, S. Caliari, F. Fici, R. Cirillo, A. R. Renzetti, A. Subissi, *et al.*, *J. Med. Chem.*, **1995**, *38*, 4806.

95JMC526　　C. A. Gandolfi, G. Beggiolin, E. Menta, M. Palumbo, C. Sissi, S. Spinelli, F. Johnson, *J. Med. Chem.*, **1995**, *38*, 526.

95JMC587　　C. Subramanyam, B. Ault, D. Sawutz, E. R. Bacon, B. Singh, P. O. Pennock, M. D. Kelly, M. Kraynak, D. Krafte, A. Treasurywala, *J. Med. Chem.*, **1995**, *38*, 587.

95JMC745　　A. Rosowsky, C. E. Mota, S. F. Queener, M. Waltham, E. Ercikan-Abali, J. R. Bertino, *J. Med. Chem.*, **1995**, *38*, 745.

95JMC994　　P. R. Marsham, A. L. Jackman, A. J. Barker, F. T. Boyle, S. J. Pegg, J. M. Wardleworth, R. Kimbell, B. M. O'Connor, A. H. Calvert, L. R. Hughes, *J. Med. Chem.*, **1995**, *38*, 994.

95JMS273　　E. Kleinpeter, St. Thomas, G. Fischer, *J. Mol. Struct.*, **1995**, *355*, 273.

95JOC1461　　P. G. Baraldi, B. Cacciari, S. Manfredini, G. P. Pollini, D. Simoni, G. Spalluto, V. Zanirato, *J. Org. Chem.*, **1995**, *60*, 1461.

95JOC1583　　J. Ohkanda, A. Katoh, *J. Org. Chem.*, **1995**, *60*, 1583.

95JOC1908　　H. Zimmer, A. R. Safwat, D. Ho, A. Amer, M. Badawi, *J. Org. Chem.*, **1995**, *60*, 1908.

95JOC246　　A. R. Katritzky, B. Yang, J. Jiang, P. J. Steel, *J. Org. Chem.*, **1995**, *60*, 246.

95JOC3131　　K. P. Chan, A. S. Hay, *J. Org. Chem.*, **1995**, *60*, 3131.

95JOC3781　　N. Plé, A. Turck, K. Couture, G. Quéguiner, *J. Org. Chem.*, **1995**, *60*, 3781.

95JOC3928　　D. Barrett, H. Sasaki, H. Tsutsumi, M. Murata, T. Terasawa, K. Sakane, *J. Org. Chem.*, **1995**, *60*, 3928.

95JOC5069　　E. D. Edstrom, Y. Wei, *J. Org. Chem.*, **1995**, *60*, 5069.

95JOC5250　　G. Zvilichovsky, V. Gurvich, S. Segev, *J. Org. Chem.*, **1995**, *60*, 5250.

95JOC5690　　Y. Kosugi, K. Itoho, H. Okazaki, T. Yanai, *J. Org. Chem.*, **1995**, *60*, 5690.

95JOC5838　　S. M. Kher, S. X. Cai, E. Weber, J. F. W. Keana, *J. Org. Chem.*, **1995**, *60*, 5838.

95JOC624　　D. J. Fenick, H. S. Carr, D. E. Falvey, *J. Org. Chem.*, **1995**, *60*, 624.

95JOC6684　　E. C. Taylor, H. H. Patel, J.-G. Jun, *J. Org. Chem.*, **1995**, *60*, 6684.

95JOC748　　T. L. Draper, T. R. Bailey, *J. Org. Chem.*, **1995**, *60*, 748.

95JOC7625　　A. R. Katritzky, G. Zhang, J. Jiang, P. J. Steel, *J. Org. Chem.*, **1995**, *60*, 7625.

95JOC7947　　E. C. Taylor, W. B. Young, *J. Org. Chem.*, **1995**, *60*, 7947.

95JOC8283　　J. Pohmer, M. V. Lakshmikantham, M. P. Cava, *J. Org. Chem.*, **1995**, *60*, 8283.

95JOM123　　M. Lucarini, G. F. Pedulli, *J. Organomet. Chem.*, **1995**, *494*, 123.

95JOM229   M. Akazome, J. Yamamoto, T. Kondo, Y. Watanabe, *J. Organomet. Chem.*, **1995**, *494*, 229.
95JPP167   C. Anselmino, J. Cadet, *J. Photochem. Photobiol., B*, **1995**, *27*, 167.
95JPS661   I. O. Donkor, C. L. Klein, L. Liang, N. Zhu, E. Bradley, A. M. Clark, *J. Pharm. Sci.*, **1995**, *84*, 661.
95LA1303   B. Wuensch, S. Nerdinger, G. Hoefner, *Liebigs Ann.*, **1995**, 1303.
95LA1371   A. A. El-Barbary, N. R. El-Brollosy, H. M. Abdel-Bary, E. B. Pedersen, P. Stein, C. Nielsen, *Liebigs Ann.*, **1995**, 1371.
95LA1871   M. Hasan, N. Rashid, K. M.d Khan, S. Perveen, G. Snatzke, H. Duddeck, W. Voelter, *Liebigs Ann.*, **1995**, 1871.
95LA661   L. Baumann, A. Folkerts, P. Imming, T. Klindert, W. Massa, G. Steitz, S. Wocadlo, *Liebigs Ann.*, **1995**, 661.
95LA775   S. F. Vasilevsky, E. V. Tretyakov, *Liebigs Ann.* **1995**, 775.
95M211   N. Haider, W. Staschek, *Monatsh. Chem.*, **1995**, *126*, 211.
95M789   M. Chakrabarty, A. Batabyal, M. S. Morales-Rios, P. Joseph-Nathan, *Monatsh. Chem.*, **1995**, *126*, 789.
95MC106   V. S. Bogdanov, K. L. Cherkasova, V. A. Dorokhov, O. V. Shishkin, Y. T. Struchkov, *Mendeleev Commun.*, **1995**, 106.
95MC193   A. V. Kadushkin, D. B. Nilov, D. D. Nekrasov, N. P. Solov'eva, V. G. Granik, *Mendeleev Commun.* **1995**, 193.
95MI101   T. W. Kensler, K. J. Helzlsouer, *J. Cell. Biochem. (Suppl. 22)*, **1995**, 101.
95MI1081   M. L. Gilpin, M. Fulston, D. Payne, R. Cramp, I. Hood, *J. Antibiot.*, **1995**, *48*, 1081.
95MI1083   J. Ishida, H. Arakawa, M. Takada, M. Yamaguchi, *Analyst*, **1995**, *120*, 1083.
95MI117   H. J. Prochaska, S. J. Chavan, P. Baron, B. Polsky, *J. Cell. Biochem. (Suppl. 22)*, **1995**, 117.
95MI153   P. Schadewaldt, H.-W. Hammen, U. Wendel, U. Matthiesen, *Anal. Biochem.*, **1995**, *229*, 153.
95MI167   M. A. Naylor, *Contrib. Oncol.*, **1995**, *49*, 167.
95MI221   P. Periti, *J. Chemother. (Florence)*, **1995**, *7*, 221.
95MI259   M. A. Naylor, G. E. Adams, A. Haigh, S. Cole, T. Jenner, N. Robertson, D. Siemann, M. A. Stephens, I. J. Stratford, *Anti-Cancer Drugs*, **1995**, *6*, 259.
95MI397   M. S. P. Sarma, P. Wilson, B. A. Otter, R. S. Klein, *Nucleosides Nucleotides*, **1995**, *14*, 397.
95MI45   B. K. Bhattacharya, M. V. Chari, R. H. Durland, G. R. Revankar, *Nucleosides Nucleotides*, **1995**, *14*, 45.
95MI551   A. Gueiffier, Y. Blache, J. P. Chapat, A. Elhakmaoui, E. M. Essassi, G. Andrei, R. Snoeck, E. De Clercq, O. Chavignon, *et al.*, *Nucleosides Nucleotides*, **1995**, *14*, 551.
95MI6705   K. P. Chan, Y.-F. Wang, A. S. Hay, X. L. Hronowski, R. J. Cotter, *Macromolecules*, **1995**, *28*, 6705.
95NPR465   J. P. Michael, *Nat. Prod. Rep.*, **1995**, *12*, 465.
95NPR77   J. P. Michael, *Nat. Prod. Rep.*, **1995**, *12*, 77.
95P361   S. El-Gengaihi, M. S. Karawya, M. A. Selim, H. M. Motawe, N. Ibrahim, L. M. Faddah, *Pharmazie*, **1995**, *50*, 361.
95P565   C. Orlewska, H. Foks, M. Janowiec, Z. Zwolska-Kwiek, *Pharmazie*, **1995**, *50*, 565.
95PAC691   J. S. Bradshaw, P. Huszthy, J. T. Redd, X. X. Zhang, T. Wang, J. K. Hathaway, J. Young, R. M. Izatt, *Pure Appl. Chem.*, **1995**, *67*, 691.
95PC169   H. Taguchi, T. Yokoi, Y. Okada, *Pept. Chem.*, **1995**, *32*, 169.
95PJC1018   M. G. Assy, A. A. Hataba, H. Y. Moustafa, *Pol. J. Chem.*, **1995**, *69*, 1018.
95PJC235   H. J. Barton, M. Paluchowska, J. Bajorski, B. Rys, *Pol. J. Chem.*, **1995**, *69*, 235.
95PJC33   S. A. El-Abbady, M. K. Awad, *Pol. J. Chem.*, **1995**, *69*, 33.

95PJC583   M. Anwar. Abdo, M. Farghaly Abdel-Megeed, M. Atia. Saleh, G. Abdel-Rahman. El-Hiti, *Pol. J. Chem.*, **1995**, *69*, 583.
95PJC61   Z. K. Abd El-Samii, S. A. El-Feky, M. I. Jaeda, M. A. A. Moustafa, *Pol. J. Chem.*, **1995**, *69*, 61.
95PJC685   M. G. Assy, E. Abd El-Ghani, *Pol. J. Chem.*, **1995**, *69*, 685.
95PJC70   E. Wagner, L. Becan, *Pol. J. Chem.*, **1995**, *69*, 70.
95PJC873   M. G. Assy, A. M. Amer, *Pol. J. Chem.*, **1995**, *69*, 873.
95PJC887   M. G. Assy, A. El-Kafrawy, M. M. Hassanien, *Pol. J. Chem.*, **1995**, *69*, 887.
95PJC892   M. G. Assy, N. H. Ouf, R. M. Fikry, *Pol. J. Chem.*, **1995**, *69*, 892.
95PNA1127   E. D. Cohen, R. F. Miller, *Proc. Natl. Acad. Sci. USA*, **1995**, *92*, 1127.
95PS143   E. A. Bakhite, A. A. Geies, A. M. Kamal El-Dean, H. S. El-Kashef, *Phosphorus, Sulfur Silicon Relat. Elem.*, **1995**, *104*, 143.
95PS179   H. F. Zohdi, R. M. Mohareb, W. W. Wardakhan, *Phosphorus, Sulfur Silicon Relat. Elem.*, **1995**, *101*, 179.
95PS57   R. M. Mohareb, S. M. Sherif, A. M. Samy, *Phosphorus, Sulfur Silicon Relat. Elem.*, **1995**, *101*, 57.
95RRC165   M. A. Abdel-Rahman, A. El-Badieh, A. G. Ghattas, G. A. El-Saraf, A. K. H. Mahmoud, *Rev. Roum. Chim.*, **1995**, *40*, 165.
95S518   K. Ikuno, T. Kobayashi, U. Chin, M. Noguchi, *Synthesis*, **1995**, 518.
95S920   M. Guillaume, Z. Janousek, H. G. Viehe, *Synthesis*, **1995**, 920.
95SC1119   H. Abdel-Ghany, A. M. El-Sayed, A. K. El-Shafei, *Synth. Commun.*, **1995**, *25*, 1119.
95SC2165   M. J. Beach, R. Hope, D. H. Klaubert, R. K. Russell, *Synth. Commun.*, **1995**, *25*, 2165.
95SC2223   S. Himdi-Kabab, K. Lavrador, J. P. Bazureau, J. Hamelin, *Synth. Commun.*, **1995**, *25*, 2223.
95SC2319   D. Villemin, B. Martin, *Synth. Commun.*, **1995**, *25*, 2319.
95SC3089   B. Tamami, M. M. Lakouraj, *Synth. Commun.*, **1995**, *25*, 3089.
95SC3271   X. Zhao, R. Zhang, *Synth. Commun.*, **1995**, *25*, 3271.
95SC569   B. Ojo, B. K. Chowdhury, *Synth. Commun.*, **1995**, *25*, 569.
95SL186   Y. Kinoshita, H. Watanabe, T. Kitahara, K. Mori, *Synlett*, **1995**, 186.
95SL349   D. H. Lee, Y. H. Kim, *Synlett*, **1995**, 349.
95T10253   P. Victory, J. Cirujeda, A. Vidal-Ferran, *Tetrahedron*, **1995**, *51*, 10253.
95T10361   M. Martín-Martínez, M. T. García-López, R. Herranz, R. Gónzalez-Muñiz, *Tetrahedron*, **1995**, *51*, 10361.
95T11855   G. Grassi, F. Risitano, F. Foti, *Tetrahedron*, **1995**, *51*, 11855.
95T13045   A. Turck, N. Plé, V. Tallon, G. Quéguiner, *Tetrahedron*, **1995**, *51*, 13045.
95T3221   P. de Tullio, B. Pirotte, L. Dupont, B. Masereel, D. Laeckmann, T. Podona, O. Diouf, P. Lebrun, J. Delarge, *Tetrahedron*, **1995**, *51*, 3221.
95T5901   J. Ma. Quintela, C. Peinador, M. J. Moreira, *Tetrahedron*, **1995**, *51*, 5901.
95T7361   H. Taguchi, T. Yokoi, M. Tsukatani, Y. Okada, *Tetrahedron*, **1995**, *51*, 7361.
95T9031   R. Gertzmann, R. Fröhlich, M. Grehl, E.-U. Würthwein, *Tetrahedron*, **1995**, *51*, 9031.
95TAS321   F. J. Urban, R. Breitenbach, C. W. Murtiashaw, B. C. Vanderplas, *Tetrahedron: Asymmetry*, **1995**, *6*, 321.
95TL2017   J. Tulinsky, S. A. Mizsak, W. Watt, L. A. Dolak, T. Judge, R. B. Gammill, *Tetrahedron Lett.*, **1995**, *36*, 2017.
95TL3241   R. S. Atkinson, J. Fawcett, D. R. Russell, P. J. Williams, *Tetrahedron Lett.*, **1995**, *36*, 3241.
95TL563   M. Kuroboshi, K. Mizuno, K. Kanie, T. Hiyama, *Tetrahedron Lett.*, **1995**, *36*, 563.
95TL5703   M. S. South, T. L. Jakuboski, *Tetrahedron Lett.*, **1995**, *36*, 5703.
95TL6777   N. E. Alexandrou, G. E. Mertzanos, J. Stephanidou-Stephanatou, C. A. Tsoleridis, P. Zachariou, *Tetrahedron Lett.*, **1995**, *36*, 6777.

Chapter 6.3

Six-Membered Ring Systems: Triazines, Tetrazines and Fused Ring Polyaza Systems

Derek T. Hurst
Kingston University, Kingston upon Thames, UK

6.3.1 INTRODUCTION

The polyaza ring systems continue to attract a considerable amount of attention in the literature and, once again, a large number of references has been collected during 1995. Almost all aspects of study seem to have received at least some coverage during the year and the intention of this chapter is to review some of the more important and more interesting topics which have appeared. More extensive reviews of ring fused 1,2,4-triazines have been published recently [94AHC(59)41; 94AHC(61)207]. A review of the use of organometallic reagents in coupling reactions of π-deficient azaheterocycles has also appeared [95AHC(62)306].

6.3.2 SYNTHESIS

6.3.2.1 Triazines

A new, simple, synthesis of 2,4-diaryl-1,3,5-triazines is shown in Scheme 1. It arose from an attempt to obtain the pyrano[4,3-*d*]pyrimidine system by reacting aryl amidines with the 3-methoxymethylenedihydropyran-2,4-dione (1; X = CH₂). As well as the desired products, diaryl-1,2,3-triazines were obtained in 30-40% yield. The use of 5-methoxymethylene-2,2-dimethyl-1,3-dioxan-4,6-dione (1; X = O)(derived from Meldrum's acid) gives the triazines in better yield (> 50%). It was also observed that 3-methoxymethylenefuran-2,4-dione reacted with *S*-methylisothiouronium bromide to yield 2,4-bismethylthio-1,3,5-triazine [95M99].

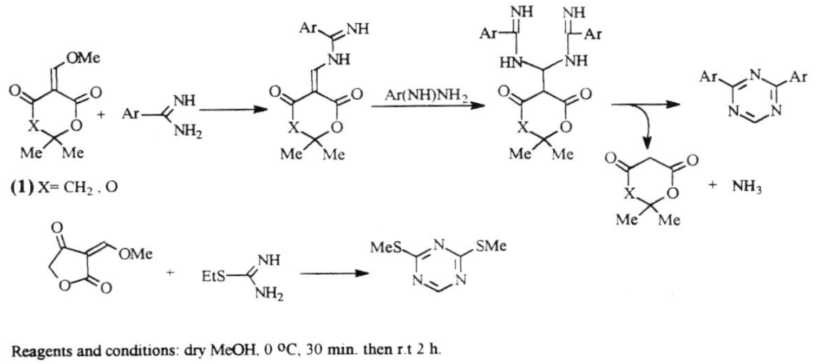

Reagents and conditions: dry MeOH, 0 °C, 30 min. then r.t 2 h.

Scheme 1

255

An unexpected formation of 2,4-disubstituted-1,3,5-triazines (3) occurs when 3-dimethoxy-methyl-2-(*N*-cyanamino)thiazolidine (2) reacts with secondary amines. When the reaction is carried out in the presence of methanol or ethanol, or with a mixture of amines, a mixture of substituted products is obtained. The proposed mechanism for the reaction is shown in Scheme 2 [94CC2301].

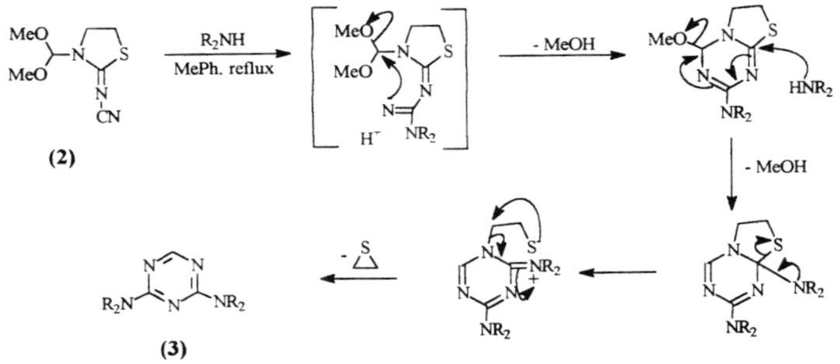

Scheme 2

3-Hydrazono-1,1,1-trifluoroalkan-2-ones (4) react with aldehydes in the presence of aqueous ammonia to yield 5-trifluoromethyl-2,3-dihydro-1,2,4-triazines which can be oxidised to give 5-trifluoromethyl-1,2,4-triazines (5) or 5-trifluoromethyl-2,5-dihydro-5-hydroxy-1,2,4-triazines (6) [94H(39)155], whilst hydrazines react with α-lactams to give 1,2,4-triazine-3,6-diones [95JOC4121; 95JOC5992] (Scheme 3).

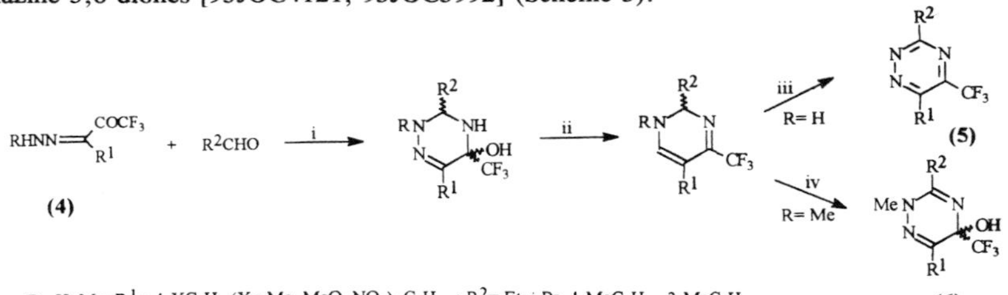

R= H. Me: R^1= 4-XC$_6$H$_4$ (X= Me. MeO. NO$_2$). C$_6$H$_{13}$; R^2= Et. *i*-Pr. 4-MeC$_6$H$_4$, 2-MeC$_6$H$_4$

Reagents and conditions: i; aq. NH$_4$OH, r.t., 1 d. ii; 1M HCl. or SiO$_2$ column. iii; DDQ, MeCN. r.t., 1 h. iv; H$_2$O$_2$, FeCl$_2$. MeCN. r.t., 2 d.

Scheme 3

1,5-Dichloro-(substituted)-2-azoniaallene salts (7) react as bifunctional nucleophiles with amines or hydrazones to yield 1,3,5-triazinium salts (8)[95JPR274].

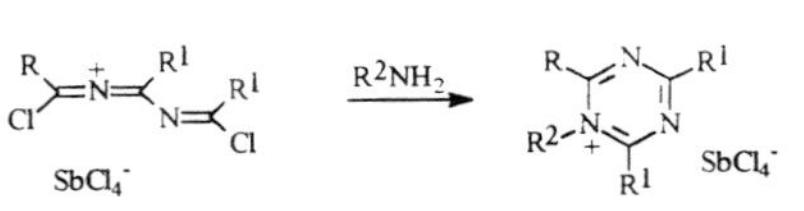

Some pyrrolo[2,1-*f*][1,2,4]triazines which are analogues of purines have been obtained from 1-aminopyrrole-2-carbonitrile (or carboxamide) (Scheme 4)[94JHC781].

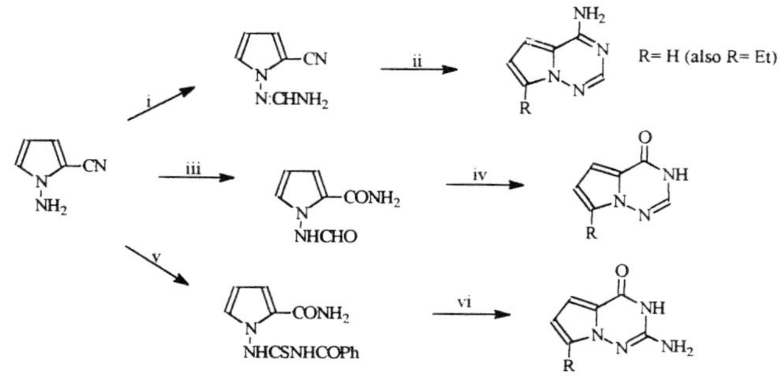

Reagents and conditions: i; $H_2NCH:NH$, AcOH, EtOH, reflux. ii; K_2CO_3, H_2O, 25 ºC. iii; KOH, H_2O, 25 ºC, then HCO_2H.
iv; NaOMe, MeOH, reflux. v: KOH, H_2O, 25 ºC then PhCONCS. Me_2CO.
vi; K_2CO_3, H_2O, Me_2CO, MeOH, reflux, then 1M NaOH, $Cu(OAc)_2$, reflux.

Scheme 4

A pyrimidine to triazine rearrangement has been observed and now a likely route has been suggested which is that shown in Scheme 5 [92CHE804; 95JHC697].

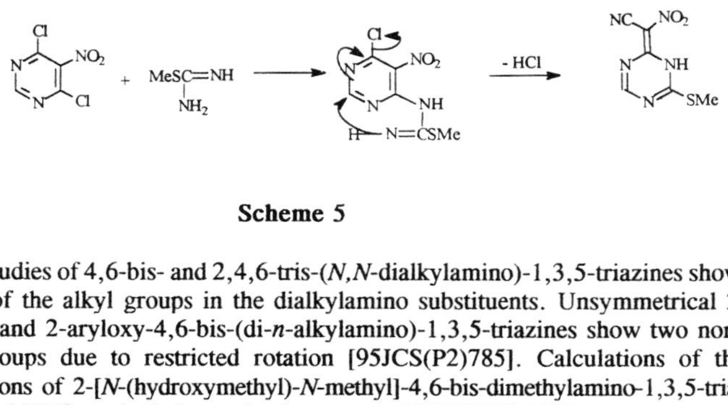

Scheme 5

NMR studies of 4,6-bis- and 2,4,6-tris-(N,N-dialkylamino)-1,3,5-triazines show correlated rotations of the alkyl groups in the dialkylamino substituents. Unsymmetrical 2-chloro-, 2-alkoxy- and 2-aryloxy-4,6-bis-(di-*n*-alkylamino)-1,3,5-triazines show two non-equivalent *n*-alkyl groups due to restricted rotation [95JCS(P2)785]. Calculations of the favoured conformations of 2-[*N*-(hydroxymethyl)-*N*-methyl]-4,6-bis-dimethylamino-1,3,5-triazine using MNDO and PM3 methods have also been made [95JCS(P2)469].

A new and unexpected synthesis of the 1,3,4,5-thiatriazine ring system is given by the treatment of substituted 1,2,3-thiatriazolium-1-imides with dry hydrogen sulfide. The mechanism suggested for this transformation is shown in Scheme 6 [94JCR(S)350].

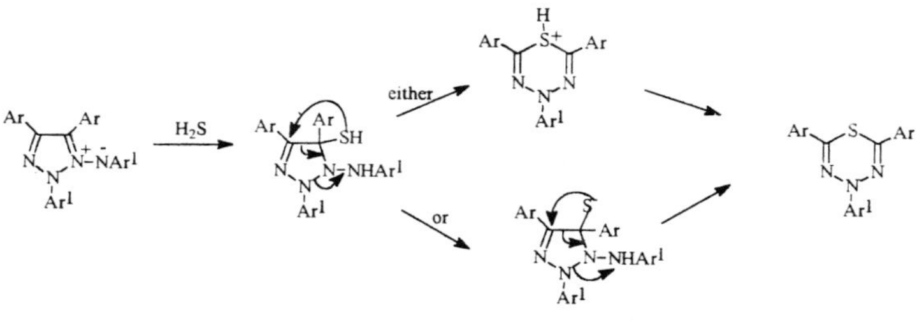

Conditions: dry H_2S , CH_2Cl_2 , 15 min. r.t.

Scheme 6

6.3.2.2 Tetrazines

A simple route to unsymmetrically substituted 1,2,4,5-tetrazines is the reaction of triethyl orthoformate (or acetate), or DMFDMA, with S-methylisothiocarbonohydrazide salt (**9**) in the presence of triethylamine and air. The use of iminium chlorides (**10**) gives similar products. The methylthio group can be readily displaced by nucleophiles to give other substituted tetrazines [94JOC8284].

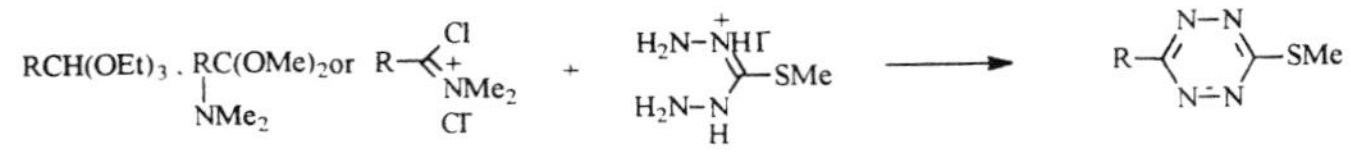

(**10**) R= alkyl   (**9**)

Another reaction to yield unsymmetrically substituted 1,2,4,5-tetrazines is that of sodium ethoxide in ethanol with S-(1-aryl-1H-tetrazol-5-yl) N-(p-nitrophenyl)benzothiohydrazonates (**11**). The mechanism of the reaction is complex and seems to involve a competitive Smiles rearrangement, fragmentation and dimerisation (Scheme 7) [95JCR(S)224].

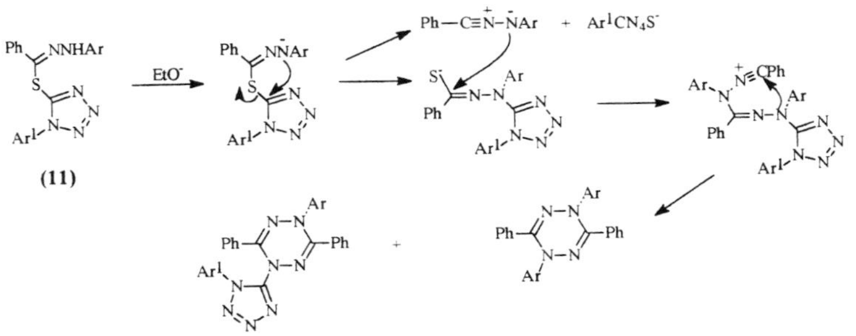

(**11**)

Scheme 7

A new and convenient synthesis of 3-(substituted)-2,4,6-triphenylverdazyls involves crown ether assisted solid-liquid phase transfer catalysis of reactions of triphenylformazans with alkyl bromides (or 1-alkylbenzotriazoles) also using barium hydroxide hydrate catalysis (Scheme 8) [94CJC1849].

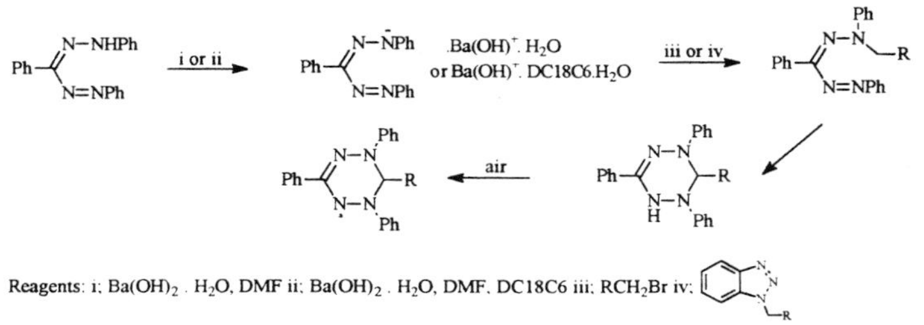
i or ii
Ba(OH)⁺. H₂O
or Ba(OH)⁺. DC18C6.H₂O
iii or iv
air
Reagents: i; Ba(OH)₂ . H₂O, DMF ii; Ba(OH)₂ . H₂O, DMF, DC18C6 iii; RCH₂Br iv;

Scheme 8

The bistetrazine (**13**) is produced when the bishydrazide (**12**), formed from benzoylhydrazine and dimethyl oxalate is heated with phosphorus pentachloride, the product then being refluxed with hydrazine in ethanol. Aromatisation is completed by treatment with nitrous acid. The bistetrazine acts as a reactive diazadiene in [4+2] cycloaddition reactions [94TL7935].

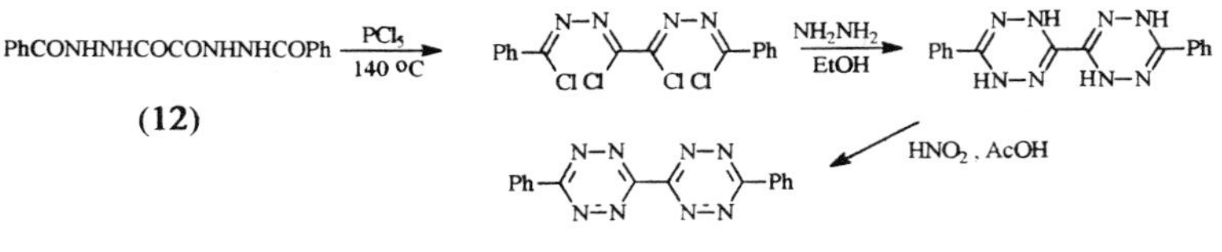
PhCONHNHCOCONHNHCOPh
PCl₅
140 °C
NH₂NH₂
EtOH
HNO₂ . AcOH

(12)

(13)

Fused ring tetrazines are easily obtained by electrophilic amination of *N*-heterocycles having good leaving groups in the adjacent position followed by treatment with base (Scheme 9) [94LA1049].

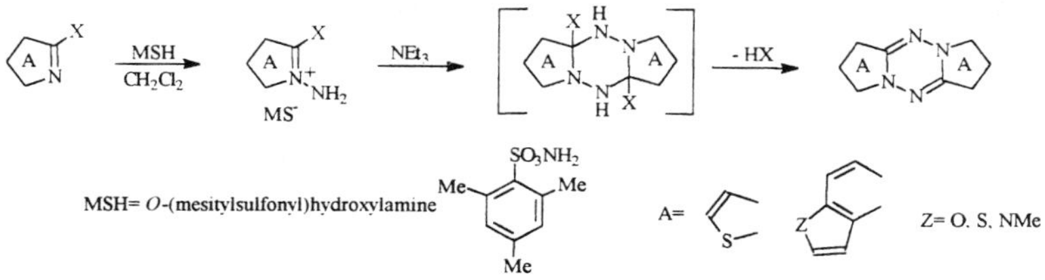
MSH
CH₂Cl₂
NEt₃
- HX
MSH= O-(mesitylsulfonyl)hydroxylamine
A=
Z= O, S, NMe

Scheme 9

6.3.2.3 Purines and purine analogues

A new synthesis of purines is illustrated by the reaction of 1,3-dimethyl-6-aminouracil with *N,N*-dimethyldichloromethyleneiminium chloride (phosgeneiminium chloride), trimethylsilyl azide and arylamines in dry chloroform, followed by treatment with 20% aqueous potassium hydrogen carbonate. The reaction probably proceeds *via* a 4-amino-5-(chloroformamidin-1'-yl)uracil (Scheme 10) [94JHC1185].

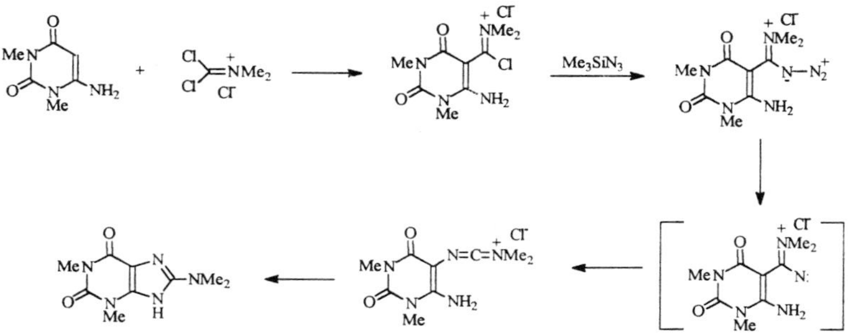

Scheme 10

Another new synthesis of purines resulting in 7-substituted purines starts from 4-nitroimidazoles and their elaboration to yield the intermediates (14) which cyclise to yield the products (15) with ammoniacal ethanol [95SL253].

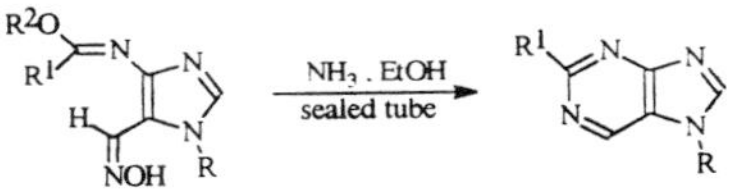

(14) R= Me. Et: R^1= H. Me. PhCH$_2$. *n*-Bu: (15)
    R^2= Me. Et

Amidines have been shown to react with 2-amino-3-cyanofurans (16) to yield, not the expected furo[2,3-*d*]pyrimidines, but pyrrolo[2,3-*d*]pyrimidines (17). Ethyl 4-[2-(2-amino-3-cyanofuran-4-yl)ethyl]benzoate (18) and guanidine give 2,4-diamino-5-[2-(4-carbethoxy-phenyl)ethyl]-pyrrolo[2,3-*d*]pyrimidine (19) [95JOC6684].

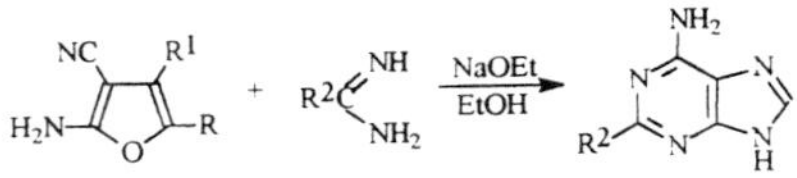

(16) R. R^1= H. alkyl. aryl   (17) R^2= Me. Ph. MeS. NH$_2$. Me$_2$N

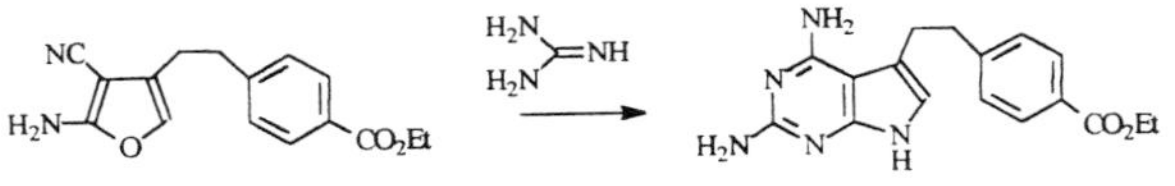

(18)   (19)

Routes to the pyrrolo[3,2-*d*] pyrimidine folate analogues (20) and an analogous route to 9-deazaguanine (21) have also been developed (Scheme 11) [95JOC7947].

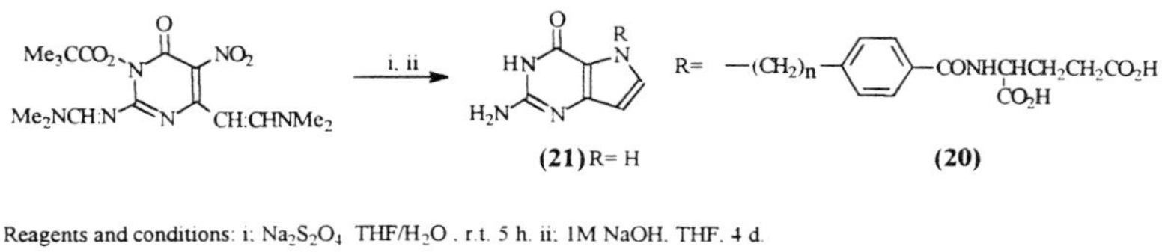

Reagents and conditions: i: Na$_2$S$_2$O$_4$ THF/H$_2$O . r.t. 5 h. ii: 1M NaOH. THF. 4 d.

Scheme 11

A simple, single step, synthesis of azolo[1,5-*a*]pyrimidines and related compounds is the reaction of arylhydrazonomalonitriles with aminoazoles. The reaction is illustrated in Scheme 12 [95JCR(S)290].

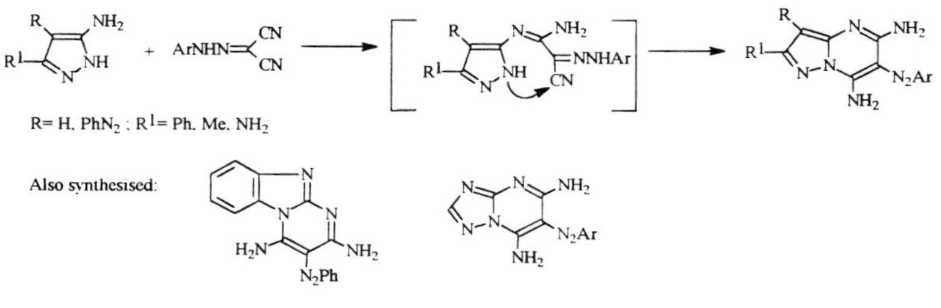

Scheme 12

Also 2-phenyl-4-phenylmethylideneoxazol-5(4*H*)-one (**22**) yields pyrazolo- and triazolo-pyrimidines when reacted with aminoazoles (Scheme 13) [94JCR(S)416].

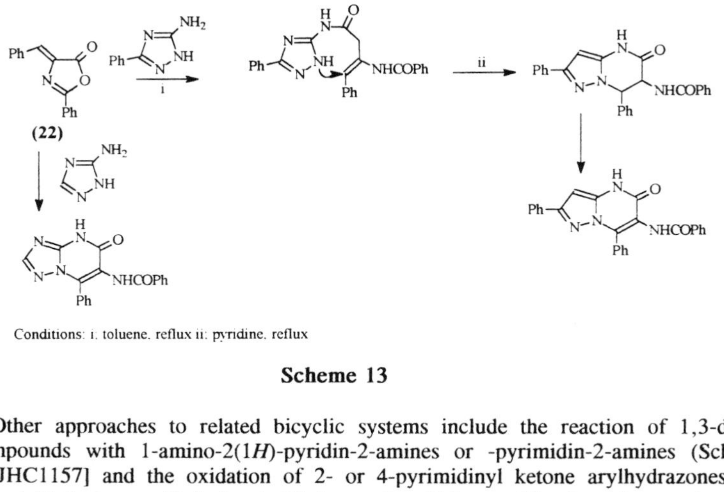

Conditions: i. toluene. reflux ii: pyridine. reflux

Scheme 13

Other approaches to related bicyclic systems include the reaction of 1,3-dicarbonyl compounds with 1-amino-2(1*H*)-pyridin-2-amines or -pyrimidin-2-amines (Scheme 14) [94JHC1157] and the oxidation of 2- or 4-pyrimidinyl ketone arylhydrazones to yield triazolo[1,5-*a*]- or -[1,5-*c*]pyrimidinium salts (Scheme 15). In this reaction 2,4,4,6-

tetrabromocyclohexa-2,5-dien-1-one (TBB; **23**) is used as the oxidant and the products are isolated as tetrafluoroborate salts on treatment with the silver salt [94JHC1041].

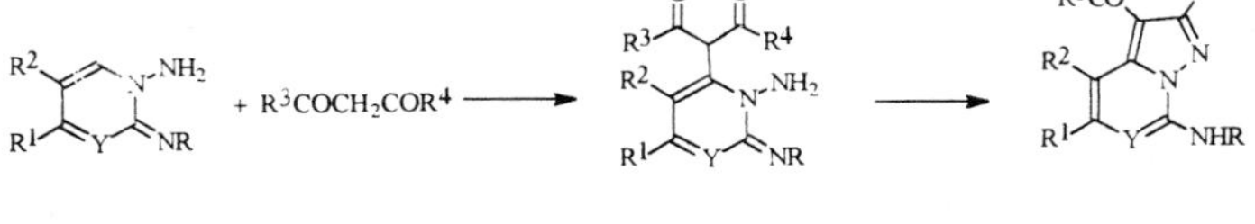

Y= CH, N; R^n= var. alkyl. aryl

Conditions: MeOH (and other solvents). reflux

Scheme 14

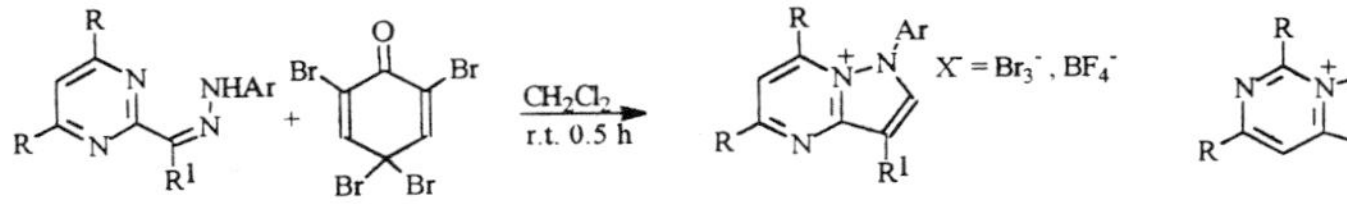

(**23**)

R= H, Me, MeO; R^1= Me, Ph, 4-ClC$_6$H$_4$

Scheme 15

2-Substituted vinamidinium salts react with 3-amino-1,2,4-triazole under basic conditions to give 6-(substituted)-triazolo[1,5-*a*]pyrimidines (**24**) (Scheme 16) [95H(40)729].

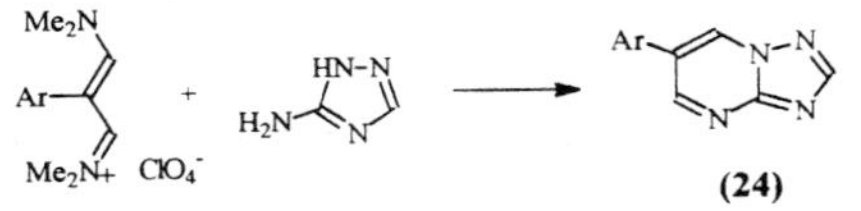

(**24**)

Conditions: NaH, DMF, 100 °C, 8 h.

Scheme 16

Thermal electrocyclic reactions of 1-azahexatriene systems can be used to obtain imidazo[4,5-*c*]pyridines (**25**) [95H(41)161] and the thermal cyclisation of 2-alkynylbenzene-diazonium salts (the Richter reaction) has been extended to the synthesis of pyrazolopyridazines (**26**) (Scheme 17) [95LA775].

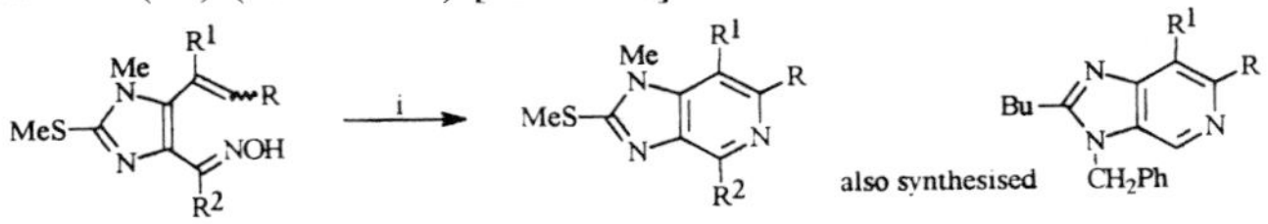

also synthesised

(**25**) R^n= H. alkyl. Ph

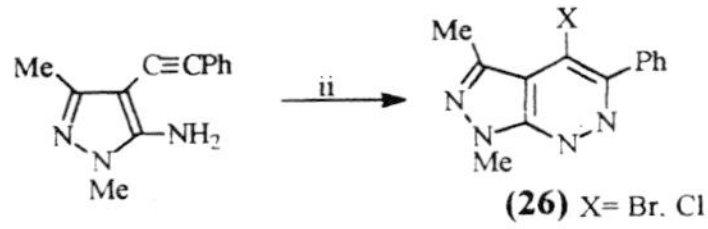

(**26**) X= Br. Cl

Reagents and conditions: i. *o*-dichlorobenzene. reflux. ii. HNO$_2$. HX. -15 °C to r.t.

Scheme 17

The reaction of 1,3-(disubstituted)-5-amino-4-nitrosopyrroles (27) with dimethylphenacyl-sulfonium bromides in boiling pyridine gives 1,3,6-(trisubstituted)-pyrazolo[3,4-*b*]pyrazine 4-oxides (28) and/or 1,3,6-(trisubstituted)-pyrazolo[3,4-*b*]pyrazin-5(4*H*)-ones (29) (Scheme 18). This is a new route to pyrazolo[3,4-*b*]pyrazines but either 4- or 5-substituted products are obtained. In some cases both 4- and 5-substituted compounds are obtained as inseparable mixtures. The reaction seems to pass through an oxaziridine intermediate (30) and there is a tendency for electron-withdrawing substituents to give 4- rather than 5-substitution. The formation of the 4-oxides by rearrangement of the oxaziridine is similar to the formation of nitrones from simple nitroso compounds and sulfonium ylides, but the common rearrangement is that to the amide *e.g.* 29 [95H(41)1667].

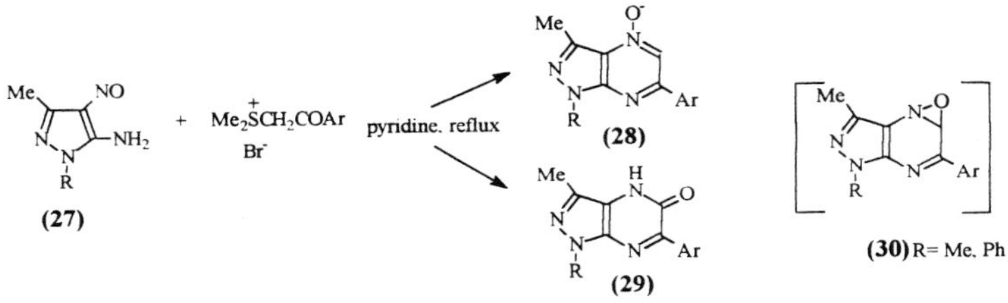

Scheme 18

The new ring systems 9,10-di(m)ethoxy-5*H*-2,3,7,8,12b,13-hexahydroimidazo[1',2':3,4]-pyrimido[6,1-*a*]isoquinolin-5-one (32a) and 11,12-di(m)ethoxy-2*H*,6*H*-3,4,8,9,13b,14-hexahydropyrimido[1',2':3,4]pyrimido[6,1-*a*]isoquinolin-6-one (32b) are formed by a tandem cyclisation of the tetrahydroisoquinoline ureas (31) on treatment with methanolic sodium methoxide [95S863].

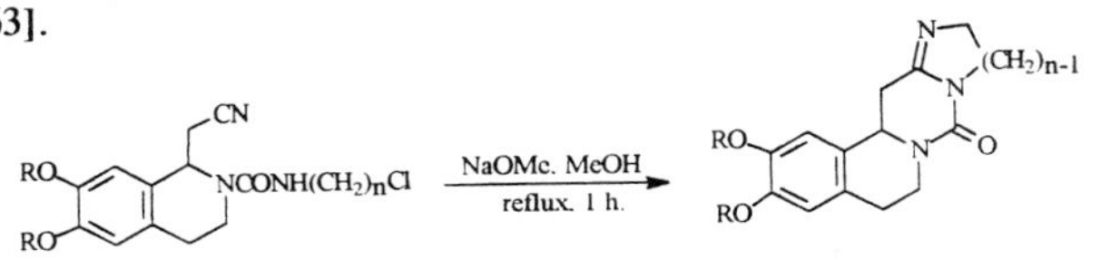

(31) → (32; a, n= 1; b, n= 2)

A number of 5-benzyl-5*H*-imidazo[4,5-*e*]-1,2,4-triazine 1-oxides (33) has been prepared by the reactions shown in Scheme 19 [94JCS(P1)2253].

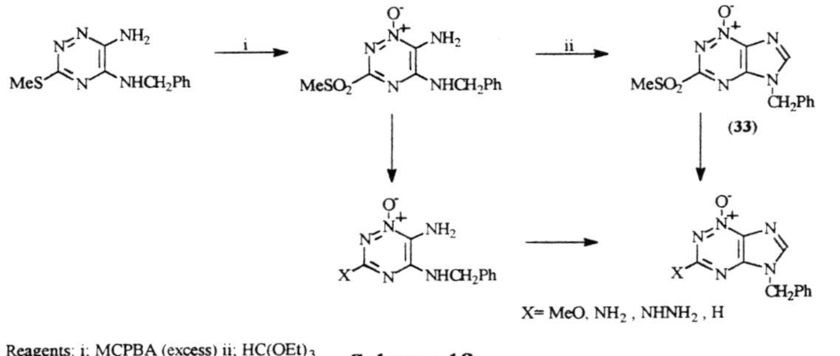

X= MeO, NH$_2$, NHNH$_2$, H

Reagents: i: MCPBA (excess) ii: HC(OEt)$_3$ **Scheme 19**

The condensation of 3-(substituted)-1,2,4-triazoles with an N-cyanocarbonimidate at high temperatures gives [1,2,4]triazolo[1,5-a][1,2,3]triazines (34) which are converted to other such products by standard metatheses. At lower temperatures [1,2,4]triazolo[4,3-a][1,3,5]-triazines (35) can also be obtained which rearrange to the more stable [1,5-a] isomers on heating. Cyclisation of the hydrazides (36) also leads to [1,5-a] fused triazines (Scheme 20) [95JCS(P1)801].

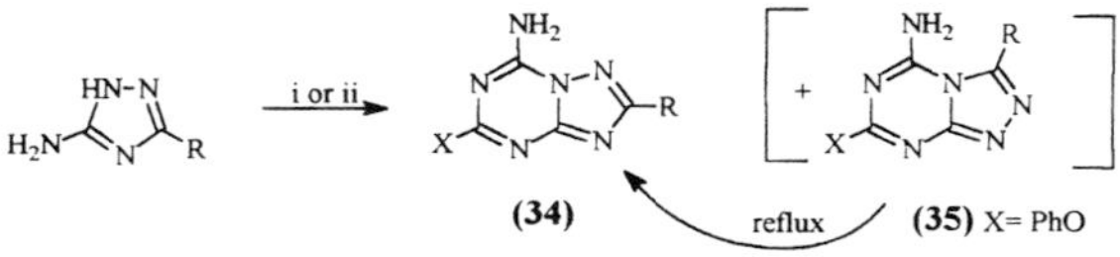

Reagents and conditions: i: (MeS)$_2$C:NCN, 160 °C (no solvent) ii: MeCN, r.t.

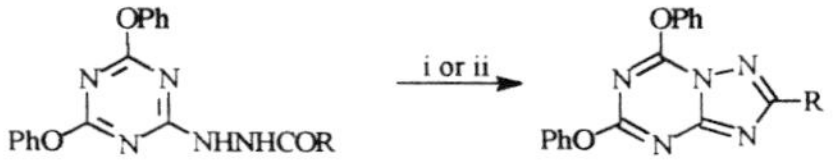

(36) R= 2-furyl, isoxazol-5-yl, 3-methylisoxazol-5-yl

Reagents and conditions: i: P$_2$O$_5$, xylene, reflux ii: tosyl chloride, pyridine, 100 °C.

Scheme 20

Aminotriazines (37) undergo Curtius rearrangement with diethyl dimorpholinomalonate and thiosemicarbazide to give imidazotriazines (6-azapurines) (38) [95MI1].

(37)   (38)

A very easy cyclodehydration of the pyrimidine (39) using silicon tetrachloride and base yields the tricyclic adenine derivative (40), a conformationally strained analogue of the anticonvulsant compound BWA78U [95TL4249].

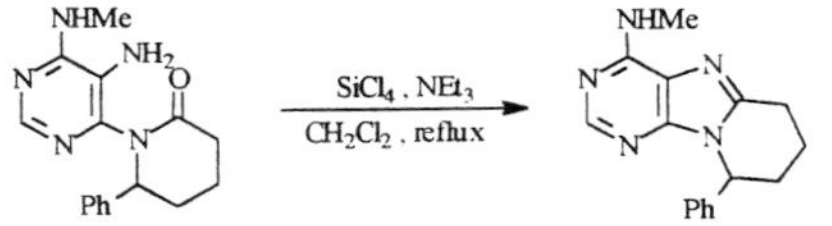

(39)   (40)

Benzylideneaminoguanidines (41) react with ethyl cyanoformimidate at room temperature to yield the intermediates (42) which cyclise to the dihydrotriazolotriazines (43) on brief reflux in methanol. These products are readily oxidised, *e.g.* by iodine, to the fully aromatic compounds [95MI2].

The stable triazolotriazine anionic σ-adducts (44) can be prepared by reacting nitroacetaldehyde with hydrazinotriazines [94KGS52], whilst pyrazolotriazinones (45) are readily obtained from aminopyrazole carboxamides [94S1437].

ArCR:NNHC(NHR^1):NH $\longrightarrow$ ArCR:NNH(NHR^1):NCH:NCN $\longrightarrow$

(41)　　　　　　　　　　　(42)　　　　　　　(43) Ar= 2-FC$_6$H$_4$, 4-ClC$_6$H$_4$;
R, R^1= H, Me

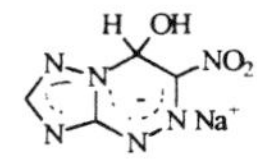

(44) 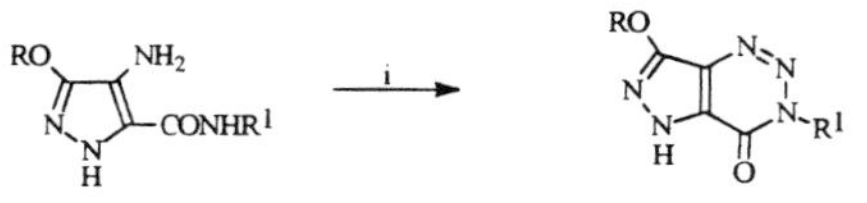　　　　　　　　　　　(45)

Reagents and conditions: i: NaNO$_2$, H$_2$O, AcOH, 0 °C, 1 h.

6.3.2.4 Pteridines and pteridine analogues

Improvements to the techniques of synthesis of 8-alkyl-$N5$-deazapterins have been reported for reactions between 2-amino-6-alkylaminopyrimidin-4(3H)ones and either 1,3-dicarbonyl compounds or 1,2-unsaturated carbonyl compounds which require the use of sodium bisulfite and the control of pH followed by chromatographic purification. The pKa data and protonation sites of the compounds which were prepared were recorded [94JHC1385].

2,6-(Disubstituted)-5-acetyl-4-aminopyrimidines react with DMF, or its acetals, and methanolic sodium methoxide to give 2,4-(disubstituted)-8H-pyrido[2,3-d]pyrimidin-5-ones (46) [94IZV1469].

Some 6-acyllumazines (47) have been isolated from the marine polychaete *Odontosyllis undecimdonta* [95H(41)789].

A new synthesis of pyrido[4,3-d]pyrimidin-5(6H)ones (48) involves treatment of methyl 2,4-dimethoxy-6-methylpyrimidine-5-carboxylate with LDA in THF at -70 °C followed by the addition of a diarylimine. The cycloadducts are aromatised by treatment with NBS *via* a benzylic bromination-dehydrobromination sequence [91CPB1189].

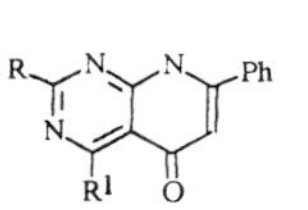

(46) 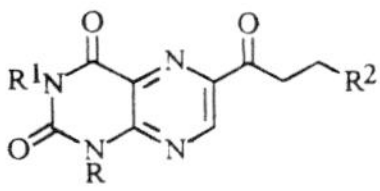　　　　　　(47) R, R^1= H, Me; R^2= H, Me, OH, OMe 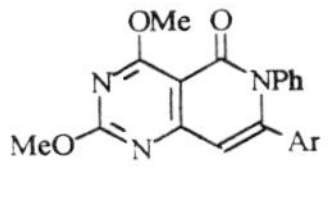　　　　(48)

The oxadiazinone (50), obtained from the pyrimidine (49), undergoes a hetero Diels-Alder addition with carbon dioxide elimination on heating with enamines to yield the 6-alkylated lumazine derivatives regioselectively (Scheme 21) [95JHC807].

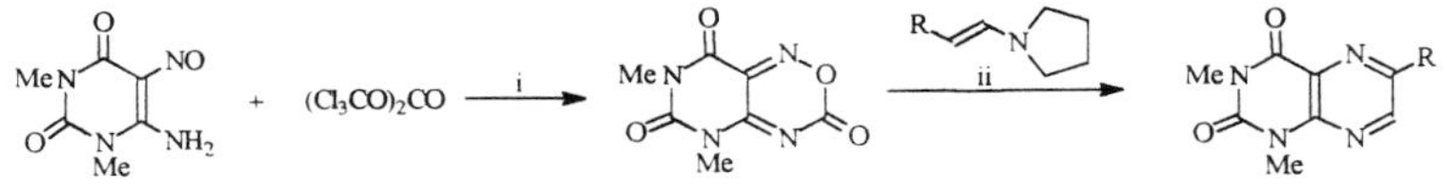

(49)　　　　　　　　　　　(50)

Conditions: i: THF, r.t., 12 h. ii: THF, -78°C, then r.t. 12 h.

Scheme 21

1,2,4-Pyridothiadiazine 1,1-dioxides (**51a-e**), novel pyridyl analogues of the 1,2,4-benzothiadiazines have been prepared by the sequence of reactions shown in Scheme 22. The 6N analogues have not been obtained due to the nonavailability of the pyridine starting materials [95T3221].

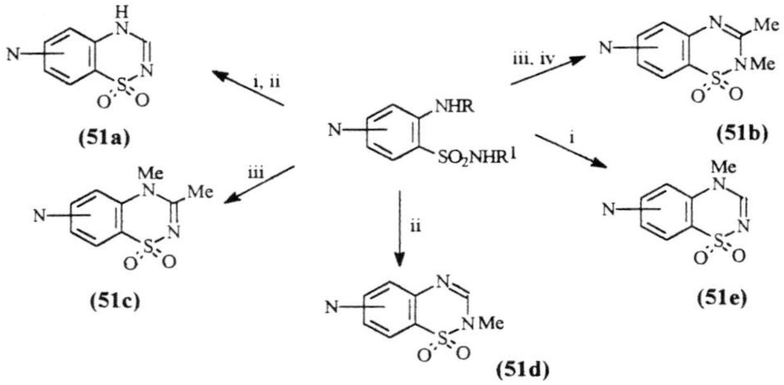

(51a) (51b) (51c) (51d) (51e)

Reagents: i: HCO$_2$COMe ii: HC(OEt)$_3$ iii Ac$_2$O iv: MeC(OEt)$_3$

Scheme 22

6.3.2.5 Miscellaneous ring systems

Intramolecular [3+2] cycloaddition of pyrazinium dicyanomethylides have been developed which yield 7-azaindolizines (**52**) (Scheme 23) [95H(40)69].

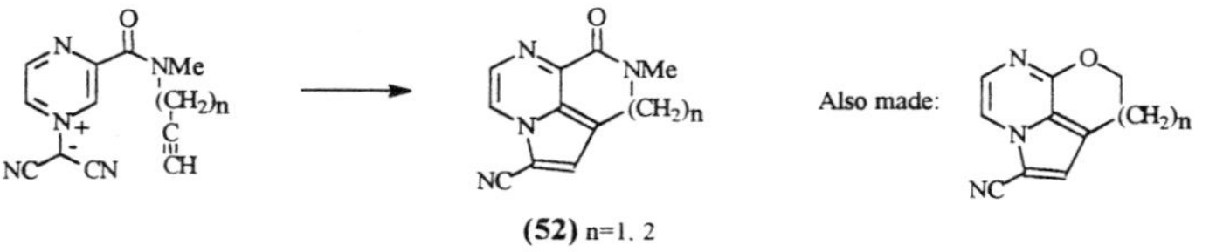

(52) n=1, 2

Conditions: Toluene, 110 °C, 3 h.

Scheme 23

The pyrimidinylhydrazine (**53**) is transformed into the 2,4,7,9-tetramethyl-1,2,3,4,7,8,9,10-octahydropyrimido[4,5-*c*]pyridazino[3,4-*d*]pyrimidine-1,3,8,10-tetrone (**54**) under diazo transfer conditions. The azopyrimidines (**55**) can also be obtained from **53** and they cyclise to triazolo[4,5-*d*]pyrimidines (**56**) on heating in DMF [94MC208].

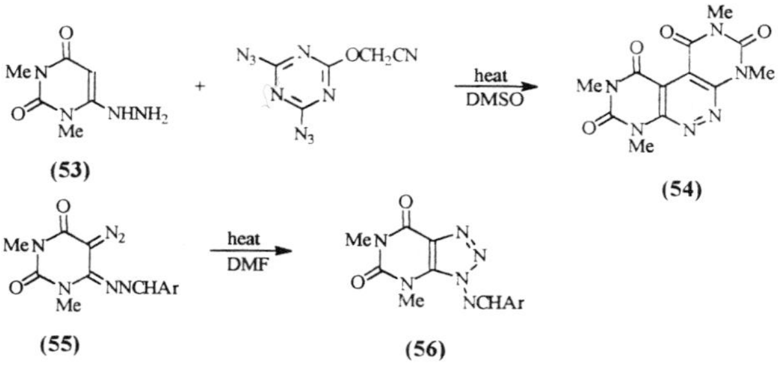

(53) (54) (55) (56)

8-Aminotheophylline reacts with 2-chlorobenzoic acid to yield 8,10-dimethylpurino[7,8-*a*] quinazoline-5,9,11(6*H*,8*H*,10*H*)-trione (57). Under similar conditions 8-aminocaffeine reacts to give the amide (58) which cyclises on heating with PPA to give 1,3,5-trimethylpurino [8,9-*b*]quinazoline-2,4,11(1*H*,3*H*,5*H*)trione (59). 8-Bromotheophylline and ethyl anthranilate yield 1,3-dimethylpurino[8,7-*b*]quinazoline-2,4,6(1*H*,3*H*,11*H*)trione (60) [95JHC941].

The reaction of 2-mercapto-5-(phenylazo)-4,6-dimethylpyridine-2-carbonitrile with appropriate halogeno compounds yields *S*-alkylated products which can be cyclised to yield pyridothieno-pyrimidines (61a) or -triazines (61b) [94PS(90)85]. Related reactions have been employed to yield further fused ring heterocycles [95PS(104)143].

The new heterocyclic system 5*H*-1-thia-3,4,5,6,8-pentaazanaphthylene (63) has been obtained by the diazotisation of the thienopyrimidine (62) [95JCR(S)286].

A variety of other polycyclic systems of this type have been synthesised including the tetracyclic system pyrido[3'',2'':4',5']thieno[2',3':5,6]pyrido[2,3-*d*]pyrimidine (64) [94H(38)2065; 95H(41)37].

6.3.3 REACTIONS

6.3.3.1 Triazines

1,3,5-(Trisubstituted)-hexahydro-1,3,5-triazines (65) are the oligomeric forms of *N*-methylene-imines to which they usually polymerise. These act as a stable source of the reactive dimeric zwitterion (66) as well as the monomeric species. The reaction of 65 (R= Ar) with isocyanates yields 1,3,5-(trisubstituted)-1,3,5-triazin-2-ones (67) [95JHC995;

94JCS(P1)1643]. The trialkyl derivatives of **65** react with oxalyl chloride, followed by ethanol, to give 4,5-imidazolones (**68**) when reacted in hexane or ether whereas they were unreactive in dichloromethane. The triaryl compounds were reactive in each solvent [93T10609; 95M103].

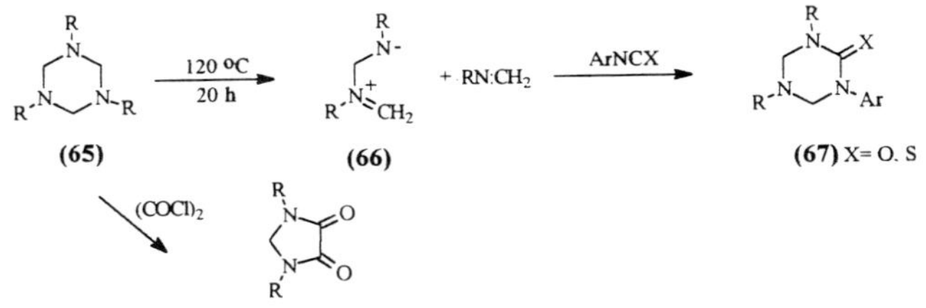

(**65**)   (**66**)   (**67**) X= O. S

(**68**) R= Me. Et. *etc.*

Monocyclic 1,2,3-triazines react with ketene silyl acetal, or silyl enol ether, in the presence of 1-chloroethyl chloroformate to give 5-(substituted)-2-(1-chloroethoxycarbonyl)-2,5-dihydrotriazines which are readily oxidised, and hydrolysed, with ceric ammonium nitrate in aqueous acetonitrile to 5-(substituted)-triazines (Scheme 24) [95CPB881].

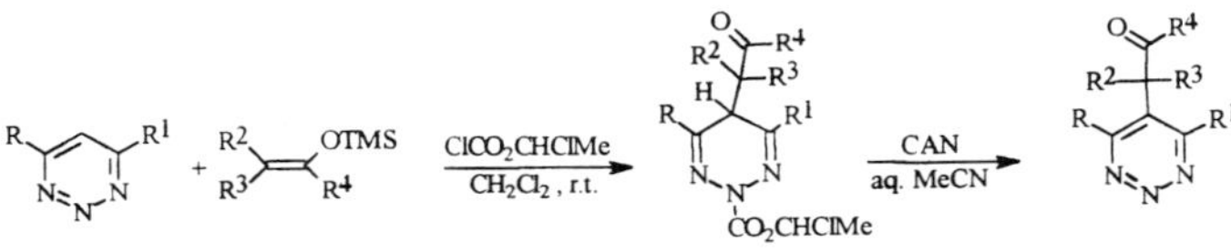

R, R^1. R^2= H. Me. Et. Ph; R^3= H. Me; R^4 = OMe. Ph

Scheme 24

Phenylmagensium bromide reacts with 5-arylmethyl-3-phenyl-1,2,4-triazin-6(1H)-ones to form 5-phenylated products which are easily oxidised to 3,5-diphenyl-1,2,4-triazin-6(1H)-one. Further derivatives have been obtained by standard metatheses (Scheme 25) [94JCR(S)453].

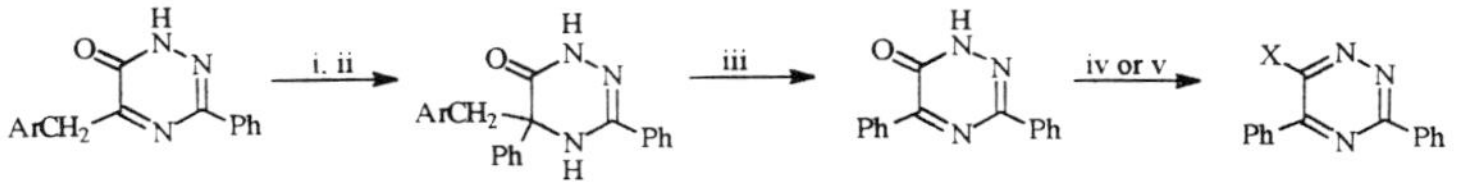

Reagents: i. PhMgBr. Et$_2$O ii: H$_2$O iii: CrO$_3$, HX iv: POCl$_3$ (for X= Cl) v: Lawesson's reagent (for X= SH)

Scheme 25

The synthesis of 2,4,6-tris(trinitromethyl)-1,3,5-triazine (**69**) has been achieved for the first time by nitration of the corresponding tris(dicarboxymethyl) compound, obtained by hydrolysis of the hexa-*t*-butyl ester. Nitration of the hexa-methyl or -ethyl esters gave (**69**). The trinitromethyl group undergoes ready displacement by nucleophiles (Scheme 26) [95MC17].

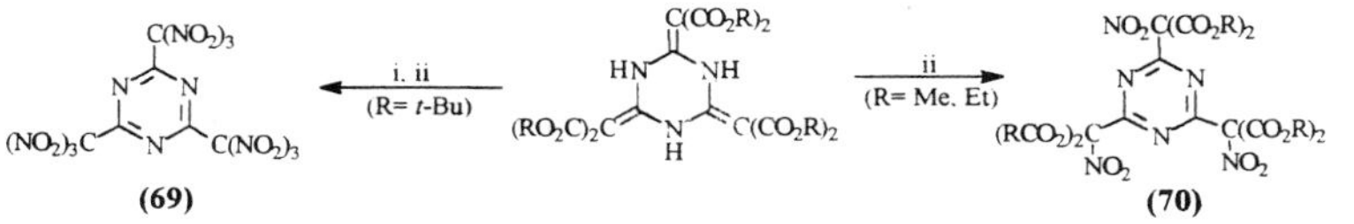

(69) **(70)**

Reagents and conditions: i: TFA. 0-5 °C. 15 min. ii: HNO₃ . CH₂Cl₂ . 0 °C or 15 °C

Scheme 26

The first report of cycloaddition reactions of 3-dimethylamino-1-methyl-1,2,4-triazinium-5-olates (71) with DMAD shows that 4-dimethylamino-1-methyl -6-oxo-1,3a,6,6a-tetrahydro-pyrrolo[3,4-c]pyrazole-3,3a-dicarboxylate derivatives (72) are obtained in each case [95AJC1175].

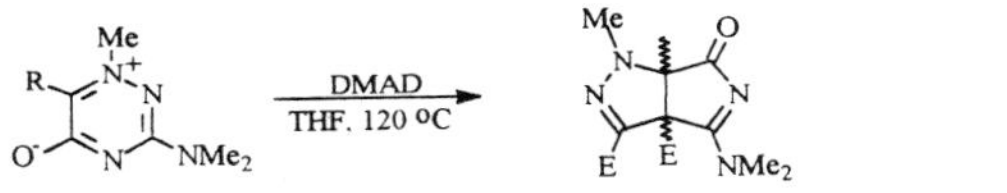

(71) **(72)** R= H. Me. Ph; E= CO₂Et

An unusually easy conversion of *N*-alkylazinium cations into the uncharged azines occurs when the iodides (73) are treated with triethylamine at room temperature. The reaction pathway seems to involve a free radical intermediate (Scheme 27) [95MC104].

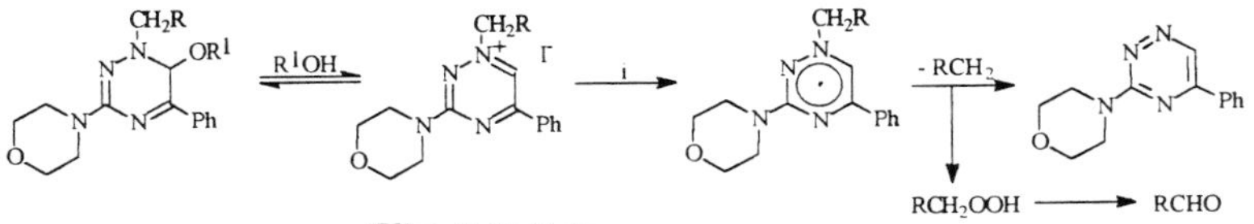

(73) R= H. Me. Et, Pr

Reagents: Et₃N. R¹OH. r.t.

Scheme 27

The tricyclic furo-fused 1,2,4-triazinium salt (74; X= O) reacts with nucleophiles such as sodium hydrogen sulfide, sodium diethyl malonate, or sodium ethyl cyanoacetate to yield the new ring systems thieno[2,3-e]pyrido[1,2-b]-1,2,4-triazinium perchlorate (74; X= S) and cyclopenta[e]pyrido[1,2-b]-1,2,4-triazines (75) [94CB1799].

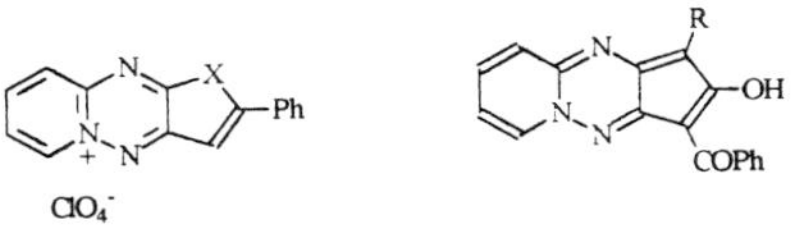

(74) **(75)**

6.3.3.2 Tetrazines

No reports of reactions of simple tetrazines have been collected during the past year. However, studies of the protonation and acid stability of the fused ring tetrazine antitumour agent "Temozolomide" (76) have been carried out and the NMR spectra of a number of Temozolomide derivatives carrying NMR active nuclei (^{13}C, ^{15}N) at different positions have been recorded [95JCS(P1)249].

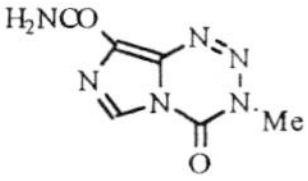

(76)

6.3.3.3 Purines and related compounds

The electrophilic substitution reactions of 1,3-dimethylpyrrolo[3,2-*d*]pyrimidine-2,4-dione (77) resulting in halogenation, aminomethylation, acylation and azo coupling yield 7-substituted products. However, nitration in acetic acid gives primarily attack at position 6. In some reactions 6,7-disubstitution is observed [95CHE(30)1077].

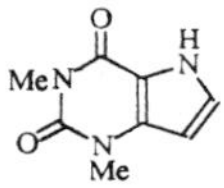

(77)

2',3',5'-Tri-*O*-acetylxanthosine (78) reacts with triphenyl phosphine-carbon tetrachloride (2 equiv.) in dichloromethane at reflux to give the 6-chloro derivative in good yield. This product yields the pyridinium salt (79) with aqueous pyridine which is a versatile reagent for the synthesis of other substituted purines (Scheme 28) [95JCS(P1)15].

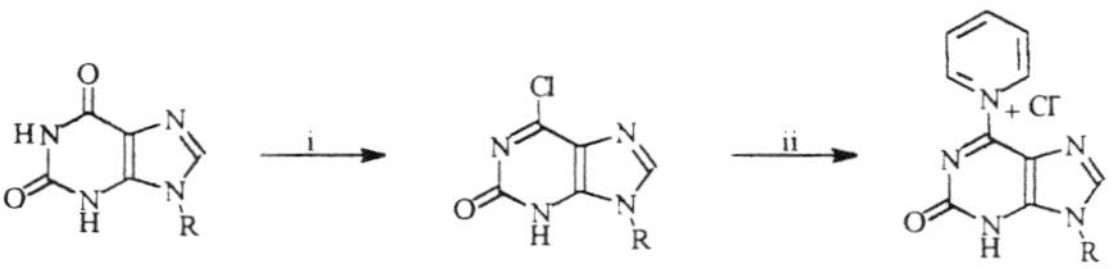

(78) R= 2',3',5'-tri-*O*-acetylribosyl   (79)

Reagents and conditions: i: PPh$_3$ .CCl$_4$, CH$_2$Cl$_2$. reflux. 3 h. ii; aq. pyridine. 50 °C, 3 h.

Scheme 28

The reaction of adenosine, and some other derivatives, with DMAD has been shown to yield a mixture of different pyrimido[2,1-*i*]purines depending on the reaction conditions. The kinetically favoured products (80) usually crystallise from the reaction medium, but if they are soluble then the thermodynamically favoured products (81) result *via* a Dimroth rearrangement [95H(41)1197].

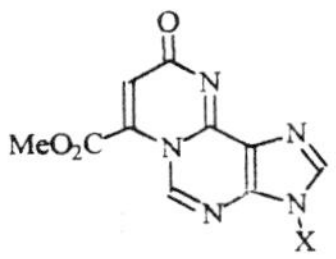

(80) 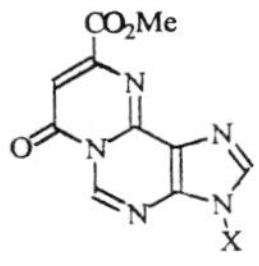   (81)

A number of pyrrolo[2,3-d]pyrimidines (82) have been made but all attempts to cyclise them to the tricyclic purine analogue (83) have failed, although the tricyclic system (84) has been known for many years [71TL4757]. Modelling and calculations show that there is considerable strain associated with the formation of the compound which is borne out by the failure to synthesise it [95JCS(P1)1225].

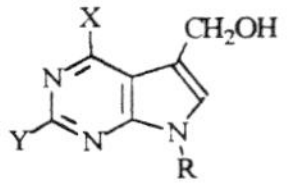

(82) R= H, Me; Y= MeSO$_n$ (83)   (84)
X= Cl, NHOH

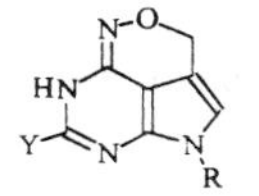

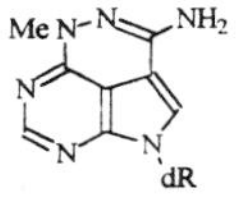

6.3.3.4 Pteridines and related compounds

Regioselective 6-alkoxylation of pteridines has been carried out by reacting 1,3-dimethyllumazine (85) or 2-dimethylamino-4(3H)-oxopteridine (86) with NBS in methanol or ethanol. Some 6-bromo product is also formed but this does not seem to be an intermediate in the reaction since these compounds are stable in refluxing ethanol and a pathway involving an intermediate bromonium ion is proposed (Scheme 29) [95H(41)781].

(85)   (86)

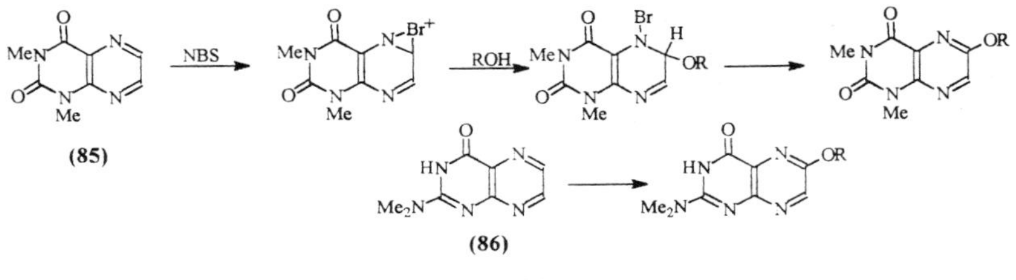

Scheme 29

Treatment of L-biopterin with DMFDMA (or DMFDEA), then acetic anhydride in pyridine, gives 1',2'-di-O-acetyl-N^2-(N,N-dimethylaminoethylene)-L-biopterin (87). This can be converted by the Mitsunobu reaction into 3-methyl and 3-p-nitrophenethyl derivatives. The protective groups on the side chain diols and N^2 of these compounds can be selectively cleaved to give biopterin. These reactions indicate their potential for biopterin modification [95MI3].

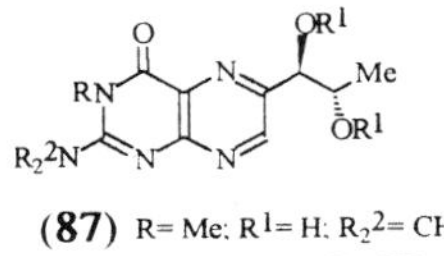

(87) R= Me; R^1= H; R$_2$^{2}= CHNMe$_2$
R= pNO$_2$C$_6$H$_4$CH$_2$CH$_2$; R^1= H; R$_2$^{2}= CHNMe$_2$
R= Me, pNO$_2$C$_6$H$_4$CH$_2$CH$_2$; R^1= R^2= H

1,3-Dimethylpyrimido[4,5-*d*]pyrimidine-2,4(1*H*,3*H*)-dione (**88**) reacts with alkylamines in liquid ammonia in the presence of an oxidising agent such as potassium permanganate to give 7-amino derivatives which corresponds to the 2-position of the pyrimidine ring. This is the first case of regioselective amination of condensed pyrimidines at the 2-position. In the case of dimethylamine both 5- and 7- amination is observed [94CHE(30)1083].

Studies of the reactivity of halogenoquinoxaline[2,3-*c*]cinnolines (**89**) have shown that the 10-chloro compound undergoes ready methoxy-dechlorination when treated with sodium methoxide but that the 1, 2, 3, 4, and 9-chloro isomers are unreactive towards this reagent. However, the 9,10-dichloro compound undergoes substitution of both chlorine atoms the 10-being the more reactive position. The 9 and 10-bromo analogues are both reactive towards sodium methoxide but the 9 and 10-fluoro derivatives are both highly reactive [94JCS(P1)2751].

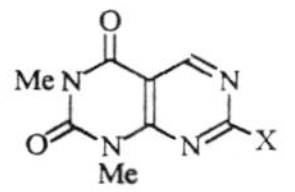

(**88**) 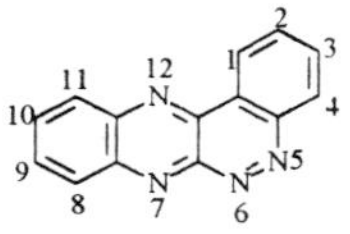　　　　　(**89**)

Fervenulin 1-oxide (**90**) reacts with secondary amines to give low yields of 8-alkyamino-theophyllines (**91**), but with ammonia or with primary amines the final product is 1,3-dimethyl-5-imino-6-hydroxyiminouracil (**92**) (Scheme 30) [94CHE(30)1087].

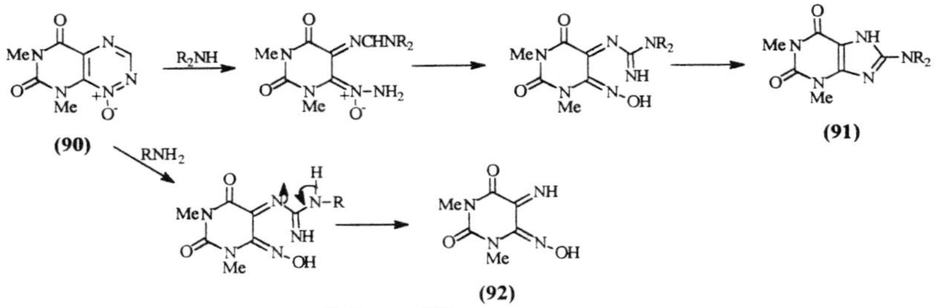

Scheme 30

6.3.3.5 Miscellaneous ring systems

The reaction of 1,2,4-triazino[5,6-*b*]indole-3-thione (**93a**; X= SH) with tetracyanoethylene affords, as one of three products, the thiazolotriazinoindole (**94**). The 3-hydrazino compound (**93b**; X= NHNH$_2$) gives the triazolotriazinoindole (**95**) and triazepinotriazinoindole (**96**) [94T9997].

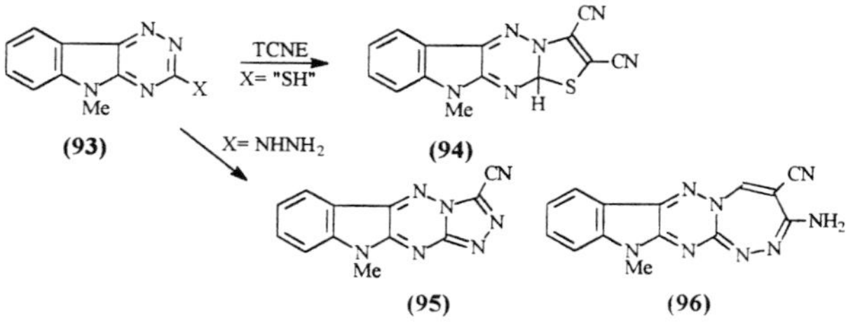

(**93**)　　(**94**)　　(**95**)　　(**96**)

2-Aryl-7,8-diamino-1,2,4-triazolo[1,5-c]pyrimidines (**97**; R = H) selectively acylate on the 8-amino group to give the amides (**97**; R = R^{1}CO) which cyclise on heating with PPA to yield 2-aryl-8-fluorobenzyl-1,2,4-triazolo[5,1-i]purines (**98**) [94JHC1171].

(**97**)

(**98**) R= var. fluorobenzyl

REFERENCES

71TL4757	K. H. Schram and L. B. Townsend, *Tetrahedron Lett.*, **1971**, 4757.
91CPB1189	A. Wada, S. Hirai and M. Hanaoka, *Chem. Pharm. Bull.*, **1991**, *39*, 1189; *Chem. Abstr.*, **1995**, *122*, 160616.
92CHE804	M. P. Nemeryuk, A. L. Sedov, V. A. Makarov, N. P. Solv'eva and T. S. Safonova, *Chem. Heterocycl. Compd. (Engl. Transl.)*, **1992**, *27*, 804.
93T10609	A. G. Giumanini, G. Verardo, F. Gorassini, P. Strazzolini and M. Tolazzi, *Tetrahedron*, **1993**, *46*, 10609.
94AHC(59)41	E. S. H. El Ashry, N. Rashed, M. Taha and E. Ramadan, *Adv. Heterocycl. Chem.*, **1994**, *59*, 39.
94AHC(61)207	E. S. H. El Ashry, N. Rashed, A. Mousaad and E. Ramadan, *Adv. Heterocycl. Chem.*, **1994**, *61*, 207.
94CB1799	Z. Riedl, G. Hajos, G. Kollenz and A. Messmer, *Chem. Ber.*, **1994**, *127*, 1799.
94CC2301	T. Tanaka, M. Watanabe, Y. Nakamoto, K. Okuno, K. Maekawa and C. Iwata, *J. Chem. Soc., Chem. Commun.*, **1994**, 2301.
94CHE(30)1083	A. V. Gulevskaya, A. F. Pozharskii, S. V. Shorshnev and E. A. Zheltushkina, *Chem. Heterocycl. Compd. (Engl. Transl.)*, **1994**, *30*, 1083.
94CHE(30)1087	A. V. Gulevskaya, A. F. Pozharskii and S. V. Shvidchenko, *Chem. Heterocycl. Compd. (Engl. Transl.)*, **1994**, *30*, 1087.
94CJC1849	A. R. Katritzky, S. A. Belyakov, H. D. Durst, R. Xu and N. S. Dalal, *Can. J. Chem.*, **1994**, *72*, 1849.
94H(38)2065	C. Peinador, M. C. Veiga, V. Ojea and J. M. Quintella, *Heterocycles*, **1994**, *38*, 2065.
94H(39)155	Y. Kamitori, M. Hojo, R. Masuda, M. Sukegawa, K. Hayashi and K. Kouzeki, *Heterocycles*, **1994**, *39*, 155.
94IZV1469	A. V. Kromakov, B. I. Ugrak, V. S. Azev, O. L. Guselnikova and O. N. Chupakin, *Izv. Akad. Nauk SSSR, Ser. Khim.*, **1994**, 1469; *Chem. Abstr.*, **1995**, *122*, 160592.
94JCR(S)350	R. N. Butler and D. F. O'Shea, *J. Chem. Res. (S)*, **1994**, 350.
94JCR(S)416	E. Zaghoul, A. M. Farag, A. M. Negm, A. K. Khalafalla, M. A. M. Rasslan and M. H. Elnagdi, *J. Chem. Res. (S)*, **1994**, 416.
94JCR(S)453	A. K. Mansour and M. M. Eid, *J. Chem. Res. (S)*, **1994**, 453.

94JCS(P1)1643   G. Verardo, A. G. Giumanini, F. Gorassini, P. Strazzolini, F. Benetollo and G. Bombieri, *J. Chem. Soc., Perkin Trans. 1*, 1994, 1643.

94JCS(P1)2253   C.-C. Tzeng, D.-C. Wei, L.-C. Hwang, M.-C. Cheng and Y. Wang, *J. Chem.Soc., Perkin Trans. 1*, 1994, 2253.

94JCS(P1)2751   A. Ahmed, L. J. Dunbar, I. G. Green, I. W. Harvey, T. Shepherd, D. M. Smith and R. K. C. Wong, *J. Chem.Soc., Perkin Trans. 1*, 1994, 2751.

94JHC781   S. A. Patil, B. A. Otter and R. S. Klein, *J. Heterocycl. Chem.*, 1994, *31*, 781.

94JHC1041   S. Batori and A. Messmer, *J. Heterocycl. Chem.*, 1994, *31*, 1041.

94JHC1157   P. Koecknitz, B. Riemer, A. Mchler, A. Hassoun and J. Liebscher, *J. Heterocycl. Chem.*, 1994, *31*, 1157.

94JHC1171   F. Gatta, M. R. Del Giudice, A. Borioni, C. Mustazza and C. Fazio, *J. Heterocycl. Chem.*, 1994, *31*, 1171.

94JHC1185   B. Kokel, *J. Heterocycl. Chem.*, 1994, *31*, 1185.

94JHC1385   M. T. G. Ivery and J. E. Gready, *J. Heterocycl. Chem.*, 1994, *31*, 1385.

94JOC8284   S. C. Fields, M. H. Parker and W. R. Erickson, *J. Org. Chem.*, 1994, *59*, 8284.

94KGS52   V. L. Rusinov, A. Yu. Petrov, G. G. Aleksandrov and O. N. Chupakin, *Khim. Geterotsikl. Soedin.*, 1994, 52; *Chem. Abstr.*, 1995, *122*, 56011.

94LA1049   M. Stumpf and H. Balli, *Liebigs Ann. Chem.*, 1994, 1049.

94MC208   Y. A. Azev, O. L. G and O. N. Chupakin, *Mendeleev Commun.*, 1994, 208.

94PS(90)85   A. M. K. El-Dean, *Phosphorus Sulfur*, 1994, *90*, 85: *Chem. Abstr.*, 1995, *122*, 105802.

94S1437   P. G. Baraldi, L. Garuti and M. Roberti, *Synthesis*, 1994, 1437.

94T9997   A. A. Hassan, N. K. Mohamed, B. A. Ali and A.-F. E. Mourad, *Tetrahedron*, 1994, *50*, 9997.

94TL7935   N. Biedermann and J. Sauer, *Tetrahedron Lett.*, 1994, *35*, 7935.

95AHC(62)306   K. Undheim and T. Benneche, *Adv. Heterocycl. Chem.*, 1995, *62*, 306.

95AJC1175   R. P. Musgrave, N. W. Jacobsen, G. Bourne, C. H. L. Kennard and G. Smith, *Aust. J. Chem.*, 1995, *48*, 1175.

95CHE(30)1077   E. B. Tsupak, Yu. N. Tkachenko and A. F. Pozharskii, *Chem. Heterocycl. Compd.*, 1995, *30*, 1077.

95CPB881   T. Itoh, Y. Matsuya, H. Hasegawa, K. Nagata, M. Okada and A. Ohsawa, *Chem. Pharm. Bull.*, 1995, *43*, 881.

95H(40)69   M. Engelbach, P. Imming, G. Seitz and R. Tegethoff, *Heterocycles*, 1995, *40*, 69.

95H(40)729   S. A. Petrich, Z, Quian, L. M. Santiago, J. T. Gupton and J. A. Sikorski, *Heterocycles*, 1995, *40*, 729.

95H(41)37   C. Peinador, M. C. Veiga, V. Ojea and J. M. Quintella, *Heterocycles*, 1995, *41*, 37.

95H(41)161   H. Yashioka, T. Choshi, E. Sugino and S. Hibino, *Heterocycles*, 1995, *41*, 161.

95H(41)781   T. Sugimoto and W. Pfleiderer, *Heterocycles*, 1995, *41*, 781.

95H(41)789   H. Kakoi, H. Tanino, K. Okada and S. Inoue, *Heterocycles,* **1995**, *41*, 789.

95H(41)1197   R. F. de Boer, D. G. I. Petra, M. J. Wanner, A. Boessart and G.-J. Koomen, *Heterocycles,* **1995**, *41*, 1197.

95H(41)1667   M. Takahishi and M. Hatazaki, *Heterocycles,* 1995, *41*, 1667.

95JCR(S)224   R. N. Butler, E. P. Ni Bhradaigh, P. McArdle and D. Cunningham, *J. Chem. Res. (S),* **1995**, 224.

95JCR(S)286   S. Tumkevicius and R. Pupeikyte, *J. Chem. Res. (S),* 1995, **286.**

95JCR(S)290   Z. E. Kandeel, *J. Chem. Res. (S),* **1995**, 290.

95JCS(P1)15   L. De Napoli, D. Montesarchio, G. Piccialli, C. Santacroce and M. Varra, *J. Chem. Soc., Perkin Trans. 1,* **1995**, 15.

95JCS(P1)249   R. T. Wheelhouse, D. E. V. Wilman, W. Thomson and M. F. G. Stevens, *J. Chem. Soc., Perkin Trans.1,* **1995**, 249.

95JCS(P1)801   P. W. R. Caulkett, G. Jones, M. McPartlin, N. D. Renshaw, S. K. Stewart and B. Wright, *J. Chem. Soc., Perkin Trans. 1,* **1995**, 810.

95JCS(P1)1225   D. M. Williams and D. M. Brown, *J. Chem. Soc., Perkin Trans. 1,* **1995**, 1225.

95JCS(P2)469   R. J. Simmonds and G. Dua, *J. Chem. Soc., Perkin Trans.2,* **1995**, 469.

95JCS(P2)785   A. R. Katritzky, D. C. Oniciu and I. Ghivirirga, *J. Chem. Soc., Perkin Trans.2,* **1995**, 785.

95JHC697   D. T. Hurst, *J. Heterocycl. Chem.,* **1995**, *32*, 697.

95JHC807   M. Igarashi and M. Tada, *J. Heterocycl. Chem.,* **1995**, *32*, 807.

95JHC941   A. Da Settimo, G. Primofiore, B. M. Cristina, F. Da Settimo and A. M. Marini, *J. Heterocycl. Chem.,* **1995**, *32*, 941.

95JHC995   G. Verardo, A. G. Giumaninni, F. Gorassini, P. Strazzolini, F. Benetollo and G. Bombieri, *J. Heterocycl. Chem.,* **1995**, *32*, 995.

95JOC4121   R. V. Hoffmann, N. K. Nayyar and W. Chen, *J. Org. Chem.,* **1995**, *60*, 4121.

95JOC5992   R. V. Hoffmann and N. K. Nayyar, *J. Org. Chem.,* **1995**, *60*, 5992.

95JOC6684   E. C. Taylor, H. H. Patel and J.-G. Jun, *J. Org. Chem.,* **1995**, *60*, 6684.

95JOC7947   E. C. Taylor and W. B. Young, *J. Org. Chem.,* **1995**, *60*, 7947.

95JPR274   A. Hamed, M. Sedeak, A. H. Ismail, R. Stumpf, H. Fischer and J. C. Jochims, *J. Prakt. Chem./Chem.-Ztg.,* **1995**, *337*, 274.

95LA775   S. F. Vasilevsky and E. V. Tretyakov, *Liebigs Ann. Chem.,* **1995**, 775.

95M99   P. Wessig and J. Schwarz, *Monatsh. Chem.,* **1995**, *126*, 99.

95M103   G. Verardo, A. G. Giumanini, F. Gorassini and P. Strazzolini, *Monatsh. Chem.,* **1995**, *126*, 103.

95MC17   A. V. Shastin, T. I. Godonikova, S. P. Golova, V. S. Kuz'min, L. I. Khemel'nitskii and B. L. Korsunskii, *Mendeleev Commun.,* **1995**, 17.

95MC104   O. N. Chupakin, B. V. Rudokov, P. McDermott, S. G. Alexeev, V. N. Churushin and F. Hegarty, *Mendeleev Commun.,* **1995**, 104.

95MI1   X.-L. Sui, Z.-J. Yang, M. Han, M.-S. Cai and T.-M. Chang, *Huaxue Xuebao,* **1995**, *53*, 199; *Chem. Abstr.,* **1995**, *122*, 239650.

95MI2   Y. Miyamoto, H. Khono, W. Pfleiderer, P. Boeger and K. Wakabayashi, *Nippon Noyaku Gakkaishi,* **1995**, *20*, 119; *Chem. Abstr.,* **1995**, *123*, 83325.

95MI3   T. Hanaya, *Pteridines*, **1995**, *6*, 1; *Chem. Abstr.*, **1995**, *122*, 314347.
95PS(104)143 E. A. Bakhite, A. A. Geies, A. M. K. El-Dean and H. S. El-Kashef, *Phosphorus Sulfur*, **1995**, *104*, 143: *Chem.Abstr.*, **1995**, *123*, 339997.
95S863   F. Fuelop, H. Wamhoff and P. Sohar, *Synthesis*, **1995**, 863.
95SL253   S. Ostrowski, *Synlett*, **1995**, 253.
95T3221   P. Tullio, B. Pirotte, L. DuPont, B. Masereel, D. Laeckmann, T. Podona, O. Diouf, P. Lebrun and J. Delarge, *Tetrahedron*, **1995**, *51*, 3221.
95TL4249   L. Desaubry, C. G. Wermuth and J.-J. Bourguignon, *Tetrahedron Lett.*, **1995**, *36*, 4249.

Chapter 6.4

Six-Membered Ring Systems: With O and/or S Atoms

John D. Hepworth and B. Mark Heron
University of Central Lancashire, Preston, UK

Introduction

The pyran unit features in a range of naturally occurring materials and much effort has been devoted to the synthesis and structure elucidation of such of those compounds which show potent pharmacological activity. Total syntheses have been reported for brevetoxin B (95JA10227), swinholide A (95T9393), lankacidin C (95JA8258), onchitriol I (95TL5357) and tautomycin (95JOC5048). Several styryllactones have been synthesised (95CC743, 95JOC3121, 95T1429), as has the fungal pigment, dermolactone, an anthra[2,3-*c*]pyran-1-one (95JCS(P1)1215). All the stereoisomers of yingzhaosu C, a naturally occurring anti-malarial sesqui-terpenoid, have been synthesised (95JOC3039).

Reviews on marine macrolides (95CRV2041), natural insecticides (95ACR343), the chemistry of fruit flies (95CRV789), saturated and unsaturated lactones (95COS133) and saturated oxygen heterocycles (95COS189) all feature pyran derivatives. The value of dispiroketals in synthesis has been surveyed (95COS365). A review of pyran chemistry has been published (95AHC19).

A review on cyclic peroxides covers the recent chemistry of 1,2-dioxanes and 1,2,4-trioxanes (95COS225) and the value of 1,3-dioxanes in the diastereoselective synthesis of chloromycetine and related compounds has been reviewed (95H(41)2327).

Reviews of dithioacetals and thioaldehydes contain much material relevant to Sections 6.4.2.1 and 6.4.4.1 (B-95MI).

As always, space limitations have precluded the inclusion of many publications of merit.

277

6.4.1 HETEROCYCLES CONTAINING ONE OXYGEN ATOM

6.4.1.1 Pyrans

The synthesis of 3,4-dihydro-2H-pyrans using Diels-Alder methodology continues to attract interest. A combination of high pressure and lanthanide catalysis facilitates the synthesis of highly substituted dihydropyrans (95T8383), whilst microwave irradiation dramatically assists the reaction of a chiral ketene acetal with chalcone which exhibits appreciable facial selectivity (95JOC4160). A β-methyl group in α,β-unsaturated aldehydes has a significiant effect in their reaction with 1,1-dimethylbuta-1,3-dienes catalysed by BBr$_3$, the hetero-Diels-Alder reaction competing successfully with the normal cycloaddition (95JOC8128).

Cyclisation of pent-4-en-1-ols features in a variety of guises in pyran syntheses. Reaction of the unsaturated alcohol with iodine reagents affords the tetrahydropyran with high diastereoselectivity associated with the bulky silyl substituent and which is enhanced by substitution at the terminal carbon atom (95SL663).

Optically active ω-bromocyanohydrins yield 2-cyano-tetrahydropyrans without racemisation (95CC989) and both the unsaturated alcohol (1) and the diol (2) afford the same tetrahydropyran through stereospecific cyclisation of a common episulfonium ion (95TL1909).

Examples of fused pyrans which can be obtained in a similar manner include 6-oxasteroids (95JCS(P1)1089) and bicyclic vinyl ethers (95CC1117), whilst a double radical cyclisation of β-alkoxyacrylates features in a synthesis of 3Z-dactomelyne (95JA8017).

Treatment of 5-bromo-3,4-dihydro-2H-pyran with complex bases generates 3,4-dehydrodihydropyran (3), which reacts with ketone enolates to yield fused cyclobutanols (4) and the derived ketones (5) (95T1973). Both (4) and (5) are of value in the synthesis of polycyclic O-heterocycles (95SL742).

1,5-Ketoacetals are available from the Lewis acid catalysed Michael addition of hemiacetal vinylogues to 3,4-dihydropyrans. The products are a source of hydroxy- and amino- acetals and hence give access to annulated tetrahydropyrans (95JCS(P1)2103).

6.4.1.2   Benzopyrans (Chromenes)

It has been thought that the use of 3-methylbut-2-enal derivatives in the synthesis of chromenes was restricted to the reaction with electron rich phenols. Not so! The reaction is efficiently catalysed by pyridine and 3-methylpyridine and is most successful with the more acidic phenols, indicating the need for a careful balance between acid and base catalysis (95JOC3397).

Examples of epoxidation (95SL197, 95TL3669) and aziridination (95JA5889) of chromenes with high enantioselectivity have been reported.

The reaction of chromenes with mono- and bis- imides of 1,4-benzoquinones (6, X = O or NCOPh) is promoted by Lewis acids and affords pterocarpans and azapterocarpans, respectively (95TL2713). A total synthesis of the pterocarpan, neorautenane, involves a chemoselective coupling of a benzodipyran with o-chloro-mercuriophenol (95JCS(P1)949).

6.4.1.3 Dihydrobenzopyrans (Chromans)

The cyclisation of *o*-alkenylphenols features in two approaches to the chroman ring system. The Hg-mediated cyclisation of (7) affords the chroman-4-ols (8) and (9) which can be separated after debenzylation, providing the chroman unit of the calophyllum coumarins (95S630). 2-Cyclohexenylphenols undergo a 6-*endo* cyclisation to fused chromans on treatment with pyridine hydrobromide perbromide (95CJC1727).

Reagents: (i) Hg(OAc)$_2$, THF; (ii) NaBH$_4$, NaOH.

The intramolecular nucleophilic addition of the formyl group to the electron deficient alkene unit in the propenoate (10) affords a benzofuranone when catalysed by a thiazolium salt. However, when NaCN is used as the catalyst, an initial Michael addition to the acrylate function is followed by an intramolecular aldol condensation and the chroman (11) is formed. The corresponding butanoates afford chroman-4-ones under the influence of thiazolium cations, but give benzoxepins in the presence of a basic catalyst (95S1311).

Attention has been drawn to the favourable buttressing effect of substituents in the thermal cyclisation of the 2-substituted 1-allyloxybenzenes (95JCS(P1)2551).

R	Temp. °C	Yield (%)
H	80 - 140	0
Me	80	90

The chemoselectivity of the thermal cyclisation of the arylideneacetylacetone derivative (12) is influenced by the choice of catalyst. Thus, with Li and Ba perchlorates, a hetero-Diels-Alder reaction leads to the benzopyrano[3,4-*c*]pyran (13), whilst this mode is suppressed by $Mg(ClO_4)_2$ and the ene product, benzopyran (14) is formed (95TL2855).

(14)   (12)   (13)

Reagents: (i) $LiClO_4$, Δ; (ii) $Mg(ClO_4)_2$, Δ

3-Methylenetetrahydropyran-2-one undergoes a tandem Michael-Claisen annulation with 1,1-bis(methylthio)butan-2-one to give tetrahydrochromans which are readily aromatised (95T9559).

Reagents: (i) NaH, CH_2Cl_2; (ii) AcOH, 60 °C; (iii) TsOH, C_6H_6

A Sharpless asymmetric epoxidation features in a synthesis of (*S*)-chromanethanol (15). In the key cyclisation step, the absolute configuration of the diol is retained by a double inversion (95SL1255). *trans*-6-Cyano-2,2-dimethylchroman-3,4-diol is obtained from the racemic diol with excellent optical purity by the stereoselective acylation using *Candida cylindraceae* lipase (95TA123).

Reagents: (i) $Ph_3C^+BF_4^-$, CH_2Cl_2;
(ii) H_2, Pd-C, Et_2O

(15)

Formation of the isochroman system is considered to trigger the synthesis of the dibenzopyran (17, $X = H_2$) by the acid catalysed cyclisation of *cis*-enediynes (16, $X = H_2$). In a similar manner, the carboxyl function in (16, $X = O$) promotes cylisation to a dihydropyranone derivative which is followed by a Myers cycloaromatisation to the dibenzopyranone (17, $X = O$) (95TL9165).

(16)   (17)

The intramolecular Pd-catalysed Heck arylation of the nitroalkene (18) which affords the isochroman (19) is unusual in that Ag_2CO_3 is the essential base and that benzene is the preferred solvent. The nitroalkane derivative (20) is a significant by-product, but its conversion to the nitroalkene can be accomplished in three steps in 70% yield (95JOC1013).

(18)   (43%)   (ii), (iii),   (40%)
        (19)   (iv), (v)   (20)

Reagents: (i) $Pd(OAc)_2$, Ph_3P, Ag_2CO_3, 25 °C; (ii) n-BuLi, THF, 0 °C;
(iii) PhSeBr; (iv) H_2O_2, THF; (v) $SnCl_4$, CH_2Cl_2, -78 °C

6.4.1.4   Pyranones

Oxidation of 4-alkylamino-5-methoxy-1,2-benzoquinones yields 4-alkyaminopyran-2-ones probably through sequential Baeyer-Villiger ring expansion, epoxide formation and ring contraction (95TL6669).

Further examples of pyran-2-ones obtained from 1,3-dicarbonyl compounds and $HC(OEt)_3$ include several hetero-fused analogues (95H(41)1299) and cyclodehydration of a γ-keto acid yields a pyranopyrrole (95JCS(P1)1131).

The conversion of furans into pyran-3(6H)-ones can be achieved using hypervalent iodine compounds (95TL3553), whilst the pyranones undergo a base catalysed isomerisation to a hydroxycyclopent-2-enone (95CC1971).

Spirolactones result from the reaction of epoxides with (2-buten-1,4-diyl) magnesium complexes and subsequent carbonation (95JOC5143).

Trifluoroacylketenes, generated by the reaction of acid chlorides with $(CF_3CO)_2O$ and pyridine, can be trapped by ethyl vinyl ether and enamines yielding dihydropyran-4-ones and pyran-4-ones, respectively (95T2585).

Reagents: (i) 1-morpholinocyclohexene, Δ; (ii) ethyl vinyl ether, Δ

Dihydropyran-4-ones are formed with good enantiomeric excess by a chiral Lewis acid catalysed reaction of aldehydes with Danishefsky's diene and cyclisation of the initial aldol product. The overal process equates to a hetero-Diels-Alder cycloaddition (95JOC5998). Lactams also react with the electron rich diene under the influence of a Lewis acid, yielding 7-aza-1-oxaspiroalkenones (95JOC7724).

The copolymerisation of CO_2 and 1,4-bis-(N,N-diethylamino-ethynyl)benzene affords a quantitative yield of a poly(pyran-4-one) ($M_n \sim 10000$) without the need for a catalyst. Its repeat unit has been synthesised to assist in the structure elucidation of the polymer (95CC2417).

6.4.1.5   Coumarins

Approaches to seselin and angelicin derivatives, naturally occurring angular fused coumarins, using Wittig methodology (95T3087) include a tandem Claisen rearrangement and Wittig reaction (95TL7109), whilst a photochemical aromatic annulation features in a synthesis of the linear furocoumarin, bergapten (95SL573). A regioselective arylation using aryllead triacetate is combined with a standard chroman-4-one synthesis in a route to the linear 3-arylpyranocoumarins, robustin and robustic acid (95JCS(P1)2531).

The conversion of nitrocoumarins into the amino compounds has been achieved by hydrogen transfer (95JCR(S)372) and an intramolecular hydride transfer features in the formation of Mannich bases of 4-aminocoumarins from 4-alkylaminocoumarin-3-carbaldehyde (95S633). Amine derivatives of coumarin-3-carboxaldehyde undergo a thermal 1,3-cycloaddition involving an oxime nitrone isomerisation on reaction with N-methyl-hydroxylamine yielding hetero-fused coumarins (95JCS(P1)1857).

4-Hydroxycoumarins can be converted into 4-arylcoumarins *via* the Pd-catalysed coupling of 4-stannylcoumarins with aryl iodides (95SC2883), whilst the three component reaction of 4-hydroxy-coumarins, triethyl orthoformate and hydrazines yields N-derivatives of 3-methylenechroman-2,4-diones (95M579).

A variety of 3-substituted coumarins react with an excess of dimethylsulfoxonium methylide, presumably forming the 3,4-fused cyclopropane derivative which rearranges to the cyclopenta[*b*] benzofuran (95TL5603).

Reagents: (i) Me$_3$S$^+$(O)I$^-$, NaH, DMF

8-Hydroxyisocoumarins are accessible from 3-hydroxybenzyl ketones using directed lithiation as the key step (95G111) and isocoumarins have been prepared from 2-iodobenzoic acid and alkynes through a Pd-mediated annulation (95JOC3270, 3711). The cyclisation of tertiary alcohols derived from the reaction of *o*-cyanobenzyllithium with aldehydes and ketones yields 3,4-dihydroisocoumarins (95S1102).

6.4.1.6 Chromones

In an unusual modified chromone synthesis, enaminones formally derived from *o*-hydroxyacetophenone react with selenium oxychloride prior to cyclisation resulting in the formation of Se-bridged bischromones. Various reactions at Se are described, including fission of an Se-Se bond, leading to chromone-3-seleninic acid (95JHC43).

The cycloaddition of ketene acetals to 3-formylchromone exhibits good diastereoselectivity and methanolysis of the pyrano[4,3-*b*]-pyran affords the chromanone ester (21) without racemisation. The chiral auxiliary, the diol (22), can be recyclised and the overall process represents an asymmetric conjugate addition to the chromone (95JCS(P1)2293).

The intramolecular C-H insertion of α-diazocarbonyl compounds proceeds with excellent regioselectivity affording chroman-4-ones and with good enantioselectivity when Rh (II) carboxylates are used as the catalyst (95JCS(P1)1373).

The transformation of chroman-4-ones into (*S*)-chroman-4-ols by *Mortierella isabellina* has been applied to naphtho[2,3-*b*]pyran-4-one to provide a synthesis of naturally occurring (*S*)-4-hydroxy-lapachone (95CJC1399) and various chroman-4-ones have been enantioselectively reduced by $NaBH_4$ in the presence of optically active Co (II) complexes (95AG(E)2145).

The base catalysed reaction of 3-azidochroman-4-one with simple aldehydes affords the aldol product, but reaction of the enolate with acetone is slower than loss of N_2 from the azido function and

3-aminochromone is formed along with a bischromanone (95JOC2368).

6.4.1.7 Flavonoids

2'-Hydroxychalcones undergo an intramolecular Michael addition in the solid state below their melting point to give flavanones (95JCS(P2)325) and the cyclodehydrogenation of hydroxychalcones to flavones can be achieved using iodobenzene diacetate (95LA1711).

Isoflavones result from the arylation of 3-(allyloxycarbonyl) chroman-4-ones with aryllead (IV) triacetates. Of particular interest is the introduction of a 2'-hydroxy function through incorporation of a protected phenolic unit into the aryllead reagent (95JCS(P1)1679).

The conversion of flavanones to flavones or isoflavones can be accomplished selectively using iodobenzene diacetate and iodosobenzene, respectively (95JCR(S)213).

Further illustrations of the value of isoxazole and Heck methodologies in flavone synthesis have been published (95ACS524) and a route to 3-aminoflavone-8-acetic acid has been described (95TL1845). The use of an imidazolidinone chiral auxiliary enables isoflavans to be formed in good yield and in high enantiomeric excess from phenacyl chlorides (95CC1317).

6.4.1.8 Xanthones

A series of rearrangements is proposed to account for the formation of symmetrically substituted xanthenes when hydroquinones react with 2-methylprop-2-en-1-ol (95S693). In an equally simple reaction, dibenzo[a,j]xanthenes are produced when aliphatic aldehydes react with an excess of 2-naphthol under acidic conditions (95JCR(S)502).

6.4.1.9 Pyrylium Salts

Interest in the use of pyrylium salts in synthesis continues. 2-Methylpyridinium salts are converted into the 2-arylpyridinium compound on reaction with 2,4,6-triarylpyrylium salts in the presence of base. The methylpyridinium salt is deprotonated to the anhydrobase which behaves as an enamine, attacking the pyrylium salt at C-2, promoting a ring opening - ring closure sequence which culminates in the effective arylation of the pyridinium salt.

4-Methylpyridinium and the corresponding quinolinium salts behave in a similar manner (95JHC563, 991).

When 2-methyleneindolines (Fischer's bases) are used as the nucleophilic species, 2-spiroannulated indolines result with high diastereomeric purity (95JPR368). When R^1 = Ph, an acid catalysed isomerisation leads to a highly substituted benzophenone (23).

Pyrylium behaves as the synthetic equivalent of the pentadienal cation in its reactions with organometallic reagents, allowing the stereoelective formation of $2Z,4E$-dienals. This approach to the synthesis of retinoids using a variety of pyrylium salts has been most successful (95JCS(P1)2385).

6.4.2 HETEROCYCLES CONTAINING ONE SULFUR ATOM

6.4.2.1   Thiopyrans and analogues

Activated thioamides can serve as the dienophile in cycloaddition reactions, giving access to amino-substituted dihydrothiopyrans (95CC1897).

The dihydrothiopyran unit has been fused onto [60]fullerene through reaction with a thioacrylamide and an acyl chloride (95CC565). Cycloadditions also feature in the synthesis of benzo[b]thioxanthenes in which $2H$-benzo[b]thiete behaves as a source of a heterodiene. Reaction with either 1,4-naphthoquinones or 1,4-epoxynaphthalenes affords the tetracycle which can be further manipulated (95JPR379).

A detailed study of the halocyclisation of unsaturated benzyl sulfides has shown that tetrahydrothiopyran formation is favoured from alkenyl sulfides through 6-*endo-trig* and 6-*exo-trig* modes. However, for alkynyl sulfides only the 6-*exo-dig* cyclisation is predominant, leading to dihydrothiopyrans (95JOC6468).

Pentadienyl cations complexed to Fe(CO)$_3$ can be trapped intramolecularly by sulfides to yield tetrahydrothiopyrans with high stereoselectivity. Conversion to the sulfoxide is facile and occurs with good diastereoselectivity (95TL1849).

Reagents: (i) Amberlyst 15, CH$_2$Cl$_2$, RT; (ii) Oxone

The radical cyclisation of *o*-bromophenyl sulfones affords the benzothiopyran 1,1-dioxide in which the *trans* isomer is either exclusive or predominant (95SL943).

$1H$-2-Benzothiopyrans are available through alkyne insertion into Pd-complexes derived from *o*-iodobenzyl sulfides and subsequent depalladation. The reaction is regiospecific, unsymmetrical phenylacetylenes yielding the 3-phenylisothiochroman (95JOC1005).

Reagents: (i) Pd(dba)$_2$, PhMe; (ii) PhCCR', CH$_2$Cl$_2$;
(iii) AgBF$_4$, CH$_2$Cl$_2$; (iv) PhCl, Δ

4-Silyloxybenzopyrylium salts, readily derived from thiochromones, undergo a diastereoselective annulation on reaction with silyloxybutadienes. The resulting silyl enol ethers can be hydrolysed to the dioxothioxanthene (95AG(E)647).

Selenoacylamidines also take part in Diels-Alder reactions yielding 4*H*-selenopyrans through a cycloaddition-cycloreversion-cycloaddition sequence (95TL237). 5,6-Dihydro-2*H*-selenopyrans have also been obtained by hetero-Diels-Alder protocol (95JA10922).

6.4.3 HETEROCYCLES CONTAINING TWO OR MORE OXYGEN ATOMS

6.4.3.1 Dioxins

Tris(hydroxymethyl)nitromethane is a good precursor of 1,3-dioxan-5-ones. An initial acid catalysed condensation with aldehydes and ketones forms the heterocyclic ring and routine functional group interconversions subsequently produce the 5-carbonyl group. The generation and reactions of the Li enolates have been investigated; aldol reactions are threo-selective (95CJC1616).

2,2-Dimethyl-1,3-dioxane-4,6-dione, Meldrum's acid, is alkylated at C-5 on reaction with aromatic aldehydes in the presence of formic acid and Et_3N. The initially formed benzylidene derivative is spontaneously reduced at ca. 50 °C. Higher temperatures cleave the heterocycle, affording 3-arylpropanoic acids (95SC3067). The pyrolysis of 5-alkylsulfamylmethylene derivatives of Meldrum's acid gives high yields of 3-hydroxythiophenes (95JCS(P1)1209).

2-Substituted 1,4-benzodioxins yield the 7-aryl compound exclusively under Friedel-Crafts conditions, but the 2,3-dihydro derivatives give a mixture of the 6- and 7- isomers in which the latter predominates (95T2619). The reaction of the tetraoxabicyclo-[4.4.0]decanes with allyltrimethylsilane provides good yields of 2,3-diallyl-1,4-dioxanes in which the *meso* compound predominates (95CC607).

6.4.3.2 Trioxins

The antimalarial properties of the artemisinins have stimulated interest in the 1,2,4-trioxine system. In the search for simpler molecules which retain the antimalarial activity, *cis*-fused cyclopenteno-1,2,4-trioxanes have been synthesised from 1,4-aryl-cyclopenta-1,3-diene, the racemic product being resolved on a chiral column (95HCA647). Other tricyclic analogues have been obtained from cyclohexanones using enamine and Wittig methodologies, the trioxane ring being formed by skeletal rearrangement of a 1,2-dioxetane (95HA105).

Analogues of artemisinin which have been prepared include the 13-carba (95TL3965) and 11-aza (95TL829) analogues.

The mode of action of the artemisinins results from cleavage of the peroxide link involving Fe^{2+}, haem or a high valent iron species which leads to a C-centred radical, the probable lethal agent (95HCA647, 95JA5885, 95TL7551).

6.4.4 HETEROCYCLES CONTAINING TWO OR MORE SULFUR ATOMS

6.4.4.1 Dithiins

The synthesis of 1,2-benzodithiin has been achieved through cyclisation of the bisthiolate obtained from either phenylacetylene or benzo[*b*]thiophene (95TL1421). These yellow solids are more stable than both 1,2-dithiins and can be oxidised at either sulfur atom and also under Swern conditions to give the 3-aldehyde.

Reagents: (i) $PhCH_2SH$, base; (ii) Na, NH_3; (iii) $K_3[Fe(CN)_6]$, H_2O

1,2-Dithianes are ring opened by organolithium reagents and subsequent reaction with electrophiles provides unsymmetrically substituted dithia compounds (95JCS(P1)2381).

The value of 1,3-dithianes in stereoselective synthesis ensures a healthy interest in their chemistry. A simple synthesis of 2-acetyl-1,3-dithiane and its microbiological reduction to R-2(1-hydroxyethyl)-1,3-dithiane have been described (95OPP555).

A Pummerer reaction may feature in the epimerisation of syn-2-acyl-2-alkyl-1,3-dithiane 1-oxides by TFAA (95S73).

2,3-Dichlorobenzoquinones react with 1,3-dithiol-2-ylphosphonate esters to give 1,4-dithiin-fused quinones rather than the Wittig-Horner product (95TL7153). 2,5-Diaryl-1,4-dithiins are rearranged to 2,6-diaryl-1,4-dithiafulvenes on treatment with Bu$_4$NOH (95ACS503).

6.4.5 HETEROCYCLES CONTAINING BOTH OXYGEN AND SULFUR IN THE SAME RING

6.4.5.1 Oxathiins

Chiral cyclic sultines result from the reaction of unsaturated alcohols with N-sulfinyl-4-toluenesulfonamide under Lewis acid catalysis. An N-toluenesulfonamide intermediate is proposed (95JOC8067).

Vinylsulfonates (24) undergo a facile intramolecular Diels-Alder reaction affording the *exo*-sultones (25) with excellent diastereo-selectivity. Oxidative desulfurisation of the sultones gives access to γ-hydroxyketones and hence vinylsulfonyl chloride used to prepared (24) behaves as a ketone equivalent (95T711).

A Pummerer rearrangement features in two approaches to 1,3-oxathiins. Refluxing γ,δ-unsaturated sulfinyl compounds (26) in xylene containing TsOH effects conversion to the 3,1-benzoxathiin (27) *via* a sulfonium ion intermediate (95CC1197), whilst 2-(hydroxymethyl)phenyl sulfoxides (28), readily cyclise to the benzoxathiin (95T6819).

(26)   (27)   (28)

Highly functionalised 1,4-oxathiins have been obtained by the cycloaddition of electron rich alkenes and alkynes to α-oxo and α,α'-dioxo- thiones (95JOC6416, 95TL6755). The derived 1,4-oxathiin S-oxides undergo a facile retro-Diels-Alder reaction generating the α,α'-dioxosulfine which can be trapped with dienophiles and dienes to give more elaborate 1,4-oxathiin S-oxides and thiopyran S-oxides, respectively (95TL5089).

Optically pure 1,3-oxathiins have been used as chiral auxiliaries for the synthesis of (R)-monoaryl epoxides (95JOC3494) and β-substituted ketones (95SL501), whilst the desulfurisation of some dihydro-1,4-oxathiins affords E-alkyl vinyl ethers (95SL1274).

6.4.6   REFERENCES

95ACR343   J. B. Gloer, *Acc. Chem. Res.*, 1995, **28**, 343.

95ACS503   M. L. Andersen, M. F. Nielsen, O. Hammerich, *Acta Chem. Scand.*, 1995, **49**, 503.

95ACS524   S. Ellemose, N. Kure, K. B. G. Torssell, *Acta Chem. Scand.*, 1995, **49**, 524.

85AG(E)647   U. Beifuss, H. Gehm, M. Noltemeyer H.-G. Schmidt, *Angew. Chem. Int. Ed. Engl.*, 1995, **34**, 647.

95AG(E)2145   T. Nagata, K. Yorozu, T. Yamada, T. Mukaiyama, *Angew. Chem. Int. Ed. Engl.*, 1995, **34**, 2145.

95AHC19   J. Kuthan, P. Sebek, S. Böhm, *Adv. Heterocycl. Chem.*, 1995, **62**, 19.

95CC565   M. Ohno, S. Kojima, S. Eguchi, *J. Chem. Soc. Chem. Commun.*, 1995, 565.

95CC607   H. Pellisier, M. Santelli, *J. Chem. Soc. Chem. Commun.*, 1995, 607.

95CC743   Z.-C. Yang, W.-S. Zhou, *J. Chem. Soc. Chem. Commun.*, 1995, 743.

95CC989   E. Menéndez, R. Brieva, F. Rebolledo, V. Gotor, *J. Chem. Soc. Chem. Commun.*, 1995, 989.

95CC1117   K. Ishihara, N. Hanaki, H. Yamamoto, *J. Chem. Soc. Chem. Commun.*, 1995, 1117.

95CC1197   H. Abe, J. Itani, C. Masunari, S. Kashino, T. Harayama, *J. Chem. Soc. Chem. Commun.*, 1995, 1197.

95CC1317   M. Versteeg, B. C. B. Bezuidenhoudt, D. Ferreira, K. J. Swart, *J. Chem. Soc. Chem. Commun.*, 1995, 1317.

95CC1897   R. Arnaud, P. Y. Chavant, K. Molvinger, Y. Vallée, *J. Chem. Soc. Chem. Commun.*, 1995, 1897.

95CC1971   S. Caddick, S. Khan, *J. Chem. Soc. Chem. Commun.*, 1995, 1971.

95CC2417   T. Tsuda, H. Hokazono, K. Toyota, *J. Chem. Soc. Chem. Commun.*, 1995, 2417.

95CJC1399   H. L. Holland, J. Qi, T. S. Manoharan, *Can. J. Chem.*, 1995, **73**, 1399.

95CJC1616   M. Majewski, D. M. Gleave, P. Nowak, *Can. J. Chem.*, 1995, **73**, 1616.

95CJC1727   K. C. Majumdar, A. K. Kundu, *Can. J. Chem.*, 1995, **73**, 1727.

95COS133   T. Laduwahetty, *Contemp. Org. Synth.*, 1995, **2**, 133.

95COS189   C. J. Burns, *Contemp. Org. Synth.*, 1995, **2**, 189.

95COS225   K. J. McCullough, *Contemp. Org. Synth.*, 1995, **2**, 225.

95COS365   S. V. Ley, R. Downham, P. J. Edwards, J. E. Innes, M. Woods, *Contemp. Org. Synth.*, 1995, **2**, 365.

95CRV789   M. T. Fletcher, W. Kitching, *Chem. Rev.*, 1995, **95**, 789.

95CRV2041   R. D. Norcross, I. Paterson, *Chem. Rev.*, 1995, **95**, 2041.

95G111   A. Ramacciotti, R. Fiaschi, E. Napolitano, *Gazz. Chim. Ital.*, 1995, **125**, 111.

95H(41)1299   V. Kepe, M. Kocevar, S. Polanc, *Heterocycles*, 1995, **41**, 1299.

95H(41)2327   M. Darabantu, S. Mager, G. Plé, C. Puscas, *Heterocycles*, 1995, **41**, 2327.

95HA105   G. H. Posner, C. H. Oh, L. Gerena, W. K. Milhous, *Heteroatom Chem.*, 1995, **6**, 105.

95HCA647   C. W. Jefford, S. Kohmoto, D. Jaggi, G. Timári, J.-C. Rossier, M. Rudaz, O. Barbuzzi, D. Gérard, U. Burger, P.

Kamalaprija, J. Mareda, G. Bernardinelli, I. Manzanares, C. J. Canfield, S. L. Fleck, B. L. Robinson, W. Peters, *Helv. Chim. Acta,* 1995, **78**, 647.

95JA5885   G. H. Posner, J. N. Cumming, P. Ploypradith, C. H. Oh, *J. Am. Chem. Soc.,* 1995, **117**, 5885.

95JA5889   Z. Li, R. W. Quan, E. N. Jacobsen, *J. Am. Chem. Soc.,* 1995, **117**, 5889.

95JA8017   E. Lee, C. M. Park, J. S. Yun, *J. Am. Chem. Soc.,* 1995, **117**, 8017.

95JA8258   A. S. Kende, K. Liu, I. Kaldor, G. Dorey, K. Koch, *J. Am. Chem. Soc.,* 1995, **117**, 8258.

95JA10227   K. C. Nicolaou, C.-K. Hwang, M. E. Duggan, D. A. Nugiel, Y. Abe, K. B. Reddy, S. A. DeFrees, D. R. Reddy, R. A. Awartani, S. R. Conley, F. P. J. T. Rutjes, E. A. Theodorakis, *J. Am. Chem. Soc.,* 1995, **117**, 10227.

95JA10922   S. Wilker, G. Erker, *J. Am. Chem. Soc.,* 1995, **117**, 10922.

95JCR(S)213 O. Prakash, M. P. Tanwar, *J. Chem. Res. (S),* 1995, 213.

95JCR(S)372 S.-T. Lin, F.-M. Yang, H.-J. Yang, K.-F. Huang, *J. Chem. Res. (S),* 1995, 372.

95JCR(S)502 O. Sirkecioglu, N. Talinli, A. Akar, *J. Chem. Res. (S),* 1995, 502.

95JCS(P1)949 R. A. Lichtenfels, A. L. Coelho, P. R. R. Costa, *J. Chem. Soc. Perkin Trans. 1,* 1995, 949.

95JCS(P1)1089 D. Nicoletti, A. A. Ghini, A. L. Brachet-Cota, G. Burton, *J. Chem. Soc. Perkin Trans. 1,* 1995, 1089.

95JCS(P1)1209 G. A. Hunter, H. McNab, *J. Chem. Soc. Perkin Trans. 1,* 1995, 1209.

95JCS(P1)1131 C.-A. Harrison, P. M. Jackson, C. J. Moody, J. M. J. Williams, *J. Chem. Soc. Perkin Trans. 1,* 1995, 1131.

95JCS(P1)1215 A. S. Cotterill, M. Gill, N. M. Milanovic, *J. Chem. Soc. Perkin Trans. 1,* 1995, 1215.

95JCS(P1)1373 T. Ye, C. F. García, M. A. McKervey, *J. Chem. Soc. Perkin Trans. 1,* 1995, 1373.

95JCS(P1)1679 D. M. X. Donnelly, J.-P. Finet, B. A. Rattigan, *J. Chem. Soc. Perkin Trans. 1,* 1995, 1679.

95JCS(P1)1857 M. Gotoh, T. Mizui, B. Sun, K. Hirayama, M. Noguchi, *J. Chem. Soc. Perkin Trans. 1,* 1995, 1857.

95JCS(P1)2103 P. Duhamel, A. Deyine, G. Dujardin, G. Plé, J.-M. Poirier, *J. Chem. Soc. Perkin Trans. 1,* 1995, 2103.

95JCS(P1)2293 T. W. Wallace, I. Wardell, K.-D. Li, P. Leeming, A. D. Redhouse, S. R. Challand, *J. Chem. Soc. Perkin Trans. 1,* 1995, 2293.

95JCS(P1)2381 K. Smith, M. Tzimas, *J. Chem. Soc. Perkin Trans. 1,* 1995, 2381.

95JCS(P1)2385 R. J. K. Taylor, K. Hemming, E. F. De Medeiros, *J. Chem. Soc. Perkin Trans. 1*, 1995, 2385.

95JCS(P1)2531 D. M. X. Donnelly, D. J. Molloy, J. P. Reilly, J.-P. Finet, *J. Chem. Soc. Perkin Trans. 1*, 1995, 2531.

95JCS(P1)2551 J. E. Bishop, K. A. Flaxman, B. S. Orlek, P. G. Sammes, D. J. Weller, *J. Chem. Soc. Perkin Trans. 1*, 1995, 2551.

95JCS(P2)325 B. S. Goud, K. Panneerselvam, D. E. Zacharias, G. R. Desiraju, *J. Chem. Soc. Perkin Trans. 2*, 1995, 325.

95JHC43 W. Löwe, T. Rütjes, *J. Heterocycl. Chem.*, 1995, **32**, 43.

95JHC563 T. Zimmermann, *J. Heterocycl. Chem.*, 1995, **32**, 563.

95JHC991 T. Zimmermann, *J. Heterocycl. Chem.*, 1995, **32**, 991.

95JOC1005 J. Spencer, M. Pfeffer, A. DeCian, J. Fischer, *J. Org. Chem.*, 1995, **60**, 1005.

95JOC1013 S. E. Denmark, M. E. Schnute, *J. Org. Chem.*, 1995, **60**, 1013.

95JOC2368 T. Patonay, R. V. Hoffman, *J. Org. Chem.*, 1995, **60**, 2368.

95JOC3039 X.-X. Xu, H.-Q. Dong, *J. Org. Chem.*, 1995, **60**, 3039.

95JOC3121 T. K. M. Shing, H.-C. Tsui, Z.-H. Zhou, *J. Org. Chem.*, 1995, **60**, 3121.

95JOC3270 R. C. Larock, E. K. Yum, M. J. Doty, K. K. C. Sham, *J. Org. Chem.*, 1995, **60**, 3270.

95JOC3397 J. T. North, D. R. Kronenthal, A. J. Pullockaran, S. D. Real, H. Y. Chen, *J. Org. Chem.*, 1995, **60**, 3397.

95JOC3494 A. Solladié-Cavallo, A. Diep-Vohuule, *J. Org. Chem.*, 1995, **60**, 3494.

95JOC3711 H.-Y. Liao, C.-H. Cheng, *J. Org. Chem.*, 1995, **60**, 3711.

95JOC4160 A. Díaz-Ortiz, E. Díez-Barra, A. de la Hoz, P. Prieto, A. Moreno, F. Langa, T. Prangé, A. Neuman, *J. Org. Chem.*, 1995, **60**, 4160.

95JOC5048 M. Oikawa, T. Ueno, H. Oikawa, A. Ichihara, *J. Org. Chem.*, 1995, **60**, 5048.

95JOC5143 R. D. Rieke, M. S. Sell, H. Xiong, *J. Org. Chem.*, 1995, **60**, 5143.

95JOC5998 G. E. Keck, X.-Y. Li, D. Krishnamurthy, *J. Org. Chem.*, 1995, **60**, 5998.

95JOC6416 G. Capozzi, R. W. Franck, M. Mattioli, S. Menichetti, C. Nativi, G. Valle, *J. Org. Chem.*, 1995, **60**, 6416.

95JOC6468 X.-F. Ren, E. Turos, C. H. Lake, M. R. Churchill, *J. Org. Chem.*, 1995, **60**, 6468.

95JOC7724 A. P. Degnan, C. S. Kim, C. W. Stout, A. G. Kalivretenos, *J. Org. Chem.*, 1995, **60**, 7724.

95JOC8067 C. M. Marson, P. R. Giles, *J. Org. Chem.*, 1995, **60**, 8067.

95JOC8128 W.-M. Dai, C. W. Lau, S. H. Chung, Y.-D. Wu, *J. Org. Chem.*, 1995, **60**, 8128.

95JPR368 T. Zimmermann, M. Pink, *J. Prakt. Chem.*, 1995, **337**, 368.

95JPR379	D. Gröschl, A. Mayer, M. Schmidt, H. Meier, *J. Prakt. Chem.*, 1995, **337**, 379.
95LA1711	G. Litkei, K. Gulácsi, S. Antus, G. Blaskó, *Liebigs Ann. Chem.*, 1995, 1711.
95M579	H. Junek, C. Reidlinger, *Monatsh. Chem.*, 1995, **126**, 579.
B-95MI	'Organosulfur Chemistry Synthetic Aspects', ed. P. Page, Academic Press, London, 1995.
95OPP555	F. Bracher, T. Litz, *Org. Prep. Proced. Int.*, 1995, **27**, 555.
95S73	P. C. Bulman Page, S. J. Shuttleworth, M. J. McKenzie, M. B. Schilling, D. J. Tapolczay, *Synthesis*, 1995, 73.
95S630	P. P. Deshpande, D. C. Baker, *Synthesis*, 1995, 630.
95S633	I. C. Ivanov, S. K. Karagiosov, *Synthesis*, 1995, 633.
95S693	L. Novák, P. Kovács, G. Pirok, P. Kolonits, E. Szabó, J. Fekete, V. Weiszfeiler, C. Szántay, *Synthesis*, 1995, 693.
95S1102	T. Kanda, S. Kato, T. Sugino, N. Kambe, A. Ogawa, N. Sonoda, *Synthesis*, 1995, 1102.
95S1311	E. Ciganek, *Synthesis*, 1995, 1311.
95SC2883	P. G. Ciattini, E. Morera, G. Ortar, *Synth. Commun.*, 1995, **25**, 2883.
95SC3067	G. Tóth, K. E. Kövér, *Synth. Commun.*, 1995, **25**, 3067.
95SL197	T. Fukuda, R. Irie, T. Katsuki, *Synlett*, 1995, 197.
95SL501	K. Utimoto, T. Kodama, S. Matsubara, *Synlett*, 1995, 501.
95SL573	R. L. Danheiser, M. P. Trova, *Synlett*, 1995, 573.
95SL663	T. Minami, A. Moriyama, M. Hanaoka, *Synlett*, 1995, 663.
95SL742	B. Jamart-Grégoire, S. Mercier-Girardot, S. Ianelli, M. Nardelli, P. Caubère, *Synlett*, 1995, 742.
95SL943	C. D. S. Brown, A. P. Dishington, O. Shishkin, N. S. Simpkins, *Synlett*, 1995, 943.
95SL1255	E. Mizuguchi, K. Achiwa, *Synlett*, 1995, 1255.
95SL1274	R. Caputo, L. Longobardo, G. Palumbo, S. Pedatella, *Synlett*, 1995, 1274.
95T711	P. Metz, M. Fleischer, R. Fröhlich, *Tetrahedron*, 1995, **51**, 711.
95T1429	Z. Yang, W. Zhou, *Tetrahedron*, 1995, **51**, 1429.
95T1973	B. Jamart-Grégoire, S. Mercier-Girardot, S. Ianelli, M. Nardelli, P. Caubère, *Tetrahedron*, 1995, **51**, 1973.
95T2585	J. Boivin, L. El Kaim, S. Z. Zard, *Tetrahedron*, 1995, **51**, 2585.
95T2619	V. Thiéry, G. Coudert, L. Morin-Allory, G. Guillaumet, *Tetrahedron*, 1995, **51**, 2619.
95T3087	Y. R. Lee, *Tetrahedron*, 1995, **51**, 3087.
95T6819	I. D. Kersey, C. W. G. Fishwick, J. B. C. Findlay, P. Ward, *Tetrahedron*, 1995, **51**, 6819.
95T8383	D. A. L. Vandenput, H. W. Scheeren, *Tetrahedron*, 1995, **51**, 8383.

95T9393   I. Paterson, J. G. Cumming, R. A. Ward, S. Lamboley, *Tetrahedron*, 1995, **51**, 9393.

95T9559   G. Solladié, D. Boeffel, J. Maignan, *Tetrahedron*, 1995, **51**, 9559.

95TA123   R. N. Patel, A. Banerjee, C. G. McNamee, L. J. Szarka, *Tetrahedron Asymm.*, 1995, **6**, 123.

95TL237   D. Dubreuil, J. P. Pradère, N. Giraudeau, M. Goli, F. Tonnard, *Tetrahedron Lett.*, 1995, 237.

95TL829   D. S. Torok, H. Ziffer, *Tetrahedron Lett.*, 1995, 829.

95TL1421   W. Schroth, H. Jordan, R. Spitzner, *Tetrahedron Lett.*, 1995, 1421.

95TL1845   D. Dauzonne, L. Martinez, *Tetrahedron Lett.*, 1995, 1845.

95TL1849   A. Hachem, L. Toupet, R. Grée, *Tetrahedron Lett.*, 1995, 1849.

95TL1909   P. Bird, J. Eames, A. G. Fallis,, R. V. H. Jones, M. Roddis, C. F. Sturino, S. O'Sullivan, S. Warren, M. S. Westwell, J. Worrall, *Tetrahedron Lett.*, 1995, 1909.

95TL2713   T. A. Engler, K. O. Lynch Jr., W. Chai, S. P. Meduna, *Tetrahedron Lett.*, 1995, 2713.

95TL2855   G. Desimoni, G. Faita, P. P. Righetti, *Tetrahedron Lett.*, 1995, 2855.

95TL3553   A. De Mico, R. Margarita, G. Piancatelli, *Tetrahedron Lett.*, 1995, 3553.

95TL3669   W. Adam, J. Jekö, A. Lévai, C. Nemes, T. Patonay, P. Sebök, *Tetrahedron Lett.*, 1995, 3669.

95TL3965   M. A. Avery, P. Fan, J. M. Karle, R. Miller, K. Goins, *Tetrahedron Lett.*, 1995, 3965.

95TL5089   G. Capozzi, P. Fratini, S. Menichetti, C. Nativi, *Tetrahedron Lett.*, 1995, 5089.

95TL5357   H. Arimoto, Y. Okumura, S. Nishiyama, S. Yamamura, *Tetrahedron Lett.*, 1995, 5357.

95TL5603   M. Yamashita, K. Okuyama, I. Kawasaki, S. Ohta, *Tetrahedron Lett.*, 1995, 5603.

95TL6669   L. Vaillon, O. Reinaud, P. Capdevielle, M. Maumy, *Tetrahedron Lett.*, 1995, 6669.

95TL6755   G. Capozzi, C. Falciani, S. Menichetti, C. Nativi, R. W. Franck, *Tetrahedron Lett.*, 1995, 6755.

95TL7109   R. S. Mali, N. A. Pandhare, M. D. Sindkhedkar, *Tetrahedron Lett.*, 1995, 7109.

95TL7153   N. Martín, L. Sánchez, C. Seoane, J. Garín, J. Orduna, *Tetrahedron Lett.*, 1995, 7153.

95TL7551   A. J. Bloodworth, A. Shah, *Tetrahedron Lett.*, 1995, 7551.

95TL9165   Y. Naoe, J. Kikuishi, K. Ishigaki, H. Iitsuka, *Tetrahedron Lett.*, 1995, 9165.

Chapter 7

Seven-Membered Rings

David J. LeCount
*Formerly of Zeneca Pharmaceuticals, UK,
1, Vernon Avenue, Congleton, Cheshire, UK*

7.1 INTRODUCTION

This is the final volume to b published under the guidance of Professor Hans Suschitzky, who during the year under review celebrated his 80th birthday. It is on this occasion that the author would like to dedicate this chapter to Professor Suschitzky.

7.2 RING SYSTEMS CONTAINING ONE HETEROATOM

7.2.1 Azepines

Maximally unsaturated azepines feature during the period under review. Cyclisation of the β,γ-unsaturated aldehyde (**1**) by treatment with trifluoroacetic acid, followed by treatment with base (DABCO or DMAP) affords 2*H*-azepine <95AG(E)1469>. The compound itself is difficult to isolate but it is remarkably stable in solution, no trace of the thermodynamically favoured 3*H*-azepine being observed after 48h at room temperature. In addition, the bicyclic adduct (**2**) is formed, probably arising from [2 + 4] cycloaddition of isobutene formed *in situ* and the intermediate immonium ion (**3**).

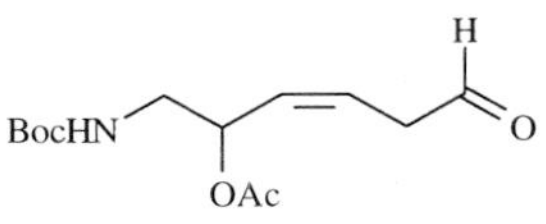

(**1**)

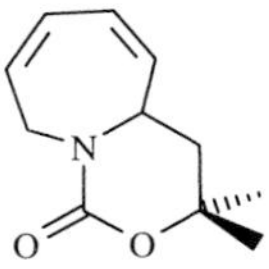

(**2**)

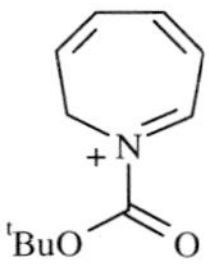

(**3**)

When 1,3-dimethoxybenzene is heated in benzene with 1a-acetyl-1-phthalamido-1a,6b-dihydro-benzofuro[2,3-*b*]azirine as a source of phthalimidonitrene, 2,4-dimethoxy-7-phthalimido-3*H*-azepine is isolated in modest yield <95JCS(P1)809>. If the reaction is carried out over a shorter time period (5h instead of 18h), it is the 2*H*-azepine which is isolated in 18% yield. A number of other analogues have been prepared and the X-ray structure of 5,7-dimethoxy-3-methyl-2-phthalimido-2*H*-azepine has been determined.

1,6-Diethoxy-1,5-hexadiene-3,4-dione reacts with ammonia and primary amines to give a mixture of the aminoalkyl- and bis(aminoalkyl)-dienes (4) and (5), which on heating in *o*-dichlorobenzene furnishes the 1*H*-azepine-4,5-diones (6, R = H, alkyl) <95JHC57>. These diones react conventionally with *o*-diaminobenzenes to yield a number of 3*H*-azepino[4,5-*b*]quinoxalines.

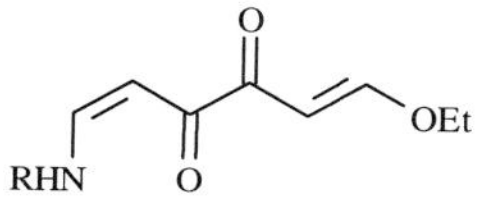

(4)

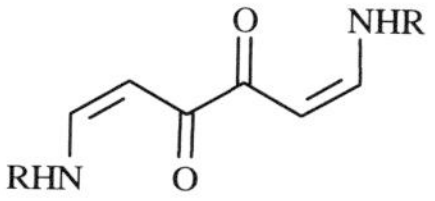

(5)

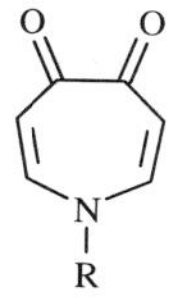

(6)

Cyclisation of the acid (7) in a mixture of DCC, DMAP and DMAP.HCl gives the azepane (8), an intermediate in the preparation of Cobactin T (9), a key component of mycobactins (Scheme 1) <95TL6379>, and cyclisation of the bisepoxide (10) with benzylamine affords the azepane (11) in a 7-*endo*-tet cyclisation <95JOC5958>. In contrast to the corresponding 3,4-benzyl ethers of the bisepoxides, no cyclisation to 6-membered species is observed.

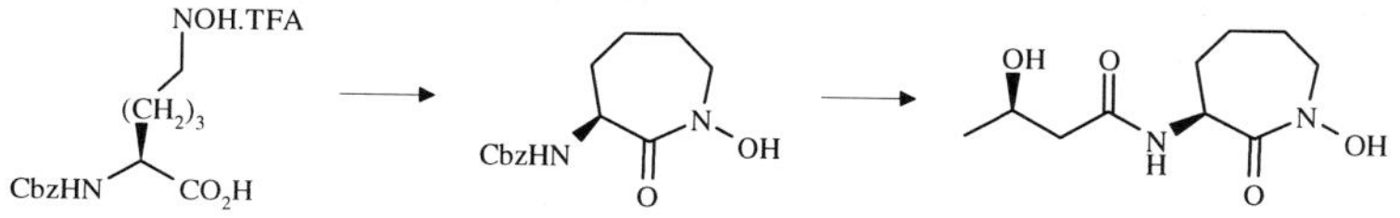

(7)

(8)

(9)

Scheme 1

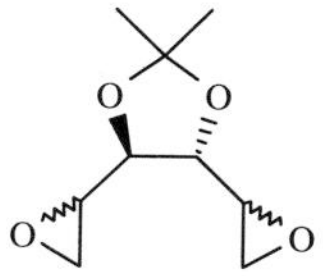

(10)

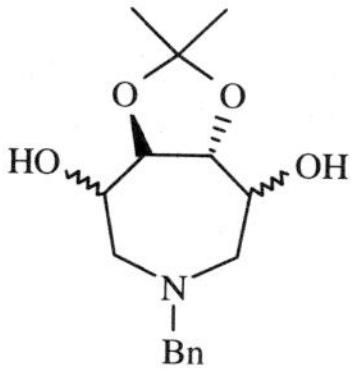

(11)

The ring expansion of cyclohexanone derivatives is a well established route to azepanes and a number of further examples have been published <95JHC491; 95SC3863; 95TL3659>. In one example it has been demonstrated that hydroxylamine-*O*-sulphonic acid reacts with cyclohexanone over SiO_2 under microwave irradiation to give the corresponding lactam in 86% yield <95JCS(CC)1101>. 3-Bromo-1-(4'-methylphenylsulphonyl)piperidin-4-one undergoes carbene insertion with ethyl diazoacetate to give 3-bromo-5-ethoxycarbonyl-1-(4'-methylsulphonyl)azepan-4-one <95JCS(P1)2355>. Cyclocondensation and Picter-Spengler cyclisations have been employed to prepare a number of 1- and 3-benzazepine derivatives <95JMC3514, 4284, 2395>, <95TL6733>.

Reaction of the quinone (12) with vinyl aziridine affords the dihydroazepinoquinone (14) in good yield <95TL4787>. The reaction proceeds via an aza-Claison rearrangement of the intermediate (13) followed by a sigmatropic rearrangement (Scheme 2).

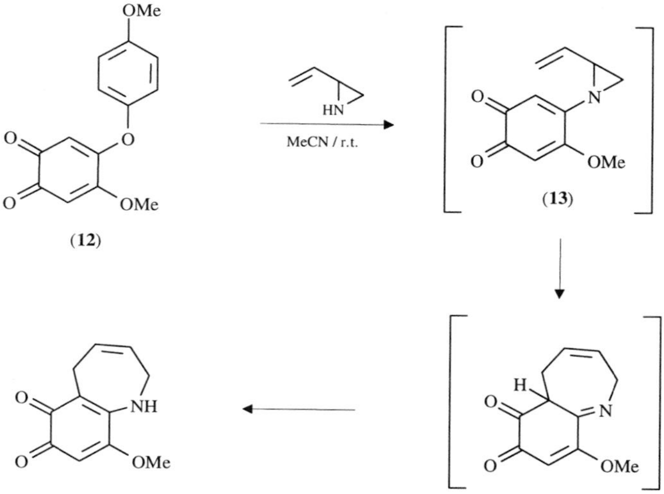

Scheme 2

Thermolysis of 3-(2,2-dicyanovinyl)-4-(1-piperidyl)pyridine (15, $X = CH_2$) in DMSO produces the naphthyridine (16, $X = CH_2$) by means of the "*tert*-amino effect" proposed by Meth-Cohn and Suschitzky <95SL622>. Where, however, X is a N, O or S an alternative cyclisation takes place, when the pyridoazepines (17) are formed. This new variant of the "*tert*-amino effect" is postulated to arise by the intermediate formation of (18).

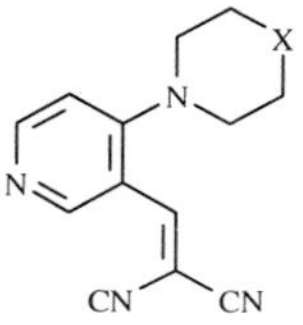

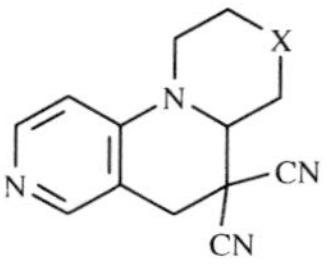

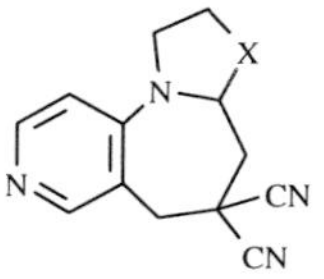

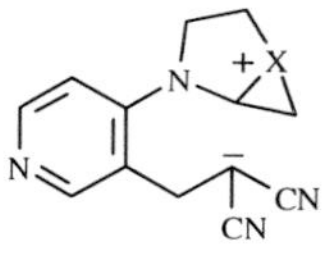

In further examples of sequential cycloaddition - palladium catalysed cyclisations, Grigg and co-workers have demonstrated the formation of polycyclic β-lactams, e.g. (20) from the imine (19) (Scheme 3) <95TL9053>.

Comprehensive data on the 1,7 electrocyclisation of diene conjugated nitrile ylides of the type (21), where cyclisation onto the unsubstituted 2-phenyl group is in competition with the substituent on the 6-position, have been published (Scheme 4) <95JCS(P1)2565>. Alkenyl groups and thiophene ring are more than 100 times more reactive than phenyl. It has also been established that where the 6-substituent is a substituted phenyl group, 3'- and 4'-substituents accelerate ring closure, irrespective of their electronic properties, whereas a 2'-methyl group hinders cyclisation by steric interaction. The relative rates are consistent with differences in the olefinic nature of the double bonds in the various substrates. However, the effects of the substituents on the phenyl ring are less readily explicable.

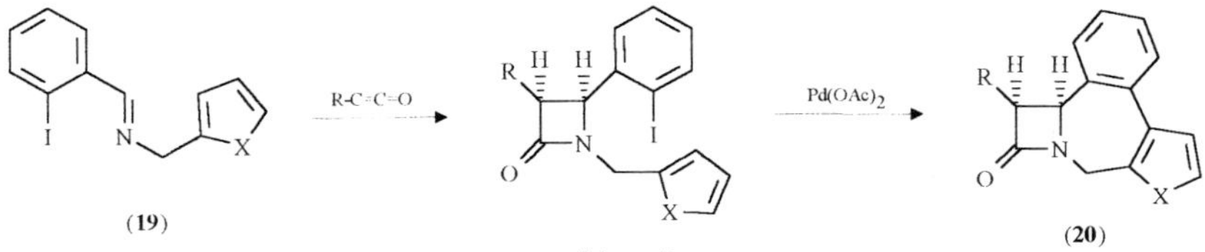

(19)   (20)

Scheme 3

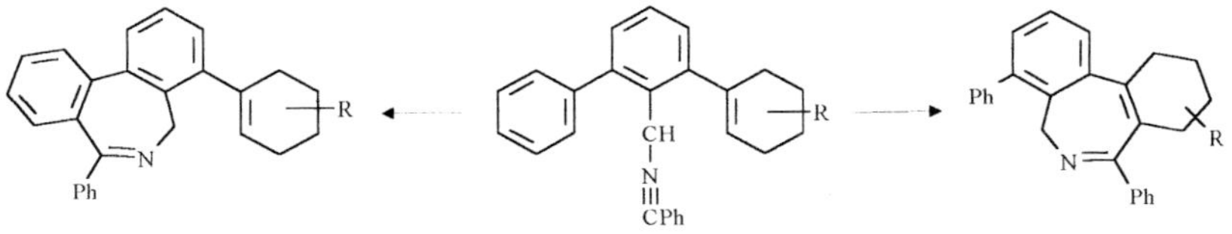

(21)

Scheme 4

Following on from a preliminary report <91TL6727>, Nitta and co-workers have published details of the formation of a number of 5-azaazulenes by the reaction of cyclopentadienyl aldehydes with vinylphosphoranes, the simplest product being the phenyl derivative, 3-phenylcyclohepta[c]azepine <95JCS(P1)1001>.

Electrochemical reduction of the pyridinium compounds (22, R = H, Bu^t), prepared by reaction of 6-bromohexan-2-one and the respective pyridine, yields mixtures of the the fused azepines (23) and (24), albeit in low yield <95AG(E)2007>. A new synthesis of claviciptic acid has been published <95JOC1486>.

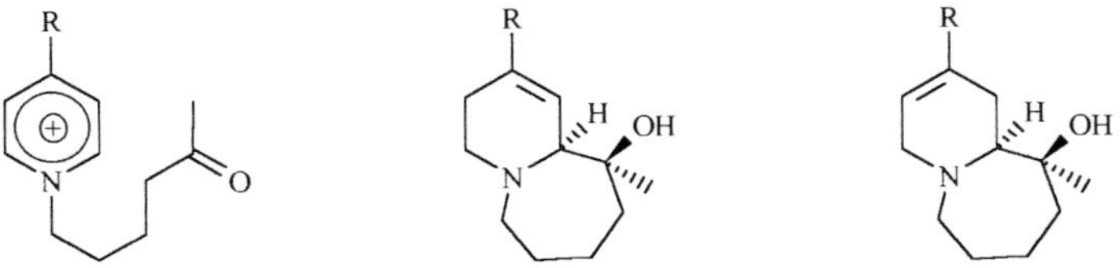

(22)   (23)   (24)

Azepines are frequently the products of ring transformation reactions. Thus 1-arylindoles have been converted into 5H-dibenz[b,f]azepines in an unusual acid-catalysed rearrangement <95T2091> and a number of 3-acyl-4-(indol-3-yl)-2-methyl-4,5-dihydro-1H-1-benzazepines have

have been prepared by the acylation of indole trimer followed by acetic acid catalysed rearrangement <95BSF337>.

Base treatment of helical biliverdins with 2-chloroethyl side chains leads to intramolecular rearrangement to yield derivatives with extended conformations <89JA1525>. This work has been extended to include *inter alia* the syntheses of Neobiliverdin Ixd (**26**), a natural product from the ovaries of the sea snake *Turbo cornutus*, by reaction of (**25**) with base <95T2243, 2255>.

(**25**)   (**26**)

The pentacyclic dimers (**27**) and (**28**) are obtained from quinoline by treatment with a Zn/Ac$_2$O/THF reagent <95SL603> and bromination of the azabicyclo[7.3.1]enediyne (**29**) affords the pyrroloazepine (**30**) <95TL4539>.

(**27**)   (**28**)

(**29**)   (**30**)

The direct functionalisation of 10H-azepino[1,2-a]indole (**31**) has been reported <95JCS(P1)203>. Bromination and Vilsmeier, Mannich and Friedel-Crafts reagents give 11-substituted azepinoindoles, whilst alkyation of the lithium anion gives a mixture of 8H-8-alkyl and 10H-10-alkyl derivatives. Electrochemical oxidation of 2,5-dihydro-1H-1-benzazepines affords 5H-1-benzazepines <95T9611>. 2-Phenylazepanes are readily prepared by reaction of the corresponding unsubstituted N-chloramine with 2.5 equivalents of phenyl lithium in diethyl ether <95SC3789>. Azepane-N-methyldiazoacetamide undergoes C-H insertion to give the lactam (**32**) in high yield and entiomeric selectivity upon treatment with chiral dirhodium (II) catalysts <95SL1075>.

(**31**)   (**32**)

Treatment of the thiolactam (**33**, R = Me, X = S) with (chlorocarbonyl)phenylketene gives the betaine (**34**, R = Me, X = S) which on heating is transformed into the intramolecular cycloaddition product (**35**, R = Me, X = S) and the tricyclic derivative (**36**) <95JOC3795>. In contrast the oxygen analogue (**33**, R = H, X = O) gives only the cycloaddition product (**35**, R = H, X = O). The intermediate betaine was not isolated, nor was it possible to induce extrusion of carbon dioxide on heating, only decomposition products being obtained.

(**33**)   (**34**)   (**35**)   (**36**)

Although DBU is well known as a non-nucleophilic base, it is less well recognised as an amidine capable of reactions of such systems. However, under certain circumstances it is capable of acting as a nucleophile towards a number of strong electrophiles. The successful cycloaddition of dimethyl acetylenedicarboxylate is now added to this list <95JCS(CC)2251>.

7.2.2 Oxepines and thiepines

There has been a resurgence in the interest of oxepines, due in part to the total synthesis of a number of natural products. In their successful completion of the synthesis of brevetoxin B, a

(**37**)   (**38**)

natural product containing two *trans*-fused oxepane rings isolated from the algae *Gymnodinium breve*, Nicolau *et al.* have investigated a number of routes for construction of the azepane ring systems <95JA10252>. In addition to lactonisation, photolytic and reductive

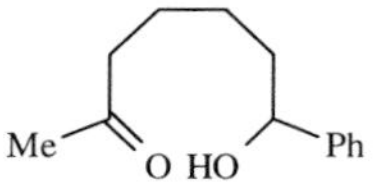

(39)

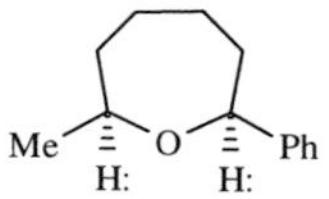

(40)

cyclisations have also been investigated. Thus, photolysis of the thioester (37) in toluene affords the enol ether (38) which equilibrated to a single enantiomer on hydrolysis, and in a second route cyclisation of (39) using Et_3SiH and TMSOTf affords the oxepane (40).

In a synthesis of hemibrevetoxin B, isolated from the same species, Yamamoto and co-workers twice used the method outlined in Scheme 5 in the same molecule to form the oxepane ring <95TL5777> and cyclisation of the alcohol (41) afforded the spirooxapane (42), a key intermediate in the synthesis of (-)-ptilomycalin by Overman and co-workers <95JA2657>.

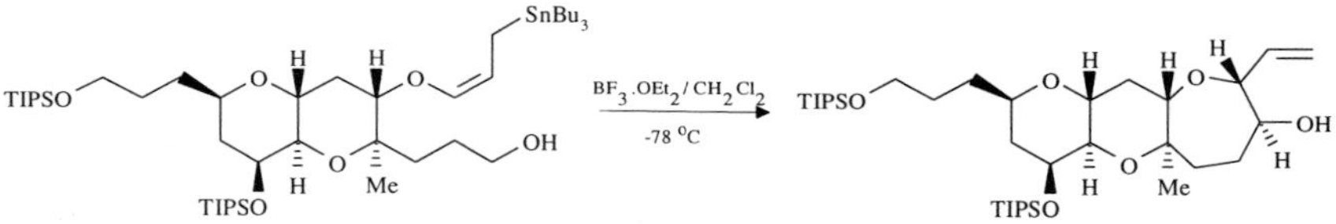

Scheme 5

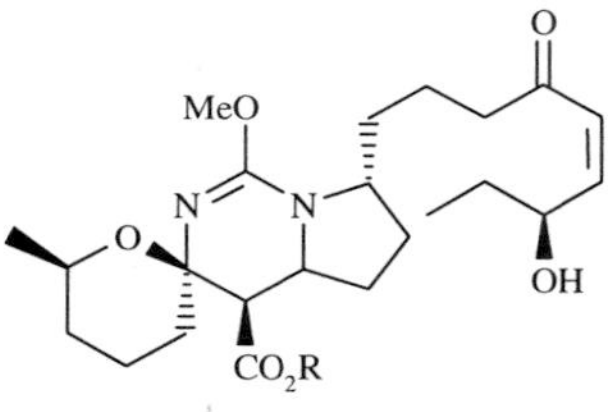

R = $(CH_2)_{15}CO_2All$

(41)

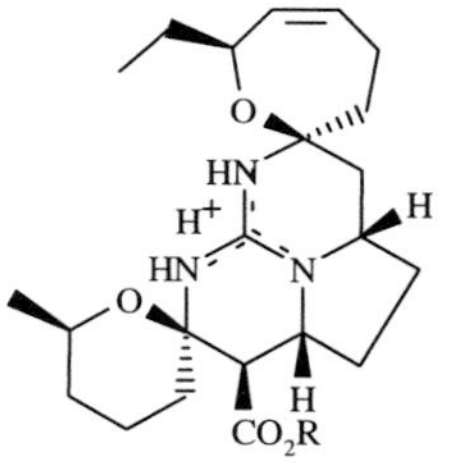

(42)

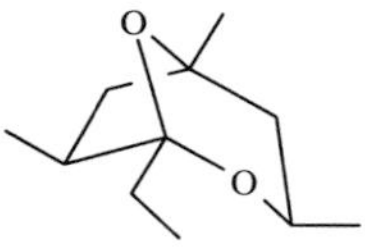

(43)

Further applications of the Baeyer-Williger oxidation of cyclohexanones to the formation of caprolactones have been reported. Regioselective oxidation wth *m*-CPBA has been used in the synthesis of the male-produced pheromone of the banana weevil (43) <95TL1043>. The oxidation of a number of cyclohexanes to the corresponding lactones has been achieved employing magnesium monoperoxyphthalate in acetonitrile in the presence of bentonite clay <95SC3765>, with myristic acid catalysed by *Candida anatarctica* <JCS(P1)89> and with a monooxygenase from *Pseudomonas putida* NCIMB 10007 <95JCS(CC)1563>.

Alkynes too have found application in the synthesis of oxepanes. The A/B ring system (45) of ciguatoxin has been formed in a stereoselective manner by cyclisation of the alkyne cobalt complex (44) with boron trifluoride followed by reductive removal of the chromium with hydrogen and Wilkinson's catalyst under high pressure <95SL1179> and the $CpW(CO)_3$ complex (**46**) cyclises in the presence of trifluorosulphonic acid with removal of the complexing agent with trifluoroacetic acid to yield the lactone (**47**) <95JA2933>.

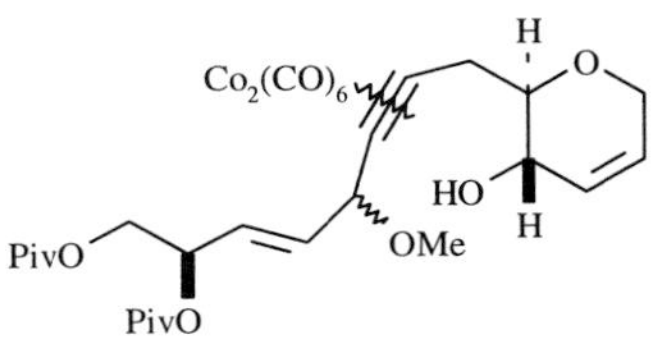

(**44**)

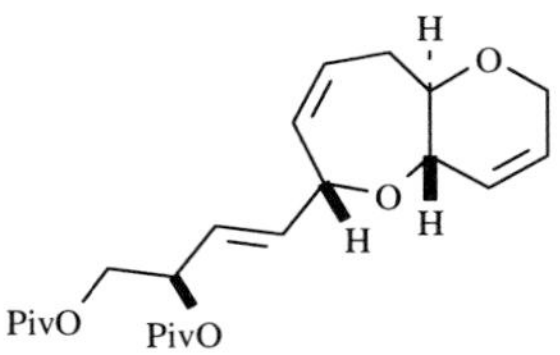

(**45**)

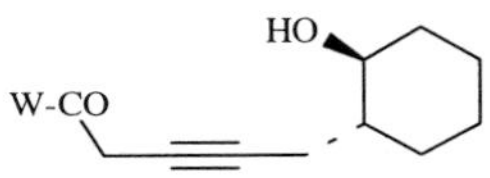

(**46**)

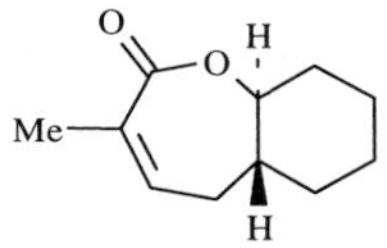

(**47**)

The concurrent formation of two rings by chromium catalysis is demonstrate in Scheme **6** <95TL3027>. Conversion of the hydrazone (**48**) into the complex (**49**) and subsequent reaction with hex-6-yn-1-ol affords the annulated complex (**50**) which is decomplexed by irradiation in benzene. The stereochemistry of the intermediate complex (**50**) was determined by recomplexation of the final product (**51**), which gave a separable mixture of the two possible diastereoisomers.

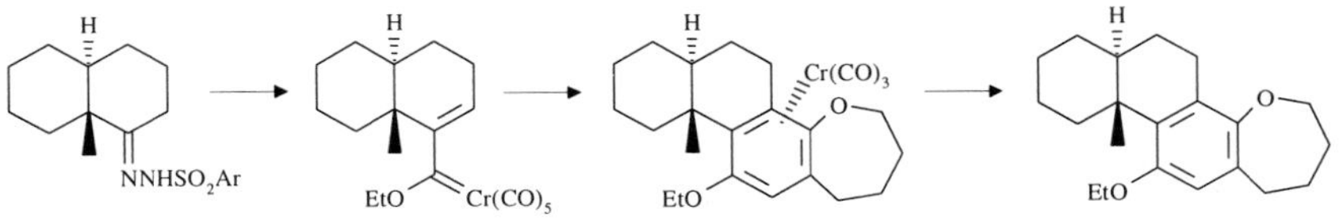

(**48**)

(**49**)

(**50**)

(**51**)

Scheme **6**

The epoxy alcohol (**52**) forms (**53**) in an allowed 6-*exo*-tet cyclisation when treated with acid, as illustrated in Scheme **7**. It has been found, however, that if the cyclisation is carried out with the antibody 26D9 the disfavoured oxepane (**54**) is formed with almost complete regiocontrol in a 7-*endo*-tet process <95JA2659>. The enantiomeric excess is 78%.

5-Hepten-1-ols are reported to undergo transformation into 2-iodomethyloxepines in an *endo*-mode cyclisation when treated with bis (*sym*-collidine) iodine (I) hexafluorophosphate <95SL323> and 2-alkyl-ε-caprolactones are formed in good overall yields and in high enantiomeric purity by alkylation of the SAMP-hydrazones and subsequent oxidative cleavage of the hydrazone with ozone <95S947>.

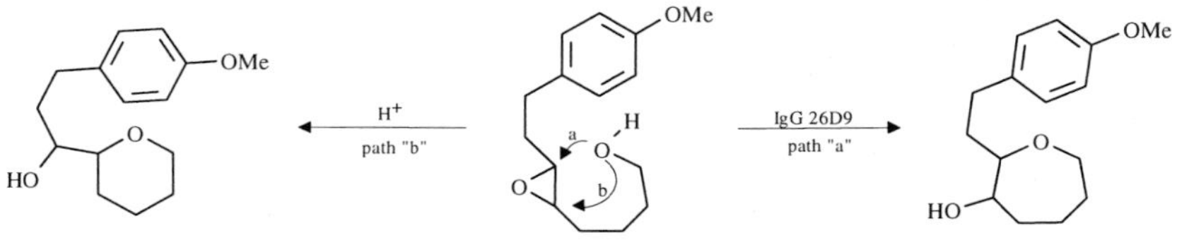

(53)   (52)   (54)

Scheme 7

Treatment of 1,2-C-methylene carbohydrates, prepared by cyclopropanation of unsaturated sugars, with Lewis acids and trapping of the intermediate oxonium ion with a nucleophile is a convenient route to 2-substituted-2,3,6,7-tetrahydrooxepines <95TL6831>. Thus rearrangement of (55) with TMSOTf in acetonitrile in the presence of MeCN affords (56). The trapping nucleophile may be a substituent of the original carbohydrate, as demonstrated by the conversion of (57) into the bridged bicyclic oxepine (58).

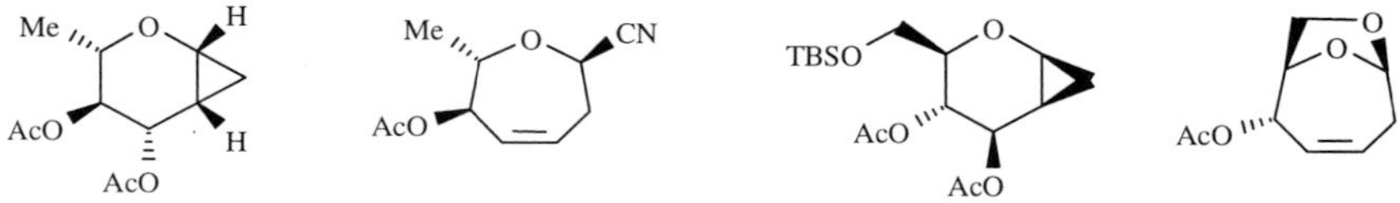

(55)   (56)   (57)   (58)

Oxonium ions as a source of the oxepane ring are also formed by the irradiation of cyclohexene epoxides <95CPB1621>. In this work the oxonium ion is also trapped in an intramolecular process to form spiro-derivatives which may undergo further rearrangement as illustrated in Scheme (8).

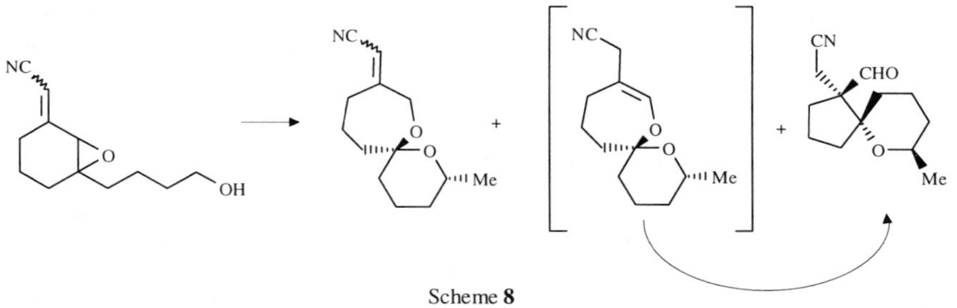

Scheme 8

(59)   (60)

A theoretical study of thieno[3,4-*d*]thiepine and furo[3,4-*d*]thiepine as dienes in the Diels-Alder reaction has been published <95JHC1499>.

The *ortho*-bromophenyl sulphone (**59**) undergoes a 7-*endo* radical cyclisation with Bu_3SnH to afford (**60**) in good yield and in high stereoselectivity <95SL943>. If the double bond does not carry the two substituents both 6-*exo* and 7-*endo* cylisations are observed, the former being the expected major product.

Treatment of the cyclopalladate complex (**61**) with with diphenylacetylene (DPA) gives the new complex (**62**), which on treatment with $AgBF_4$ and subsequent thermolysis in chlorobenzene yields the dibenzo[*bd*]thiepine salt (**63**) (Scheme 9). Longer treatment of the salt in chlorobenzene results in conversion to the thiepine (**64**) <95JOC1005>.

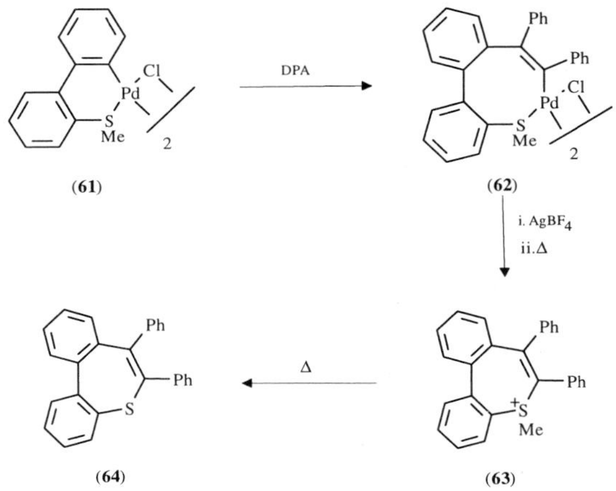

Scheme **9**

An interesting conversion of thiochromane to 1-benzthiepane has been reported <95TL4459>. Cleavage of the heterocyclic ring with lithium 4,4'-di-*tert*-butylbiphenylide and treatment with formaldehyde gives 2-(4'-hydroxybutyl)thiophenol which cyclises on heating in acid and subsequent base treatment.

7.2.3 Atoms other than nitrogen, oxygen or sulphur

1,1-Diphenyl-1-sila-cyclohexan-4-one, prepared from divinyldiphenylsilane, is converted into 1,1-diphenyl-1-silacycloheptan-4-one, first by treatment with ethyl diazoacetate and LDA at -78 °C then rhodium diacetate at room temperature <95SL111>.

A synthesis of 5-methyl-1-phenylpyrrolo[3,4-*d*]borepine has been reported <95JCS(CC)1249>.

Flash vacuum pyrolysis of 2a,7b-dihydrocyclobuta[*b*]-1-benzometalloles results in valence tautomerisation to afford the corresponding 7-membered ring systems (**65**, R = H, M = $SiMe_2$, SiMePh, $GeMe_2$, PPh, POPh, AsPh, AsOPh) <94CPB2441>. The compounds behave in a manner analogous the the corresponding azepines in that they revert to the 6,5,4-ring systems on irradiation and they react with dienophiles to give cycloaddition products. 2-Alkyl-1-benzotellurepines and selenepines (**65**, R = H, M = Te, Se) are obtained by sodium borohydride reduction of di[o-(1-buten-3-ynyl)phenyl] ditellurides and selenides (**66**, R = alkyl, M = Te, Se) <95CPB19>.

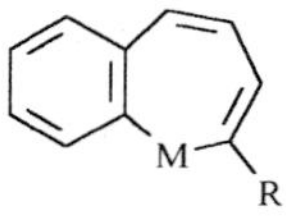

(**65**) 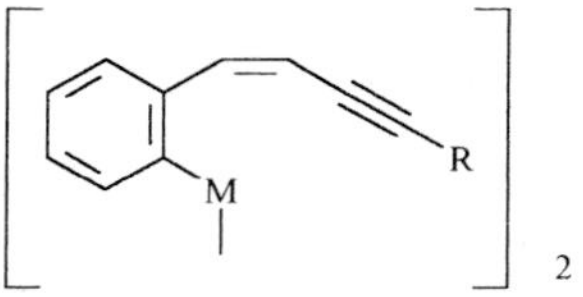   (**66**)

7.3 RING SYSTEMS CONTAINING TWO HETEROATOMS

7.3.1 Diazepines

Although there have been reports of the synthesis of a number of diazepinodiazepines fused with phenyl rings, the synthesis of the bicyclic system has been rarely reported. It has now been demonstrated that the reaction of the amine (**67**, n = 2) with dimethyl allenedicarboxylate provides a good route into this ring sytem, affording (**68**, n = 1) <95H(41)1709>. Use of the amine (**67**, n = 3) produces the previously unreported diazepinodiazocine (**68**, n = 2).

Five methods for the preparation of 6-amino-1-benzyl-4-methylhexahydro-1H-1,4-diazepine, each starting from N-benzyl-N'-methylethylenediamine have been described <95JHC637>.

Reaction of (**69**) with the tetramethylene diamine at temperatures below 50 °C affords the azepinopyridine derivative (**70**). A complex reaction mechanism has been proposed, involving the intermediate formation of the pyridone (**71**), which undergoes a Smiles type rearrangement to give the final product <95JHC477>.

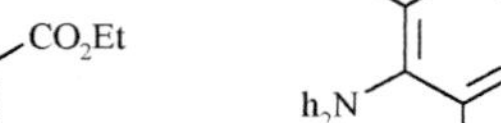

(**67**) 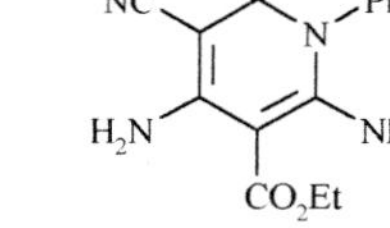   (**68**)

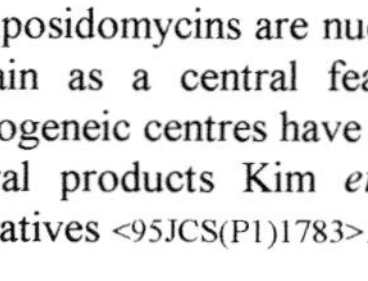

(**69**) 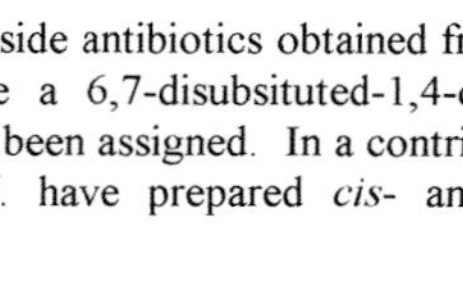   (**70**) 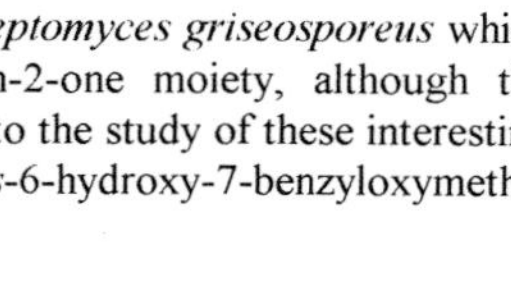   (**71**)

Liposidomycins are nucleoside antibiotics obtained from *Streptomyces griseosporeus* which contain as a central feature a 6,7-disubstituted-1,4-diazepan-2-one moiety, although the stereogeneic centres have not been assigned. In a contribution to the study of these interesting natural products Kim *et al.* have prepared *cis*- and *trans*-6-hydroxy-7-benzyloxymethyl derivatives <95JCS(P1)1783>.

The chemical properties of 2,3-dihydro-1,4-diazepines are dominated by the presence of the diene portion of the molecules, either by electrophilic attack at the 1, 4 or 6 positions, or nucleophilic attack at positions 5 or 7. There have previously been no observations of the involvement of the saturated part of the molecule. It has now been demonstrated, however, that in vacuum flash pyrolysis there is a suprafacial 1,5 hydrogen shift of a proton from position 7 to position 3 <JCS(CC)2337>. This has been confirmed by deutero-labelling studies when 7-deutero-2,3-dihydro-methyl-1,4-diazepine is converted into the 3-deutero-isomer. When the study is repeated with the bicyclic *cis*-2,3-cyclohexano derivative the *trans*-isomer is isolated, confirminf a suprafacial shift mechanism

Fused diazepines are, of course, widely recognised for their activity in a number of biological systems, and further reports have been published describing the synthesis and activity of 1,4/1,5-fused diazepines as PAF antagonists <95JMC3514, 3524>, as orally active nonpeptide fibrinogen antagonists <95TL9433>, as probes for "diazepam insensitive" $GABA_A$ receptors <95JMC1679>, HIV-1 transcriptase anatagonist <95JMC771, 1406>and in benzodiazepine receptor binding studies <95JHC169>. Biological activity is not limited to these diazepines, however. There are reports of the activity of 1,2-diazepines against HeLa cells <95LA817> and of antiarrythmic activity of a number of 2,4-benzodiazepines <95JMC2551>.

An important feature of the synthesis of substituted benzodiazepines is the stereochemistry of the substituents in the reduced heterocyclic ring. In this context, further studies on the preparation of enantiomeric 3-amino- and 3-methyl-benzodiazepines have been published <95JOC730>, <95T(A)849>, <95H(40)717>. The asymmetric reduction of the 3,4-double bond in 4-methyl-2,3-benzodiazepines is also reported <95JCS(P1)1423>.

There are further reports of the use of solid phase techniques in the preparation of benzodiazepines <95JOC5742>, <95JOC5744>, <95JA3306>.

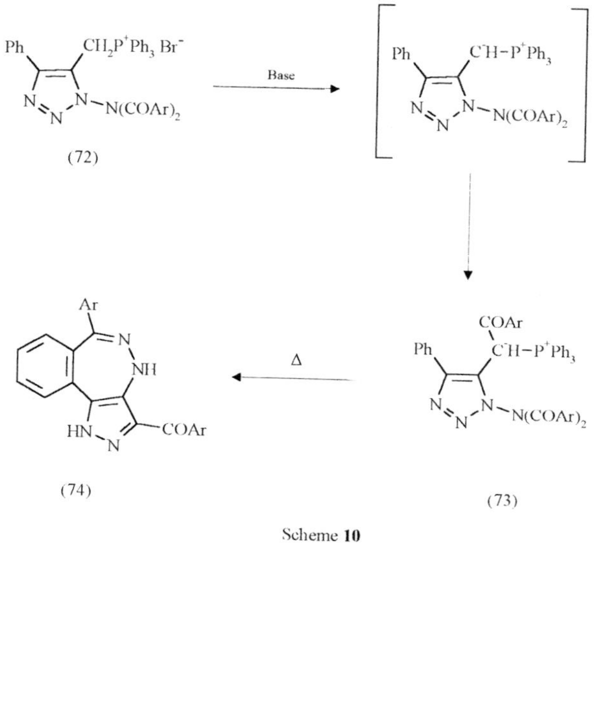

(72)

(73)

(74)

Scheme **10**

Treatment of the phosphonium bromides (**72**) with base followed by rearrangement of the intermediate ylid gives the very stable isomeric ylids (**73**) in good yield <95TL5637>. Thermolysis of (**73**) in xylene produces the 2,3-benzodiazepines (**74**) in a Dimroth rearrangment/1,7-electrocyclic ring closure sequence.

Condensation of α-amino acids esters with o-azidobenzoyl chlorides followed by an intramolecular tandem Staudinger/aza-Wittig reaction has been used in the preparation of a number of 1,4-benzodiazepine derivatives, exemplified in two independent syntheses of the antibiotic DC-81 (**75**) <95T5617>, <95JOC4006>. The pyrrolo[2,1-c][1,4]benzodiazepine ring systems (**76**, R = OMe, X = H_2, O) have been prepared by cyclisation of the triflates (**77**, R = OMe, R^1 = CH_2OTs, CO_2Me) with ammonia <95TL7595>. The dione (**76**, R = H, X = O) is resistant to reaction with $POCl_3$, the starting material being recovered unchanged after refluxing for 14 hours. In an attempt to force the reaction by using microwave irradiation rearrangement took place, affording the isomeric ring system (**78**) <95TL6673>.

(**75**)   (**76**)   (**77**)   (**78**)

(**79**)   (**80**)

Intramolecular cyclisation of the azides (**79**) by refluxing in toluene has produced the [1,2,3]triazolo[1,5-a][1,4]diazepines (**80**) <95S647>. Removal of the Boc protecting group in the benzodiazepine derivative (**81**), prepared in three steps from 2-fluoro-5-nitro-benzoic acid, results in ring expansion to (**82**) *via* a Smiles rearrangement <95SL539>.

(**81**)   (**82**)

Pyrimidino[1,5]diazepin-2,4-diones are formed by the treatment of 1,2-diaminopyrimidines with carbon suboxide <95H(41)303>. The reaction may be extended to the formation of pyrimidino[1,5]thiazepines. Hexahydrocyclopenta[*b*][1,5]benzodiazepines are isolated as minor products in the reaction of phenylene diamines with cyclopentadiene and formaldehyde <95T12383>. A number of optically active 4-methyl-1,3,4,5-tetrahydro-2*H*-1,5-benzodiazepines have been synthesised by the reaction of phenylene diamines and crotonic acid and their CD spectra have been investigated <95LA1861>.

The novel pyrazolo[1,5-*a*]azepine (**84**) is prepared by the cycloaddition reaction of 3a,6a-diazepentalene (**83**) with dimethyl acetylenedicarboxylate <95JCR(S)338>.

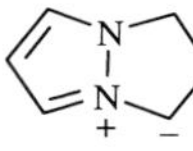

(**83**)

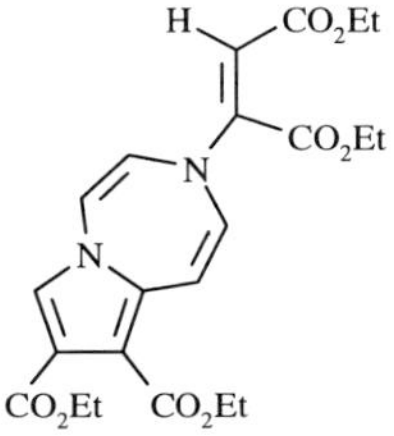

(**84**)

7.3.2 Dioxepanes and dithiapanes

Hydroxyacetals of structure (**85**, X = O) undergo a 7-*exo*-tet cyclisation in the presence of diphenylphosphine and carbon tetrachloride, for which the mechanism in Scheme 11 has been proposed <95SL1119>. The cyclisation has also been extended to the sulphur and nitrogen analogues (**85**, X = S or N).

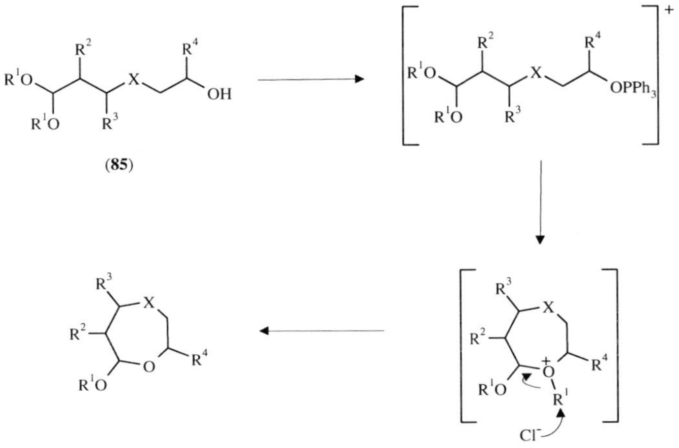

(**85**)

Scheme **11**

The diol (**86**) cyclises in the presence of acid and molecular sieve to give products the nature of which are dependent upon the nature of the acid. In methanolic sulphuric acid the mixed acetal (**87**) is produced, but with TFA a mixture of the bisdioxepane (**88**) and the novel

14-crown-4 crown ether (89) is obtained <95T9757>.

The spirobis[2,4]-benzodithiepine (90) has been prepared from 1,2-bis(chloromethyl)-4,5-dimethylbenzene and sodium trithiocarbonate prepared *in situ* and a conformational analysis has been carried out using ^{1}H- and ^{13}C-NMR, X-ray analysis and semi-empirical calculations <95JOC6335>. In the solid state it exists in a chair-twisted boat conformations whereas in solution it undergoes two dynamic processes, namely pseudorotation at lower temperatures and ring inversion at higher temperatures.

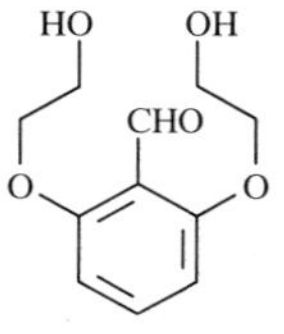

(86) 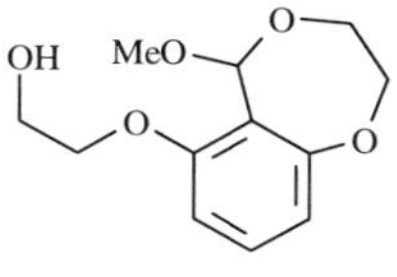　　　　　　　　　(87) 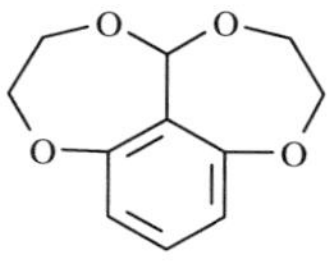　　　　　　　　(88)

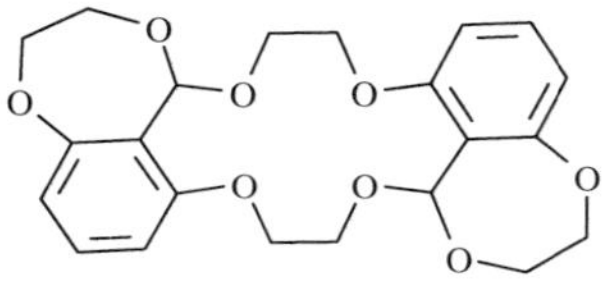

(89) 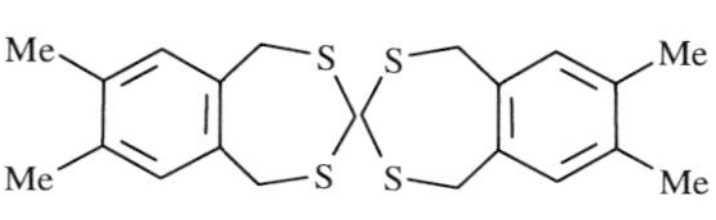　　　　　　　　　　　(90)

Dithiolanes bearing a 2-cyclobutenone substituent undergo a one-carbon ring insertion on thermolysis with concomitant formation of a spirobutenolide ring <95JOC735>. The initial step is carbon insertion into the dithialane ring from a ketene generated from the cyclobutene forming a ten-membered intermediate which undergoes intramolecular rearrangement to give the final product (Scheme 12). Polymerisation resistant dithiolanes react with acetylides in protic solvents to form dihydrothiepins as illustrated in Scheme 13 <JCS(CC)1763>. The intermediate is stable in aprotic solvents and may be trapped, for example, as a silyl sulphide.

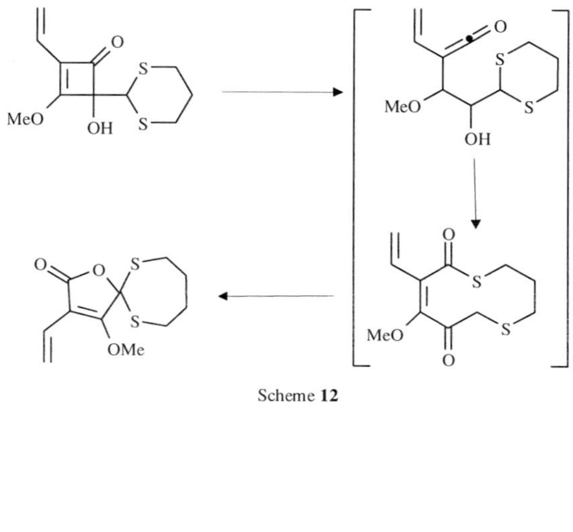

Scheme 12

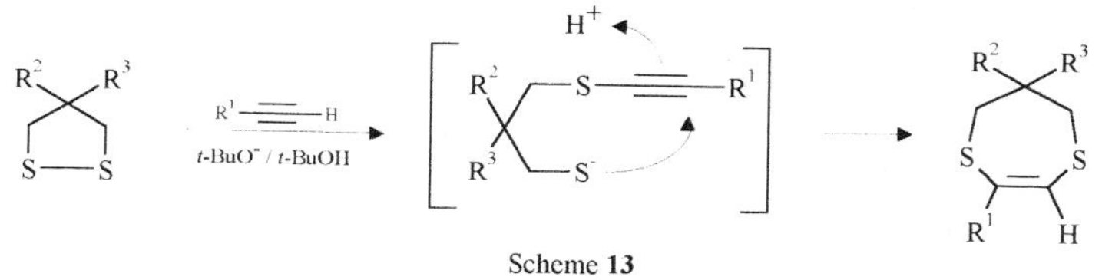

Scheme **13**

7.3.3 Oxazepines and thiazepines

Reaction of the 1-aryl-2-phenacylcyclopropanes with chlorosulphonyl isocyanate and subsequent removal of the chlorosulphonyl group with benzenethiol in pyridine affords the 4,5-dihydro-1,3-oxazepines (**91**) <95SC1939> and in a reaction sequence in which an aziridine is the source of nitrogen, methyl 1-benzyloxycarbonylaziridine-2-carboxylate reacts with 2-(N-benzyl-N-*tert*-butoxycarbonyl)aminoethanol to give the derivative (**92**) which, after removal of the Boc group, is subject to a reductive cyclisation to yield the hexahydro-1,4-oxazepine (**93**) <95CPB1137>.

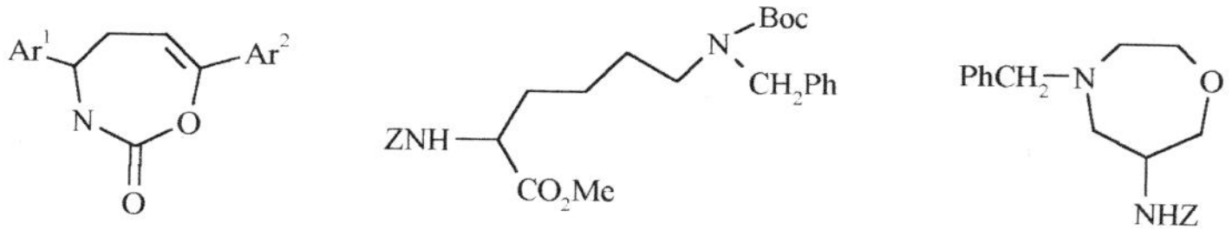

(**91**)

(**92**)

(**93**)

Intramolecular nitrene insertion of pyranoside azides is a further route to oxazepanes <95JCS(P1)1747>. Thus thermolysis of the diazide (**94**) affords the tetrazolooxazepane (**95**) in high yield. When the rearrangement is carried out under ultra-violet irradiation the yield of (**95**) is reduced when it is also accompanied by small amounts of the isomer (**96**).

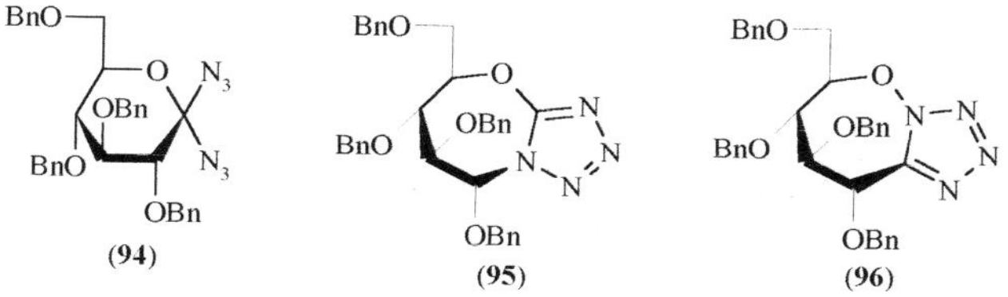

(**94**)

(**95**)

(**96**)

Trans-perhydro-1,4-benzazoxepine is prepared by the reaction of *trans*-methylaminocyclohexanol with ethyl chloroacetate and subsequent reduction with LAH <95JHC161>. Intramolecular cycloaddition of nitrilamines to a nitrile group is the key step in the synthesis of [1,2,4]-triazolo[1,5-*a*][1,4]benzoxazepines (Scheme 14) <95S1483>.

In addition to their formation by transformation of smaller ring heterocycles, oxazepines are capable of contraction as demonstrated by the carbene transformation of the oxazepane dione (**97**) in the presence of catalytic amounts of copper or rhodium to the dihydropyrrolone (**98**) by loss of CO_2 <95AG(E)78>.

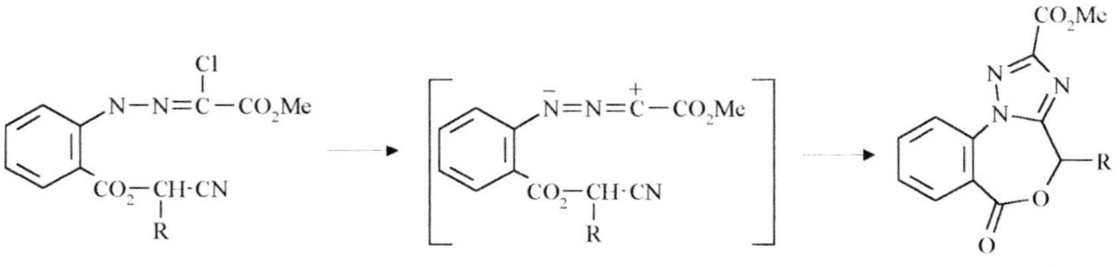

Scheme 14

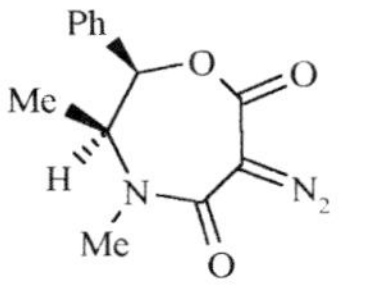

(97) 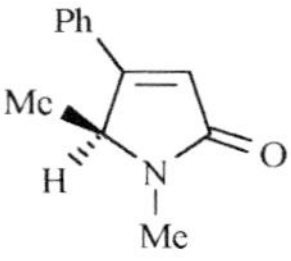   (98)

A simple route to the preparation of monocyclic thiazepines is the reaction of the propenethioamides (99, R = CO_2Me, CN, X = cyclic amino) with phenacyl bromide <95JHC463>. In TsOH the thiazepines (100) are formed, but in TFA the reaction takes a slightly different course. Where R = CO_2Me the thiazepinone (101) is isolated, however, where R = CN a thiophene (102) is formed.

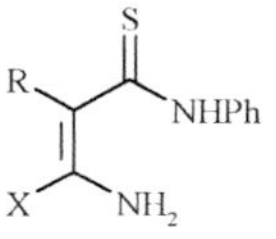

(99) 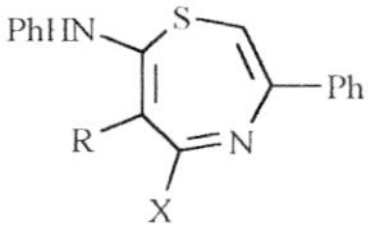   (100) 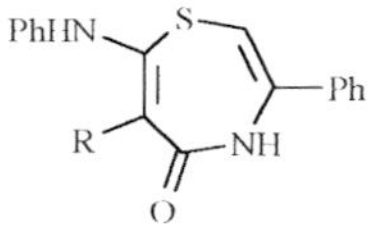   (101) 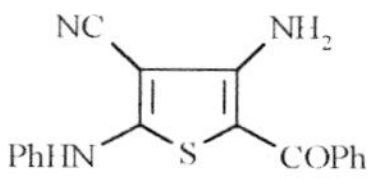   (102)

The calcium antagonist of diltiazem ensures a continuing interest in 1,5-benzothiazepines, with papers published on thieno derivatives <95H(41)709>, <95M569>, <95LA453>. Diastereoisomers of 2-benzoyl-3-phenyl-7,8-dimethoxy-2,3,4,5-tetrahydro-1,4-benzothiazine have been prepared by the reaction of 6,7-dimethoxy-2-phenyl-3,4-dihydrothiazine with phenacylbromide or 2-benzoylmethyl-4,5-dimethoxybenzylamine with benzaldehyde <95TL753>. Benzothiazepinones have been prepared from thioflavanones by a trimethylsilyl azide mediated Schmidt rearrangement <95SC1495>. A comprehensive review of annelated derivatives has appeared <95AHC61>.

7.4   RING SYSTEMS CONTAINING 3 OR MORE HETEROATOMS

The dibornenodithiine (103) is readily converted into the trithiine (104) by a number of methods, namely by reaction with sulphur, by reaction with 3,6-diphenyldithiine as sulphur donor in the presence of light, or by disproportionation, when the molecule acts as both sulphur donor and acceptor <95T13247>.

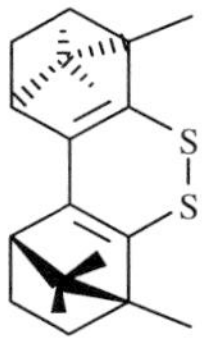

(103) 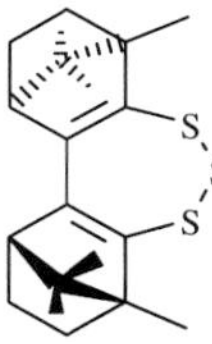　　　　　　　　(104) 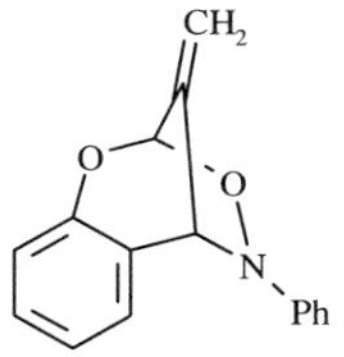　　　　　　　　(105)

The reaction of *o*-(1,2-propadienyloxy)benzaldehyde with phenylhydroxylamine results in the formation of (105) by way of an intramolecular cycloaddition of the intermediate N-phenyl nitrone <95T89>.

When treated with active methylene compounds e.g. malononitrile, in K_2CO_3/DMSO systems the azides (106) cyclise to form the imidazotetrazoles (107) which may be isolated as their alkali metal salts <95JHC457>. On treatment with acid these salts are transformed into imidazoyl triazoles (Scheme 15).

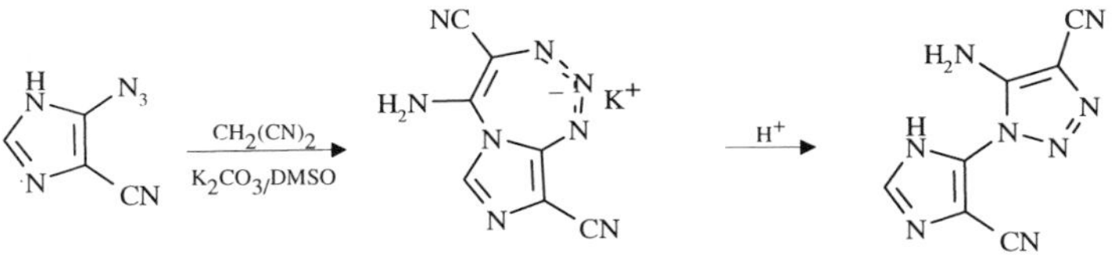

(106)　　　　　　　　(107)

Scheme 15

7. 5   REFERENCES

89JA1525　　　　J. B. I. Iturraspe, S. E. Bari, B. Frydman, *J. Am. Chem. Soc.* **1989**, *111*, 1525
91TL6727　　　　M. Nitta, S, Mori, Y. Iino, *Tetrahedron Lett.*, **1991**, *32*, 6727
94CPB2441　　　S. Shiratori, S. Yasuike, J. Kurita, T. Tsuchiya, *Chem. Pherm. Bull.* **1994**, *42*, 2441
95AG(E)78　　　G. Chelucci, A. Saba, *Angew. Chem. Int. Ed. Engl.* **1995**, *34*, 78
95AG(E)1469　　D. Hamprecht, K. Polborn, W. Steglich, *Angew. Chem (Int. Ed. Engl.)* **1995**, *34*, 1469.
95AG(E)2007　　R. Gorny, H. J. Schäfer, R. Fröhlich, *Angew. Chem. Int. Ed. Engl.* **1995**, *34*, 2007
95AHC61　　　　A. Chirmirri, R. Gitto, S. Grasso, A. M. Monforte, M. Zappalà, *Adv. Heterocycl. Chem.* **1995**, *63*, 61
95BSF337　　　　E. Gonzalez, *Bull. Soc. Chim. Fr.* **1995**, *132*, 337
95CPB19　　　　H. Sashida, K. Ito, T. Tsuchiya, *Chem. Phar. Bull.*, **1995**, *43*, 19
95CPB1137　　　T. Morie, S. Kato, H. Harada, N. Yoshida, I. Fujiwara, J. Matsumoto, *Chem. Pharm. Bull.* **1995**, *43*, 1137

95CPB1621   M. Kotera, K. Ihii, M. Sakamoto, *Chem. Phar. Bull.* **1995**, *43*, 1621
95H(40)717   H. R. Pfaendler, F. Weisner, *Heterocycles* **1995**, *40*, 717
95H(41)303   L. Bonsignore, F. Cottogla, G. Loy, D. Secci, *Heterocycles* **1995**, *41*, 303
95H(41)709   I. Puschmann, T. Erker, *Heterocycles* **1995**, *41*, 709
95H(41)1709   T. Okawara, S. Ehara, A. Takenaka, T. Hiwatashi, M. Furukawa, *Heterocycles*, **1995**, *41*, 1709
95JA2657   L. E. Overman, M. H. Rabinowitz, P. A. Renhowe, *J. Am. Chem. Soc.* **1995**, *117*, 2657
95JA2659   K. D. Janda, C. G. Shevlin, R. A. Lerner, *J. Am. Chem. Soc.* **1995**, *117*, 2659
95JA2933   C.-C. Chen, J.-S. Fan, G.-H. Lee, S.-M. Peng, S.-L. Wang, R.-S. Liu, *J. Am. Chem. Soc.* **1995**, *117*, 2933
95JA3306   M. J. Plunkett, J. A. Ellman, *J. Am. Chem. Soc.* **1995**, *117*, 3306
95JA10227   K. C. Nicolaou, C.-K. Hwang, M. E. Duggan, D. A. Nugiel, Y. Abe, B. Reddy, S. A. DeFrees, D. R. Reddy, R. A. Awartani, S. R. Conley, F. P. J. T. Rutjes, E. A. Theodorakis, *J. Am. Chem. Soc.* **1995**, *117*, 10227
95JA10252   K. C. Nicolaou, F. P. J. T. Rutjes, E. A. Theodorakis, J. Tiebe, M. Sato, E. Untersteller, *J. Am. Chem. Soc.* **1995**, *117*, 10252
95JCR(S)338   K. Matsumoto, H. Lida, T. Hinomoto, T. Uchida, *J. Chem. Res. (S)* **1995**, 338
95JCS(CC)1101   A. Laurent, P. Jacqualt, J.-L. Di Martino, J. Hamelin, *J. Chem. Soc, Chem. Commun.* **1995**, 1101
95JCS(CC)1249   Y. Sugihara, R. Miyatake, I. Murata, A. Imamura, *J. Chem. Soc., Chem. Commun.* **1995**, 1249
95JCS(CC)1563   B. Adger, M. T. Bes, G. Grogon, R. McCague, S. Pedragosa-Moreau, S. M. Roberts, R. Villa, P. W. H. Wan. A. J. Willets, *J. Chem. Soc., Chem. Commun.*, **1995**, 1563
95JCS(CC)1763   M. Tazaki, M. Kumakura, S. Nagahama, M. Takagi, *J. Chem. Soc., Chem. Commun.* **1995**, 1763
95JCS(CC)2251   L. Ma, D. Dolphin, *J. Chem. Soc., Chem. Commun.* **1995**, 2251
95JCS(CC)2337   M. J. Ellis, D. Lloyd, H. McNab, M. J. Walker, *J. Chem. Soc., Chem. Commun.* **1995**, 2337
95JCS(P1)89   S. C. Lemoult, P. F. Richardson, S. M. Roberts, *J. Chem. Soc., Perkin Trans 1*, **1995**, 89
95JCS(P1)203   G. Jones, M. W. Kempa, M. B. Hursthouse, K. A. Malik. *J. Chem. Soc., Perkin Trans 1*, **1995**, 203
95JCS(P1)809   D. W. Jones, M. Thornton-Pett, *J. Chem. Soc., Perkin Trans 1.* **1995**, 809
95JCS(P1)1001   M. Nitta, Y. Iino, S. Mori, T. Takayasu, *J. Chem. Soc., Perkin Trans 1* **1995**, 1001
95JCS(P1)1423   I. Ling, B, Podányi, T. Hámori, S. Sólyom, *J. Chem. Soc., Perkin Trans1*, **1995**, 1423
95JCS(P1)1747   M. Yokoyama, S. Hirano, M. Matsushita, T. Hachiya, N. Kobayashi, M. Kubo, H. Togo, H. Seki, *J. Chem. Soc., Perkin Trans. 1* **1995**, 1747
95JCS(P1)1783   K. S. Kim, I. H. Cho, Y. H. Ahn, J. I. Park, *J. Chem. Soc., Perkin Trans. 1*, **1995**, 1783

95JCS(P1)2355   C. P. Adams, S. M. Fairway, C. J. Hardy, D. E. Hibbs, M. B. Hursthouse, A. D. Morley, B. W. Sharp, N. Vicker, I. Warner, *J. Chem. Soc., Perkin Trans 1* **1995**, 2355

95JCS(P1)2565   K. E. Cullen, J. T. Sharp, *J. Chem. Soc., Perkin Trans. 1* **1995**, 2565

95JHC57   H. G. Bonacorso, K.-E. Mack, F. Effenberger, *J. Hetercycl. Chem.* **1995**, *32*.57

95JHC161   L. Simon, S. G. Talpas, F. Fülöp, G. Bernáth, G. Argay, A. Kálmán, P. Sohár, *J. Heterocycl. Chem.* **1995**, *32*, 161

95JHC169   G. Biagi, I. Giorgi, O. Livi, V. Scartoni, S. Velo, *J. Hetercycl. Chem.* **1995**, *32*, 169

95JHC457   A. P. Freitas, M. Fernanda, J. R. P. Proença, *J. Heterocycl. Chem.* **1995**, *32*, 457

95JHC463   M. T. Cocco, C. Congiu, V. Onnis, *J. Heterocycl. Chem.* **1995**, *32*, 463

95JHC477   W. Winnik, *J. Heterocycl. Chem.* **1995**, *32*, 477

95JHC491   J. G. Avila Z, *J. Heterocycl. Chem.* **1995**, *32*, 491

95JHC637   S. Kato, H. Harada, T. Morie, *J. Heterocycl. Chem.* **1995**, *32*, 637

95JMC771   H. J. Breslin, M. J. Kukla, D. W. Ludovici, R. Mohrbacher, W. Ho, M. Miranda, J. D. Rodgers, T. K. Hitchins, G. Leo, D. A. Gauthier, C. Y. Ho, M. K. Scott, E. De Clercq, R. Pauwels, K. Andries, M. A. C. Janssen, P. A. J. Janssen, *J. Med. Chem.* **1995**, *38*, 771

95JMC1406   J. R. Proudfoot, U. R. Patel, S. R. Kapadia, K. D. Hargrave, *J. Med. Chem.* **1995**, *38*, 1406

95JHC1499   B. S. Jursic, *J. Heterocycl. Chem.* **1995**, *32*, 1499

95JMC1679   P. Zhang, W. Zhang, R. Liu, B. Harris, P. Skolnick, J. M. Cook, *J. Med. Chem.* **1995**, *38*, 1679

95JMC2395   S. E. Snyder, F. A. Aviles-Garay, R. Chakraborti, D. E. Nichols, V. J. Watts, R. B. Mailman, *J. Med. Chem.* **1995**, *38*, 2395

95JMC2551   R. E. Johnson, P. J. Silver, R. Becker, N. C. Birsner, E. A. Bihnet, G. M. Briggs, C. A. Busacca, P. Canniff, P. M. Carabateas, C. C. Chadwick, T. D'Ambra, R. L. Dundore, J.-S. Dung, A. M. Ezrin, W. Gorczyca, P. G. Habeeb, P. H, D. S. Krafte, G. M. Pilling, B. O'Connor, M. T. Saindane, D. C. Schlegel, G. P. Stankus, J. Swestock, W. A. Volberg, *J. Med. Chem.* **1995**, *38*, 2551

95JMC3514   M. J. Fray, K. Cooper, M. J. Parry, K. Richardson, J. Steele, *J. Med. Chem.* **1995**, *38,* 3514

95JMC3524   M. J. Fray, D. J. Bull, K. Cooper, M. J. Parry, and M. H. Stefaniak, *J. Med. Chem.* **1995**, *38*, 3524

95JMC4284   J. H. Shah, S. Izenwasser, B. Geter-Douglass, J. M. Witkin, A. H. Newman, *J. Med. Chem.* **1995**, *38*, 4284

95JOC1005   J. Spencer, M. Pfeffer, A. DeCian, J. Fischer, *J. Org. Chem.* **1995**, *60*, 1005

95JOC1486   Y. Yokoyama, T. Matsumoto, Y. Murakami, *J. Org. Chem.* **1995**, *60*, 1486

95JOC3795   K. T. Potts, T. Rochanapruk, A. Pawda, S. J. Coats, L. Hadjiarapoglou, *J. Org. Chem.* **1995**, *60*, 3795

95JOC4006   S. Eguchi, K. Yamashita, Y. Matsushita, A. Kakehi, *J. Org. Chem.* **1995**, *60*, 4006

95JOC730   R. G. Sherrill, E. E. Sugg, *J. Org. Chem.* **1995**, *60*, 730

95JOC730　　R. G. Sherrill, E. E. Sugg, *J. Org. Chem.* **1995**, *60*, 730

95JOC735　　K. H. Lee, H. W. Moore, *J. Org. Chem.* **1995**, *60*, 735

95JOC5742　C. G. Boojamra, K. M. Burow, J. A. Ellman, *J. Org. Chem.*, **1995**, *60*, 5742

95JOC5744　D. A. Goff, R. N. Zuckermann, *J. Org. Chem.* **1995**, *60*, 5744

95JOC5958　B. B. Lohray, Y. Jayamma, M. Chatterjee, *J. Org. Chem.* **1995**, *60*, 5958

95JOC6335　M. Mikolajczyk, M. J. Potrzebowski, S. Kazmieski, H. Gross, B. Costisella, I. Keitel, M. W. Wieczorek, I. Wawer, *J. Org. Chem.* **1995**, *60*, 6335

95LA453　　I. Laimer, T. Erker, *Justus Liebigs Ann. Chem.* **1995**, 453

95LA817　　V. Arán, M. Flores, P. Muñoz, J. R. Ruiz, P. Sánchez-Verdú, M. Stud, *Justus Liebigs Ann. Chem.* **1995**, 817

95LA1861　F. Malik, M. Hasan, K. M. Khan, S. Perveen, G. Snatzke, H. Duddeck, W. Voelter, *Justus Liebigs Ann. Chem.* **1995**, 1861

95M569　　I. Puschmann, T. Erker, *Monatsh. Chem.* **1995**, *126*, 569

95S647　　G. Broggini, G. Molteni, G. Zecchi, *Synthesis*, **1995**, 647

95S947　　D. Enders, R. Gröbner, J. Runsink, *Synthesis*, **1995**, 947

95S1483　　G. Broggini, L. Garanti, G. Molteni, G. Zecchi, *Synthesis* **1995**, 1483

95SC1495　P. T. Kaye, M. J. Mphahele, *Synth. Commun.* **1995**, *25*, 1495

95SC1939　E. S. Kumar, D. N. Dhar, *Synth. Commun.* **1995**, *25*, 1939

95SC3765　M. Hirano, Y. Ueno, T. Morimoto, *Synth. Commun.* **1995**, *25*, 3765

95SC3789　M. A. M. Healey, S. A. Smith, G. Stemp, *Synth. Commun.* **1995**, *25*, 3789

95SC3863　V. J. Majo, M. Venugopal, A. A. M. Prince, P. T. Perumal, *Synth. Commun.* **1995**, *25*, 3863

95SL111　　D. Damour, A. Renaudon, S. Mignani, *Synlett.*, **1995**, 111

95SL323　　Y. Brunel, g. Rousseau, *Synlett*, **1995**, 323

95SL539　　A. Borchardt, W. C. Still, *Synlett.* **1995**, 539

95SL603　　M. Grignon-Dubois, J.-C. Gauffre, *Synlett.* **1995**, 603

95SL622　　V. Ojea, I. Muinelo, M. C. Figueroa, M. Ruiz, J. M. Quintela, *Synlett.* **1995**, 622

95SL943　　C. D. S. Brown, A. P. Dishington, O. Shishkin, N. S. Simpkins, *Synlett.*, **1995**, 943

95SL1075　M. P. Doyle, A. V. Kalinin, *Synlett.* **1995**, 1075

95SL1119　A. Espinosa, M. A. Gallo, J. Campos, J. A. Gómez, *Synlett.* **1995**, 1119

95SL1179　S. Hosokawa, M. Isobe, *Synlett.* **1995**, 1179

95T89　　　A. Padwa, M. Meske, Z. Ni, *Tetrahedron*, **1995**, *51*, 89

95T2091　　G. P. Tokmakov, I. I. Grandberg, *Tetrahedron* **1995**, *51*, 2091

95T2243　　J. Iturraspe, S. E. Bari, B. Frydman, *Tetrahedron* **1995**, *51*, 2243

95T2255　　S. E. Bari, J. Iturraspe, B. Frydman, *Tetrahedron* **1995**, *51*, 2255

95T5617　　P. Molina, I. Díaz, A. Tárraga, *Tetrahedron* **1995**, *51*, 5617

95T9611　　B. Kharraz, P. Uriac, L. Toupet, J. P. Hurvois, C. Moinet, A. Tallec, *Tetrahedron Lett.* **1995**, *51*, 9611

95T9757　　F. Lucchesini, V. Bertini, M. Pocci, G. De Munno, A. Crispini, *Tetrahedron* **1995**, *51*, 9757

95T12383　J. M. Mellor, G. D. Merriman, P. L. Mitchell, *Tetrahedron* **1995**, *51*,

12383
95T13247 W. Schroth, E. Hintzsche, R. Spitzner, D. Ströhl, J. Sieler, *Tetrahedron*, **1995**, *51*, 13247

95TA849 G. Curotto, D. Donati, G. Finizia, A. Ursini, *Tetrahedron Asymmetry* **1995**, *6*, 849

95TL753 L/ Fodor, J. Szabó, G. Bernáth, P. Sohár, *Tetrahedron Lett.* **1995**, *36*, 753

95TL1043 J. Beauhaire, P.-H. Ducrot, C. Malosse, D. Rochat, I. O. Ndiege, D. O. Otieno, *Tetrahedron Lett.* **1995**, *36*, 1043

95TL3027 R. L. Beddoes, J. D. King, P. Quayle, *Tetrahedron Lett.* **1995**, *36*, 3027

95TL3659 H. Hu, G. E. Jagdmann, Jr., *Tetrahedron Lett.* **1995**, *36*, 3659

95TL4459 T. Cohen, F. Chen, T. Kulinski, S. Florio, V. Capriati, *Tetrahedron Lett.* **1995**, *36*, 4459

95TL4787 L. Viallon, O. Reinaud, P. Capdevielle, M. Maumy, *Tetrahedron Lett.* **1995**, *36*, 4787

95TL5439 P. Magnus, R. Fairhurst, S. Eisenbeis, D. Grandjean, *Tetrahedron Lett.* **1995**, *36*, 4539

95TL5617 P. Molina, I. Díaz, A. Tárraga, *Tetrahedron* **1995**, *51*, 5617

95TL5637 E. Laskos, P. S. Lianis, N. A. Rodios, A. Terzis, C. P. Raptopoulou, *Tetrahedron Lett.* **1995**, *36*, 5637

95TL5777 I. Kadota, P. Jung-Youl, N. Koumura, G. Pollaud, Y. Matsukawa, Y. Yamamoto, *Tetrahedron Lett.* **1995**, *36*, 5777

95TL6379 J. Hu, M. J. Miller, *Tetrahedron Lett.* **1995**, *36*, 6379

95TL6673 S. Rault, A.-C. Gillard, M.-P. Foloppe, M. Robba, *Tetrahedron Lett.* **1995**, *36*, 6673

95TL6733 H. Ishibashi, H. Kawanami, H. Iriyama, M. Ikeda, *Tetrahedron Lett.* **1995**, *36*, 6733

95TL6831 J. O. Hoberg, J. J. Bozell, *Tetrahedron Lett.* **1995**, *36*, 6831

95TL7595 G. A. Kraus, P. Liu, *Tetrahedron Lett.* **1995**, *36*, 7595

95TL9053 M. Burwood, B. Davies, I. Diaz, R. Grigg, P. Molina, V. Sridharan, M. Hughes, *Tetrahedron Lett.* **1995**, *36*, 9053

95TL9433 W. H. Miller, T. W. Ku, P. E. Ali, W. E. Bondinell, R. R. Calvo, L. D. Davis, K. F. Erhard, L. B. Hall, W. F. Huffman, R. M. Keenan, C. Kwon, K. A. Newlander, S. T. Ross, J. M. Samanen, D. T. Takata, C.-K. Yuan , *Tetrahedron Lett.* **1995**, *36*, 9433

Chapter 8

Eight-Membered and Larger Rings

George R. Newkome
University of South Florida, Tampa, FL, USA

8.1 INTRODUCTION

In the first half of the nineties, there has been a continuing trend from synthetic studies of classical "crown ethers" towards the polyazamacromolecules and the introduction of multiple heteroatoms, including most recently the metal atom centers. As supramolecular chemistry [95MI1] gains an ever increasing role in science, researchers in peripheral areas, for example material sciences and macromolecular chemistry, have turned to the incorporation of these meso- and macrocyclic rings into larger molecular arrays. In that "molecular recognition is one of the corner stones of supramolecular chemistry," [95CSR197] the utilization of tailored polyfunctional macroheterocycles has an important role in future synthetic endeavors.

The continued topics of catenanes for novel molecular assemblies [95PAC233, 95CBR33], specifically the self-assembly of a gold(I) catenane [95AG(E)2107]; molecular encapsulation with carceplexes and hemicarceplexes [95T3395]; sensors and switches [95CSR197]; molecular [95JPC339, 95T343, 95MI4] and cation [94MI5] recognition; medium ring lactones [95T2777] and ethers [94COS457]; crown ethers with cyanine dyes [95MI2], special functions/applications [94MI3], polysiloxane [93MI3], and polymer sorbents of metal ions [93MI1] as well as in monomers and cancer [94MI4] therapy; calixcrowns [94SS103, 94MI1]; uranyl complexes of macroheterocycles [95NJC619]; partition chromatography [95MI3]; chiroselective corand/ionophore ligands [95MCP2383]; host-guest chemistry [94COS259] and in a mass spectrometer [95JMS925]; polyrotaxanes [95MI5]; separation and sensing [94MI2]; gas chromatography [95MI6]; metal ion extraction [94MI6]; and [1n]orthocyclophanes [94SL765] have been reviewed.

Because of spatial limitations, only meso- and macrocycles possessing heteroatoms and/or subheterocyclic rings are reviewed; in general, lactones, lactams, and cyclic imides have been excluded. In view of the delayed availability of some articles appearing in previous years, several have been herein incorporated.

8.2 CARBON–OXYGEN RINGS

1,3-Alternate substitutions on calix[4]arenes were accomplished by reaction of calix[4]arene with tetraethylene glycol ditosylate [95TL6095], triethylene glycol [95CL497], pentaethylene glycol [95JA2767], and 1,8-*bis*(ethyleneoxy)anthraquinone; the related 1,4-substituted calix[6]arene crown ethers have also been reported [95T591]. The coordination of Sc^{+3} to oxacalix[3]arene macrocycles has been investigated [95IC5641]. Novel lantern-shaped macromolecules (e.g., **1**) were synthesized by utilizing resorcin[4]arene and *m*-terphenyl units as the capping and bottom fragments, respectively [95T7677].

Diverse chiral crown ethers have been reported; the chiral portion has been instilled by the molecular incorporation of sugar moieties [95TL5951, 94TL5661, 95SC3777, 95JCS(1)2339, 95JA 11198], (*R,R*)-2,3-butanediol [95TA2059], ethyl lactate [95TA1873] or 1,1'-binaphthyl, to mention but a few. Chiral recognition of host - guest complexation between crown ethers and amino acid ester ammonium ion guests has been studied with fast atom bombardment mass spectrometry [95JA7726]. Glucose was released from a diboronic acid cleft in **2**, when a metal - *bis*crown complex was formed [95CC1483]. Association constants between glycophane **3** and a series of (di)nitrophenyl glycosides with axial and equatorial configuration at the anomeric center were reported [95JA11198].

Synthesis and characterization of new hemicarcerands have been reported [95JA1659, 95CC1947, 95JOC1207]; some of the interiors are large enough, in principle, to encompass [60]fullerene [95CC1085]. A series of *bis*(5-carbomethoxy-1,3-phenylene)-(3*x* + 2)-crown-*x* ethers has been synthesized in one step from methyl 3,5-dihydroxybenzoate and oligo(ethylene glycol) dichlorides [95JOC516]. Polyester rotaxane backbones have been laced [95JA852] with diverse crown ethers by step grown polymerization using diacyl chloride - diol and transesterification reactions; the mobility of the macrocycle along the backbone without dethreading has been demonstrated. Self-assembly, by means of a slippage procedure, of a [3]rotaxane composed of three different subunits and encircled by a large crown ether was described [95CC747]. Cyclopolymerization of 1,14-*bis*(4-ethynyl-phenoxy)-3,6,9,12-tetraoxatetradecane with different metal catalysts has afforded poly(phenylacetylene) (**4**) [95M658].

The tetraoxa[26]annulenoquinone has been prepared and electrochemically transformed to the corresponding dianion [95TL4401]. The novel 1,12-dioxa[12](1,4)naphthylenophane-14-carboxylic acid has been prepared and resolved; its (-)-enantiomer was shown to have the *S*-configuration by X-ray analysis [95TA1043]. The readily accessible octamethyl-tetraoxaquaterene reacts with benzyne to yield (**5**) but could not be converted into the corresponding [1.1.1.1]paranaphthalenaphane [94T9113]. The first triptyceno-crowns were prepared by initial condensation of 9,10-*bis*(chloromethyl)anthracene with polyethylene glycols, followed by benzyne cycloaddition [95TL8163].

Aggregation of metallotriazole hemiporphyrazines possessing crown ethers was induced by alkali cations [95CC419]; and the first examples of 2,2'-tethered bifluorenylidene crown ethers were synthesized using an oxidative photochemical cyclization process [95JOC7380].

8.3 CARBON–NITROGEN RINGS

1,4,7-Triazacyclononane selectively reacts with 2-(*tert*-butoxycarbonyloxyimino)- and 2-(benzyloxycarbonyloxyimino)-2-phenylacetonitrile to give (>90 %) the diprotected derivatives, thus affording access to mono- and di-substituted *N*-derivatives [95TL9269]. Mono-*N*-functionalized tetraazamacrocycles were prepared by reaction of a five-fold excess of the free macrocycles with one equiv. of the alkylating or arylating reagent [95CJC685]. Reaction of metal tricarbonyl complexes of tetraazamacrocycles (esp. cyclen and cyclan) with enolizable aldehydes or acyl chlorides, then subsequent demetalation, selectively gave the mono-*N*-functionalized derivatives [95TL79]. 1,4,7,10-Tetraazacyclododecane regioselectively reacts in acidic solution with several chloroformates to give the 1,7-diprotected macrocycle; subsequent alkylation and deprotection afforded the 1,7-difunctionalized material [95CC185]. High dilution bridging of 1,7-difunctionalized tetraazamacrocycles with a diacid activated with 1,3-thiazolidine-2-thione afforded bicyclic polyamines after borane reduction [95S1019]. The synthesis, characterization, and selected ligation studies of three giant-sized (54-, 60-, and 64-membered) azamacrocycles have been reported [95GCI163]; similarly, large, up to 45-membered, macrocycles were prepared from piperazine and *m*- or *p*-di(bromomethyl)xylene [95LA1515]. Amazingly, treatment of 1,3,5-

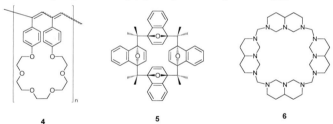

4   5   6

triamino-pentane with aqueous formaldehyde after 30 min. precipitated (100%) the nonacycle **6** [95CC1631]; a related nonacyclic compound possessing 16 bridgehead nitrogens has been prepared from 1,1-*bis*(2-aminoethyl)hydrazine [95CC1633].

Homologation of a pyrrole to a pyridine subunit within a porphyrinogen skeleton has been reported [95JA2793]. Two new expanded porphyrins have been reported by Sessler et al. [95CEJ56], specifically "orangarin", containing five pyrrolic subunits and two bridging carbon atoms, as well as "amethyrins", possessing six pyrrole rings.

The longest, yet reported, molecular ribbons (e.g., **7**) possessing several [3.3]metacyclophane units, have been prepared using a new iterative procedure [95CC1237]. Macrocycles containing two acridine subunits have been synthesized [95TL5261, 95CC1073, 95TL8279] and demonstrated to intercalate nucleic bases. A straightforward strategy for the synthesis of heterophanes containing heterocyclic betaines and constructed with both highly π-excessive and π-deficient moieties linked in a 1,3-alternating fashion has recently appeared [95CC1239, 95SL757]. Gleiter, et al. [95AG(E)789] treated 1,6-diazacyclodeca-3,8-diyne with 1,4-dibromo-2-butyne to generate the bicyclic triyne **8** possessing a topological prismane-like preorganization of the triple bonds; diverse other novel macrocycles were therein reported.

Menger and Catlin [95AG(E)2147] successfully prepared the DABCO-based cyclophane (**9**), whose cavity is lined with eight positive charges; no *intracavity encapsulation* of guest molecules was exhibited. Other water-soluble cyclophanes have been reported [95TL2707, 95TL8051, 95T8423].

a R = CO$_2$Et
b R = CH$_2$OH
c R = CH$_2$Br

7

8

9

Di- and polynuclear complexation with specifically designed macrocycles has continued to expand in popularity. Treatment of 1,4,7-triazacyclononane orthoamide with 1,8-*bis*(bromomethyl)-naphthalene afforded the desired *bis*-1,8-(triazamacrocycle), which readily forms a *bis*-Cu^{+2} complex [95JA10577]. The synthesis of the *bis*-dien macrocycle bearing two 2-pyridylmethyl moieties has been reported [95CC2439]; the corresponding *bis*-Cu^{+2} complex not only readily binds imidazolate ion in aqueous solution, but also recognizes molecules containing the imidazole moiety. Syntheses of related multibridged polyaza cryptands have been reported [95TL3889, 95T77, 95CC1649, 95JA1965, 95IC3003].

8.4 CARBON–OXYGEN/CARBON–NITROGEN (CATENANES)

Mutual molecular recognition between structural components in large rings has led to the template-directed synthesis of a wide range of catenanes. A homologous series of [2]catenanes has been constructed using macrocyclic polyethers of the *bis*(*p*-phenylene)-(3*n*+4)crown ether-*n* (*n* = 9 - 14) type as templates for the formation of the tetracationic cyclophane, cyclo*bis*(paraquat-*p*-phenylene) [95JA1271, 95JA11171]. A combination of approaches has led to the successful self-assembly, in two steps, of a linear [4]catenane together with a small amount of the [5]catenane [95JA1271]. "The successful assembly of these catenanes ..., through the transcription of programmed molecular information, in the form of noncovalent bonding interactions, lends support to the contention that self-assembly is a viable paradigm for the construction of nanometer-scale molecular and supramolecular structures incorporating a selection of simple building blocks" [95JA11142].

8.5 CARBON–SULFUR RINGS

A series of lipophilic thiacrown ethers was prepared [95T4065] in low to moderate yields, by a procedure similar to that previously reported by Kellogg et al. [94T2095], via treatment of the dihalide with cesium dithiolate under high-dilution conditions in DMF, as the solvent. The simple 1,4,7,11,14,17-hexathiacycloeicosane was prepared (30 - 40 %) analogously except with slower addition of the dibromide and increased dilution. [95CJC1023] Another approach utilized the intermolecular cyclization of *bis*(alkyl bromide)s with thioacetamide using high dilution techniques [94CB1327].

The McMurry coupling of dialdehydes affords easy access to the corresponding alkene; however, when applied to the preparation of **10**, only traces of the desired product were isolated. The precursor dialdehyde, prepared from 1,1-dichloro-2,2-di(2-thienyl)ethene by lithiation and subsequent formylation, when subjected to specific coupling conditions {$TiCl_3(DME)_{1.5}$/Zn(Cu) in DME} afforded (70 %) the cyclic dimer **10**. Subjecting **10** to a novel double Fritsch-Buttenberg-Wiechell rearrangement gave rise (30 %) to the dark red annulene **11** [95CL499].

Double-layered tetrathiafulvalenes have been prepared but with different face-to-face orientations. The coupling of **12** with triethylphosphine in toluene under reflux gave (26 %) **13**, in which the TTF planes are slightly bent into a boat shape and overlapped with each other [95CL523]. Whereas, the related dimeric structure **14**, where the two TTF moieties possess a cross-orientation, has recently been reported [95CL579, 95TL5045].

10

11

12

13

n=1, n=2, n=3

14

8.6 CARBON-SILICON RINGS

The 4-methyl-4-silyl[$3^{4,10}$][7]metacyclophane and 4-(2-propenyl)-4-methyl-4-silyl[7]-metacyclophane were prepared in very low yields from the *tris*(9-borabicyclo[3.3.1]-nonane) [9-BBN] adduct of methyltriallylsilane with 1,3,5-tribromobenzene in the presence of Pd(0) reagents [94O3728]. A series of cyclic diynes with a tetramethyldisila moiety has been prepared; thus, 1,1,2,2-tetramethyl-1,2-disilacyclododeca-3,11-diyne was synthesized (4-8%) from 1,9-decadiyne, by treatment with methylmagnesium bromide, followed with 1,2-dichlorotetramethyldisilane at 25 °C in THF [95TL4603]. Reaction of this cyclic diyne with CpCoL$_2$ afforded (50-60%) superphane **15** [95TL4607]. Similar cyclic silanole derivatives have been created from other diyne ring structures [95O1089]. The use of Pd(0) catalysts caused selective intramolecular Si-Si σ-bond metathesis [95O2556]; the oligomerization of 1,1,2,2-tetramethyl-1,2-disilacyclopentane gave cyclic oligomers up to the 40-membered octamer [95JA1665].

8.7 CARBON–NITROGEN-OXYGEN RINGS

A series of novel *bis* and *tris*(macrocyclic) molecules has been designed as models for cation-conducting channels, such as "sidearm - crown - spacer - crown - sidearm", which can function in phospholipid bilayer vesicle membranes [95CC641, 95JA7665]. Numerous moieties have been *N*-appended to azacrown ethers (*N*-lariat ethers), such as: 2-hydroxy-5-nitrobenzyl or 5-chloro-8-hydroxy-2-quinolinyl [95JOC6097], various heteroaromatics [95JCS(P1)2497], two bidentate dianionic catecholates [95CC1505], 5- [95IC6235] and 4,7-(1,10-phenanthrolinyl) [95CC687], as well as (±)-7-benzocyclobutenylcarbonyl, whose resultant amide was heated with C$_{60}$ in trichlorobenzene at 180 °C to afford adducts **16**.

n=1,2

15

16

The following aza-subunits have been incorporated in a crown ethereal macrocycle: 3,7-diazabicyclo[3.3.1]nonan-9-one [95T4819], chiral substituted diethanolamines [95TA1123], 1,2-diarylethylenediamines [95JOC3980], 1,8-naphthyridine or 4-pyridinone [95JPC451]. The first *cis*-1,3,5,7-tetraoxadecalin diazacrown ethers and the corresponding cryptands **17** have been reported [95TL9193]. Synthesis of new large cryptands **18** has been completed and X-ray analysis confirmed the presence of an encapsulated benzene guest molecule [95CC735]. Facile, one- or two-step, preparation of cryptands, possessing different subunits have been reported [95T1599, 95JOC4912]. Ten new cryptands, e.g., **19**, containing two

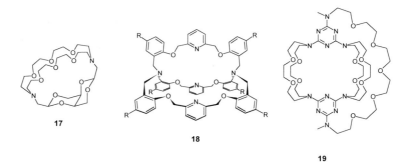

1,3,5-triazine subrings were created via simple aminolysis of cyanuric chloride with α,ω-diamines or diazacrowns [95JPC534].

A series of charged flexible cyclophanes made up of π-electron rich (hydroquinone) and deficient (bipyridinium) subunits coupled by polyethereal units has been reported [95CC2541]; however, the incorporation of two sets of these subunits in diametrically opposite locations generates a box-like shape, which has the potential to form structured two-dimensional arrays [95AG(E)1862]. Diverse novel rotaxanes have been assembled utilizing the previously known macrocyclic 1,10-phenanthroline precursor with oligobipyridines (to rigid-rack multimetallic complexes) [95CC715], with a C_{60} derivative (to a rotaxane with fullerene stoppers) [95CC781] or with a mixture of 3,5-di-*tert*-butylbenzaldehyde and 3,3'-diethyl-4,4'-dimethyl-2,2'-methylene-*bis*-1*H*-pyrrole (to a rotaxane with porphyrin caps) [95BCF340].

8.8 (CARBON-NITROGEN-OXYGEN)ⁿ (n>1) RINGS (CATENANES)

The synthesis of the first doubly interlocked [2]-catenane, based on the three-dimensional template effect of Cu^{+1}, has been completed; in principle, helices containing an odd number of metal centers lead to even numbered crossing [2]-catenanes [94JA375].

8.9 CARBON–SULFUR-OXYGEN RINGS

Simple thiametacyclophanes were prepared from commercial starting materials in which the final ring-closure (30%) between the polyethereal terminal dichloride and *m*-xylene-α,α'-dithiol employed a Cs^+-mediated procedure in DMF solution [95IC5656]. Homolytic cycloaddition of dithiols, derived from *trans*- and *cis*-1,2-cyclohexanediols, to alkynes was induced by Pr_3B-O_2, affording a simple route to *trans*- and *cis*-cyclohexano-fused 12-membered crown thioethers [95T11431]. Macrocycle **20** was synthesized from 3-bromothiophene by two different procedures [95JA9832]; **20** has been shown to form strong self-assembled complexes with paraquat [94JA9347]. This monomer (**20**) was dilithiated and subjected to cross-coupling polymerization to afford macromolecules with reasonable molecular weights. The synthesis, optical, and electrochemical properties of a related calix[4]arene-substituted polythiophene, which was shown to possess ion selective voltammetric, chromic, fluorescent, and resistive responses, have also been reported [95JA9842].

Oxa-crown porphyrazines (21) were synthesized by the Mg(II) template cyclization of crown ether derivatives of dithiomaleonitrile and shown to possess ligation of eight Ag(I) ions by utilizing both the crown ether and meso-pocket coordination sites [95AG(E)2020]. An improved preparation and the coordination chemistry with Ag(I) of oxa-crown derivatives of dithiomaleonitrile have been reported [95IC2300].

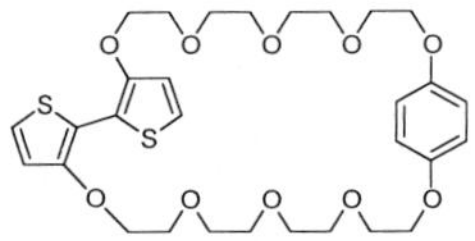

20

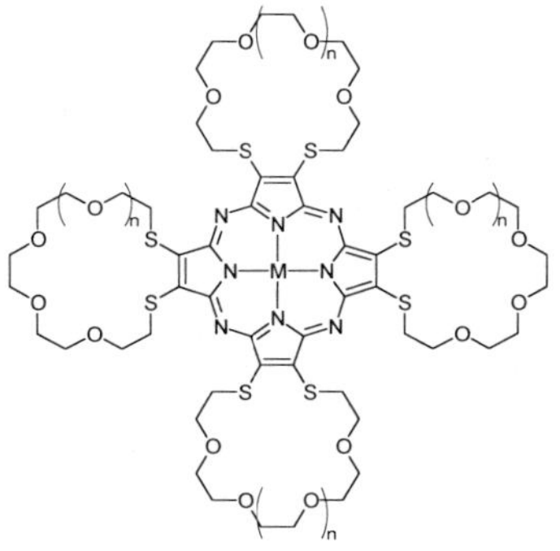

21

8.10 CARBON–NITROGEN–SULFUR RINGS

A general synthetic method for the incorporation of the dithiomaleonitrile moiety into macrocycles possessing nitrogen (as well as sulfur and oxygen) has appeared [95T8175]. A series of CNS-macrocycles with a pendant carboxylic and amino group has been synthesized [95HCA1325]. The inversion barriers and excited states of 1-thia-10-aza[2.2]meta-cyclophane have been calculated; good agreement between the experimental and calculated circular dichroism was observed [95JCS(P2)1185].

8.11 CARBON–SILICON-SULFUR (or OXYGEN or NITROGEN) RINGS

Konig et al. [95AG(E)661] have prepared a related series of Si-bridged macrocycles, including the first silacalix[4]arene, from the deprotonation of furan, thiophene, *N*-methylpyrrole or tert-butylanisole, followed by addition of dimethyldichlorosilane.

8.12 CARBON-NITROGEN-SULFUR-OXYGEN RINGS

Pyridinophanes **22** were prepared from *bis*(thiomethyl)*meta*-terphenyls and *bis*(chloromethyl)pyridine derivatives [95T2267]. The template synthesis of new cryptands possessing three distinct compartments has been shown [95T3265]. The synthesis of the novel bicyclic azetidinyl *bis*propargylic sulfone **23** was demonstrated in five steps from 4-benzoyloxyazetidinone [95TL7913]. Tetrafluoro-1,2-*bis*(chlorosulfenyl)ethane was cyclized with 1,8-diamino-3,6-dioxaoctane to produce (30 %) 1,4-dithia-7,16-diaza-10,13-dioxa-2,2,3,3-tetrafluorocyclooctadecane [94IC6123].

8.13 CARBON–NITROGEN–PHOSPHORUS-OXYGEN RINGS

A series of macrocyclic cyclophosphazene derivatives with mono-ansa, mono-spiro, spiro-ansa, and *bis*-ansa structures has been prepared by the reaction of hexachlorocyclotriphosphazene with tetraethylene glycol in the presence of sodium hydride [95ICA187]. Although possessing imine bonds, the cyclocondensation of phosphodihydrazides with 3,3'-[(3-oxapentane-1,5-diyl)dioxy]*bis*(2-hydroxybenzaldehyde) as well as with an oligomer afforded the related macrocycles [95JA1712]. Reaction of related phosphorus macrocycles with the sodium salt of a phosphodihydrazone gave macrocycles possessing five phosphorus atoms [95JA1712].

Treatment of 2,6-*bis*(bromomethyl)pyridine with 2-(methylamino)ethanol afforded 2,6-*bis*[(2-hydroxyethyl)methylaminomethyl]pyridine, which with 4-nitrophenylphosphoro dichloride under high dilution conditions gave rise to the desired cyclic phosphotriester **24**; divalent metal ions dramatically enhance the rate of hydrolysis [95TL4031].

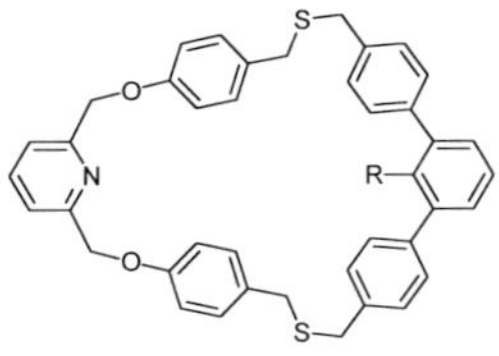

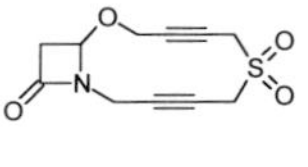

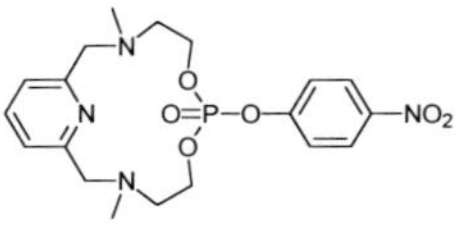

8.14 CARBON–NITROGEN-METAL RINGS

Stang et al. [94JA4981, 94O3776, 95JA1667, 95JA6273] described the self assembly of a series of unique cationic, tetranuclear, Pd(II)- and Pt(II)-based macrocyclic squares (e.g., **25**), utilizing different bidentates as the sides of these structures. The similar self-assembly complexation of dipyridyl porphyrins by *cis*- and *trans*-substituted Pd(II) or Pt(II) ions possessing square planar coordination afforded multiporphyrin arrays with a square

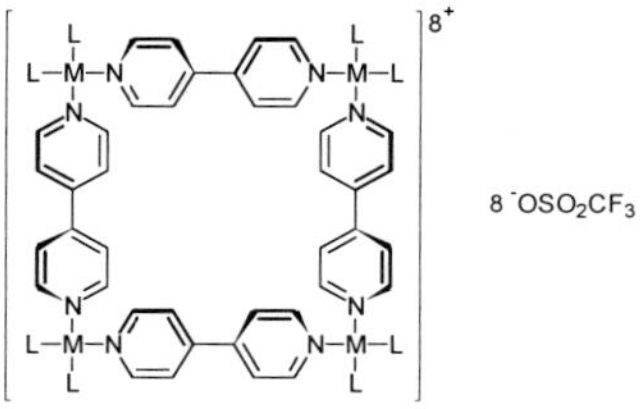

25 8 ⁻OSO₂CF₃

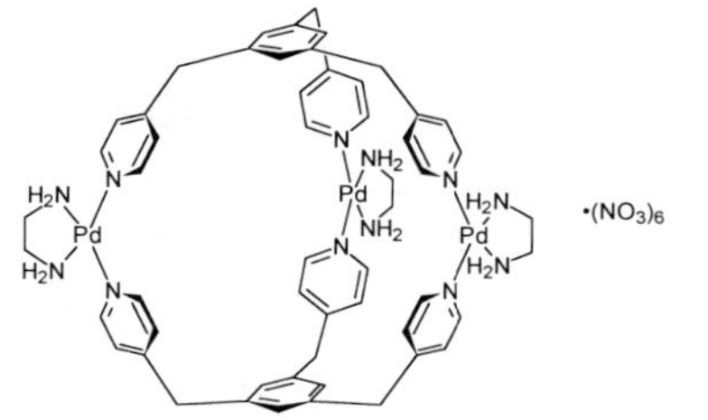

26 •(NO₃)₆

architecture [94CC2313]; also, the self-assembly of a cyclic ruthenium porphyrin tetramer has been reported [95CL765]. The creation of three-dimensional cage-like Pd(II) complexes (**26**) has been described [95JA1649]; however, **26** only assembles in the presence of specific guest molecules.

8.15 CARBON–NITROGEN-METAL/CARBON-NITROGEN-METAL RINGS (CATENANES)

The concept of a molecular lock using the dual character of a Pt(II)-pyridine coordination bond has been shown [95JA4175]; utilization of the labile nature of the Pd(II)-pyridine bond has realized the quantitative self-assembly of [2]-catenane **27** from two related monocyclic counterparts. The catenane with M = Pd(II) is in rapid equilibrium; whereas with M = Pt(II), the catenane is locked, but can be unlocked with added salt and heating or relocked by removing of the salt and cooling.

8.16 CARBON-NITROGEN-OXYGEN-METAL RINGS

Reaction of [1,1'-ferrocenediyl*bis*(methylene)]*bis*[pyridinium] salt with diaza-12-crown-4 afforded the ferrocene crown ether 1,1'':1',1'''-*bis*(ferrocenediyl)*bis*[4,10-*bis*(methylene)-1,7-dioxa-4,10-diazacyclododecane [95IC3964].

8.17 CARBON-PHOSPHORUS-OXYGEN-METAL RINGS

Photolysis of *cis*-Mo(CO)₄{Ph₂P(CH₂CH₂O)₄CH₂CH₂PPh₂-*P,P*'} in THF under nitrogen gave (45%) the corresponding *trans*-isomer, which is the first example of a metallo-crown ether possessing a *trans*-coordinated α,ω-*bis*(phosphane)polyether ligand [94O1542].

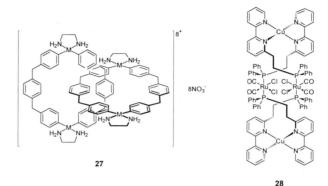

27

28

8.18 CARBON-PHOSPHORUS-NITROGEN-METAL RINGS

Treatment of 6-(2-bromoethyl)-2,2'-bipyridine with lithiophosphine afforded the corresponding 2-diphenylphosphinoethyl derivative, which when subjected to $[Ru(CO)_2Cl_2]_n$ in methanol at 25 °C to gave the 2:1 metallo-synthon possessing *trans* phosphane ligands; addition of Cu(I) generated the 36-membered metallocycle 28 [95CC2033].

8.19 REFERENCES

93MI1   V. Ya. Veselov, Yu. V. Savel'ev, A. P. Grekov, *Kompoz. Polim. Mater.* **1993**, *55*, 3.
93MI2   E. E. Ergozhin, M. Kurmanaliev, *Izv. Nats. Akad. Nauk Resp. Kaz., Ser. Khim.* **1993**, 44.
93MI3   Y. Chen, X. Lu, *Gaofenzi Tongbao*, **1993**, 1.
94CB1327   K. Mlinaric-Majerski, D. Pavlovic, M. Luic, B. Kojic-Prodic, *Chem. Ber.* **1994**, *127*, 1327.
94CC2313   C. M. Drain, J.-M. Lehn, *J. Chem. Soc., Chem. Commun.* **1994**, 2313.
94COS259   J. D. Kilburn, H. K. Patel, *Contemp. Org. Syn.* **1994**, *1*, 259.
94COS457   M. C. Elliot, *Contemp. Org. Syn.* **1994**, *1*, 457.
94IC6123   H. Plenio, *Inorg. Chem.* **1994**, *33*, 6123.
94JA375   J.-F. Nierengarten, C. O. Dietrich-Buchecker, J.-P. Sauvage, *J. Am. Chem. Soc.* **1994**, *116*, 375.
94JA4981   P. J. Stang, D. H. Cao, *J. Am. Chem. Soc.* **1994**, *116*, 4981.
94JA9347   M. J. Marsella, P. J. Carroll, T. M. Swager, *J. Am. Chem. Soc.* **1994**, *116*, 9347.
94MI1   Z. Asfari, S. Wenger, J. Vicens, *Inclusion Phenom. Mol. Recognit. Chem.* **1994**, *19*, 137.

94MI2   K. Hiratani, T. Hamaya, H. Sakaguchi, K. Taguchi, K. Kasuga, H. Sugihara, T. Hirose,Y. Himeda, T. Takahashi, *Busshita Kogaku Kogyo Gijutsu Kenkyusho Hokoku* **1994**, *2*, 499.

94MI3   X. Ye, Q. Guo, *Huaxue Shiji* **1994**, *16*, 302.

94MI4   R. Delgado, *Bol.-Soc. Port. Quim.* **1994**, *52*, 56.

94MI5   Y. Nakasuji, *Yukagaku* **1994**, *43*, 821.

94MI6   B. Z. Iofa, *Vestn. Mosk. Univ., Ser. 2: Khim.* **1994**, *35*, 441.

94MI7   Y. Kobute, *Yukagaku* **1994**, *43*, 830.

94O1542   G. M. Gray, C. H. Duffey, *Organometallics* **1994**, *13*, 1542.

94O3728   W. R. Kwochka, R. Damrauer, M. W. Schmidt, M. S. Gordon, *Organometallics* **1994**, *13*, 3728.

94O3776   P. J. Stang, J. A. Whiteford, *Organometallics* **1994**, *13*, 3776.

94SS103   Z. Asfari, S. Wenger, J. Vicens, *Supramol. Sci.* **1994**, *1*, 103.

94SL765   W. Y. Lee, *Synlett* **1994**, 765.

94T2095   J. J. H. Edema, J. Buter, R. M. Kellogg, *Tetrahedron* **1994**, *50*, 2095.

94TL5661   M. Atsumi, M. Mizuochi, K. Ohta, K. Fujita, *Tetrahedron Lett.* **1995**, *35*, 5661.

95AG(E)661   B. König, M. Rödel, P. Bubenitschek, P. G. Jones, *Angew. Chem. Int. Ed. Engl.* **1995**, *34*, 661.

95AG(E)789   R. Gleiter, K. Hövermann, J. Ritter, B. Nuber, *Angew. Chem. Int. Ed. Engl.* **1995**, *34*, 789.

95AG(E)1862 P. R. Ashton, C. G. Claessens, W. Hayes, S. Menzer, J. F. Stoddart, A. J. P. White, D. J. Williams, *Angew. Chem. Int. Ed. Engl.* **1995**, *34*, 1862.

95AG(E)2020 J. W. Sibert, S. J. Lange, C. L. Stern, A. G. M. Barrett, B. M. Hoffman, *Angew. Chem. Int. Ed. Engl.* **1995**, *34*, 2020.

95AG(E)2107 A. Grohmann, *Angew. Chem. Int. Ed. Engl.* **1995**, *34*, 2107.

95AG(E)2147 F. M. Menger, K. K. Catlin, *Angew. Chem. Int. Ed. Engl.* **1995**, *34*, 2147.

95BCF340   J.-C. Chambron, V. Heitz, J.-P. Sauvage, *Bull. Soc. Chim. Fr.* **1995**, *132*, 340.

95CBR33   E. C. Constable, D. Smith, *Chem. Brit.* **1995** (1), 33.

95CC185   Z. Kocacs, A. D. Sherry, *J. Chem. Soc., Chem. Commun.* **1995**, 185.

95CC419   F. Fernández-Lázaro, A. Sastre, T. Torres, *J. Chem. Soc., Chem. Commun.* **1995**, 419.

95CC641   K. Wang, X. Han, R. W. Gross, G. W. Gokel, *J. Chem. Soc., Chem. Commun.* **1995**, 641.

95CC675   D. Bethell, G. Dougherty, D. C. Cupertino, *J. Chem. Soc., Chem. Commun.* **1995**, 675.

95CC687   M. Schmittel, H. Ammon, *J. Chem. Soc., Chem. Commun.* **1995**, 687.

95CC715   H. Sleiman, P. Baxter, J.-M. Lehn, K. Rissanen, *J. Chem. Soc., Chem. Commun.* **1995**, 715.

95CC735   R. J. A. Janssen, L. F. Lindoy, O. A. Matthews, G. V. Meehan, A. N. Sobolev, A. H. White, *J. Chem. Soc., Chem. Commun.* **1995**, 735

95CC747   D. B. Amabilino, P. R. Ashton, M. Belohradský, F. M. Raymo, J. F. Stoddart, *J. Chem. Soc., Chem. Commun.* **1995**, 747.

95CC781   F. Diederich, C. Dietrich-Buchecker, J.-F. Nierengarten, J.-P. Sauvage, *J. Chem. Soc., Chem. Commun.* **1995**, 781.

95CC1073 P. Cudic, M. Zinic, V. Tomisic, V. Simeon, J.-P. Vigneron, J.-M. Lehn, *J. Chem. Soc., Chem. Commun.* **1995**, 1073.

95CC1085 C. von dem Bussche-Hünnefeld, D. Bühring, C. B. Knobler, D. J. Cram, *J. Chem. Soc., Chem. Commun.* **1995**, 1085.

95CC1237 S. Breidenbach, S. Ohren, M. Nieger, F. Vögtle, *J. Chem. Soc., Chem. Commun.* **1995**, 1237.

95CC1239 E. Alcalde, M. Alemany, L. Pérez-García, M. L. Rodriguez, *J. Chem. Soc., Chem. Commun.* **1995**, 1239.

95CC1483 T. D. James, S. Shinkai, *J. Chem. Soc., Chem. Commun.* **1995**, 1483.

95CC1505 E. Graf, M. W. Hosseini, R. Ruppert, A. D. Cian, J. Fischer, *J. Chem. Soc., Chem. Commun.* **1995**, 1505.

95CC1631 J. Dale, C. Rømming, M. R. Suissa, *J. Chem. Soc., Chem. Commun.* **1995**, 1631.

95CC1633 J. Dale, C. Rømming, M. R. Suissa, *J. Chem. Soc., Chem. Commun.* **1995**, 1633.

95CC1649 G. Morgan, V. McKee, J. Nelson, *J. Chem. Soc., Chem. Commun.* **1995**, 1649.

95CC1947 Y.-S. Byun, T. A. Robbins, C. B. Knobler, D. J. Cram *J. Chem. Soc., Chem. Commun.* **1995**, 1947.

95CC2033 R. Ziessel, D. Matt, L. Toupet, *J. Chem. Soc., Chem. Commun.* **1995**, 2033.

95CC2439 L. Fabbrizzi, P. Pallavicini, L. Parodi, A. Perotti, A. Taglietti, *J. Chem. Soc., Chem. Commun.* **1995**, 2439.

95CC2541 P.-L. Anelli, M. Asakawa, P. R. Ashton, G. R. Brown, W. Hayes, O. Kocian, S. R. Pastor, J. F. Stoddart, M. S. Tolley, A. J. P. White, D. J. Williams, *J. Chem. Soc., Chem. Commun.* **1995**, 2541.

95CEJ56 J. L. Sessler, S. J. Weghorn, Y. Hiseada, V. Lynch, *Chem. Eur. J.* **1995**, *1*, 56.

95CJC685 I. Meunier, A. K. Mishra, B. Hanquet, P. Cocolios, R. Guilard, *Can. J. Chem.* **1995**, *73*, 685.

95CJC1023 C. R. Lucas, S. Liu, J. N. Bridson, *Can. J. Chem.* **1995**, *73*, 1023.

95CL497 H. Yamamoto, K. Ueda, K. R. A. Samankumara, S. Shinkai, *Chem. Lett.* **1995**, 497.

95CL499 T. Kawase, H. R. Darabi, R. Uchimiya, M. Oda, *Chem. Lett.* **1995**, 499.

95CL523 K. Matsuo, K. Takimiya, Y. Aso, T. Otsubo, F. Ogura, *Chem. Lett.* **1995**, 523.

95CL579 J. Tanabe, T. Kudo, M. Okamoto, Y. Kawada, G. Ono, A. Izuoka, T. Sugawara, *Chem. Lett.* **1995**, 579.

95CL765 K. Funatsu, A. Kimura, T. Imamura, Y. Sasaki, *Chem. Lett.* **1995**, 765.

95CSR197 L. Fabbrizzi, A. Poggi, *Chem. Soc. Rev.* **1995**, 197.

95GCI163 C. Bazzicalupi, A. Bencini, A. Bianchi, P. Paoletti, V. Fusi, M. Micheloni, *Gazz. Chim. Ital.* **1995**, *125*, 163.

95HCA1037 E. Martinborough, T. M. Denti, P. P. Castro, T. B. Wyman, C. B. Knobler, F. Diederich, *Helv. Chim. Acta* **1995**, *78*, 1037.

95HCA1325 P. C. Riesen, Th. A. Kaden, *Helv. Chim. Acta* **1995**, *78*, 1325.

95IC2300   J. W. Sibert, S. J. Lange, D. J. Williams, A. G. M. Barrett, B. M. Hoffman, *Inorg. Chem.* **1995**, *34*, 2300.

95IC3003   C. Bazzicalupi, A. Bencini, A. Bianchi, V. Fusi, L. Mazzanti, P. Paoletti, B. Valtancoli, *Inorg. Chem.* **1995**, *34*, 3003.

95IC3964   H. Plenio, R. Diodone, *Inorg. Chem.* **1995**, *34*, 3964.

95IC5641   C. E. Daitch, P. D. Hampton, E. N. Duesler, *Inorg. Chem.* **1995**, *34*, 5641.

95IC5656   J. E. Kickham, S. J. Loeb, *Inorg. Chem.* **1995**, *34*, 5656.

95IC6235   Y. Shen, B. P. Sullivan, *Inorg. Chem.* **1995**, *34*, 6235.

95ICA187   K. Brandt, T. Kupka, J. Drodz, J. C. van de Grampel, A. Meetsma, A. P. Jekel, *Inorg. Chim. Acta* **1995**, *228*, 187.

95JA852   H. W. Gibson, S. Liu, P. Lecavalier, C. Wu, Y. X. Shen, *J. Am. Chem. Soc.* **1995**, *117*, 852.

95JA1271   D. B. Amabilino, P. R. Ashton, C. L. Brown, E. Córdova, L. A. Godínez, T. T. Goodnow, A. E. Kaifer, S. P. Newton, M. Pietraszkiewicz, D. Philp, F. M. Raymo, A. S. Reder, M. T. Rutland, A. M. Z. Slawin, N. Spencer, J. F. Stoddart, D. J. Williams, *J. Am. Chem. Soc.* **1995**, *117*, 1271.

95JA1649   M. Fujita, S. Nagao, K. Ogura, *J. Am. Chem. Soc.* **1995**, *117*, 1649.

95JA1659   S. K. Kurdistani, R. C. Helgeson, D. J. Cram *J. Am. Chem. Soc.* **1995**, *117*, 1659.

95JA1665   M. Suginome, H. Oike, Y. Ito, *J. Am. Chem. Soc.* **1995**, *117*, 1665.

95JA1667   P. J. Stang, K. Chen, *J. Am. Chem. Soc.* **1995**, *117*, 1667.

95JA1712   J. Mitjaville, A.-M. Caminade, J.-C. Daran, B. Donnadieu, J.-P. Majoral, *J. Am. Chem. Soc.* **1995**, *117*, 1712.

95JA1965   J.-L. Pierre, P. Chautemps, S. Refaif, C. Beguin, A. E. Marzouki, G. Serratrice, E. Saint-Aman, P. Rey, *J. Am. Chem. Soc.* **1995**, *117*, 1965.

95JA2767   A. Casnati, A. Pochini, R. Ungaro, F. Ugozzoli, F. Arnaud, S. Fanni, M.-J. Schwing, R. J. M. Egberink, F. de Jong, D. N. Reinhoudt, *J. Am. Chem. Soc.* **1995**, *117*, 2767.

95JA2793   D. Jacoby, S. Isoz, C. Floriani, A. Chiesi-Villa, C. Rizzoli, *J. Am. Chem. Soc.* **1995**, *117*, 2793.

95JA4175   M. Fujita, F. Ibukuro, K. Yamaguchi, K. Ogura, *J. Am. Chem. Soc.* **1995**, *117*, 4175.

95JA6273   P. J. Stang, D. H. Cao, S. Saito, A. M. Arif, *J. Am. Chem. Soc.* **1995**, *117*, 6273.

95JA7665   O. Murillo, S. Watanabe, A. Nakano, G. W. Gokel, *J. Am. Chem. Soc.* **1995**, *117*, 7665.

95JA7726   M. Sawada, Y. Takai, H. Yamada, S. Hirayama, T. Kaneda, T. Tanaka, K. Kamada, T. Mizooku, S. Takeuchi, K. Ueno, K. Hirose, Y. Tobe, K. Naemura, *J. Am. Chem. Soc.* **1995**, *117*, 7726.

95JA9832   M. J. Marsella, P. J. Carroll, T. M. Swager, *J. Am. Chem. Soc.* **1995** *117*, 9832.

95JA9842   M. J. Marsella, R. J. Newland, P. J. Carroll, T. M. Swager, *J. Am. Chem. Soc.* **1995**, *117*, 9842.

95JA10577   M. J. Young, J. Chin, *J. Am. Chem. Soc.* **1995**, *117*, 10577.

95JA11142   D. B. Amabilino, P.-L. Anelli, P. R. Ashton, G. R. Brown, E. Córdova, L. A. Godínez, W. Hayes, A. E. Kaifer, D. Philp, A. M. Z. Slawin, N. Spencer, J. F. Stoddart, M. S. Tolley, D. J. Williams, *J. Am. Chem. Soc.* **1995**, *117*, 11142.

95JA11171   P. R. Ashton, R. Ballardini, V. Balzani, A. Credi, M. T. Gandolfi, S. Menzer, L. Pérez-García, L. Prodi, J. F. Stoddart, M. Venturi, A. J. P. White, D. J. Williams, *J. Am. Chem. Soc.* **1995**, *117*, 11171.

95JA11198   J. Jiménez-Barbero, E. Junquera, M. Martín-Pastor, S. Sherma, C. Vicent, S. Penadés, *J. Am. Chem. Soc.* **1995**, *117*, 11198.

95JCS(P1)2339   P. P. Kanakamma, N. S. Mani, U. Maitra, V. Nair, *J. Chem. Soc. Perkin Trans 1* **1995**, 2339.

95JCS(P1)2497   K. Matsumoto, M. Hashimoto, M. Toda, H. Tsukube, *J. Chem. Soc. Perkin Trans 1* **1995**, 2497.

95JCS(P2)1103   F. Ohseta, S. Shinkai, *J. Chem. Soc. Perkin Trans 2* **1995**, 1103.

95JCS(P2)1185   D. Wortmann-Saleh, S. Grimme, B. Engels, D. Müller, F. Vögtle, *J. Chem. Soc. Perkin Trans 2* **1995**, 1185.

95JMS925   M. Vincenti, *J. Mass Spectrom.* **1995**, *30*, 925.

95JOC516   Y. Delaviz, J. S. Merola, M. A. G. Berg, H. W. Gibson, *J. Org. Chem.* **1995**, *60*, 516.

95JOC1207   J. R. Fraser, B. Borecka, J. Trotter, J. C. Sherman, *J. Org. Chem.* **1995**, *60*, 1207.

95JOC3980   N. Kise, H. Oike, E. Okazaki, M. Yoshimoto, T. Shono, *J. Org. Chem.* **1995**, *60*, 3980.

95JOC4912   A. V. Bordunov, N. G. Lukyanenko, V. N. Pastushok, K. E. Krakowiak, J. S. Bradshaw, N. K. Dalley, X. Kou, *J. Org. Chem.* **1995**, *60*, 4912.

95JOC6070   S. Kanamathareddy, C. D. Gutsche, *J. Org. Chem.* **1995**, *60*, 6070.

95JOC6097   A. V. Bordunov, P. C. Hellier, J. S. Bradshaw, N. K. Dalley, X. Kou, X. X. Zhang, R. M. Izatt, *J. Org. Chem.* **1995**, *60*, 6097.

95JOC7380   C.-H. Kuo, M.-H. Tsau, D. T.-C. Weng, G. H. Lee, S.-M. Peng, T.-Y. Luh, *J. Org. Chem.* **1995**, *60*, 7380.

95JPC339   B. König, *J. prakt. Chem.* **1995**, *337*, 339.

95JPC451   E. Weber, H.-J. Köhler, *J. prakt. Chem.* **1995**, *337*, 451.

95JPC534   H. Graubaum, F. Tittelbach, G. Lutze, *J. prakt. Chem.* **1995**, *337*, 534.

95LA1515   J. Huuskonen, J. Schulz, K. Rissanen, *Liebigs Ann.* **1995**, 1515.

95M658   T. Kakuchi, H. Kamimura, S. Matsunami, K. Yokota, K. Tsuda, *Macromolecules* **1995**, *28*, 658.

95MCP2383   K. Yokota, O. Haba, T. Satoh, T. Kakuchi, *Macromol. Chem. Phys.* **1995**, *196*, 2383.

95MI1   J.-M. Lehn, "Supramolecular Chemistry: Concepts and Perspectives", VCH, Weinheim, Germany, 1995.

95MI2   X. Luo, X. Liu, H. Xu, *Huaxue Jinzhan* **1995**, *7*, 113.

95MI3   T. Araki, *Chromatogr. Sci. Ser.* **1995**, *68*, 241.

95MI4   T. Morozumi, S. Shinkai, *Kobunshi* **1995**, *44*, 2.

95MI5   H. W. Gibson, S. Liu, Y. X. Shen, M. Bheda, S.-H. Lee, F. Wang, *NATO ASI Ser., Ser. C* **1995**, *456*, 41.

95MI6   P. Jing, R. Fu, *Fenxi Huaxue* **1995**, *23*, 104.

95MI7   K. Odashima, K. Kago, *Kagaku (Kyoto)* **1995**, *50*, 124.
95NJC619   P. Thuery, N. Keller, M. Lance, J.-D. Vigner, M. Nierlich, *New J. Chem.* **1995**, *19*, 619.
95O1089   E. Toyoda, A. Kunai, M. Ishikawa, *Organometallics* **1995**, *14*, 1089.
95O2556   T. Kusukawa, Y. Kabe, B. Nestler, W. Ando, *Organometallics* **1995**, *14*, 2556.
95PAC233   J.-C. Chambron, C. O. Dietrich-Buchecker, V. Heitz, J.-F. Nierengarten, J.-P. Sauvage, C. Pascard, J. Guilhem, *Pure Appl. Chem.* **1995**, *67*, 233.
95S1019   V. Jacques, M. Mesbahi, V. Boskovic, J. F. Desreux, *Synthesis* **1995**,1019.
95SC3777   P. P. Kanakamma, N. S. Mani, V. Nair, *Syn. Commun.* **1995**, *25*, 3777.
95SL757   E. Alcalde, M. Alemany, M. Gisbert, L. Pérez-García, *Synlett* **1995**, 757.
95T77   D. Chen, R. J. Motekaitis, I. Murase, A. E. Martell, *Tetrahedron* **1995**, *51*, 77.
95T343   A. D. Hamilton, *Tetrahedron* **1995**, *51*, 343.
95T591   A. Casnati, P. Jacopozzi, A. Pochini, F. Ugozzoli, R. Cacciapaglia, L. Mandolini, R. Ungaro, *Tetrahedron* **1995**, *51*, 591.
95T1599   K. E. Krakowiak, J. S. Bradshaw, X. Kou, N. K. Dalley, *Tetrahedron* **1995**, *51*, 1599.
95T2267   T. K. Vinod, P. Rajakumar, H. Hart, *Tetrahedron* **1995**, *51*, 2267.
95T2777   G. Rousseau, *Tetrahedron* **1995**, *51*, 2777.
95T3265   P. Ghosh, R. Shukla, D. K. Chand, P. K. Bharadwaj, *Tetrahedron* **1995**, *51*, 3265.
95T3395   J. C. Sherman, *Tetrahedron* **1995**, *51*, 3395.
95T4065   V. Guyon, A. Guy, J. Foos, M. Lemaire, M. Draye, *Tetrahedron* **1995**, *51*, 4065.
95T4819   D. St C. Black, M. A. Horsham, M. Rose, *Tetrahedron* **1995**, *51*, 4819.
95T8175   S. J. Lange, J. W. Sibert, C. L. Stern, A. G. M. Barrett, B. M. Hoffman, *Tetrahedron* **1995**, *51*, 8175.
95T8423   O. Hayashida, K. Ono, Y. Hisaeda, Y. Murakami, *Tetrahedron* **1995**, *51*, 8423.
95T9113   F. H. Kohnke, M. F. Parisi, F. M. Raymo, P. A. O'Neil, D. J. Williams, *Tetrahedron* **1995**, *50*, 9113.
95T9927   A. Kraus, A. Gügel, P. Belik, M. Walter, K. Müllen, *Tetrahedron* **1995**, *51*, 9927.
95T11431   E. I. Troyansky, R. F. Ismagilov, V. V. Samoshin, Y. A. Strelenko, D. V. Demchuck, G. I. Nikishin, S. V. Lindeman, V. N. Khrustalyov, Y. T. Struchkov, *Tetrahedron* **1995**, *51*, 11431.
95TA1043   T. Hattori, N. Harada, S. Oi, H. Abe, S. Miyano, *Tetrahedron: Asymmetry* **1995**, *6*, 1043.
95TA1123   E. F. J. de Vries, L. Ploeg, M. Colao, J. Brussee, A. van der Gen, *Tetrahedron: Asymmetry* **1995**, *6*, 1123.
95TA1873   K. Naemura, M. Asada, K. Hirose, Y. Tobe, *Tetrahedron: Asymmetry* **1995**, *6*, 1873.
95TA2059   J. Grochowski, B. Rys, P. Serda, U. Wagner, *Tetrahedron: Asymmetry* **1995**, *6*, 2059.

95TL79 V. Patinec, J. J. Yaouanc, J. C. Clément, H. Handel, H. des Abbayes, *Tetrahedron Lett.* **1995**, *36*, 79.

95TL2707 R. Breslow, P. J. Duggan, D. Wiedenfeld, S. T. Waddell, *Tetrahedron Lett.* **1995**, *36*, 2707.

95TL3889 B. P. Clark, J. R. Harris, G. H. Timms, J. L. Olkowski, *Tetrahedron Lett.* **1995**, *36*, 3889.

95TL4031 I. O. Kady, B. Tan, *Tetrahedron Lett.* **1995**, *36*, 4031.

95TL4401 G. Märkl, U. Striebl, P. Kreitmeier, A. Knorr, M. Porsch, J. Daub, *Tetrahedron Lett.* **1995**, *36*, 4401.

95TL4603 R. Gleiter, H. Stahr, F. Stadtmüller, H. Irngartinger, H. Pritzkow, *Tetrahedron Lett.* **1995**, *36*, 4603.

95TL4607 R. Gleiter, H. Stahr, B. Nuber, *Tetrahedron Lett.* **1995**, *36*, 4607.

95TL5045 K. Takimiya, Y. Shibata, K. Imamura, A. Kashihara, Y. Aso, T. Otsubo, F. Ogura, *Tetrahedron Lett.* **1995**, *36*, 5045.

95TL5261 A. Lorente, M. Fernández-Saiz, J.-F. Espinosa, C. Jaime, J.-M. Lehn, J.-P. Vigneron, *Tetrahedron Lett.* **1995**, *36*, 5261.

95TL5951 L. Tóke, L. Fenichel, M. Albert, *Tetrahedron Lett.* **1995**, *36,* 5951.

95TL6095 K. N. Koh, K. Araki, S. Shinkai, Z. Asfari, J. Vicens, *Tetrahedron Lett.* **1995**, *36*, 6095.

95TL7677 S. Watanabe, K. Goto, T. Kawashima, R. Okazaki, *Tetrahedron Lett.* **1995**, *36*, 7677.

95TL7913 A. Basak, U. K. Khamrai, *Tetrahedron Lett.* **1995**, *36*, 7913.

95TL8051 O. Hayashida, T. Hirohashi, Y. Hisaeda, Y. Murakami, *Tetrahedron Lett.* **1995**, *36*, 8051.

95TL8163 A. A. Gakh, R. A. Sachleben, J. C. Bryan, B. A. Moyer, *Tetrahedron Lett.* **1995**, *36*, 8163.

95TL8279 A. Lorente, M. Fernández-Saiz, J.-M. Lehn, J.-P. Vigneron, *Tetrahedron Lett.* **1995**, *36*, 8279.

95TL9193 K. Frische, M. Greenwald, E. Ashkenasi, N. G. Lemcoff, S. Abramson, L. Golender, B. Fuchs, *Tetrahedron Lett.* **1995**, *36*, 9193.

95TL9269 Z. Kovacs, A. D. Sherry, *Tetrahedron Lett.* **1995**, *36*, 9269.

INDEX

A-86929, 87
Ab initio calculations, 155
Ab initio Hartree-Fock-Roothaan, 83
Acetyl-1-(phenylsulfonyl)pyrrole, 109
(1*R*,2*S*,3*R*)-Acetyl-4(5)-[(1,2,3,4)-tetrahydroxybutyl]imidazole, 150
5-Acetyl-4-methyloxazole, 236
1-Acetylpyrrole osmium and ruthenium derivatives, 116
2-Acetylthiophene, 84
Acridines, 323
Acyl cobalt speces, 23
Acyl radicals, 18
Acyl-peroxo-cobalt species, 63
3-Acylamino-1,2,4-oxazoles, 172
3-Acylaminofurazans, 172
5-(Acylhydrazino)pyrazoles, 146
N-Acylindoles, 106
N-Acylindolin-2-ols, 106
1-(Acylmethyl)-2-methyl-4-nitro-5-bromoimidazoles, 151
4-Alkenoylimidazoles, 150
2-Alkyl-, 2-bromo-, and 2-methylthiotryptophans, 111
1-Alkyl-2-phenylpyrroles, 105
1-Alkyl-4,5-dinitro-1,2,3-triazole, 152
9-Alkylcarbazoles, 26
3-Alkylideneindolines, 106
3-Alkylideneoxindoles, 108
N-Alkylimidazoles, 151
3-Alkyloxindoles, 108
3-Alkylthiophenes, 86
Allenyl isoselenocyanates, 174
Allenylidene-tetrahydrofurans, 56
Aluminium chlorofluoride, 69
Aluminocyclopentadiene, 83
Amethyrins, 322
4-Amino-1,2,3-triazolo[4,5-*d*]pyridazines, 235
5-Amino-1H-1,2,4-triazole, 155
2-Amino-2-thiazoline, 167
2-Amino-3-cyanofurans, 237
5-Amino-3-cyanopyrazole, 147
3-Amino-3H-azirines, 148
2-Amino-5-aryl-1,3,4-thiadiazoles, 174
6-Amino-indole-4,7-quinones, 113
N-Aminobenzimidazoles, 151
Aminocoumarins, 284
Aminofluorenes, 36
N-Aminoimidazoles, 151
Aminomethylation, 87
2-Aminopyrroles, 109
2-Aminothiazole, 170
2-Aminothiazoline, 167
5-Aminothiazolo[4,5-*d*]pyrimidine-2,7(3H,6H)-diones, 242
3-Aminothieno-2,3-*b*]pyridines, 92
Aminothienopyrazoles, 92
2-Aminothiophene, 93
3-Aminothiophene, 94
N-Aminotriazoles, 153

Aminotriazolotropone, 153
5-Androsteno[17,16-*e*]pyrimidines, 238
Annelation of indoles, 103
ANRORC, 231, 241
Anthraquinone-photocatalysis, 28
Arene diazonium tetrafluoroborates, 22
Artemisinin, 290
2-Aryl and 2-styrylindoles, 112
1,2-Aryl radical rearrangements, 36
2-Aryl-3H-indol-3-ones, 114
2-Aryl-5-bromomethyl-4,5-dihydro-3H-pyrroles, 106
3-Aryl-N-BOC-oxaziridines, 63
Arylation of 1-vinylpyrroles under Heck conditions, 112
Arylidene-4,5-dihydropyridazines, 232
2-Arylpyrroles, 104
3-Arylpyrroles, 113
3-(Arylsulfonyl)-2-trifluoromethyl-5-hydrazinopyrazoles, 146
4-(Arylsulfonyl)pyrazoles, 147
Arylsulfonylvinamidinium salts, 147
Aryltetrazoles, 157, 158
3-Arylthiophenes, 90
Aspidospermidine, 30
Aza-Payne rearrangement, 59
Aza-Wittig rearrangement, 61
5-Azaazulene, 301
Azacrown ethers, 325
7-Azaindolizines, 266
Azamacrocycles, 322
Azanorbornanes, 117
Azanorbornenes, 117
Azatrienes, 94
Azazirconacycles, 163
Azepanes, 299
Azepines, 298
Azepino[4,5-*b*]quinoxalines, 245
Azetidines, 67
Azetidinones, 75
Azetidinyl *bis*propargylic sulfone, 328
2-Azido and 3-azido-1-methylindole, 112
2-Azido-5-methylthiophene, 94
Azidoalkylphosphonates, 153
Azidolysis, 53
Aziridinating agents, 242
Aziridination, 57, 58
Aziridines, 57-60
3,4-Aziridinopyrrolidine, 57
2H-Azirine-2-carboxylic esters, 61
Azolo[1,5-*a*]pyrimidines, 261
Baeyer-Villiger rearrangement, 77
Barreleno[*d*]pyridazine, 234
Barton-Zard pyrrole synthesis, 104
Bemarinone, 239
Benzaldimines, 63
3-Benzazepine, 300
1H-1-Benzazepine, 301
Benzimidazoles, 151
Benzisothiazoles, 163

2,4,1-Benzodiazaborines, 238
1,5-Benzodiazepines, 83
Benzodiazepines, 310, 311
Benzodiazocines, 235
1,3-Benzodioxoles, 180
1,3-Benzodiselenoles, 180
1,3-Benzoditelluroles, 180
Benzoditellurolium salts, 181
1,3,2-Benzodithiatelluroles, 186
1,2-Benzodithins, 94
1,3-Benzodithioles, 180, 181
Benzofuran dioxetane, 72
Benzofurans, 17
Benzopyrans, 279
1,3,2-Benzothiaselenatelluroles, 186
Benzothiazines, 166
Benzothiazoles, 165, 166, 169
Benzothieno[2,3-*d*]imidazoles, 87
Benzothieno[3,2-*b*]benzofuran, 136
Benzothieno[3,2-*c*]isoxazoles, 93
2H-1-Benzothiete, 91
Benzothiophenes, 93
1-, 2- or 3-(Benzotriazol-1-yl)methylindoles, 109, 110
2-(Benzotriazol-1-ylmethyl)furans, 130
Benzotriazoles, 152, 153, 170
Benzotrithioles, 186
1,2-Benzoxatelluroles, 186
Benzoxazepines, 313
Benzoxazinone,3
Benzo[*b*]furans, 135
Benzo[*b*]phenazine, 246
Benzo[*b*]thiophenes, 83, 84
Benzo[*c*]thiophenes, 83
Benzyl pyrrole-2-carboxylate, 104
1-Benzyl-2-(methylthio)-4-bromo-5-cyanoimidazole, 151
3-Benzyl-5-phenyl-7-alkylaminothiazolo[4,5-*d*]pyrimidine-2(3H)-thiones, 237
Benzyne, 321, 322
Benz[4,5]isoquino[1,2-*b*]quinazoline-7,9-dione
2,2'-Bi(4-aryl-4,5-dihydro-5-imino-1,3,4-selenadiazoles), 175
Bicyclo[5.3.0]decenone, 56
Biginelli reaction, 9
Biindoles, 107
Biopterin, 271
2,2'-Biphenylylenediphenyltellurane, 97
2,2'-Bipyrazine, 242
Bipyridinium, 326
4,4'-Bipyrimidine, 242
2,5-Bis(1,3-dithiol-2-ylidene)-2,5-dihydroselenophene, 97
1,14-*Bis*(4-ethynylphenoxy)-3,6,9,12-tetraoxatetradecane, 321
Bis(dihydro-oxazole) ligands, 58
α,ω-*Bis*(phosphane)polyether ligand, 329
3,6-Bis(trifluoromethyl)-1,2,4,5-tetrazine, 234
1,4-Bis(trifluoromethyl)pyrido[3,4-*d*]pyridazine, 234
Bis-1,8-(triazamacrocycle), 323
5,6,17,18-Bisdehydrotetrathia[24]annulene[2.2.2.2], 96
Biselenadiazoles, 175
1,4-Bis[(aminoalkyl)amino]benzo[g]phthalazine-5,10-diones, 235

Bithiophenes, 83
Boracyclobutenes, 74
Borepine, 307
Borole, 83
Brevetoxin B, 277, 303
Brodimoprim, 232
3-Bromo-2-nitrobenzo[b]thiophene
2-Bromo-3-substituted-5-nitrothiophenes, 86
2-Bromo-5-hydroxytryptophan, 110
1-Bromobenzothiophene, 85
6-(2-Bromoethyl)-2,2'-bipyridine, 330
3-(Bromomethyl)indoles, 110
3-Bromopyrroles, 103
4-Bromopyrroles, 103
2-Bromopyrroles, 112
Bromotetrazole, 157
Buspirone, 244
Butadienethiolates, 84
Butyrolactones, 22
Calixcrowns, 320
Calix[4]arenes, 321, 327
Calix[6]arenes, 321
Camalexin, 107
Camptothecin, 31
Carbazole-1,4-quinones, 108
Carbazoles, 108
4-Carbethoxythiazole, 170
Carbocyclization, 23
Carbopenem, 31
1-Carboxy-2-(tributylstannyl)indole, 112
Carceplexes, 320
Cascade radical reactions, 31
Catecholates, 325
Catenanes, 320, 323, 324, 326, 329
Cation recognition, 320
CC-1065, 30
Ceratopicanol, 56
Cerium(IV) nitrate, 16
Cetiedil, 82
Charge transfer complexes, 174
Charine, 236
Chilenine, 30
Chiral auxiliary, 76
Chiral crown ethers, 321
Chiral Lewis acids, 16
Chiral nitroxide radicals, 29
Chloroketones, 55
2-(Chloromercurio) derivatives of 1-acetyl- and 1-(phenylsulfonyl)pyrrole, 116
Chloroperoxidase, 49
Cholesteno[4,3-d]pyrimidines, 238
Cholesteno[7,6-d]pyrimidines, 238
Chroman-4-ols, 280
Chroman-4-ones, 280, 285
Chromans, 280
Chromenes, 279
Chromones, 285
Ciguatoxin, 304

Cine-substitution of 1,4-dinitro-5-methylpyrazoles, 147
Cinnolines, 231, 232, 234, 235
Cis-1,3,5,7-tetraoxadecalin diazacrown ethers, 325
Claviciptic acid, 301
CNS-macrocycles, 327
Cobactin T, 299
Conducting polymers, 95
Continine, 27
Copper(II) acetate, 25
Copper(II)triflate-catalyzed, 58
Corand/ionophore ligands, 320
Cotton effect, 68
Coumarins, 283
Crown ether macrocycles, 154
Crown ethers, 320
Cryptands, 325, 328
Cuprates, 59
Curtius rearrangement, 111
Cyanine dyes, 320
2-Cyanobenzothiazoles, 169
2-Cyanothiophene, 84
α-Cyanovinylindoles, 106
Cyclic phosphonamidates, 77
Cyclization of 1-(ω-iodoalkyl)-2-phenylsulfonylindoles, 114
Cyclization of 1-(ω-iodoalkyl)-3-formylindoles, 114
Cyclization of 2-bromo-1-(but-3-enyl)indole, 114
Cycloaddition reactions of pyrrole osmium(II)pentamine derivatives, 117
2-[α-(Cycloalkylidene)alkyl]indoles, 113
Cyclohepta[*g*]quinazolines, 236
2-(Cyclohex-1-enoyl)indoles, 113
Cyclooctatetraene, 234
Cycloocta[*d*]pyridazine, 234
Cyclopentannulation, 24
Cyclopenta[b]indoles, 115
Cyclopenta[*d*]pyrimidines, 241
Cyclopenta[*e*]pyrido[1,2-*b*]triazines, 269
Cyclophanes, 323, 326
Cyclophosphazenes, 328
Cyclopolymerization, 321
Cyclosporin, 59
Cyclo[*b*]-fused carbazoles, 93
Dactomelyne, 34
9-Deazaguanine, 260
Dehydrosulfurization, 171
Dehydrotryptophans, 111
2'-Deoxycadeguomycin, 237
7-Deoxypancratistatin, 34
Deoxyvasicine, 240
Desulfurization, 94
Dewar benzo[*c*]thiophene, 90
2,4-Di-*t*-butoxy-5-pyrimidineboronic acid, 88
1,4-Diacyl-3-acylamino-5-aryl-4,5-dihydro-1H-1,2,4-triazoles, 155
1,4-Diacyl-3-acylamino-5-phenyl-4,5-dihydro-1H-1,2,4-triazole, 154
3-Dialkylaminoisothiazole 1,1-dioxides, 164
1,3-Diaryl-2-thiobarbituric acids, 241
3,6-Diarylimidazo[1,5-*b*]pyridazines, 233
Diaryloxazolium oxides, 104

5,6-Diarylpyridazin-3-ones, 233
4,5-Diarylpyrrole-2-carboxylates, 105
1,2-Diarylpyrroles, 103
Diazacrowns, 326
1,6-Diazacyclodeca-3,8-diyne, 323
Diazafulvene, 147
Diazepines, 308
Diazepinodiazocine, 308
Diazido-barbituric acid, 5
Diazido-pyridazines, 5
Diazido-pyrimidines, 5
Diazido-quinolinediones, 1
Diazidoacetyl derivatives, 7
Diazidomethyl pyrimidines, 9
Diazine reviews, 231
4-Diazinylimidazoles, 232
Diazo ß-diketones, 2
Dibenzotellurophenes, 97
Dibenzothiophenes, 85, 90
Dibenzoxazepines, 38
Dibenzo{a,h}phenazine, 245
2,3-Dibromothiophene, 87
4,5-Dichloro-1,2,3-dithiazolium chloride, 169
2,6-Dichloropurines, 88
2,5-Dichlorothiophene, 86
8,8-Dicyanoheptafulvene, 236
4,5-Dicyanopyridazine, 234
2,5-Dicyclopropylthiophene, 90
Diels-Alder reactions with furans, 128, 129
Diepoxy[15]annulenone rearrangement, 124
5-(N,N-Diethylcarbamoyloxy) lithiation, 112
α,α-Difluoro-γ-lactones, 17
Difullerenofuran, 133
1,2-Dihydro-1,2-diborete, 74
2,5-Dihydro-1-hydroxyimidazoles, 148
3,4-Dihydro-1H-pyrido[2,3-b]pyrazin-2-one, 243
4,5-Dihydro-5,5-dimethyl-3-oxo-3H-1,2,4-triazole, 155
5,6-Dihydro-7H-imidazol[1,2-b][1,2,4]triazoles, 156
Dihydrobarreleno[d]pyridazine, 234
2,3-Dihydrobenzo-1,2-thiazole-1,1-dioxides, 164
2,3-Dihydrobenzo[b]thiophenes, 91
Dihydrocycloocta[d]pyridazine, 234
Dihydrofurans, 16
2,5-Dihydroimidazole-1-oxyls, 148
Dihydropinidine, 35
Dihydropyran-4-ones, 283
Dihydropyrazine, 110
2,3-Dihydropyrazolo[5,1-b]thiazoles, 169
Dihydropyridazines, 231
7,8-Dihydropyridazino-[4,5-g]quinoxaline-2,6,9(1H)-trione, 246
Dihydrosesamin, 25
5,6-Dihydrothiazolo[2,3-e][1,4,2]diazaphosphole, 167
6,7-Dihydrothieno[2,3-b][1,4]thiazepin-5(4H)-one, 93
6,7-Dihydrothieno[3,2-d]pyrimidine-2,4-diones, 240
Dihydrothieno[3,4-d]pyrimidine-2,3-diones, 93
Dihydrothiepins, 312
Dihydrothiophene dioxide, 94

Dihydrothiophenes, 91, 94
5,6-Dihydro[1,2,4]triazolo[5,1-*d*]-[1,3,5]oxadiazepines, 156
Dihydro[2,3-*b*]benzofurans, 138
(Diimine)copper(I)-catalysts, 57
3,6-Diiodopyridazines, 233
Dimethoxyphthalimido-azepine, 299
4,4-Dimethyl-1,3-thiazole-5(4H)-thiones, 170
Dimethyldihydropyrenes, 129
Dimethyldioxirane, 48
2,3-Dimethylene-2,3-dihydrothiophene, 93
3,4-Dimethylenepyrrole, 115
Dimethylindole zincate reagents, 112
Dimethyloxosulfonium methylide, 58
(3,5-Dimethylpyrazolo)pyrrolo[2,3-*d*]pyrimidines, 242
Dimethylpyrazolo[1,2-*a*]benzotriazoles, 244
2,5-Dimethylpyrrole-2-carboxylate esters, 106
Dimethylsulfonium methylide, 58
1,3-Dimethyluracils, 241
4,5-Dinitro-2-aryl-1,2,3-triazole 1-oxide, 152
Dinitro-2H-1,2,4-triazoles, 146
Dinitrofuroxan oxide, 152
1,2-Dioxanes, 37
1,3-Dioxanes, 39
1,2,4-Dioxazoles, 201
1,12-Dioxa[12](1,4)naphthylenophane-14-carboxylic acid, 321
Dioxepanes, 311
Dioxins, 289
Dioxiranes, 61, 62
1,3-Dioxolan-2-ones, 178, 179
1,3-Dioxolan-4-ones, 179, 180
1,3-Dioxolanes, 178, 179, 180
1,2-Dioxolanes, 184
Dioxosulfine, 292
N-(Diphenylmethylene)dehydroalanine, 111
2,3-Diphenyltetrazolium salts, 156
1,3-Dipolar cycloadditions, 174
Dipyridyl porphyrins, 328
Discorhabins, 113
1,2-Diselenol-3-ones, 185
1,3-Diselenoles, 181
Dispiroketals, 277
4,4-Disubstituted 4H-imidazoles, 148
4,6-Disubstituted dibenzofurans, 126
1,2-Disubstituted indoles, 109
3,5-Disubstituted pyrrole-2-carboxylate esters, 105
2,4-Disubstituted-1,3,5-triazines, 255, 256
1,4-Dithia-7,16-diaza-10,13-dioxa-2,2,3,3-tetrafluorocyclooctadecane, 328
Dithiadiselenafulvalenes, 182
Dithiapanes, 311
1,3-Dithietane-2,4-diylidenebis(cyanoacetic acid esters), 146
1,3-Dithietanes, 73
Dithiins, 290
1,5-Dithiocines, 94
1,3-Dithiol-2-ones, 33, 181
1,2-Dithiol-3-ones, 185
Dithiolane S-oxides, 181
1,3-Dithiolanes, 178, 181

1,2-Dithiolanes, 184
1,3-Dithiole-2-thiones, 181
1,2-Dithiole-3-thiones, 185
1,3-Dithioles, 181, 182, 183
1,2-Dithioles, 184
1,2-Dithiolium salts, 185
1,3-Dithiolium-4-olates, 181
1-Dodecyl-1-methyl-4-oxopiperidinium triflate, 50
Duocarmycin, 30
DuP 753, 88
Ebselene, 33
Ecotine, 236
Electrocyclization, 103
Electrophilic[2+2]cycloaddition, 69
Ellipticine, 234
6-*Endo* cyclization, 26
8-*Endo-trig* radical cyclization, 38
6-*Endo-trig*, 25, 27, 33, 36, 37
5-*Endo-trig*, 27
Enynes, 22
4-Epi-ethisolide, 24
4-Epibakkenolide-A, 24
Epoxidation, 44, 45, 47, 48, 50, 51, 62
Epoxides, 14, 44, 52, 53, 54, 55
Epoxy tosylhydrazones, 54
Eremantholide A, 23
Eriolanin, 24
Ethano- and ethenophthalazines, 234
2,5-Ethanopyrido[2,3-*f*]quinazoles, 236
2-Ethoxy-2-vinylcyclopropanecarboxylate esters, 153
Ethyl 4(5)-alkyl(aryl)thioimidazole-5(4)-carboxylates, 149
Ethyl 7-methoxyindole-3-acetate, 107
6-*Exo* cyclization, 33, 37
5-*Exo* cyclizations, 28, 29, 30, 33
5-*Exo-dig*, 18, 24
6-*Exo-trig (dig)*, 33
4-*Exo-trig*, 15
5-*Exo-trig*, 17, 26, 27, 37
6-*Exo-trig*, 33, 35, 36
Ferrocene crown ethers, 329
[1,1'-Ferrocenediyl*bis*(methylene)]*bis*[pyridinium] salt, 329
Ferrocenyl ligands, 146
Fervenulin 1-oxide, 272
Flavanoids, 286
Flunarizine, 244
8H-Fluoreno[3,4-*b*]thiophene, 93
Fluorinated pyrazoles, 146
Fluoro-*cis*-2,3-dialkyloxaziridines, 63
Fluorofurans, 121
3-Fluoropyrroles, 105
2-Fluoropyrroles, 114
Fluoro[2,3-*b*]pyridines, 92
2- and 3-Formylindoles, 114
5-Formylpyrrole-2-carboxylates, 114
Forskolin, 25
FPL64176, 104
Friedel-Crafts acylation of pyrrole, 109

Fries rearrangement, 155
Fritsch-Buttenberg-Wiechell rearrangement, 96, 324
[60]Fullerene, 287, 321
Fullerenes, 326
Furanoditerpines, 132
Furanylketones, 123
Furaquinocin C, 125
Furocoumarins, 137
Furonaphthoquinones, 122
Furopyrimidines, 237
Furo[2,3-*b*]quinoxalin-2-ones, 245
Furo[2,3-*d*]pyrimidines, 237, 242
Furo[3,4-*d*]thiepine, 307
Furyl[3,4-*d*]tropone, 153
Fused quinazolines, 239
Fused tetrazole, 158
Fused thiophenes, 82
Galactostatin, 167
Geminal diazides, 1
Gewald approach, 89
GI-147211C, 31
Glycophane, 321
Gramine, 110
Grossularine, 149
Group transfer methods, 19
Guanidines, 152
Hantzsch synthesis, 170
Hantzsch-type condensation, 167
HDS catalysis, 84, 85
Heck reaction, 106, 111
Hemibrevetoxin B, 304
Hemicarceplexes, 320
Hemicarcerands, 321
Heptaleno[1,2-*c*]furanes, 124
Herbicides, 146
Heterocumulenes, 60
Heterocyclic derivatives of methylidenecyclopropanaphthalene, 127
Heterocyclo[*b*]fused carbazoles, 137
Heterophanes, 323
Hexachlorocyclotriphosphazene, 328
4,5,6,7,8,9-Hexahydrocycloocta-1,2,3-selenadiazoles, 175
Hexahydroindoles, 106
1,4,7,11,14,17-Hexathiacycloeicosane, 324
Hinokinin, 25
Homolytic macrocyclization, 39
Hydrodesulfurization, 84
Hydroquinolines, 139
4-Hydroxy-2-cyclobutenones, 134
N-Hydroxyazoles, 151
Hydroxyethylpiperazine, 95
Hydroxymethine radical, 59
5-(Hydroxymethyl)thiazole, 168
Hydroxymethylaziridine, 59
N-Hydroxymethylbenzotriazole, 152
N-Hydroxypyrazoles, 147
ß-Hydroxyselenides, 52
4a-Hydroxytetrahydropterins, 240

3-Hydroxythieno[3,2-c]quinolin-4(5H)-ones, 92
3-Hydroxythiophene-2-carboxylates, 94
5-Hydroxy[1]benzopyrano[4,3-c]pyridazin-3(2H]-ones, 234
Imidazole-1-oxides, 148
Imidazole-2-thiones, 151
Imidazoles, 39, 323
Imidazoles, 148, 149, 150, 151
2-Imidazolidine-thione, 60
Imidazolium salts, 151
Imidazolosugars, 149
Imidazolo[1,2-a]pyrimidines, 242
α-(Imidazolyl)phenylacetic acids, 149
Imidazopyrimdines, 39
Imidazothiazoles, 168
Imidazotriazine 1-oxides, 263
Imidazo[1,2-a]pyrazin-3(7H)-one, 246
α-(3-Imidazo[1,2-a]pyridyl)phenylacetic ester, 149
Imidazo[1,2-a]pyrimidine-5(1H)-ones, 242
Imidazo[1,2-b]pyridazine-2-acetic acids, 235
Imidazo[1,2-b]pyridazines, 235
Imidazo[1,2-b]pyridazinones, 233
Imidazo[1,2-c]pyrimidines, 238
1H,3H-Imidazo[1,5-c]thiazole, 168
Imidazo[4',5':4,5]thieno[3,2-d]pyrimidine, 151
Imidazo[4,5-b]quinoxalines, 247
Imidazo[4,5-c]pyridines, 262
Imidazo[4,5-d]isothiazoles, 165
Imidazo[4,5-g]quinoxaline-6,7-diones, 247
2-Imino-1,3-dioxoles, 178
2-Imino-1,3-dithioles, 181
5H-Indeno[1,2-c]pyridazines, 235
Indol-2-ylborates, 113
Indol-4-ylzinc reagent, 112
Indole debenzylation, 114
Indole, 2-methylindole and 2,3-dimethylindole η^6-ruthenium(II) complexes, 117
indole-2-ylzinc species, 112
Indole-3-acetic acid palladium derivative, 116
Indole-3-carboxylate ester, 107
Indoles from aniline and ethylene glycol, 108
Indoles from o-N-diacylanilines, 107
Indolizidine 209D, 61
Indolo[1,2-a]quinoxalin-6(5H)-ones, 245
Indolo[2,3-a]carbazole, 107
2-Indolyl radicals, 114
1H-Indolyl-2-benzothiazoles, 169
3-Iodoindole-2-carboxylate, 150
2-Iodomethyloxepines, 305
Iodopyridazines, 233
Irinotecan, 31
Isoalloxazine, 244
Isochromans, 281, 282
Isocoumarins, 284
Isoellipticine, 234
Isoindolobenzazepine, 30
Isomerization of allenones, 131
Isoquinolines, 239

Isothiazole 1,1-dioxides, 164
Isothiazole dioxide, 104
Isothiazoles, 163-165
Isoxazoles, 154, 172, 192
Isoxazolidines, 194
Isoxazolines, 193
Isoxazolopyrimidines, 237
Isoxazolo[4,3-*d*]pyrimidines, 243
Isoxazolo[4,5-*d*]pyrimidines, 237
Jacobsen-type catalysts, 44, 48
Kataritzsky lithiation-carbonation-lithiation sequence, 112
Kealiiquinone, 149
Ketoaziridines, 59
Ketyl radicals, 20
Knoevenagel reaction, 167
ß-Lactams as synthons, 66
ß-Lactams, 15, 31, 168
 Lactams, 75
δ-Lactones, 34
Lanthanide-induced rearrangement, 70
Lariciresinol, 25
Lawesson's reagent, 170, 172, 173
Leimgruber-Batcho indole synthesis, 107
Lithiation of 1-(tri-*iso*-propylsilyl)-gramine, 110
Lithiation of 1-vinylpyrrole, 111
Lithiation, indoles and pyrroles, 111
2-Lithio and 3-lithio-1-(phenylsulfonyl)indole, 112
Lithioimidazole, 150
Lithioindoles, 112
Lithiopyrroles, 112
2-Lithiothiophene, 87
Lithium enolates, 70
Luffariolide E, 24
Lumazines, 265
Macrocyclic squares, 328
Macroheterocycles, 320
4-Magnesioisothiazole, 165
Makaluvamines, 113
Manganese salen complexes, 47
Manganese(III) acetate, 16 25, 30, 35
Manganese(III) reagents, 21
Manganese(IV) dioxide, 37
MAO-B inhibitors, 235
McMurry coupling, 96, 324
Meerwein's reagent, 171
Meldrum's acid, 111
Melinonine-E, 36
2-Mercapto-4(3H)-quinazolinone, 242
Mercuration, 87
3-Mercuration, 113
Mesionic tetrazoles, 156
Mesoionic 1,3-oxazolium-5-olates, 148
[3.3]Metacyclophanes, 323
Metal ion extraction, 320
Metallacyclopentenes, 163
Metallaoxetane, 47
Metallo-crown ethers, 329

Metallotriazole hemiporphyrazines, 322
1,2-Metallotropic migration, 173
6,10a-Methanopyrimido[4',5':4,5]cyclohepta[1,2-b]azocines, 236
Methanothienoazóninones, 93
Methoxypsoralen, 240
5-Methoxytryptophan, 110
Methyl 1-(phenylsulfonyl)indole-4-carboxylate, 113
Methyl 3-hydroxyindole-2-carboxylate, 236
Methyl(trifluoromethyl)dioxirane, 62
2-Methyl-1,2-dihydro-4H-pyrido[2,3-b]pyrazin-3-one, 243
5-Methyl-2(1H)-pyrazinones, 243
5-Methyl-2-bromothiophene, 88
4-Methyl-2-thiophenecarboxaldehyde, 90
9-Methyl-3-(1h-tetrazol-5-yl)-4h-pyrido[1,2-a]pyrimidin-4-one, 238
1-Methyl-3-(benzotriazol-1-ylmethyl)indole, 109
4-Methyl-4-silyl[3^{4,10}][7]metacyclophane, 325
3-Methyl-5-phenylisothiazole, 165
3-Methyl-5-phenylisoxazole, 165
Methylcarbapenem, 15
Methylenefurans, 134
Methyleneoxazolidinones, 32
Methylenetetrahydrofuranes, 131
Methylenolactocin, 24
S-Methylthiophenium salts, 83
ß-Methyltryptophan, 110
α-Methyltryptophan, 111
Miharamycin A, 20
Mitsunobu reaction, 103, 150, 151
Molecular encapsulation, 320
Molecular Ribbons, 323
Multifidene, 23
Multiporphyrin arrays, 328
Münchnones, 164
N-Methyl morpholine N-oxide, 45
N-Methyl morpholine, 51
Naphtho[2,3-c][1,2,5]thiadiazole-4,7-dione, 172
1,8-Naphthyridines, 325
Negstatin I, 150
Neobiliverdin 1xd, 302
Neorautennane, 137
ß-Nitrato alcohols, 54
Nitrene addition, 57
Nitrofuroxan, 152
Nitroimidazo[1,5-a]imidazoles, 151
5-Nitropyrimidines, 231
3-Nitrosoimidazo[1,2-a]pyrimidines, 237
Nucleophilic epoxidation, 50
Nucleosides, 240
Octahydro-2H-pyrido[1,2-a]pyrazine, 244
Octamethyltetraoxaquaterene, 321
Oligobipyridines, 326
Oligothiophenes, 88, 90
Oltipraz, 232
Optoelectronic properties, 29
Orangarin, 322
Organocobalt species, 23

[^{1}n]Orthocyclophanes, 320
Osmium complexes, 116
Oxa-crown porphyrazines, 327
Oxacalix[3]arenes, 321
1,2,4-Oxadiazol-5-yl)-2,3-dihydrodiimidazo[1,5-*a*:1',2'-*c*]quinazoline, 235
Oxadiazoles, 202
1,2-Oxaselenolanes, 186
1,2-Oxatelluroles, 186
Oxathiins, 291, 292
1,3-Oxathiolan-5-ones, 184
1,3-Oxathiolane *S*-oxides, 91
1,3-Oxathiolane-2-thiones, 184
1,3-Oxathiolanes, 178, 183, 184
1,2-Oxathiolanes, 185
Oxazepines, 313
Oxazines, 239
Oxaziridines, 62, 63
Oxazole-1,2,4-triazole, 155
Oxazoles, 168, 195
Oxazolidin-2-ones, 199
Oxazolidines, 51, 198
Oxazolidinones, 32
Oxazolines, 196
Oxazolium oxides, 104
1,3-Oxazolium-5-oxides, 168
Oxazolones, 164
Oxepanes, 305, 306
Oxepines, 303
Oxetane rearrangement, 69
Oxetanes and thietanes, 68
2-Oxetanones, 71
Oxidative amination, 113
Oxindoles from ß-nitrostyrenes, 108
Oxiranium radical cation, 54
6-Oxo-2,3,4,6,7,8-hexahydro-1*h*-pyrido[1,2-*a*]pyrimidine-9-carbonitriles, 238
2-Oxo-3-phenylisoxazolo[2,3-*a*]pyrimidines, 237
Oxone, 62
Palladium-catalyzed cross coupling, 103, 150, 157
Palladium-catalyzed transfer hydrogenolysis, 54
Papaverine, 239
Parabanic acids, 6
[1.1.1.1]Paranaphthalenaphane, 322
Paraquat, 326
Patulin, 127
Pd(II)-pyridine, 329
N-(Pent-4-enyl)-pyrroles and indoles were cyclizations, 1155
Pentaammineosmium(II) derivatives of pyrroles, 116
Pentaazapentalenes, 171
Peptidomimetic templates, 244
Peptidomimetics, 154
Peracid oxidation, 151
Perfluoroalkyl pyrazoles, 146
4-Perfluoroalkylpyrrole-3-carboxylate esters, 104
Peroxomolybdenum complexes, 146
Phenanthridines, 26, 36
1,10-Phenanthrolines, 326

Phenazine antibiotics, 231, 243
Phenazines, 231, 245
5-Phenyl-1,2,4-dithiazole-3-one, 169
1-(Phenylcyclopropyl)pyrroles, 116
4-Phenyloxazole, 153
4-Phenylpyridine N-oxide, 45
1-(Phenylsulfonyl)pyrrole osmium and ruthenium derivatives, 116
N-Phenyltetrazole, 157
1-Phenyltetrazoline-5-thiones, 157
Phosphole, 83
Phospholipid bilayer vesicle membranes, 325
Phosphorus macrocycles, 328
Photocycloaddition, 71
Photodimers, 241
Photooxidation, 12
Photosensitized electron transfer, 19
Phototranspositions, 165
Phthalazines, 231, 234
Piperidines, 37, 61
Piritrexim, 242
Platinum derivatives of gramine, tryptamine, methyl tryptophanate, 115
Poly(cycloalkyl[c]thiophenes), 92
Polyaza cryptands, 323
Polyazamacromolecules, 320
Polycyclic triazoles, 153
Polyrotaxanes, 320
Polysiloxane, 320
Polythiophenes, 327
Porphyrins, 322, 326
Pterocarpan, 279
Pterocarpanes, 137
Ptilomycalin, 304
Pummerer cyclization, 75
Pummerer reaction, 107
Pyranones, 123, 282
Pyranopyrimidines, 237
7H-Pyrano[2,3-d]pyrimidin-7-ones, 241
Pyrano[2,3-d]pyrimidines, 237
Pyrans, 34, 278
Pyrazine oxides, 246
Pyrazines, 174, 231, 232, 243
Pyrazinium dicyanomethylides, 246
2(1H)-Pyrazinones, 243
Pyrazinoquinoxalines, 247
Pyrazole-based ligands, 146
Pyrazoles, 146, 147, 242
2-Pyrazolines, 164
Pyrazolopyridazines, 235, 262
Pyrazolopyrimidines, 11
Pyrazoloquinazoline, 240
Pyrazolotriazinones, 264
Pyrazolo[1,2-a]quinoxalines, 245
Pyrazolo[3,4-b]pyrazines, 263
Pyrazolo[3,4-d]pyrimidinones, 237
5H-Pyrazolo[5.1-b][1,3]thiazines, 146
Pyridazin-3(2H)-ones, 233
Pyridazines, 231-235

Pyridazinium 4-dicyanomethylides, 235
3(2H)-Pyridazinones, 231
Pyridazinones, 233
Pyridazino[3,2-b]quinazolin-6-imine, 233
Pyridazomycin, 235
Pyridines, 322
4-Pyridinone, 325
Pyridinophanes, 328
Pyridino[2,3-d]thiazole, 233
Pyridoazepine, 300
Pyridopyrazino[2,3-d]azepines, 245
Pyridothieno-pyrimidines, 267
Pyrido[1',2':1,2]imidazo[4,5-b]pyrazines, 246
1H,5H-Pyrido[1,2,3-de]quinoxaline-5, 247
4H-Pyrido[1,2-a]pyrimidin-4-one (pirenperone), 235
4H-Pyrido[1,2-a]pyrimidin-4-ones, 242
Pyrido[2,3-d]pyridazine, 234
Pyrido[2,3-d]pyrimidines, 238, 242
Pyrido[3,2-d]pyrimidines, 242
Pyrido[3,2-f]quinoxalines, 247
Pyrido[3,4-d]pyridazine-1,4-diones, 233
Pyrido[3,4-f]quinoxaline-2,3-dione, 247
Pyrido[4,3-d]pyrimidin-5(6H)ones, 265
Pyrido[4,3-d]pyrimidines, 242
Pyridyl-2-hydroxythiophenes, 88
2-Pyridylsulfonyl as an N-protecting group, 114
2-(Pyrimidin-4-yl)estradiols, 242
Pyrimidine betaines, 241
Pyrimidine-4(3H)-ones, 242
Pyrimidinediones, 18, 240
Pyrimidines, 174, 232, 235, 236, 237
2,4,6-[1H,3H,5]Pyrimidinetrione, 235
Pyrimidino-18-crown-6 ligand, 242
Pyrimidinones, 236
Pyrimidino[4,5-b][1,4]diazepines, 238
Pyrimidino[4,5-b][1,4]thiazepines, 238
1H-pyrimidinthiones, 174
Pyrimido[2,1-i]purines, 270
Pyrimido[4',5'-4,5]selenolo[2,3-b]quinolin-4(3H)-one, 97
Pyrimido[6,1-a]isoquinolinones, 263
Pyroglutamates, 27
Pyrrol-1-ylbenzylidene pentacarbonyl chromium, 116
Pyrrol-3-yl glycosides, 104
Pyrroles from 2,5-dimethoxytetrahydrofuran, 106
Pyrroles from oxazolium oxides, 104
Pyrroles, 322
Pyrrolidin-2-ones, 27
Pyrrolidines, 16
Pyrrolo-, pyrazolo-, or imidazopyrimidines, 237
Pyrrolotriazines, 257
Pyrrolo[1',2':2,3]pyridazino[6,1-a]isoindole diones, 233
Pyrrolo[1,2-a]pyrazine, 244
Pyrrolo[1,2-a]quinoxalines, 243
Pyrrolo[1,2-c]pyrimidines, 238
Pyrrolo[1'',2'':1',6']pyrazino[2',3':4,5]thieno[2,3-b]quinolines, 243
Pyrrolo[2,3-d]pyrimidines, 242, 260, 271
Pyrrolo[4,3,2-de]quinoline, 113

Pyrylium salts, 286
Quinazolin-4(3H)-ones, 243
2,4(1H,3H)-Quinazolinediones, 242
Quinazolines, 231, 238, 239, 243
Quinazolinethione, 239
(3H)-Quinazolinethiones, 236
Quinazolinium salts, 239
Quinazolinones, 231, 239, 242
4(3H)-Quinazolinones, 236
Quinisatine, 4
Quinolines, 234
Quinolinones, 94
Quinones, 172
Quinoxalin-2-(1H)-ones, 233
Quinoxaline oxides, 231
Quinoxaline, 231, 244, 246
Radical cyclization, 75
Radical reactions, 114
Reductive N-heterocyclization, 239
Resorcin[4]arenes, 321
4-(Ribofuranosyl)imidazole nucleosides, 150
Richter reaction, 235
Ring lithiation, 232
(Rongalite), 115
Ropinirole, 108
Rotaxanes, 321, 326
Ruthenium porphyrin tetramer, 329
Ruthenium, 116
(Salen)Mn catalysts, 44, 45, 46, 48, 53
(Salen)Mn epoxidations, 45
SAR studies, 242, 246
Schollkopf intermediate, 110
Seebach oxazolidinone procedure, 111
Selenadiazoles, 174, 175
Selenasapphyrins, 97
4H-1,3-Selenazines, 97
Selenazoles, 174, 175
Selenepines, 307
Selenolo[2,3-b]pyrroles, 97
Selenolo[3,2-a]pyrroles, 97
5-(Selenophene)cytidines, 97
5-Selenophene)uridines, 97
Selenophenes, 96, 97
Selenopyrans, 97, 289
Sharpless epoxidation, 44, 49, 51
Si-bridged macrocycles, 327
[3,3]Sigmatropic rearrangements, 174
Silacalix[4]arenes, 327
Silacyclobutane, 74
Silacyclopentadiene, 83
Silanoles, 325
Silaoxacycles, 32
Silicon-bridged thiophenes, 96
5-Siloxy-1,2,3-triazole, 152
8-Silylpurines, 88
Simmons-Smith reaction, 89
Solid-state photochemical reactions, 32

Spiro-lactones, 70
Spiro-oxindoles, 26
Spiro-oxirane, 72
Spirothietanes, 72
Spiro[pyrimidine-2(1H), 2'(3'H)-[1,3,4]thiadiazoles], 174
Spiro[pyrimidine-4(1H), 2'(3'H)-[1,3,4]thiadiazoles], 174
Sporothriolide, 24
Stabilized 2H- and 3H-pyrroles, 116
O-Stannylpyrazole, 147
Stannylthiophenes, 88
Steroids, 63
Stetter reaction, 90
Stille coupling, 88, 93, 112, 113
2-Styrylthiopyranopyrimidines, 237
3-Substituted imidazole-1-oxides, 148
ß-Substituted tryptophan esters, 111
3-Substituted-3H-[1,2,4]triazino[6,1-b]quinazoline-4,10-diones, 240
Sulfinimines, 58
Sulfur-containing lactones, 39
Sulfur-substituted pyrroles, 105
Sulfuranes, 185
Sultones, 73, 291
Superheterodiene, 234
Superphanes, 325
Suzuki coupling, 88, 113
Suzuki reaction to prepare several 1-(phenylsulfonyl)-2-arylpyrroles, 112
Swern oxidation, 55, 61
Swinholide A, 277
Synthesis of gibberellins, 129
Tandem radical additions, 21
Tandem radical cyclizations, 17
21-Telluraporphyrins, 97
Tellurepines, 307
Tellurophenes, 96
Telluropyrroles, 97
TEMPO, 30
2,2'-Tethered bifluorenylidene crown ethers, 322
1,4,7,10-Tetraazacyclododecane, 322
Tetraazamacrocycles, 322
Tetrahydrobenzo[c]thiophen-4-ones, 90
Tetrahydrofuran-3-ones, 18
Tetrahydrofurans, 135
2,3,5,6-Tetrahydroimidazo[2,1-b]thiazoles, 167
Tetrahydroisoquinolines, 36
Tetraoxa[26]annulene quinone, 133, 321
2,4,5,8-Tetraphenylquinazoline, 234
Tetraphenylthiophene, 91
Tetraselenafulvalenes, 182
Tetrathiafulvalenes, 22, 181, 182, 324
Tetrathia[22]annulene[2.1.2.1], 96
1,2,4,5-Tetrazines, 258
1H-Tetrazol-5-thiol, 156
Tetrazoles, 2, 156, 157, 158
Tetrazolo[2,3-d]pyrimidines, 242
1-Thia-10-aza[2.2]metacyclophane, 327
7-Thia-2,5-diazaspiro[3,4]octan-1-one, 168
5H-1-Thia-3,4,5,6,8-pentaazanaphthylene, 267

5H-1-Thia-3,5,6,8-tetraazaacenaphthylenes, 92
2-Thia-3-azabicyclo[3.1.0]hex-3-ene 2,2-dioxides, 164
Thiacrown ethers, 324
1,2,5-Thiadiazole, 172
1,2,4-Thiadiazoles, 162, 171
1,2,3-Thiadiazoles, 171
1,3,4-Thiadiazoles, 173
[1,3,4]-Thiadiazolo[3,4-*b*]phthalazines, 232
Thiametacyclophanes, 326
Thiamin, 231
Thiapentalenes, 171
Thiaplatinacycles, 85
1,3,4,5-Thiatriazine, 257
Thiazepines, 311, 313, 314
Thiazino[2,3-*b*]quinazolines, 231
Thiazofurims, 95
5-(Thiazol-2'-yl)pyrimidines, 236
1,3-Thiazole-5(4*h*)-thione oxides, 170
Thiazoles, 165, 167, 168, 169, 170
1,3-Thiazolidine-2-thione, 322
Thiazolidinimine, 60
4-Thiazolidinones, 242
Thiazolines, 166-168
Thiazolo[2,3-*b*]quinazolines, 231
5H-[1,3]Thiazolo[3,2-*a*]pyrido[3,2-*e*]pyrimidin-5-ones, 243
5H,7H-Thiazolo[3,4-*c*]oxazolium-1-oxides, 168
Thiazolo[4',5':2,3]pyridino[4,3-*d*]pyridazines, 233
Thienamycin, 15
Thieno-fused pyrimidines, 238
Thienoazepinones, 93
Thienocyclopentapyran, 95
Thienodiazepines, 95
Thienodiltiazems, 95
Thienoimidazole, 151
Thienoisoquinolines, 37, 93
Thienol[3,4-*d*]thiepine, 307
Thienopyridines, 83, 92
Thienoquinolines, 37, 93
Thienothiophenes, 94
2-Thienoylbenzoic acids, 93
Thienozinc reagents, 87
Thieno[2,3(3,2)-*f*]indolizines, 93
Thieno[2,3-*b*]benzo[*h*]quinolines, 92
Thieno[2,3-*b*]naphthyridines, 93
Thieno[2,3-*b*]quinoline-2-carboxylates, 243
Thieno[2,3-*c*]pyridazines, 92
Thieno[2,3-*c*][1,2,5]oxadiazole, 83
Thieno[2,3-*d*]pyrimidine 7,7-dioxides, 237
Thieno[2,3-*d*]pyrimidine-2,4(1H,3H)-diones, 242
Thieno[2,3-*d*]pyrimidines, 92, 235, 237, 242
Thieno[2,3-*d*][1,3]thiazin-4-ones, 93
2H-Thieno[2,3-*e*]-1,3-oxazin-4(3H)-one, 94
Thieno[2,3-*h*][1,6]naphthyridines, 92
3H-Thieno[3,2-*c*]-1,2-dithiole-3-thione, 94
Thieno[3,4-*b*]quinoxalines, 244
Thieno[3,4-*b*][1,4]diazepine, 83
Thieno[3,4-*c*]cepham sulfones, 92

Thieno[4,5-c; 2,3-c']dipyrazoles, 90
Thienyl esters, 86
Thienyl ketones, 86
3-(3-Thienyl)alanine, 95
2-(2-Thienyl)pyridine, 84
2-Thienylboronic anhydride, 88
Thienyllithium, 85
Thienylpyridazinones, 88
Thiepines, 303
Thiiranes, 91
Thioisobenzofurans, 138
5-(Thiophene)cytidines, 95
5-(Thiophene)uridines, 95
Thiophene-1,1-dioxides, 94
Thiophene-Li$^+$ complex, 84
Thiophenecarbonylchromiun(0) complexes, 87
3-Thiophenecarboxaldehyde, 87
Thiophenes, 82
Thiophenfurin, 95
2H-Thiophenium complexes, 85
Thiopyrano[2,3-d]pyrimidines
Thiopyrans, 287
Thiopyroglutamates, 27
1,3-Thioselenoles, 181
Thiosulfinic S-esters, 91
Thorpe cyclization, 151
Thymidine, 240
Ticarcillin$^{®}$, 82
Tiospirone, 244
Tirapazamine, 247
Titanium enolates, 76
1,3-Tithiolium-4-olate, 91
Topotecan, 31
Transition metal complexes, 115
2-Tri-n-butylstannylthiophenes, 88
3-Tri-n-butylstannylthiophenes, 88
2,3,5-Triarylpyrroles, 104
1,4,7-Triazacyclononane orthoamide, 323
1,4,7-Triazacyclononane, 322
Triazepinotriazinoindole, 272
1,2,3-Triazine, 93
1,3,5-Triazine, 326
1,3,5-Triazinium salts, 256
1,2,4-Triazino[5,6-b]indole-3-thione, 272
1,2,3-Triazole 1-oxide, 152
1,2,3-Triazole, 153
1,2,4-Triazole, 154, 155, 156
1,2,4-Triazole-5-ylphosphonic acids, 155
[1,2,4]-Triazole[1,3]thiazinoquinolines, 156
Triazolines, 154
Triazolinethione, 154
Triazolium N-allylidines, 156
Triazolium salts, 154, 156
Triazolohemiporphyrazines, 156
Triazolophthalocyanines, 156
Triazolotriazines, 264

Triazolotriazinoindole, 272
[1,2,4]-Triazolo[1,2-*b*]phthalazines, 232
1,2,4-Triazolo[1,5-*a*]pyrimidines, 235
Triazolo[1,5-*a*]pyrimidines, 237
1,3,4-Triazolo[1,5-*a*]pyrimidines, 243
4H-1,2,3-Triazolo[1,5-*a*][1,4]benzodiazepin-6(5H)-one, 153
1,2,4-Triazolo[1,5-*c*]pyrimidines, 238
4-Triazolo[2,3-*d*]pyrimidines, 242
s-Triazolo[3,4-*a*]phthalazines, 234
1,2,4-Triazolo[4,3-*a*]pyrazines, 246
1,2,4-Triazolo[4,3-*a*]quinazolin-5-ones, 242
s-Triazolo[4,3-*b*]pyridazinones, 233
Triazolo[4,5-*d*]pyrimidines, 266
1,2,4-Triazolo[5,1-*i*]purines, 273
Trichloromethyldiazines, 232
2,3,5-Trichlorothiophene, 86
6-Trifluoroacetyl-4-trifluoromethylbenzo[*h*]quinazolines, 240
Trifluoromethylpyridazines, 233
Trimethylamine-N-oxide, 51
Trimethylsilyl azide, 52
2-(Trimethylsilyl)thiazole, 167
Trimetrexate, 242
1,3,3-Trinitroazetidine, 67
Trioxins, 290
(Triphenyltin)cobaloxime complex, 20
Triphenylverdazyls, 258
Triptyceno-crowns, 322
Tris(pentafluorophenyl)boron, 55
2,4,6-Tris(trinitromethyl)-1,3,5-triazine, 268
1,3,4-Trisubstituted-lactones, 70
Trithiazyl trichloride, 172
Trithiine, 314
1,2,4-Trithiolanes, 186
N-Tritylimidazole, 150
Tropone, 236
Tryptophans, 111
Uhle's ketone, 109
Uracil, 241
Uranyl complexes, 320
Urothion, 245
van Alphen Hüttel rearrangement, 11
Vicine, 236
Vinyl aziridines, 57, 61
Vinyl silanes, 62
2-Vinyl- and 3-Vinyl-1-(phenylsulfonyl)pyrroles, 109
2-Vinylindoles, 37
Vinylindoles, 106
4-Vinylpyrroles, 113
5-Vinyltetrazoles, 157
Xanthine oxidase inhibitor, 153
Xanthones, 286
Yingzhaosu C, 37
Ytterbium triisopropoxide, 53
Yuehcukene analogs, 113
Zincate reagents, 112
Zirconium metallacycles, 163